electronics
one-seven

Hayden Electronics One-Seven Series

Harry Mileaf, Editor-in-Chief

electronics one — Electronic Signals ☐ Amplitude Modulation ☐ Frequency Modulation ☐ Phase Modulation ☐ Pulse Modulation ☐ Side-Band Modulation ☐ Multiplexing ☐ Television Signals ☐ Navigation Signals ☐ Facsimile ☐ Heterodyning ☐ Harmonics ☐ Waveshaping

electronics two — Electronic Building Blocks ☐ Basic Stages ☐ The Power Supply ☐ Transmitters ☐ Receivers ☐ UHF ☐ Telemetry ☐ Television ☐ Radar and Sonar ☐ RDF ☐ Radio Navigation ☐ Radio Control

electronics three — Electron Tubes ☐ Diodes ☐ Triodes ☐ Tetrodes ☐ Pentodes ☐ Multielement Tubes ☐ Gas-Filled Tubes ☐ Phototubes ☐ Electron-Ray Indicators ☐ Cathode-Ray Tubes ☐ UHF and Microwave Tubes ☐ Magnetrons ☐ Klystrons ☐ The Traveling-Wave Tube

electronics four — Semiconductors ☐ P-N Diodes ☐ Avalanche Diodes ☐ Switching Diodes ☐ Zener Diodes ☐ Tunnel Diodes ☐ N-P-N and P-N-P Transistors ☐ Tetrode Transistors ☐ Field Effect, Surface Barrier, Unijunction, SCR Transistors ☐ Photodevices

electronics five — Power Supplies ☐ Rectifiers ☐ Filters ☐ Voltage Multipliers ☐ Regulation ☐ Amplifier Circuits ☐ A-F, R-F, and I-F Amplifiers ☐ Video Amplifiers ☐ Phase Splitters ☐ Follower Amplifiers ☐ Push-Pull Amplifiers ☐ Limiters

electronics six — Oscillators ☐ Sinusoidal and Nonsinusoidal Oscillators ☐ Relaxation Oscillators ☐ Magnetron Oscillators ☐ Klystron Oscillators ☐ Crystal Oscillators ☐ Modulators ☐ Mixers and Converters ☐ Detectors and Demodulators ☐ Discriminators

electronics seven — Auxiliary Circuits ☐ AVC, AGC, and AFC Circuits ☐ Limiter and Clamping Circuits ☐ Separator, Counter, and Gating Circuits ☐ Time Delay Circuits ☐ Radio Transmission ☐ Antennas ☐ Radiation Patterns ☐ R-F Transmission Lines

electronics
one-seven

HARRY MILEAF EDITOR-IN-CHIEF

HAYDEN BOOK COMPANY, INC.
Rochelle Park, New Jersey

Library of Congress Catalog Card Number 66-23489

Printed in the United States of America

Fifth Printing, 1970

preface

This book combines a series of volumes designed specifically to teach electronics. The series is logically organized to fit the learning process. Each volume covers a given area of knowledge, which in itself is complete, but also prepares the student for the ensuing volumes. Within each volume, the topics are taught in incremental steps and each topic treatment prepares the student for the next topic. Only *one* discrete topic or concept is examined on a page, and *each* page carries an illustration that graphically depicts the topic being covered. As a result of this treatment, neither the text nor the illustrations are relied on solely as a teaching medium for any given topic. Both are given for *every* topic, so that the illustrations not only complement but reinforce the text. In addition, to further aid the student in retaining what he has learned, the important points are summarized in text form on the illustration. This unique treatment allows the book to be used as a convenient review text. Color is used not for decorative purposes, but to accent important points and make the illustrations meaningful.

In keeping with good teaching practice, all technical terms are defined at their point of introduction so that the student can proceed with confidence. And, to facilitate matters for both the student and the teacher, key words for each topic are made conspicuous by the use of italics. Major points covered in prior topics are often reiterated in later topics for purposes of retention. This allows not only the smooth transition from topic to topic, but the reinforcement of prior knowledge just before the declining point of one's memory curve. At the end of each group of topics comprising a lesson, a summary of the facts is given, together with an appropriate set of review questions, so that the student himself can determine how well he is learning as he proceeds through the book.

Much of the credit for the development of this series belongs to various members of the excellent team of authors, editors, and technical consultants assembled by the publisher. Special acknowledgment of the contributions of the following individuals is most appropriate: Frank T. Egan, Jack Greenfield, and Warren W. Yates, principal contributors; Peter J. Zurita, S. William Cook, Jr., Steven Barbash, Solomon Flam, and A. Victor Schwarz, of the publisher's staff; Paul J. Barotta, Director of the Union Technical Institute; Albert J. Marcarelli, Technical Director of the Connecticut School of Electronics; Howard Bierman, Editor of *Electronic Design;* E. E. Grazda, Editorial Director of *Electronic Design;* and Irving Lopatin, Editorial Director of the Hayden Book Companies.

Harry Mileaf
Editor-in-Chief

contents

ELECTRONICS ONE

CONTENTS

CONTENTS

ELECTRONICS FOUR

CONTENTS

CONTENTS

CONTENTS

ELECTRONICS SIX

CONTENTS

CONTENTS

ELECTRONICS SEVEN

electronics
one

what is electronics?

Now that you are beginning the study of electronics, it might be a good idea to ask yourself, "Do I really know what electronics is?" From your familiarity with some of the everyday applications of electronics, you know that there is a relationship between *electronics* and *electricity*, since electronic devices, such as radios and televisions, all use electricity. However, all devices that use electricity are not electronic devices. The washing machine, electric iron, television, and hi-fi all use electricity; but the washing machine and the iron are *electrical* devices, while the television and hi-fi are *electronic* devices. What makes the difference? The answer can be found in the concept of *intelligence*, and it is on this basis that we will define the study of electronics.

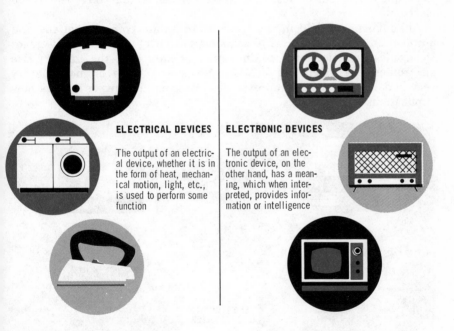

ELECTRICAL DEVICES

The output of an electrical device, whether it is in the form of heat, mechanical motion, light, etc., is used to perform some function

ELECTRONIC DEVICES

The output of an electronic device, on the other hand, has a meaning, which when interpreted, provides information or intelligence

In the study of *electricity*, you learned how electrical phenomena are used to provide *power* or *energy*. Thus, an electric iron is an electrical device because electricity is used to provide energy, in the form of heat, by its element. Similarly, electricity provides the power to turn the tub of a washing machine as well as to operate its control relays. In the study of *electronics*, though, you will learn how electricity is used to carry *intelligence*. You will find that this intelligence varies widely, from the simple doorbell, which tells you that someone is calling, to complex radar systems, which locate and track fast-moving distant targets. Nevertheless, any device that uses electricity to *tell*, *show*, or otherwise *inform* is electronic.

where is electronics used?

There is probably no aspect of our present-day life that has not been influenced to some extent by electronics. Electronic devices and equipment are used in so many ways, and for so many reasons, that it is almost impossible to adequately summarize their uses.

In certain fields, electronics plays such an important role that it is safe to say that without it, these fields could never have developed to their present status. An example of one of these fields is *communications*. Without electronic radio transmitters and receivers, rapid communication as we know it today would be impossible. Another example is industrial *automation*. Most of the monitoring and control devices that make automation possible are electronic. *Data processing* and *scientific and medical research* are other fields that rely heavily on electronics.

Although not a field in the same sense as are communications and automation, the *military establishment* is one of the largest users of electronics and electronic equipment. Not only does the military use electronics extensively, but it also spends vast sums of money every year to develop new and improved electronic equipment, as well as new applications of electronics.

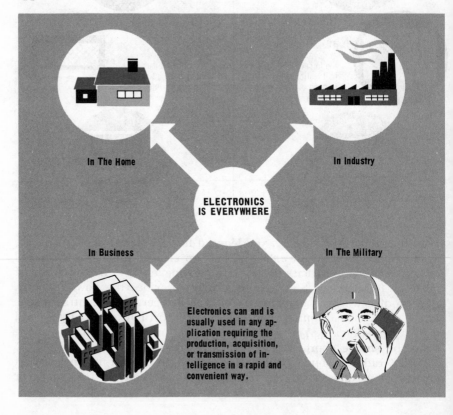

In The Home

In Industry

ELECTRONICS
IS EVERYWHERE

In Business

In The Military

Electronics can and is usually used in any application requiring the production, acquisition, or transmission of intelligence in a rapid and convenient way.

electronic signals

You will recall from what you learned about electricity that electrical currents and voltages have various *characteristics*. These range from the amplitude for d-c currents and voltages to the a-c sinusoidal waveform, frequency, period, etc. Although these characteristics must be considered when you analyze electrical circuits, the quantity you are most interested in is usually the *energy* or *power* delivered to the load.

In electronics, characteristics of signals that are extremely important because of their intelligence-carrying capability include:

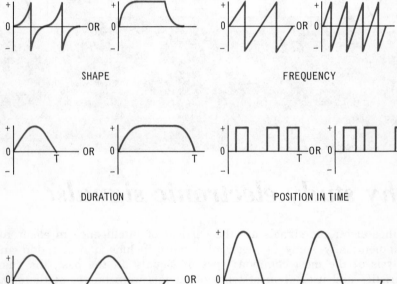

SHAPE   FREQUENCY

DURATION   POSITION IN TIME

AMPLITUDE

In the study of electronics, the situation is entirely different. The power delivered is still a consideration, but it is no longer the most important characteristic. The other characteristics of the currents and voltages are just as, if not more, important, since it is by means of these characteristics that the currents and voltages *carry intelligence*. For convenience, currents or voltages that carry intelligence are often referred to as *signals*.

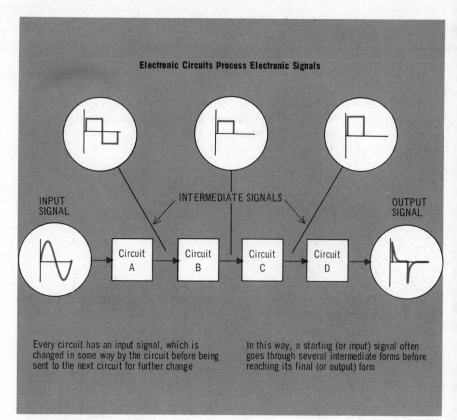

Electronic Circuits Process Electronic Signals

INPUT
SIGNAL

INTERMEDIATE SIGNALS

OUTPUT
SIGNAL

Circuit A → Circuit B → Circuit C → Circuit D

Every circuit has an input signal, which is changed in some way by the circuit before being sent to the next circuit for further change

In this way, a starting (or input) signal often goes through several intermediate forms before reaching its final (or output) form

why study electronic signals?

Since electronic signals are the carriers of intelligence in electronic equipment, any study of electronics must include a description and analysis of the most common types of signals. In the past, the characteristics and uses of most types of signals were taught at the *same time* that the circuits producing the signals were described. This was a satisfactory method for a long time. In recent years, however, rapid advances in the electronics field have opened this method to question. New circuits, new equipment, and new applications have resulted in the situation where the same basic type of signal is produced and used in a *wide variety* of ways. It seems desirable, therefore, to *divorce* signals from circuits or equipment as much as possible, and describe them from the standpoint of how they carry intelligence, how they interact with other signals, etc. This somewhat unique approach is used in this volume, which is devoted entirely to electronic signals.

Once you have a firm grasp of the principles and characteristics of electronic signals, you will find that circuits as well as entire equipments can be explained on the basis of them.

d-c signals

The use of dc amply illustrates how intelligence can be added to a voltage or current to create a signal. Consider first the case of two men separated by a great distance. If their only means of communication is a d-c circuit consisting of a battery and a current-limiting resistor, it is obvious that they cannot communicate. A steady d-c current flows in the circuit, and such a current carries no intelligence.

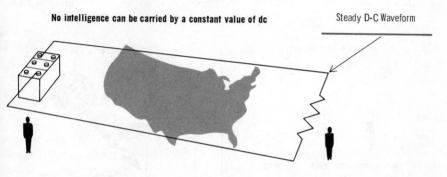

No intelligence can be carried by a constant value of dc   Steady D-C Waveform

By the addition of a *switch* into the circuit, though, the current can drop to zero when the switch is opened, and rise to its steady value when the switch is closed. So by opening and closing the switch, one man causes the current to either *flow* or *not flow*. The waveform of the current is a pulse when current flows and no pulse when current stops. If the men have a prearranged code whereby each letter of the alphabet is represented by a particular combination of pulses, the man with the switch can then cause the current waveform to carry any message he wants. This, of course, assumes that the other man has a way of "seeing" or "hearing" the waveform.

This example, although impractical, serves to illustrate that intelligence can only be carried when some characteristic of a current or voltage is made to *change* or *vary* in a meaningful way.

If dc is broken up into a series of pulses whose characteristics correspond to   D-C Pulse Waveform
some code, the dc then makes up an intelligence-carrying signal

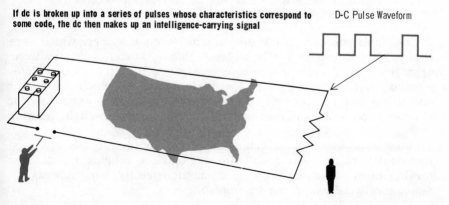

applications

As you will learn, d-c signals are not used as widely as are a-c signals, but they have many practical applications. Some applications make use of *photoelectric cells.* When light strikes a photoelectric cell, the cell emits electrons to produce a d-c current. Thus, when no light strikes the cell, there is no d-c current; and, within certain limits, when light does fall upon the cell, the *amplitude* of the d-c current is proportional to the light intensity. The d-c current, therefore, can serve as a signal which represents the *presence,* or *intensity,* of light striking the cell.

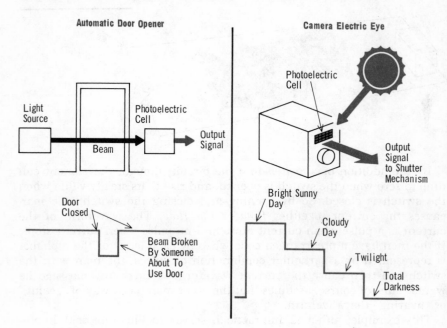

Since dc has only two characteristics that can be varied (presence or absence, and amplitude), all d-c signals have a basic similarity. But the intelligence carried by d-c signals can represent a wide variety of things

One application of this is the automatic door opener, which uses a photoelectric cell and a light beam that is broken when someone approaches the door. The interruption of the cell output then actuates a motor that opens the door. The basic signal on which the circuit operates is nothing more than a certain d-c current level when the door is closed, and a short duration of zero current when the light beam is broken.

Other applications in which similar types of d-c signals are used include devices for automatically turning on electric lights at night and turning them off at daybreak, and electric eyes used in cameras for automatically adjusting the lens opening.

disadvantages

Steady d-c currents and voltages, as shown on the previous pages, can be made to carry intelligence, and can therefore be used as signals. The signals can be formed by making the dc vary between *zero* and its *full value*, or by having it vary between *two different values*. As far as the signal is concerned, though, both types are the same. The only difference is that the zero reference level is replaced with a d-c reference level.

With the exception of certain applications, such as digital computers, and teletype, d-c signals are not used *extensively* in electronics. There are many reasons for this, with one of the more important being their lack of compatability with many electronic circuits and components. As you learn about the characteristics and uses of a-c signals, the disadvantages of d-c signals will become obvious.

An important point that you should note here is that although d-c *signals* are not used extensively in electronics, d-c *voltages* are *widely used* for supplying *power*. In fact, most of the power supplied to electronic circuits within an equipment is dc. Another point of importance here is that the d-c signals so far described are signals derived from a *constant* value of dc. *Fluctuating d-c* signals are used extensively in electronics, but their characteristics are so similar to a-c signals that they will be considered as ac.

D-c signals can vary between zero and the steady value of dc   Or they can vary between two different values of dc

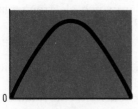

Fluctuating d-c signals, which vary in magnitude but not in direction, are widely used in electronics. They are similar in many ways to a-c signals, and will be considered as such

summary

□ Electronics can be defined as the study of how electricity is used to tell, show, or otherwise inform. To do this, the electricity must carry intelligence, and it is this intelligence that differentiates the study of electricity from the study of electronics. □ When an electrical current or voltage carries intelligence, it is referred to as a signal. Intelligence is carried on a signal by means of characteristics such as amplitude, phase, or frequency. □ Signals used in a wide variety of circuits and equipments are similar. It is possible, therefore, to divorce signals from specific circuits and equipment and study them from the standpoint of how they carry intelligence and interact with other signals.

□ Intelligence can be added to a voltage or current to create a signal in many ways. □ Probably the simplest way to produce a signal is to interrupt a steady d-c current. The result is a series of pulses when current flows and no pulses when current stops. □ If current pulses are made to correspond to some code, they carry intelligence and can be used to transmit messages. The important thing is that the pulses, or interruptions in current, must occur in some meaningful sequence.

□ D-c signals are not as widely used as are a-c signals. Nevertheless, they have many important uses, especially in applications involving computers and teletypewriter communications. □ Although d-c signals are not used extensively in electronics, d-c voltages are widely used for supplying power to the circuits in electronic equipment. □ Fluctuating d-c signals have characteristics very similar to a-c signals. Therefore, they can be treated as ac.

review questions

1. What is *electronics*?
2. How does the study of electronics differ from the study of electricity?
3. Name five fields in which electronics is widely used today.
4. What is a *signal*?
5. Give an example of an electrical signal that you encounter every day.
6. Name three characteristics of a current or voltage that can be varied to produce a signal.
7. Does a 5-ampere current carry more intelligence than a 2-ampere current?
8. Are d-c signals used in electronics?
9. Draw a simple circuit that can produce d-c signals.
10. Can intelligence be added to a fluctuating d-c voltage?

a-c signals

You are now ready to learn about a-c signals. You will see in the rest of this volume how ac, because of its extreme versatility and many desirable characteristics, is used for an almost limitless variety of electronic signals. Before proceeding, though, it is important for you to realize that practically everything you will learn has as its basis the fundamental principles of ac. There is a change in *emphasis*, to be sure, away from the transfer of electrical power and to the transmission or production of intelligence. Nevertheless, the basic concepts of ac are the same, regardless of the specific purpose for which it is being used. Whether it is providing energy to light a city, or carrying the television signal to your home, ac still varies in both magnitude and direction. It is still affected the same way by inductors and capacitors. It still has the basic properties of frequency, phase, amplitude, etc. And it still can be represented graphically by means of waveforms. In other words, a-c electricity is the starting point for learning about a-c electronic signals.

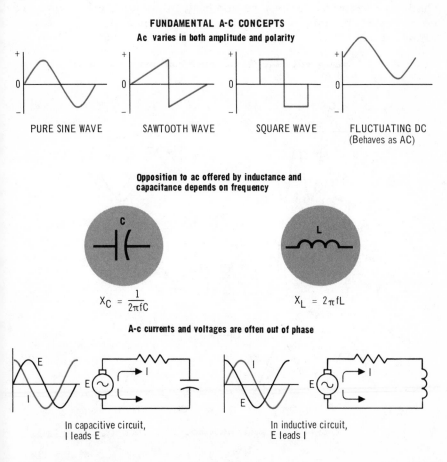

FUNDAMENTAL A-C CONCEPTS
Ac varies in both amplitude and polarity

PURE SINE WAVE   SAWTOOTH WAVE   SQUARE WAVE   FLUCTUATING DC
(Behaves as AC)

Opposition to ac offered by inductance and capacitance depends on frequency

$$X_C = \frac{1}{2\pi f C}$$

$$X_L = 2\pi f L$$

A-c currents and voltages are often out of phase

In capacitive circuit,
I leads E

In inductive circuit,
E leads I

the continuous a-c wave

In electricity, you learned that an a-c wave is made up of a *continuous* succession of sine waves. The sine waves are all *identical* in every way, having the same amplitude the same period, the same frequency, etc. Because of this absolute similarity, every individual cycle, or sine wave, of a continuous a-c wave looks exactly like every other cycle. Thus, as a carrier of intelligence, the continuous a-c wave is similar to a steady level of dc. It has no *meaningful* variations or changes which, as you know, are necessary for intelligence. Of course, the amplitude of the wave does change. But the changes are exactly the same during each cycle.

You recall that even though a steady value of dc carries no intelligence, it can be broken into a series of pulses that can then represent intelligence. Essentially, the same can be done with a continuous a-c wave. In addition, a-c waves have other characteristics that can be varied, such as the *amplitude* and the *frequency*, as well as some others that are shown. Before describing how intelligence can be inserted on a continuous a-c wave, however, certain basic information will be reviewed on the type and ranges of frequencies commonly used in electronic signals.

Characteristics of continuous a-c waves that are important when they are used as signals are

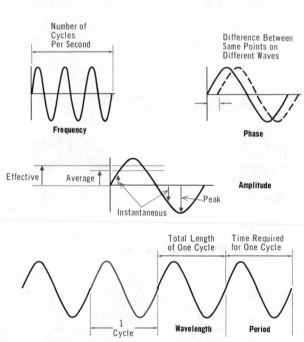

Each cycle of a continuous a-c wave is identical to every other cycle

audio frequencies

The frequency of a continuous a-c wave is the number of times per second that the wave makes a complete cycle from zero, through to its maximum positive value, then through to its maximum negative value, and back to zero. Each full cycle is one complete sine wave. The frequency is normally expressed in cycles per second (cps), so the higher the frequency of a wave, the more times it reverses direction each second. A-c waveforms can be produced having frequencies from as low as a few cps to billions and even trillions of cps. Because of this extremely wide range, frequencies are usually divided into *subranges*, or *bands*. Each band is a range of frequencies that have similar properties and are used in similar ways in electronic applications.

One extremely important band of frequencies consists of those frequencies that correspond to the frequency range of the *human ear:* those frequencies that people can hear. These frequencies start at about 20 cps, and extend to about 20,000 cps. The frequencies in this 20-to-20,000-cps range are therefore called *audio frequencies,* since they correspond to audible sound.

Often, audio frequencies are also referred to as *sonic frequencies* because they are *sound frequencies.* As a result, frequencies below 20 cps can be referred to as *subsonic,* and those just above the audio band can be called *supersonic, ultrasonic* or *hypersonic* signals.

This Complex Sound Wave is Made Up of Many Simple Waves

Sound waves are normally complex and are not the simple type of audio sinusoidal wave with which you are familiar

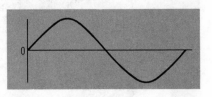

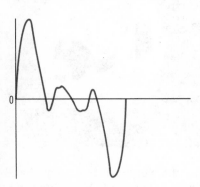

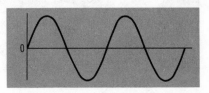

The complex sound waves are made up of many simple sinusoidal audio waves. When the human ear hears a sound represented by a complex sound wave, it is actually sensitive to all the constituent simple sinusoidal waves that are in the audio range

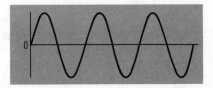

higher frequencies

Signal frequencies as high as thousands of *megacycles* are used in electronics. You already know that those frequencies between 20 and 20,000 cps are called audio frequencies. They are often, however, also called *very-low frequencies,* since they are the lowest frequencies used for electronic signals. The frequencies above the audio, or very-low, frequencies are also divided into bands, and these bands have designations, such as low-frequency, medium-frequency, etc., which describe the *relative* highness or lowness of the frequencies in the band. Similarly, any frequency in the medium-frequency band is higher than any in the low-frequency band.

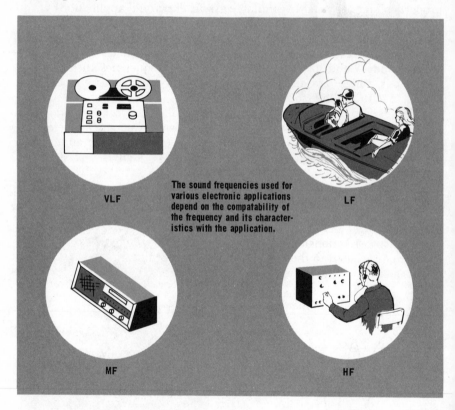

VLF

The sound frequencies used for various electronic applications depend on the compatability of the frequency and its characteristics with the application.

LF

MF

HF

The designations of the bands above the very-low frequency band (VLF) are: low frequency (LF), medium frequency (MF), high frequency (HF), very-high frequency (VHF), ultra-high frequency (UHF), super-high frequency (SHF), and extremely-high frequency (EHF). In addition, you have probably heard people refer to *short waves* and *microwaves.* These designations also refer to frequency ranges, but do so in terms of *wavelength,* as meter or centimeter bands. This is possible, since the frequency and wavelength of a wave are directly related.

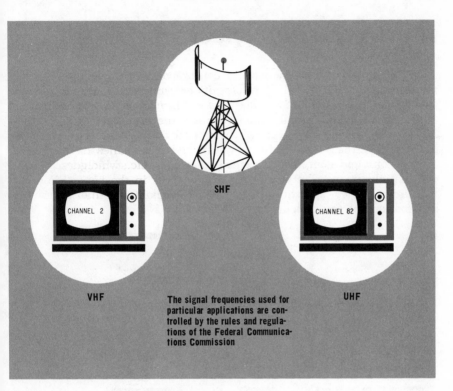

SHF

VHF

CHANNEL 2

CHANNEL 82

UHF

The signal frequencies used for particular applications are controlled by the rules and regulations of the Federal Communications Commission

higher frequencies (cont.)

The exact relationship of frequency and wavelength is that the wavelength is equal to the velocity of the wave, which is normally taken as the speed of light, divided by the frequency:

$$\text{Wavelength (meters)} = \frac{\text{speed of light (meters/sec)}}{\text{frequency (cycles/sec)}}$$

$$\lambda = \frac{300,000,000}{f}$$

With this method, you can say that signals are in the 30-meter band, 50-meter band, and so on; or in the 10-centimeter band, etc. The frequency range covered by the terms short wave and microwave are not exact, with different groups and organizations using different ranges. For this reason, the designations of LF, MF, HF, etc. are preferred, since the more precise definitions are widely accepted. Similarly, in the field of radar, letters such as K, X, and L are often used to designate certain frequency bands. These designations were originally used for purposes of military secrecy, but have now come into general use. Like short waves and microwaves, though, the limits of these bands are not precisely defined.

the frequency spectrum

All of the possible frequencies of continuous a-c waves make up the *frequency spectrum*. For the purposes of electronic signals, the frequency spectrum starts at about 20 *cps* and continues up to approximately 30,000 *megacycles*. Actually, the frequency spectrum extends far beyond 30,000 megacycles. However, at these high frequencies, a-c waves no longer have the characteristics normally associated with electronic applications and equipment. Instead, they are in the category of heat waves, light waves, X-rays, and so on.

The frequency spectrum of electronic signals, together with the designations of the various frequency bands, is shown.

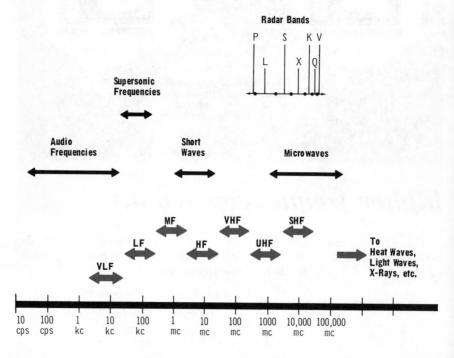

THE FREQUENCY SPECTRUM	
Band	**Frequency Range**
Very-low frequency, VLF	< 3 kc to 30 kc
Low frequency, LF	30 kc to 300 kc
Medium frequency, MF	300 kc to 3000 kc
High frequency, HF	3 mc to 30 mc
Very-high frequency, VHF	30 mc to 300 mc
Ultra-high frequency, UHF	300 mc to 3000 mc
Super-high frequency, SHF	3000 mc to 30,000 mc
Extremely high frequency, EHF	Above 30,000 mc

the interrupted continuous wave

As stated, a continuous a-c wave, like a steady value of dc, carries no intelligence. However, if the wave can be *interrupted* so that it becomes a series of *pulses* that corresponds to some known code, then the wave carries intelligence. Such signals provide *interrupted continuous-wave* (CW) *transmission,* since they do nothing more than go *on* and *off*.

A pulse of a continuous wave actually consists of many cycles of the current or voltage that makes up the wave. However, it is the *presence* of the pulse, or its *duration,* that makes the intelligence, not the number of cycles contained in a pulse. For example, if a one-second pulse represented the letter A, it would make no difference whether a 100-cps or a 1000-cps frequency was used.

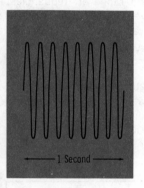

For the purposes of carrying intelligence, these CW pulses are identical, even though one is derived from an 8-cps wave and the other from a 2-cps wave. What makes them the same is that they are both 1-second long

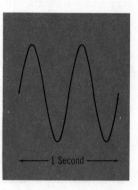

Interrupted CW transmission is widely used in radiotelegraphy, where the continuous wave is broken into pulses that correspond to the familiar dots and dashes of the Morse code. The dots are short pulses, and the dash pulses are three times longer. Each letter of the alphabet then has its own combination of dots and dashes. Thus, pulses corresponding to any combination of dots and dashes can be produced.

In Morse Code, the interrupted CW signal for the letter I (dot – dot) would look like this:

Similarly, the signal for the letter R (dot–dash–dot) would look like this:

summary

☐ A continuous a-c wave is made up of a succession of identical sine waves. Such a wave has no meaningful variations, and therefore does not carry intelligence. ☐ If an a-c wave is broken into a series of pulses that correspond to some known code, it then becomes a signal, since it carries intelligence. A signal of this sort is called an interrupted CW signal. ☐ Interrupted CW transmission is widely used in radio telegraphy, where the signal interruptions correspond to the dots and dashes of the Morse code.

☐ A-c waves can be produced having frequencies from as low as a few cps to as high as many billions of cps. ☐ Frequencies from about 20 to 20,000 cps correspond to audible sound, and are called audio frequencies. ☐ All of the possible frequencies of the continuous a-c waves make up the frequency spectrum. For the purposes of electronics, the frequency spectrum is divided into various bands, with each band covering a certain range of frequencies. ☐ The frequency bands and their designations are: very-low frequency (VLF), low frequency (LF), medium frequency (MF), high frequency (HF), very-high frequency (VHF), ultra-high frequency (UHF), super-high frequency (SHF), and extremely-high frequency (EHF).

☐ A-c waves can be described in terms of wavelength as well as frequency. This is because the frequency and wavelength of a wave are directly related. ☐ Wavelength is equal to the velocity, normally taken as the speed of light, divided by the frequency. As an equation, $\lambda = 300,000,000/f$; where λ is the wavelength in meters, and f is the frequency in cps.

review questions

1. Does a steady continuous a-c wave carry intelligence? Why?
2. What is the wavelength of a 10-megacycle a-c wave?
3. How can an interrupted continuous a-c wave be made to carry intelligence?
4. A 50-kilocycle wave is in what frequency band?
5. Which has a longer wavelength: an audio frequency or a subsonic frequency?
6. Which has the higher frequency: a UHF or a VHF frequency?
7. Which has the shorter wavelength: a UHF or a VHF frequency?
8. Which has the greater amplitude: a UHF or a VHF frequency?
9. What is the frequency of a 1-meter wave?
10. Increasing the amplitude of a continuous a-c wave has what effect on the wavelength?

the modulated continuous wave

You have seen how intelligence can be added to a continuous a-c wave by interrupting it in such a way that it is broken into a series of pulses that correspond to some known code. Although this type of signal is widely used, it has certain disadvantages; the most important being that it cannot easily carry intelligence that corresponds to *sound,* such as the human voice or music. Therefore, when a signal is to be used for carrying sound, other means of adding the intelligence are usually used. In these methods, some characteristic of the *continuous* a-c wave is *controlled* by the sound in such a way that it varies in exactly the same manner as the sound wave. The continuous a-c wave is then said to be *modulated* by the sound.

Modulation is a process whereby some characteristic
of a wave is varied by another wave

A Carrier

Can Be
Amplitude Modulated

Or
Frequency Modulated

Two of the most commonly used
types of modulation are amplitude
and frequency modulation

Both are widely used for inserting sound, or audible, intelligence on carrier waves

The two most common characteristics of an a-c wave that are modulated by sound are the *amplitude* and the *frequency.* When the sound controls the amplitude of the wave, it is *amplitude modulation;* and when the frequency is controlled by the sound, it is *frequency modulation.* The a-c wave is called the *carrier,* since it is made to "carry" the sound intelligence.

In actual practice, amplitude and frequency modulation are used to add many other types of intelligence, besides sound, to a carrier wave. However, the principles are the same regardless of the type of intelligence involved, as you will learn.

amplitude modulation

When the *amplitude* of one wave is varied in accordance with another wave that represents some form of intelligence, the process is called amplitude modulation. The wave being modulated is the *carrier,* and the other is the *modulating signal* or wave. In amplitude modulation, the *peak-to-peak* amplitude of the a-c carrier is varied with the intelligence; the carrier then consists of sine waves whose amplitudes follow the amplitude variations of the modulating wave, so that the carrier is contained in an *envelope* formed by the modulating wave.

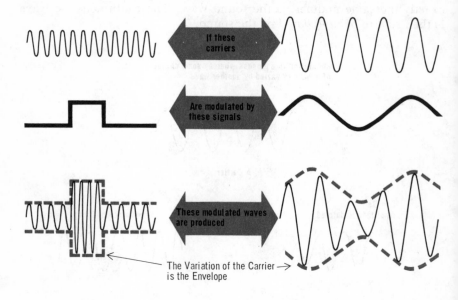

If the carrier and the lower half of the envelope could be removed from a modulated wave, the remaining upper half of the envelope would exactly duplicate the modulating wave, which represents the intelligence being carried. This is done to recover, or remove, the intelligence from the modulated wave. The process is called DEMODULATION, and will be covered later

You may now wonder why a signal that already carries intelligence (the modulating wave) should be used to modulate another wave (the carrier). As you will learn, radio transmission of higher frequency signals is *cheaper* and more *reliable* than transmission of very low-frequency signals. You need a lot of power to transmit a low-frequency signal, and it cannot be transmitted very far. Thus, low-frequency intelligence is placed on, or modulates, a higher frequency signal, which is often called a *radio-frequency* (r-f) *carrier* since it is suitable for radio transmission. The term "radio frequency" does not define any specific frequency band. It just means that the frequency is high enough for practical radio transmission.

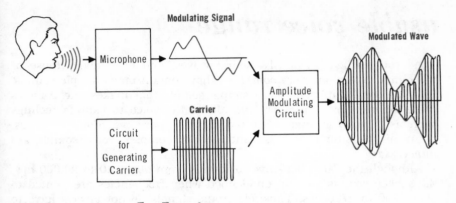

voice modulation

One of the most common types of intelligence carried by electronic signals is the sound of the *human voice*. And when such intelligence is to be transmitted by radio, an electrical voice signal is first produced, which is then used to modulate a higher frequency carrier. Amplitude modulation is used most often for this purpose.

In a typical voice modulation setup, a person speaks into a microphone, which produces an audio-frequency signal that corresponds to the sound waves created by the speaker's voice. The audio-frequency signal is then used to modulate a carrier that has a frequency usually well above the audio range. After modulation, the peak-to-peak amplitude of the carrier varies according to the modulating signal. Thus, the modulated wave varies in two ways: one of these is the *rapid* (high-frequency) variations of the instantaneous amplitude and polarity of the carrier; and the other is the *slower* (audio-frequency) variations of the peak-to-peak amplitude of the carrier. An important point to understand here is that the audio-frequency variations of the carrier, which actually represent the sound intelligence being transmitted, vary in both frequency and amplitude. The frequency variations represent the pitch of the sound, and the amplitude variations, the loudness of the sound. The carrier on the other hand, only varies in amplitude. Its frequency does not change.

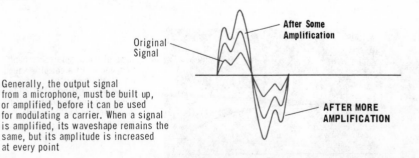

Generally, the output signal from a microphone, must be built up, or amplified, before it can be used for modulating a carrier. When a signal is amplified, its waveshape remains the same, but its amplitude is increased at every point

usable voice range

As you learned previously, sound waves, and particularly those of the human voice, are very *complex*. They contain many simple sounds. It is the combination of these simple sounds that makes one person's voice different from another, and allows the voice to express feelings such as sorrow or anger. For basic *voice communications* purposes, many of the simple sounds contained in complex voice sounds are *unnecessary*.

Although the ear is sensitive to sounds from about 20 to 20,000 cps, the spoken sounds are still understood when frequencies are limited to about 200 to 2700 cps. Thus, electronic signals do not always have to duplicate the sound waves. This often makes it possible to reduce the complexity and cost of the electronic circuits used for sound reproduction and transmission. Of course, in certain areas, such as the high-fidelity reproduction of music, the electronic sound signal must duplicate closely the original sound waves. For standard AM radio broadcasting, on the other hand, audio frequencies above 5000 cps are eliminated, yet the quality of the sound is satisfactory for most purposes.

First Person   **Second Person**

If two people pronounced the letter O, the waveforms of their sounds would be similar and yet different in some respects

The differences arise from the fact that, although in both cases the sound O was recognizable, the two waveforms are made up of a somewhat different combination of frequencies

This Sound Wave   MIGHT BE REPRODUCED   **This Electronic Sound**
                        INTELLIGIBLY BY   **Signal**

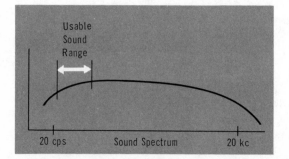

Usable Sound Range

20 cps   Sound Spectrum   20 kc

Some of the simple component frequencies of a complex sound wave can be omitted and the sound will still be intelligible. When frequencies are removed, the waveform of the sound changes

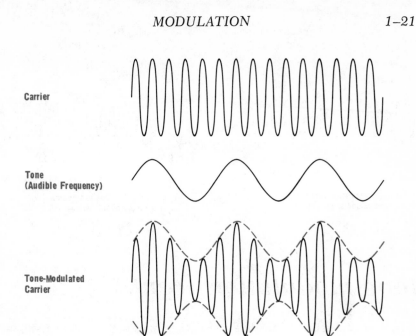

Carrier

Tone
(Audible Frequency)

Tone-Modulated
Carrier

If a continuous-wave carrier is amplitude modulated by an
audible frequency, the result is a tone-modulated carrier.
Such a signal can carry intelligence in various ways

tone modulation

Previously, you learned about interrupted CW signals. These consist
of pulses that conform to the dots and dashes of the Morse code, and
which we made by interrupting a continuous a-c wave. Although interrupted CW signals provide a good means for transmitting intelligence,
they are subject to certain conditions that can render them unintelligible.
The reason for this is that the on–off conditions of the carrier are really
only d-c levels, which must be changed to a signal you can hear at the
receiver. Sometimes, because of *instabilities* in the electronic circuits
and equipment used, the CW signal will change, or *drift*, in frequency.
The circuits that convert the signal to audible sounds then can no
longer perform their function, and the signal is, in effect, lost.

One way of overcoming this problem is by amplitude modulating
the continuous wave with an *audible* signal. Sinusoidal signals of 500
or 1000 cps are frequently used for this. When the continuous wave is
modulated in this way, it can still be interrupted to form dot-and-dash
pulses. However, now each pulse contains an audio-frequency envelope,
and the dot-and-dash sounds are already in the signal. So, to convert
the pulses to audible sounds, all that is required is for the carrier and
one-half of the envelope to be removed in some way. Circuits for
accomplishing this are relatively simple and reliable.

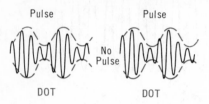
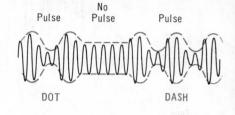

DOT DOT DOT DASH

The modulated carrier can be interrupted to form pulses

OR

Only the tone can be interrupted to form pulses

tone modulation (cont.)

It is also possible to modulate a carrier with a tone, and then just *interrupt the tone* to produce the pulses for carrying the intelligence. The *no-pulse* condition is then represented by the *unmodulated carrier*. With this method, the signal is continuous and only the intelligence portion is interrupted. In radio transmission, as you will learn later, this method makes it possible to *maintain radio contact* even when no intelligence is being sent.

Tone modulation can also be used for the methods in which more than a single tone modulates a carrier. In these methods, one tone can correspond to a pulse and another to no pulse; or one tone can be a dot and another tone can be a dash; or the various tones can even represent different intelligence. Of course, when multiple tones are used, they must have different frequencies so that they can be distinguished from each other.

Sometimes a single *continuous tone* is used to modulate a *continuous-wave carrier*. In this case, the modulated wave itself carries *no* intelligence, but the way in which the wave is used does. You will learn more about the uses of this type of signal later.

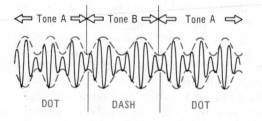

DOT DASH DOT

More than one tone can be used

A single tone can continuously modulate the carrier

pulse modulation

When intelligence is to be transmitted by radio at UHF and SHF frequencies, the power requirements of the electronic equipment is an important consideration. One way of decreasing the power required is to break up the intelligence into *small bits* or *samples,* which can be used to reproduce the original intelligence after transmission. In effect, only a *portion* of the intelligence is transmitted, but it is sufficient to allow the *total* intelligence to be recreated from it. One method of accomplishing this type of transmission is called *pulse modulation.* In this type of modulation, the modulating signal is first converted to a series of pulses whose amplitudes correspond to the instantaneous amplitudes of the modulating signal. These *amplitude-modulated pulses* are then used to amplitude modulate a carrier wave, with the result that the modulated carrier consists of a series of pulses having amplitudes that correspond to the intelligence being transmitted.

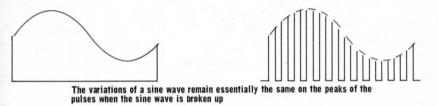

The variations of a sine wave remain essentially the same on the peaks of the pulses when the sine wave is broken up

Actually, the type of pulse modulation just described is called *pulse amplitude modulation* (PAM). There are other methods of pulse modulation frequently used. These other methods, as well as a more detailed description of PAM, are covered later.

For an identical carrier and modulating signal the peak and minimum transmitted power is the same whether continuous or pulse modulation is used. However, since with the pulse method there are periods when the signal is not being transmitted at all, the average power of the pulse signal is much less than that of the continuous one.

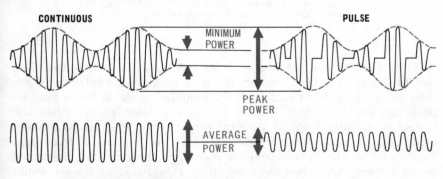

Although a continuous and a pulse signal may have the same peak and minimum power, the average power of the pulse signal is much lower

percentage of modulation

In the discussion of amplitude modulation, nothing has been said about the *relative amplitudes* of the modulating signal and the unmodulated carrier. The relationship between these two amplitudes is the *percentage of modulation,* which expresses the extent to which the carrier is modulated. When the peak-to-peak amplitude of the modulating signal *equals* the peak-to-peak amplitude of the unmodulated carrier, the carrier is said to be *100 percent* modulated. Thus, in the case of 100 percent modulation, the modulating signal goes far enough positive to double the peak-to-peak amplitude of the carrier, and far enough negative to reduce the peak-to-peak amplitude of the carrier to zero.

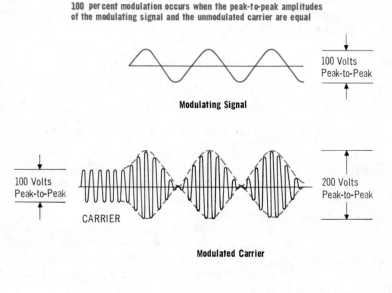

100 percent modulation occurs when the peak-to-peak amplitudes of the modulating signal and the unmodulated carrier are equal

100 Volts
Peak-to-Peak

Modulating Signal

100 Volts
Peak-to-Peak

CARRIER

200 Volts
Peak-to-Peak

Modulated Carrier

The peak-to-peak amplitude of the modulated carrier, therefore, varies from a minimum of zero to a maximum of twice its unmodulated value

If the peak-to-peak amplitude of the modulating signal is *less* than that of the unmodulated carrier, the percentage of modulation is less than 100 percent. For example, if the modulating signal has a peak-to-peak amplitude one-half that of the unmodulated carrier, then the carrier is modulated by 50 percent; or, put another way, 50 percent modulation is used. When the modulating signal reaches its maximum positive value, the peak-to-peak amplitude of the carrier is increased by 50 percent. And when the modulating signal reaches its maximum negative value, the carrier's peak-to-peak amplitude is decreased by 50 percent.

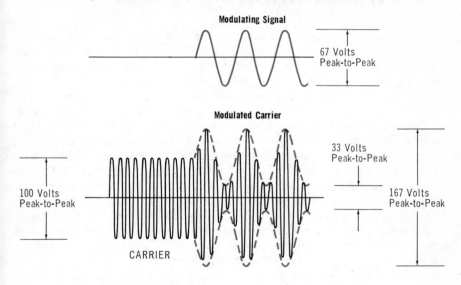

67 percent modulation occurs when the peak-to-peak amplitude of the modulating signal is two-thirds, or 67 percent, that of the unmodulated carrier

Modulating Signal

67 Volts
Peak-to-Peak

Modulated Carrier

33 Volts
Peak-to-Peak

167 Volts
Peak-to-Peak

100 Volts
Peak-to-Peak

CARRIER

The peak-to-peak amplitude of the modulated carrier, therefore, varies from a minimum value 67 percent less than its unmodulated value, to a maximum 67 percent greater than its unmodulated value

percentage of modulation (cont.)

There are various formulas for calculating the percentage of modulation of an amplitude-modulated carrier. One of the easiest is

$$\text{Percentage of modulation} = \frac{E_{MAX} - E_{MIN}}{E_{MAX} + E_{MIN}} \times 100$$

where E_{MAX} is the greatest peak-to-peak amplitude of the modulated carrier, and E_{MIN} is the smallest. For example, if the peak-to-peak values of a modulated carrier vary from a maximum of 167 volts to a minimum of 33 volts, the percentage of modulation is

$$\text{Percentage of modulation} = \frac{167 - 33}{167 + 33} \times 100$$

$$= 0.67 \times 100$$

$$= 67\%$$

The equation can only be used for modulation of 100 percent or less. Modulation greater than 100 percent is called *overmodulation*, and is generally undesirable.

overmodulation

Generally, the higher the percentage of modulation, the more effective and efficient is the transmission of an amplitude-modulated signal. But *overmodulation* is usually undesirable, since it *distorts* the modulation envelope of the carrier.

The way in which overmodulation causes distortion of a modulated signal can be seen from the illustration. If the peak-to-peak amplitude of the modulating signal is greater than that of the unmodulated carrier, the maximum positive values of the modulating signal will cause peak-to-peak values of the modulated carrier greater than twice the unmodulated value. There is nothing wrong with this. But when the modulating signal reaches its maximum negative values, it is greater than the amplitude of the unmodulated carrier. This cancels, or *cuts off*, the carrier, since its peak-to-peak amplitude cannot fall below zero. As a result, the carrier variations do not follow those of the modulating signal when the modulating signal goes through its extreme negative values. Part of the negative cycle is *clipped* off. Because of this distortion of the modulated signal caused by overmodulation, percentages of modulation greater than 100 percent are seldom used. Such overmodulation is not used in voice communication systems because the voice will sound clipped or garbled.

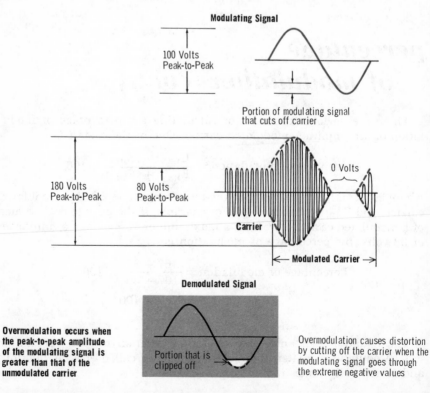

Modulating Signal

100 Volts
Peak-to-Peak

Portion of modulating signal
that cuts off carrier

180 Volts
Peak-to-Peak

80 Volts
Peak-to-Peak

0 Volts

Carrier

|← **Modulated Carrier** →|

Demodulated Signal

Overmodulation occurs when the peak-to-peak amplitude of the modulating signal is greater than that of the unmodulated carrier

Portion that is clipped off

Overmodulation causes distortion by cutting off the carrier when the modulating signal goes through the extreme negative values

summary

☐ When sound or other intelligence controls some characteristic of an a-c wave, the wave is said to be modulated. If the amplitude of the wave is controlled, it is amplitude modulated; and if the frequency is controlled, it is frequency modulated. ☐ An a-c wave being modulated is called the carrier. The signal that is adding the intelligence is called the modulating signal.

☐ In amplitude modulation the peak-to-peak amplitude of the carrier is varied in accordance with the intelligence. After being modulated, the carrier is contained in an envelope formed by the modulating wave. ☐ Simple audio tones, as well as complex voice signals, can be amplitude modulated onto a carrier wave. Tones can carry intelligence by being interrupted to form the dots and dashes of Morse code. ☐ Before intelligence is modulated onto a carrier, the intelligence can be broken into small bits or samples that can be used to reproduce the original intelligence after transmission. This is called pulse modulation. ☐ In one type of pulse modulation, called pulse amplitude modulation (PAM), the modulating signal is converted to a series of pulses whose amplitudes correspond to the instantaneous amplitudes of the modulating signal. ☐ The advantage of pulse modulation is that it requires less average power to transmit a given amount of intelligence.

☐ In amplitude modulation, the relationship between the amplitudes of the modulating signal and the unmodulated carrier is expressed as the percentage of modulation. Percentage of modulation can be calculated by $(E_{MAX} - E_{MIN})/(E_{MAX} + E_{MIN}) \times 100$; where E_{MAX} and E_{MIN} are the maximum and minimum peak-to-peak values of the modulated carrier, respectively. ☐ Modulation greater than 100 percent is called overmodulation and is generally undesirable, since it can cause distortion of the intelligence carried by the signal.

review questions

1. What is a *carrier*?
2. Draw and label the components of an amplitude-modulated signal.
3. What is *tone modulation*?
4. What is *pulse amplitude modulation*?
5. Why is pulse amplitude modulation used?
6. What is *overmodulation,* and why is it undesirable?
7. Draw and label an amplitude-modulated wave that is modulated by 50 percent.
8. Draw an overmodulated wave.
9. Why are voice signals modulated onto a carrier before being transmitted?
10. How does a tone-modulated signal carry intelligence?

side bands

Until now we have been interested in the modulated carrier that results when the amplitude of a carrier is varied by a modulating signal. You have learned that the modulated carrier is a constant-frequency waveform whose amplitude changes in accordance with the modulating signal. Mathematically, though, it can be proven that the modulated carrier consists of *other frequencies* in addition to the carrier frequency. These frequencies are generated as a result of the modulation process, and make up what are known as *side-band frequencies*. Side-band frequencies are not merely mathematical abstractions. They can actually be separated from the modulated carrier, and form the basis for a widely used system of radio transmission.

When this signal...

...Modulates this carrier...

...This modulated carrier is produced, and consists of the following components:

CONSTANT-AMPLITUDE, UPPER SIDE-BAND FREQUENCY

CONSTANT-AMPLITUDE CARRIER FREQUENCY

CONSTANT-AMPLITUDE, LOWER SIDE-BAND FREQUENCY

The amplitude of the modulated carrier at every instant is equal to the algebraic sum of the instantaneous amplitudes of its three components

side bands (cont.)

Side-band frequencies can best be understood by first considering a carrier modulated by a simple sinusoidal modulating signal. The modulating process produces two entirely new frequencies. This results from a process called *heterodyning*, which you will learn about later. One of the new frequencies is equal to the *sum* of the carrier and modulating signal frequencies, and is called the *upper side-band frequency* since it is above the carrier in frequency. The other new frequency equals the *difference* between the carrier and the modulating signal frequencies, and is called the *lower side-band frequency*.

The modulated carrier consists essentially of the two side-band frequencies and the carrier frequency, all having *constant amplitudes*. When the waveforms of these three component frequencies are added, they produce the waveform of the modulated carrier. Thus, the effect of the side-band frequencies is to provide the *amplitude variations* for the carrier frequency.

As an example of the generation of the side-band frequencies, consider a 30-kc carrier modulated by a 1-kc signal. The upper side-band frequency would be 30 + 1, or 31 kc; and the lower side-band frequency, 30 − 1, or 29 kc. The amplitude-modulated carrier, therefore, consists of a 29-kc, a 30-kc, and a 31-kc component, each having a constant amplitude.

SPECTRUM REPRESENTATION OF THE SIDE BANDS

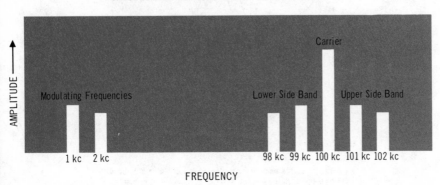

You have seen that when a carrier is amplitude modulated by a single frequency, two side-band frequencies are produced. When a modulating signal consists of more than one frequency, such as in voice modulation, two side-band frequencies are produced for *every* frequency contained in the modulating signal. Thus, if the modulating signal contains two frequencies, four side-band frequencies are produced: two higher than the carrier frequency, and two lower than it. Similarly, if there are ten frequencies in the modulating signal, twenty side-band frequencies are produced; ten on each side of the carrier frequency.

side bands and bandwidth

You can see, then, that there are always *exactly* the same number of side-band frequencies *higher* than the carrier frequency as there are *lower* than it. Together, all of the side-band frequencies above the carrier frequency make up the *upper side band*. In a similar manner, all those below the carrier frequency make up the *lower side band*. The frequencies in the *upper* side band represent the *sum* of the individual modulating frequencies and the carrier frequency, while those in the *lower* side band represent the *difference* between the modulating frequencies and the carrier frequency.

The side-band nature of an amplitude-modulated carrier can be depicted in two ways. One is by use of a spectrum diagram, which shows the amplitude and frequencies of the modulation components in a graphical way (see page 1-29). The other is a pictorial representation of the component waveforms.

PICTORIAL REPRESENTATION OF SIDE BANDS

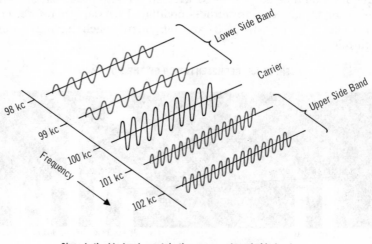

Since both side bands contain the same number of side-band frequencies, they have the same frequency width, or bandwidth

The *bandwidth* of an amplitude-modulated signal is the *frequency range* between the lowest, lower side-band frequency and the highest, upper side-band frequency. Since both of the extreme side-band frequencies are produced by the same modulating frequency, namely the *highest*, the bandwidth can be expressed in terms of the highest modulating frequency. The exact relationship is that the bandwidth is equal to *twice* the highest modulating frequency. For example, if the highest modulating frequency is 3 kc, the bandwidth is 6 kc.

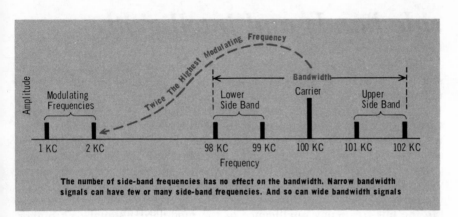

The number of side-band frequencies has no effect on the bandwidth. Narrow bandwidth signals can have few or many side-band frequencies. And so can wide bandwidth signals

bandwidth

The bandwidth of a signal is important for a variety of reasons. One of these is that it is determined by the frequencies in the intelligence being carried by the signal; so if the intelligence is to be carried with no distortion, all of the electronic circuits that process the signal must be able to do their job over the entire bandwidth. From knowledge of inductors and capacitors, you know that these components behave differently at different frequencies. This should give you some idea of the difficulties in building circuits that can handle a wide bandwidth with no distortion. For example, circuits used for processing signals carrying intelligence consisting of only a 1000-cps tone (2-kc bandwidth) can be much simpler than circuits that have to process a range of voice frequencies from say 50 to 15,000 cps (30-kc bandwidth).

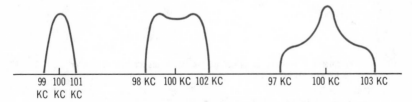

Bandwidth or bandpass curves such as these are usually used to show the side-band frequencies that go with the carrier. The shape of the curve depends on the amplitudes of the side bands

To simplify the circuit requirements, therefore, it is common practice to keep the bandwidth of signals as *narrow* as possible without destroying the intelligibility of the information being carried by the signal. This is why in voice modulation many of the higher audio frequencies are often *eliminated* before modulation and so not included in the signal. Although this introduced some distortion in the signal, it does not destroy the basic information.

side bands and intelligence

You know that when all of the *instantaneous amplitudes* of the upper side-band frequencies, the lower side-band frequencies, and the unmodulated carrier are *added,* the result is the modulated carrier. This shows that it is the side bands that cause the amplitude variations of the carrier, which you know represent the intelligence. In other words, then, the *side bands carry the intelligence.* This may be hard to visualize at first, but it is a fact, and it is useful, therefore, to think of the modulated carrier wave not as a single wave, but as an unmodulated carrier wave with upper and lower side-band waves. When you think in these terms, the purpose of the unmodulated carrier is to serve as a means of *increasing* the low-frequency intelligence of the modulating signal to a higher frequency; namely the side-band frequencies. In the demodulation process, the carrier also provides the means for converting the intelligence contained in the side bands back to its original lower (usually audio) frequency form. Thus, the only purpose of the carrier is to convert the intelligence from one frequency to another.

By means of a carrier, audio-frequency intelligence is converted to high frequencies in the form of upper and lower side bands

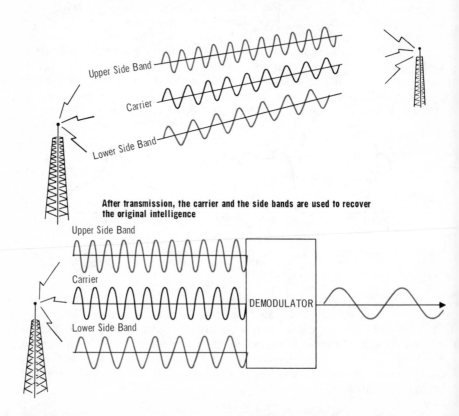

After transmission, the carrier and the side bands are used to recover the original intelligence

Upper Side Band

Carrier

DEMODULATOR

Lower Side Band

the intelligence
of a single side band

If you carefully inspect the waveforms of the side bands and unmodulated carrier, you will see that the addition of only one of the side bands and the unmodulated carrier will produce a waveform that has the same relative amplitude variations that would result if both side bands and the carrier were added. With only one side band, the peak-to-peak amplitudes of the resulting wave, and therefore the modulation envelope, are smaller, but the amplitude *variations* follow the intelligence of the modulating signal. This means, therefore, that the two side bands each contain the entire signal intelligence. As a result, all that is really necessary to recover the intelligence is the unmodulated carrier and one of the side bands, either the upper or lower.

An interesting point here concerns the intelligence carried by radio signals in the commercial AM broadcast band. To conserve bandwidth, these signals are limited by the FCC to a bandwidth of 10 kc. But since both side bands carry the same intelligence, the actual signal intelligence is limited to a maximum frequency of 5 kc. The other 5 kc of the bandwidth has the same intelligence, only at different frequencies.

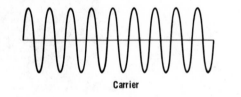

Carrier

Lower Side Band   Upper Side Band

Intelligence Envelope

Modulated Carrier   Modulated Carrier

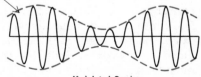

If only the lower side band combines with the unmodulated carrier, the amplitude variations of the carrier are similar, although smaller, than when both side bands are used

If only the upper side band combines with the unmodulated carrier, the amplitude variations of the carrier are also similar to those produced when both side bands are used

side-band power

Every electronic signal has a certain amount of electrical *energy*. Depending on the nature of the signal, its electrical energy may be measured in terms of voltage, current, or power. The energy of amplitude-modulated signals is usually expressed as *power*, and it determines to a large extent how far the signal can be sent, as well as how much buildup, or amplification, will be required to increase the signal to a usable level after transmission.

When a signal is transmitted by radio, only a very small portion of it is picked up by a receiving antenna

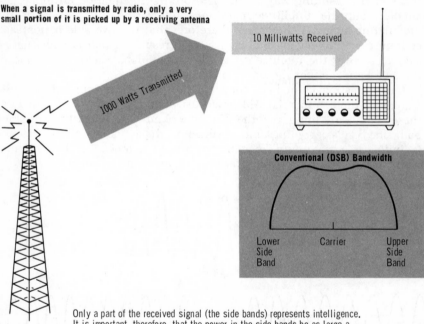

10 Milliwatts Received

1000 Watts Transmitted

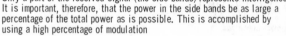

Conventional (DSB) Bandwidth

Lower Side Band   Carrier   Upper Side Band

Only a part of the received signal (the side bands) represents intelligence. It is important, therefore, that the power in the side bands be as large a percentage of the total power as is possible. This is accomplished by using a high percentage of modulation

The power in an amplitude-modulated signal is *divided* among the carrier and the side bands. The relative amounts of power in the carrier and the side bands depends on the percentage of modulation. But in all cases, the two side bands generally contain *equal power*, and their combined power is less than that contained in the carrier. At 100-percent modulation, the total side-band power is one-half the carrier power. Thus, the side bands together hold 33.3 percent of the total signal power, or each side band has 16.7 percent of the total power. These percentages drop sharply when the modulation is less than 100 percent.

Since, as you know, the side bands contain the intelligence, the power in the side bands represents *signal power*. It is important, therefore, to have as much power as possible in the side bands; and this is why a high percentage of modulation is normally desirable.

summary

☐ For each modulating frequency, two side-band frequencies are produced: one above the carrier frequency and one below it. ☐ The upper side-band frequencies represent the sum of the individual modulating frequencies and the carrier frequency. ☐ The lower side-band frequencies represent the difference between the modulating frequencies and the carrier frequency.

☐ The bandwidth of an amplitude-modulated signal is the frequency range between the lowest, lower side-band frequency and the highest, upper side-band frequency. The bandwidth is always equal to twice the highest modulating frequency. ☐ Since bandwidth is determined by the frequencies in the modulating signal, all circuits that process a signal must accommodate the entire bandwidth.

☐ The intelligence in an amplitude-modulated signal is carried in the side bands. In effect, the unmodulated carrier merely serves as a means of increasing the low-frequency intelligence of the modulating signal to a higher frequency; namely, the side-band frequencies. ☐ Both side bands of an amplitude-modulated signal carry the identical intelligence. Therefore, to recover the intelligence, all that is required is the unmodulated carrier and one of the side bands. ☐ Power in an amplitude-modulated signal is divided among the carrier and the two side bands, with each band containing equal power. ☐ Since the side bands contain the signal intelligence, it is important to have as much power as possible in the side bands, and this is accomplished by using a percentage of modulation close to 100 percent.

review questions

1. If a 1-kilocycle tone amplitude modulates a 1-megacycle carrier, what are the side-band frequencies?
2. What is the bandwidth of the modulated signal in Question 1?
3. Why are side bands important?
4. What effect does the carrier frequency have on bandwidth?
5. Is all the power in an AM signal carried in the side bands?
6. If one side band is removed from an AM signal, will the signal power be affected?
7. If one side band is removed from an AM signal, will the signal intelligence be affected?
8. A modulating signal containing three frequencies will produce how many side-band frequencies?
9. If the modulating frequencies in Question 8 are 2, 4, and 6 kilocycles, what is the bandwidth of the modulated signal?
10. How does percentage of modulation affect side-band power?

single side-band modulation

You have seen that both side bands of an amplitude-modulated signal contain all of the intelligence being transmitted, So, to recover the intelligence, all that is required is one side band and the carrier. If one of the side bands, therefore, was removed from the modulated carrier immediately after modulation, it would have no harmful effects on the transmission of the intelligence. The intelligence would be transmitted in the other side band, and the unmodulated carrier would accompany it for later use in converting the intelligence to its original lower frequency.

This technique of removing one side band from an amplitude-modulated signal is called *single side-band modulation* (SSB), and has certain advantages over conventional transmission in which both side bands are used. The most important advantage to be gained by eliminating one side band is that the bandwidth of the signal is cut in half.

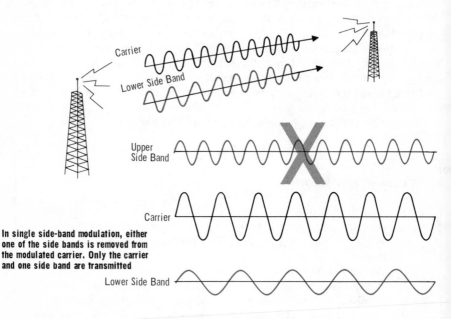

Carrier

Lower Side Band

Upper Side Band

Carrier

In single side-band modulation, either one of the side bands is removed from the modulated carrier. Only the carrier and one side band are transmitted

Lower Side Band

You recall that with both side bands, half of the bandwidth is above the carrier frequency and half below. But both halves represent the same intelligence, only at different frequencies. So by eliminating one side band, the range of frequencies that carry the intelligence is cut in half. This reduction in bandwidth improves reception of the signal by receiving equipment and circuits, since the narrower the bandwidth, the less atmospheric noise, or static, that will enter the receiving circuits with the signal. Also, if each carrier uses less bandwidth in a given range, more carrier signals can be sent, or there will be less interference between different carrier signals.

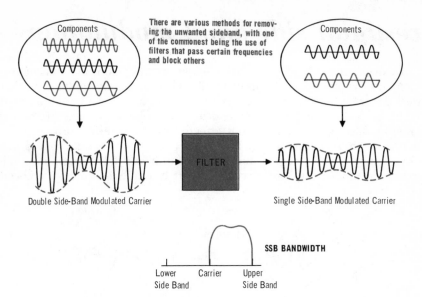

Components

There are various methods for removing the unwanted sideband, with one of the commonest being the use of filters that pass certain frequencies and block others

Components

Double Side-Band Modulated Carrier

FILTER

Single Side-Band Modulated Carrier

SSB BANDWIDTH

Lower
Side Band

Carrier

Upper
Side Band

single side-band modulation (cont.)

The filters or other components used to remove the unwanted side band from a single side-band signal are not perfect devices. There is no filter that will completely eliminate, or block, say a frequency of 100 kc (100,000 cps), and at the same time pass a frequency of 100,001 or 99,999 cps without any reduction, or attenuation, in amplitude. Instead, *practical* filters used to eliminate an unwanted side band completely block certain frequencies, attenuate others, and pass all remaining frequencies.

In terms of a frequency spectrum, the attenuated frequencies are on either side of and close to the blocked frequencies, while the frequencies passed with no attenuation are relatively far from the blocked frequencies. As a result of these filter characteristics, it is difficult to remove a side band completely when the modulating signal that produces the side bands contains *low frequencies*. This is because low modulating frequencies produce pairs of side-band frequencies that are *close* to each other, as well as to the carrier. For example, the side-band frequencies produced by a modulating frequency of 50 cps are only 100 cps apart and 50 cps from the carrier; whereas a relatively high modulating frequency of say 2000 cps will produce side-band frequencies that are 4000 cps apart and 2000 cps from the carrier. If an attempt is made, therefore, to completely remove a side band that contains frequencies very close to the carrier, both the carrier and some frequencies of the other side band will be attenuated, and this is undesirable.

vestigial side-band modulation

To overcome this problem of attenuation when low modulating frequencies are involved, the unwanted side band *is not completely eliminated.* Instead, frequencies relatively far from the carrier are eliminated, while those close to the carrier are only *attenuated,* so that the carrier and the other side band are not affected by the filtering process. This method of modulation is called *vestigial side-band modulation,* and has, although to a lesser degree, the narrow bandwidth advantages of single side-band modulation. In effect, only part of one side band is removed.

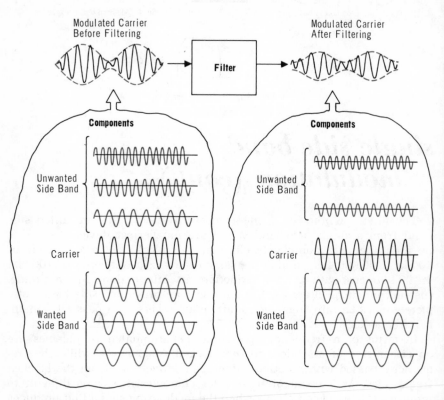

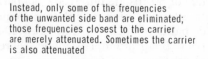

In vestigial side-band modulation, one side band is not completely eliminated as it is in single side-band modulation

Instead, only some of the frequencies of the unwanted side band are eliminated; those frequencies closest to the carrier are merely attenuated. Sometimes the carrier is also attenuated

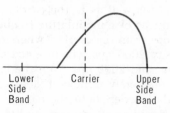

Vestigial SB Bandwidth

suppressed carrier modulation

When you think in terms of side bands, the purpose of the carrier is to convert audio-frequency (a-f) intelligence to radio-frequency (r-f) intelligence before transmission; and after transmission, to reconvert the r-f intelligence to its original audio form. Thus, the side bands (either one, or both) are transmitted to send the intelligence from one place to another. The carrier, although it contains no intelligence, is also transmitted just so it is *available* for demodulation at the receiving end.

Since the carrier contains much more power than the side bands, and since this power is supplied by the transmitting equipment, the transmission of the carrier is a *large percentage* of the power that must be supplied at the transmitting end. A considerable *savings* in power can be accomplished, therefore, by eliminating the carrier before transmission and just transmitting one side band. Of course, the carrier must be regenerated and *reinserted in the signal* at the receiving end to reconvert the intelligence to its original audio form.

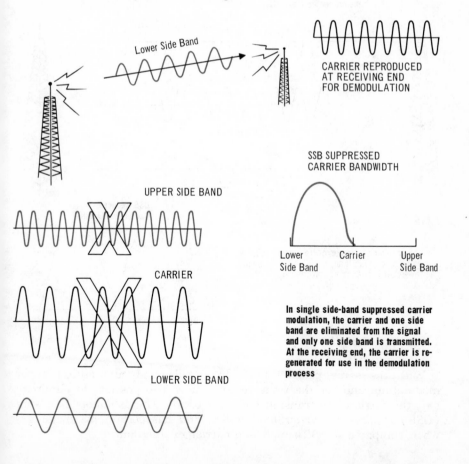

Lower Side Band

CARRIER REPRODUCED
AT RECEIVING END
FOR DEMODULATION

SSB SUPPRESSED
CARRIER BANDWIDTH

Lower   Carrier   Upper
Side Band   Side Band

UPPER SIDE BAND

CARRIER

LOWER SIDE BAND

In single side-band suppressed carrier modulation, the carrier and one side band are eliminated from the signal and only one side band is transmitted. At the receiving end, the carrier is regenerated for use in the demodulation process

suppressed carrier modulation (cont.)

The carrier can be eliminated before transmission because, since it is a constant-frequency, constant-amplitude wave, it is easily generated, and at a much lower powel level than that of a transmitted carrier. Actually, the carrier generated at the receiving end might only require a power level of a few watts, whereas transmitted carriers normally have power levels of kilowatts.

The elimination of the carrier, as well as one side band, prior to transmission is called *single side-band modulation with suppressed carrier,* or just *single side-band suppressed carrier modulation.* To some people and in some literature, the term "single side-band modulation" automatically means with a suppressed carrier. To avoid confusion, care should be taken in using the term.

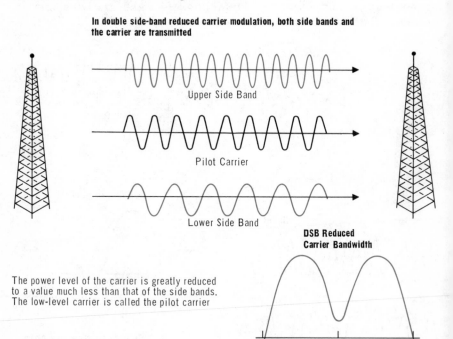

In double side-band reduced carrier modulation, both side bands and the carrier are transmitted

Upper Side Band

Pilot Carrier

Lower Side Band

DSB Reduced Carrier Bandwidth

The power level of the carrier is greatly reduced to a value much less than that of the side bands. The low-level carrier is called the pilot carrier

Lower Side Band   Pilot Carrier   Upper Side Band

With the same principles of single side-band suppressed carrier modulation, and for the same reasons, it is also possible to eliminate *only* the carrier, and transmit both side bands. This is *double side-band* (DSB) *suppressed carrier modulation,* and has certain disadvantages when compared to SSB suppressed carrier modulation.

suppressed carrier modulation (cont.)

The main disadvantage of DSB suppressed carrier modulation is the difficulties involved in the demodulation process. To achieve satisfactory demodulation, the phase of the regenerated carrier at the receiving end must be the *same*, or nearly the same, as the phase of the carrier that produced the side bands. If the *difference in phase* is too large, severe distortion of the signal intelligence results. This problem does not exist to as large a degree for SSB suppressed carrier modulation.

To ensure the correct phase relationship between the carrier used for modulation, the carrier at the transmitting end (modulation carrier) is not completely eliminated when DSB modulation is employed. Instead, the carrier is transmitted along with the side bands, but at a greatly *reduced* power level. Such a reduced carrier is called a *pilot carrier*, and is used at the receiving end of the system to maintain the correct phase of the regenerated carrier.

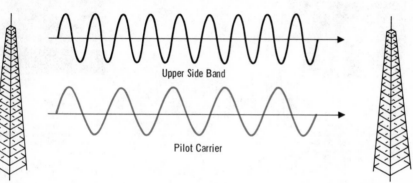

Upper Side Band

Pilot Carrier

Single side-band reduced carrier modulation is the same as DSB reduced carrier, except that only one side band is transmitted with the pilot carrier

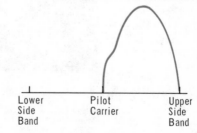

SSB REDUCED CARRIER BANDWIDTH

Lower Side Band   Pilot Carrier   Upper Side Band

A pilot carrier is often used with SSB modulation, especially when music is the intelligence transmitted. When both side bands are transmitted with a pilot carrier, it is DSB reduced carrier modulation; and when only one side band and a pilot carrier are used, it is SSB reduced carrier modulation.

types of amplitude modulation

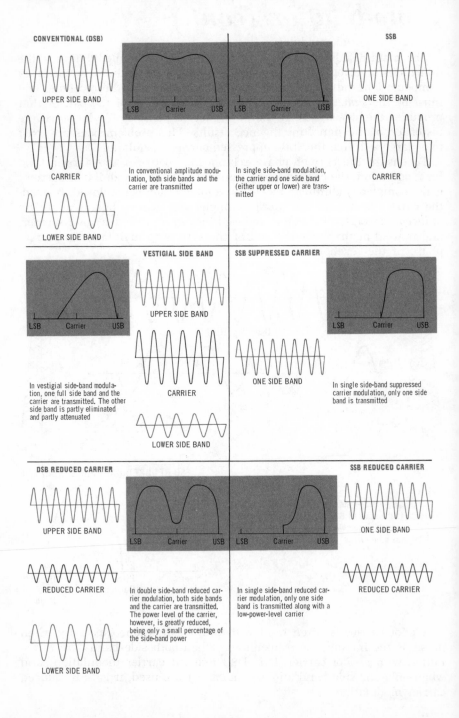

CONVENTIONAL (DSB)

UPPER SIDE BAND

CARRIER

LOWER SIDE BAND

LSB   Carrier   USB   LSB   Carrier   USB

In conventional amplitude modulation, both side bands and the carrier are transmitted

In single side-band modulation, the carrier and one side band (either upper or lower) are transmitted

SSB

ONE SIDE BAND

CARRIER

VESTIGIAL SIDE BAND   **SSB SUPPRESSED CARRIER**

LSB   Carrier   USB

UPPER SIDE BAND

CARRIER

LOWER SIDE BAND

ONE SIDE BAND

In vestigial side-band modulation, one full side band and the carrier are transmitted. The other side band is partly eliminated and partly attenuated

LSB   Carrier   USB

In single side-band suppressed carrier modulation, only one side band is transmitted

---

DSB REDUCED CARRIER

UPPER SIDE BAND

REDUCED CARRIER

LOWER SIDE BAND

LSB   Carrier   USB   LSB   Carrier   USB

In double side-band reduced carrier modulation, both side bands and the carrier are transmitted. The power level of the carrier, however, is greatly reduced, being only a small percentage of the side-band power

In single side-band reduced carrier modulation, only one side band is transmitted along with a low-power-level carrier

SSB REDUCED CARRIER

ONE SIDE BAND

REDUCED CARRIER

AM demodulation or detection

AM *demodulation* is the process of *recovering* the signal intelligence from an amplitude-modulated carrier wave. It is also called *detection*. It can best be described from the standpoint of the overall modulated carrier wave rather than from its components, which you know are side bands and an unmodulated carrier. If the carrier was suppressed or reduced before transmission, a carrier of the proper phase, frequency, and amplitude must first be generated and combined with the side band before the signal can be demodulated. This is called *carrier reinsertion*.

When an amplitude-modulated signal is ready for demodulation, therefore, it consists of a carrier frequency whose peak-to-peak amplitude varies in accordance with the intelligence being carried. The demodulation or detection process consists of sending such a modulated wave through a circuit called a *detector* or *demodulator*, which does two operations to the wave: it first cuts off either the top or bottom half of the wave (this is called *rectification*); and then the detector removes the r-f portion of the remaining half of the wave, but leaves a signal that follows the *envelope* of that half of the wave. In effect, therefore, the detector eliminates all of the modulated carrier wave, except one-half of the envelope. And since the variations of both halves of the envelope represent the intelligence, reducing the wave to one-half of the envelope completes the demodulation process.

AM demodulation is accomplished by removing everything from the modulated signal except one-half of the envelope, which represents the intelligence

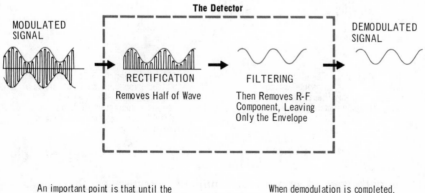

The Detector

MODULATED SIGNAL

RECTIFICATION

Removes Half of Wave

FILTERING

Then Removes R-F Component, Leaving Only the Envelope

DEMODULATED SIGNAL

An important point is that until the completion of demodulation, the envelope of the modulated signal is not a physical quantity – it just shows amplitude variations of the carrier

When demodulation is completed, however, the envelope is actually a varying voltage or current that corresponds to the original intelligence

disadvantages

As a means of carrying intelligence, amplitude modulation has many advantages. However, it also has some disadvantages that under certain conditions limit its usefulness and make other forms of modulation more desirable. The major disadvantage of amplitude modulation is that it is easily affected by atmospheric noise (static), other electronic signals having similar frequencies, and interference from such electrical equipment as motors and generators. All of these tend to *amplitude modulate* a carrier in the same way as does its own modulating signal. And as a result, they become a part of the modulated signal, and remain with it right through the demodulation process. After demodulation, they appear as *noise* or *distortion*, which, if severe enough, can completely mask the intelligence and make the demodulated signal worthless. Even if they are not severe enough to diminish intelligibility, they can be extremely annoying.

Probably the most common type of interference that affects amplitude-modulated signals is atmospheric static, which is especially severe during violent thunderstorms

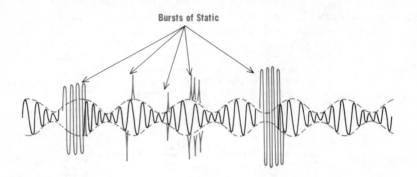

Bursts of Static

The static is caused by electrical discharges in the atmosphere which result in large-amplitude pulses being amplitude modulated on the carrier

After demodulation, these pulses appear as loud bursts of noise if they are on a voice-modulated signal, or as brief periods of complete distortion if the signal is carrying some other form of intelligence

The only way to prevent or eliminate interference that tends to amplitude modulate a carrier is to place the intelligence on the carrier in some way other than by amplitude variations. In other words, use some type of modulation other than amplitude modulation. One such type of modulation that has good *interference-resistant* properties is *frequency modulation.*

summary

☐ Single side-band modulation (SSB) is a form of amplitude modulation in which one side band is removed from the signal. ☐ In vestigial side-band modulation, the unwanted side band is not completely removed.

☐ In single side-band suppressed carrier modulation, only one of the side bands is transmitted. Both the carrier and the other side band are removed from the signal before transmission. ☐ SSB modulation with suppressed carrier requires considerably less transmitted power than does a comparable conventional SSB signal. This is because the carrier, which is suppressed, represents a large percentage of the total signal power. ☐ When single side-band suppressed carrier modulation is used, the carrier must be regenerated and reinserted in the signal at the receiving end to reconvert the intelligence to its original form. This adding of the carrier back into the signal is called carrier reinsertion. ☐ To ensure that the reinserted carrier has the required phase, a pilot carrier is sometimes used. This means that instead of being suppressed, the carrier is transmitted at a greatly reduced power level.

☐ Demodulation, or detection, is the process of recovering the signal intelligence from a modulated carrier wave. It is accomplished by a circuit called a detector or demodulator. ☐ The first step in detection is rectification, in which one-half of the modulated carrier wave is removed. Then the r-f portion of the remaining half of the wave is removed. This leaves a signal that follows the envelope of one-half of the modulated wave. ☐ The major disadvantage of amplitude modulation is that it is easily affected by static, other electronic signals, and interference from electrical motors and generators.

review questions

1. What is *vestigial side-band modulation?*
2. Can single side-band modulation be used when the modulating signal consists of many frequencies?
3. What is the principal advantage of suppressed carrier modulation?
4. A carrier transmitted at a greatly reduced power level is called _____.
5. What is meant by *carrier reinsertion?*
6. Name three types of single side-band modulation.
7. What is *demodulation?*
8. What is another name for demodulation?
9. What is the major disadvantage of amplitude modulation?
10. What is the major advantage of single side-band modulation?

frequency modulation

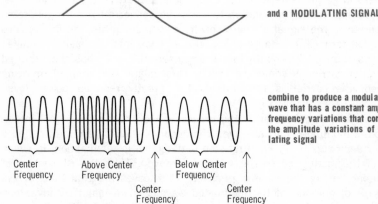

In frequency modulation, a constant-amplitude CARRIER

and a MODULATING SIGNAL

combine to produce a modulated wave that has a constant amplitude, and frequency variations that correspond to the amplitude variations of the modulating signal

Center
Frequency

Above Center
Frequency

Center
Frequency

Below Center
Frequency

Center
Frequency

In frequency modulation (FM), an r-f carrier wave is varied in accordance with a modulating signal. However, in *AM*, the *amplitude* of the carrier is changed, whereas in *FM*, it is the *frequency* of the carrier that is varied. When the carrier is frequency modulated, its amplitude is unchanged, while its frequency increases and decreases in accordance with the *amplitude* variations of the modulating signal. The frequency of the unmodulated carrier is called the *center* or *resting* frequency; the carrier fluctuates above and below its center frequency.

A frequency-modulated carrier is at its center frequency when the modulating signal has *zero amplitude*. As the amplitude of the modulating signal increases in the *positive* direction, the frequency of the carrier also *increases*, reaching a maximum when the amplitude of the modulating signal is at its maximum positive value. Then, when the modulating signal decreases in amplitude, the frequency of the carrier also decreases, returning to its center frequency when the modulating signal again reaches zero amplitude.

In the same way, the frequency variations of the carrier follow the *negative* amplitude variations of the modulating signal, except that the carrier frequency *decreases* as the modulating signal becomes more negative, and then increases, reaching its center frequency again when the modulating signal completes its negative half cycle and returns to zero.

frequency generation

You have seen that the frequency of an FM wave varies, or *deviates*, above and below its center frequency according to the amplitude variations of the modulating signal. The total range, or swing from the center frequency to the *lowest frequency*, which corresponds to the *maximum negative amplitude* of the modulating signal, or from the center frequency to the *highest frequency*, which corresponds to the *maximum positive amplitude* of the modulating signal, is called the *maximum frequency deviation* of the carrier.

It is obvious that the greater the amplitude of the modulating signal, the larger is the frequency deviation of the FM carrier. For example, a weak (small-amplitude) modulating signal might cause a carrier having a center frequency of 100 mc to vary from a low frequency of 99.99 mc to a high frequency of 100.01 mc. The maximum frequency deviation would thus by 100.01 mc minus 100.00 mc, or ±10 kc. A strong signal, on the other hand, might vary the same carrier from 99.95 mc to 100.05 mc, for a maximum frequency deviation of ±50 kc. Thus, the frequency deviation of the carrier indicates the amplitude of the modulating signal.

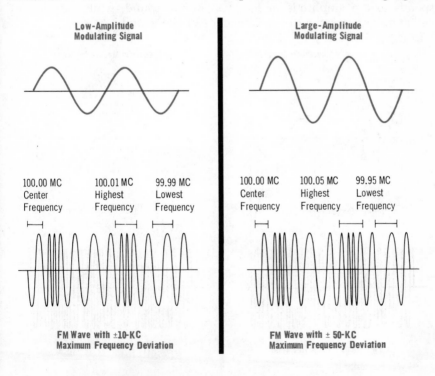

Low-Amplitude Modulating Signal			Large-Amplitude Modulating Signal		
100.00 MC Center Frequency	100.01 MC Highest Frequency	99.99 MC Lowest Frequency	100.00 MC Center Frequency	100.05 MC Highest Frequency	99.95 MC Lowest Frequency
FM Wave with ±10-KC Maximum Frequency Deviation			FM Wave with ± 50-KC Maximum Frequency Deviation		

The total frequency swing of an FM wave above or below its center frequency is called the maximum frequency deviation, and is proportional to the amplitude of the modulating signal. The amplitude of the modulated wave is unaffected by the amplitude of the modulating signal

rate of frequency deviation

The amplitude of the modulating signal determines the maximum frequency deviation of the modulated carrier. Each time the modulating signal goes through one full cycle, assuming it is sinusoidal, the carrier also goes through *one full frequency deviation*. This consists of starting at the center frequency, increasing to its maximum frequency, then decreasing to its minimum frequency, passing through the center frequency on the way, and finally increasing back to the center frequency. Thus, if the modulating signal has a frequency of 10 kc, the carrier goes through 10,000 full frequency deviations every second. In other words, the rate of frequency deviation of the carrier, or the rate at which the carrier deviates, is determined by the frequency of the modulating signal. How far the carrier deviates, though, is still only affected by the amplitude of the modulating signal.

You can see now that the intelligence carried by an FM wave is represented by the maximum frequency deviation of the carrier, as well as by the rate at which the carrier goes through the maximum deviation. In the case of audio intelligence, the amount of carrier deviation corresponds to the amplitude or loudness of the sound, while the rate of deviation corresponds to the frequency of the sound.

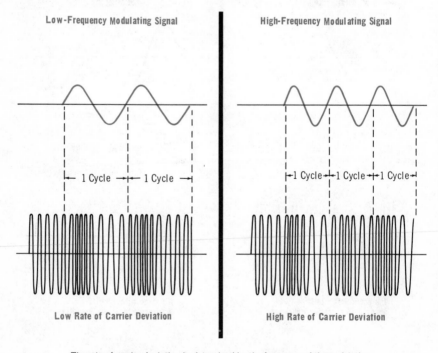

The rate of carrier deviation is determined by the frequency of the modulating signal. Low-frequency intelligence, therefore, causes slow deviation of the carrier frequency, while high-frequency intelligence causes the carrier to deviate more rapidly

generation of side bands

During the process of frequency modulation, just as during amplitude modulation, new frequencies, called side-band frequencies, are produced above and below the unmodulated carrier frequency. These side-band frequencies contain the signal intelligence, as in amplitude modulation, and combine with the unmodulated carrier to produce the modulated carrier previously described.

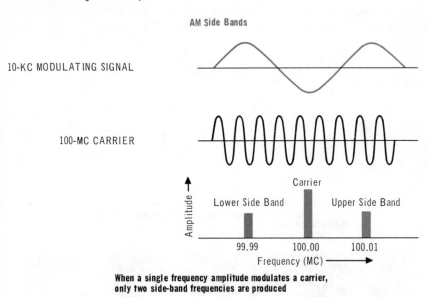

When a single frequency amplitude modulates a carrier, only two side-band frequencies are produced

A significant difference between AM and FM side-band frequencies is the *number produced*. If you recall, in amplitude modulation, two side-band frequencies are produced for every modulating frequency. One of these side-band frequencies is equal to the *sum* of the modulating and carrier frequencies, and is *above* the carrier frequency. The other is equal to the *difference* between the modulating and carrier frequencies, and is *below* the carrier. In FM, each modulating frequency produces a similar pair of sum and difference side-band frequencies. However, in addition to the basic pair, a theoretically infinite number of additional side-band frequencies are produced. These additional frequencies are equal to *whole number multiples* of the basic pair.

For example, if a 1-mc carrier is frequency modulated by a single frequency of 10 kc, the basic pair of side-band frequencies will be 1010 kc and 990 kc. The additional frequencies will be at 1020 and 980 kc, 1030 and 970 kc, 1040 and 960 kc, and so on. Although theoretically these side-band frequencies extend outward from the carrier indefinitely, only a limited number of them contain *sufficient power* to be significant. Even so, this limited number is still always far greater than the number produced by comparable amplitude modulation.

generation
of side bands (cont.)

The number of significant side-band frequencies produced in any particular case depends on the amplitude and frequency of the modulating signal. The larger the amplitude or the lower the frequency of the modulating signal, the greater is the number of significant side-band frequencies. The exact number can be found using a ratio called the *modulation index*. You will learn about this later.

FM Side Bands

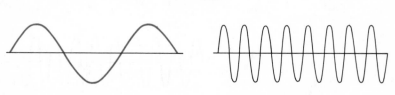

10-KC Modulating Signal   100-MC Carrier

When a single frequency frequency modulates a carrier, many side-band frequencies are produced. Each of these side-band frequencies is separated from adjacent ones by the modulating frequency

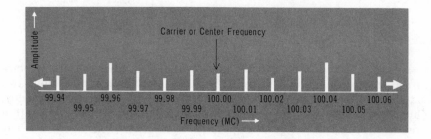

You recall that in amplitude modulation, the amplitudes of the side-band frequencies, or the power contained in them, were independent of the amplitude of the unmodulated carrier, and depended only on the amplitude, or power, of the modulating signal. In frequency modulation, the situation is different. The side bands derive their power from the carrier, which means that the unmodulated carrier component of an FM wave has less power, or smaller amplitude, *after* modulation than it does before. The amount of power removed from the carrier and placed in the side bands depends on the modulating frequencies and the maximum deviation of the carrier. It is possible, under certain conditions, for the carrier power to be *zero*, with all of the power in the side bands. This, of course, is desirable, since the carrier itself contains no intelligence.

generation
of side bands (cont.)

The amplitudes of the individual side-band frequencies depend on the *modulation index*, which is described later. The pattern of the individual amplitudes is highly *irregular*. There is no continuous increase in amplitude as frequencies go further from the carrier, nor is there a continuous decrease. However, in all cases, there is a point relatively distant from the carrier where the amplitudes of the side-band frequencies drop below *1 percent* of the amplitude of the unmodulated carrier. Past this point, the side bands are insignificant, and can be ignored.

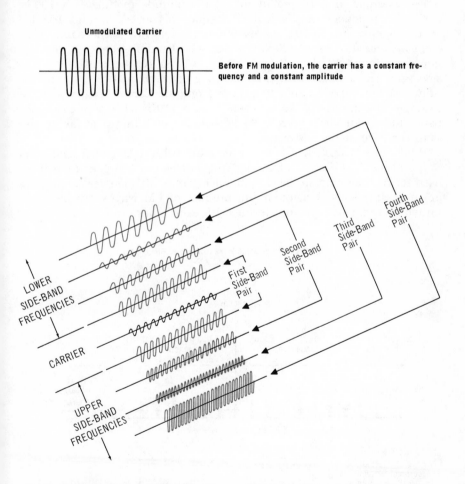

Unmodulated Carrier

Before FM modulation, the carrier has a constant frequency and a constant amplitude

LOWER SIDE-BAND FREQUENCIES

CARRIER

UPPER SIDE-BAND FREQUENCIES

First Side-Band Pair

Second Side-Band Pair

Third Side-Band Pair

Fourth Side-Band Pair

After modulation, the carrier component of the FM wave still has the same constant frequency, but its amplitude has been reduced as a result of the power taken from it by the side bands

The side-band frequencies also have constant amplitudes, which when combined with the carrier component produce the modulated wave with its constant amplitude but varying frequency

FM bandwidth

In AM, you learned that the term *bandwidth* meant the entire range of frequencies in a modulated wave. Because of the many side-band frequencies contained in an FM wave, bandwidth when applied to FM is more restrictive: It includes only the *significant frequencies*. The bandwidth of an FM wave is the frequency range between the *extreme upper* and *extreme lower* side-band frequencies whose amplitudes are 1 percent or more of the unmodulated carrier amplitude. Since these extreme side-band frequencies are multiples of the modulating frequencies, you can see that the bandwidth of an FM wave can be many times greater than that of an AM wave.

For example, if a frequency of 1 kc amplitude modulates a 100-kc carrier, it produces only side-band frequencies at 99 kc and 101 kc; so the bandwidth is 101 minus 99, or 2 kc. But if the same 1 kc *frequency modulates* a 100-kc carrier, side-band frequencies are produced at 99 and 101 kc, 98 and 102 kc, 97 and 103 kc, and so on. The side-band frequencies with amplitudes greater than 1 percent of the unmodulated carrier can extend far from the carrier frequency; for example, to 92 and 108 kc, or even 81 and 119 kc. In these cases, the bandwidth would be 16 kc or 38 kc, which you can see is far greater than the 2 kc of the AM wave.

When an FM wave has a very wide bandwidth, it is called *wide-band FM*, and requires the use of carrier frequencies much higher than those used for AM carrying similar intelligence. These high carrier frequencies are necessary so that a maximum number of FM waves can be transmitted by radio without interfering with each other.

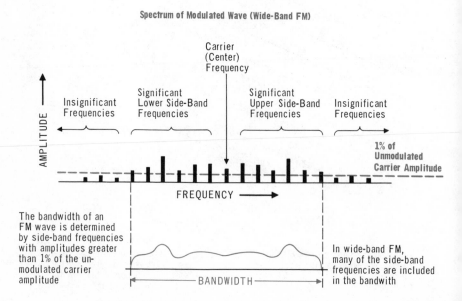

Spectrum of Modulated Wave (Wide-Band FM)

Spectrum of Modulated Wave (Narrow-Band FM)

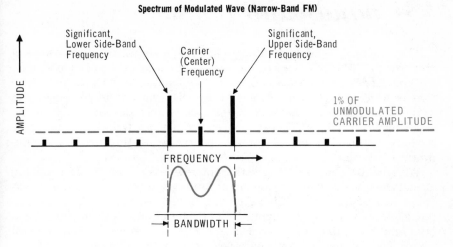

In narrow-band FM, only the two basic side-band frequencies have significant amplitudes. The bandwidth of such a wave, therefore, is the same as an AM wave

FM bandwidth (cont.)

It is possible, by limiting the maximum deviation of the FM carrier, to produce FM having the same bandwidth as an AM wave carrying the same intelligence. This is called *narrow-band FM*. While this process causes some distortion of the intelligence, it allows carrier frequencies to be used that are lower than some required for wide-band FM.

You should understand at this point that the bandwidth of a modulated wave is important for two reasons: first, it determines how much *space* or room in the radio-frequency spectrum the wave will occupy; and second, it determines the range of frequencies over which the electronic circuits used to receive and process the wave must be capable of operating.

As far as the radio-frequency spectrum is concerned, all of the modulated waves transmitted by radio in any one geographic area must occupy *different* places in the spectrum or else they will interfere with each other. For example, the lower frequencies of a modulated wave with a 20-kc carrier and a 8-kc bandwidth would overlap and interfere with the upper frequencies of a 14-kc carrier with an 8-kc bandwidth. You can see that interference between radio waves can be avoided either by *reducing* bandwidths or by moving carrier frequencies *farther apart*.

If bandwidths are made too narrow, though, distortion of the intelligence carried by the wave will result, since many of the side bands, which contain the intelligence, will be eliminated. On the other hand, if carrier frequencies are too far apart, a very limited number of radio waves would *completely fill* the radio spectrum.

FM bandwidth (cont.)

The practical solution to the problem of bandwidth allocation is a compromise, whereby the Federal Communications Commission (FCC) assigns carrier frequencies and limits bandwidths to a frequency range that is wide enough to prevent extreme distortion of intelligence, and narrow enough to prevent interference between adjacent waves in the radio spectrum. The FCC also licenses and assigns frequencies to transmitter operations to control the use of airwaves so that there is a minimum of interference.

With bandwidths set by government regulation, electronic receiving circuits can be designed to respond accordingly. To receive all the intelligence in a signal, the receiving circuits must respond to all of the frequencies included in the bandwidth. If the circuits cannot, distortion over and above that already set by the FCC bandwidth limitations will occur. You should be aware here that the distortion of the intelligence caused by the FCC bandwidth limitations is insignificant, since only the extreme side-band frequencies are eliminated, and these contribute little to the overall intelligence.

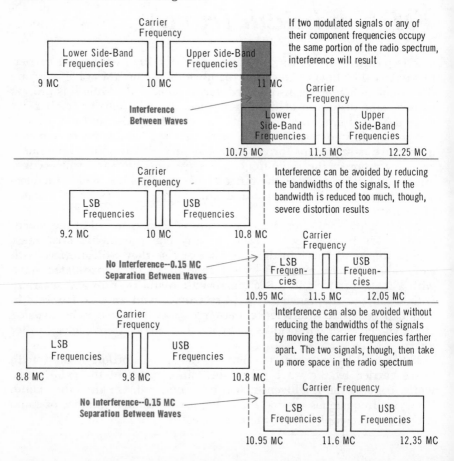

the modulation index

Since the bandwidth is the range between the upper and lower *significant* side-band frequencies, you may think that the more significant side-band frequencies there are, the wider is the bandwidth. This is not always the case. Remember that with a single modulating frequency, the side-band frequencies are separated by a space equal to the modulating frequency. Thus, the side-band frequencies produced by high modulating frequencies are much farther apart than are those produced by low modulating frequencies.

It is possible to have a relatively wide bandwidth when the side-band frequencies are far apart even if only a few of them have significant amplitudes. Similarly, closely spaced side-band frequencies produced by a low modulating frequency can result in a relatively narrow band-pass even though many of them have significant amplitudes. The situation is further complicated by the fact that the number of side-band frequencies that have significant amplitudes depends on the *maximum frequency deviation* of the FM carrier, which in turn, as you know, depends on the amplitude of the modulating signal. You can see, then, that the bandwidth of an FM wave is determined, in a complicated way, by the frequency (or highest frequency) of the modulating signal, and the maximum deviation of the carrier caused by that frequency.

The ratio of the maximum carrier deviation to the modulating frequency is called the *modulation index:*

$$\text{Modulation index} = \frac{\text{maximum carrier deviation}}{\text{maximum modulating frequency}}$$

Using a special form of mathematics, tables like the one below show the relationship between the modulation index, and the bandwidth and number of significant side-band frequencies of an FM wave. As an example of how to use the table, consider a modulating frequency of 1 kc that causes a maximum carrier deviation of 7 kc. The modulation index is 7 kc/1 kc, or 7. So there are 11 significant side bands in the wave, and the bandwidth is 22 × 1 kc, or 22 kc.

Modulation Index	Number of Side-Band Frequencies	Bandwidth (F = modulating frequency)	Modulation Index	Number of Side-Band Frequencies	Bandwidth (F = modulating frequency)
0.5	2	4 × F	11	15	30 × F
1	3	6 × F	12	16	32 × F
2	4	8 × F	13	17	34 × F
3	6	12 × F	14	18	36 × F
4	7	14 × F	15	19	38 × F
5	8	16 × F	16	20	40 × F
6	9	18 × F	17	21	42 × F
7	11	22 × F	18	23	46 × F
8	12	24 × F	19	24	48 × F
9	13	26 × F	20	25	50 × F
10	14	28 × F			

percentage of modulation

In AM, you recall, the percentage of modulation expressed the degree to which the modulating signal caused the peak-to-peak amplitude of the carrier to vary. Thus, at 100 percent amplitude modulation, the peak-to-peak *amplitude* of the carrier varies between zero and twice its unmodulated value. If the same type of system was used to express the percentage of modulation of FM waves, 100 percent modulation would mean that the carrier *frequency* varied between zero and twice its unmodulated value. This is entirely impractical; so instead, the percentage of modulation for FM is defined in terms of the maximum frequency *deviation* that can be produced by the electronic equipment generating the wave.

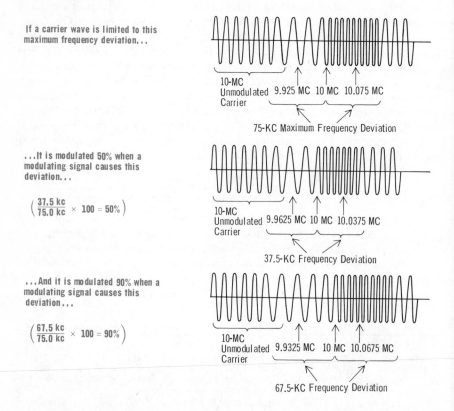

If a carrier wave is limited to this maximum frequency deviation...

10-MC Unmodulated Carrier　　9.925 MC　10 MC　10.075 MC

75-KC Maximum Frequency Deviation

...It is modulated 50% when a modulating signal causes this deviation...

$$\left(\frac{37.5\ kc}{75.0\ kc} \times 100 = 50\% \right)$$

10-MC Unmodulated Carrier　　9.9625 MC　10 MC　10.0375 MC

37.5-KC Frequency Deviation

...And it is modulated 90% when a modulating signal causes this deviation...

$$\left(\frac{67.5\ kc}{75.0\ kc} \times 100 = 90\% \right)$$

10-MC Unmodulated Carrier　　9.9325 MC　10 MC　10.0675 MC

67.5-KC Frequency Deviation

Generally, this maximum frequency deviation is set by FCC regulations, and the percentage of modulation is then the percentage of this maximum deviation that is produced by a modulating signal. For example, the maximum carrier deviation set by the FCC for commercial FM broadcasting is 75 kc. If a modulating signal causes the full 75-kc deviation, it has undergone 100 percent modulation. Similarly, a deviation of 37-1/2 kc represents a modulation of 50 percent.

summary

□ In a frequency-modulated signal, the frequency of an r-f carrier varies in accordance with the amplitude and frequency of a modulating signal. □ The frequency of the unmodulated carrier is called the center, or resting, frequency. When the carrier is frequency modulated, it then fluctuates above and below its center frequency. □ The frequency swing from the center frequency to either the highest or lowest modulated frequency is called the frequency deviation. The larger the amplitude of the modulating signal, the greater is the frequency deviation. □ The rate of frequency deviation is determined by the frequency of the modulating signal.

□ Theoretically, each modulating frequency produces an infinite number of side-band frequencies in an FM signal. However, the bandwidth of an FM signal is the frequency range between the extreme upper and lower side-band frequencies whose amplitudes are one percent or more of the unmodulated carrier amplitude. □ A wide-band FM signal has a much wider bandwidth than an AM signal that carries the same intelligence. □ A narrow-band FM signal has the same bandwidth as an AM signal carrying the same intelligence.

□ The exact number of significant side-band frequencies in an FM signal can be found by applying a ratio called the modulation index. This is the ratio of the maximum carrier deviation to the modulating frequency. □ In frequency modulation, the side bands derive their power from the carrier. Thus, the unmodulated carrier component of the signal has less power after being modulated than it does before.

review questions

1. The unmodulated carrier *frequency* of an FM signal is called _____?
2. What is meant by the *maximum frequency deviation* of an FM signal?
3. How does the amplitude of the modulating signal affect the frequency deviation of an FM signal?
4. How does the frequency of the modulating signal affect the frequency deviation of an FM signal?
5. In an FM signal, which side-band frequencies are significant?
6. What is *narrow-band FM*?
7. What is the disadvantage of narrow-band FM?
8. What is the modulation index used for?
9. Can the power in the unmodulated carrier component of an FM signal ever be zero?
10. Explain the reason for your answer to Question 9.

preemphasis

When a carrier is modulated by a complex signal, the deviation of the carrier depends only on the *amplitudes* of the modulating frequencies, not on the frequencies themselves. In human speech, or in music, *higher frequencies* have *lower amplitudes* than do the lower frequencies. So, in an FM wave carrying speech or music, higher frequencies have smaller deviations than the lower frequencies. If not for noise, this would be no problem. But, when a modulated wave is demodulated, the noise that it "picked up" during its transmission is demodulated as well.

Although the noise is present at all frequencies, the ratio of the noise level to the signal level is greater at the higher (lower-amplitude) frequencies: the signal-to-noise ratio is less at high frequencies. To increase the signal-to-noise ratio of the higher frequencies, certain changes, called *preemphasis,* are made before frequency modulation takes place. These changes consist of emphasizing the amplitudes of the higher modulating frequencies.

Preemphasis distorts the sound signal to some extent, but after transmission and demodulation, the reverse of preemphasis, called *deemphasis,* takes place. The frequencies are then reduced in amplitude to restore the sound signal back to its original form.

It may not seem obvious that these processes increase the signal-to-noise ratio of the higher frequencies, but they do. The important point is that preemphasis increases the level of the high frequencies *before* the noise is encountered, while deemphasis reduces the high frequencies back to their *normal levels,* but at the *same time reduces* the *noise* accompanying these frequencies to *below* its normal level.

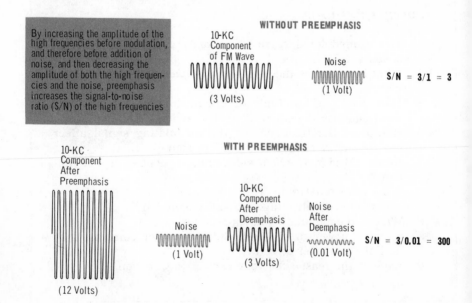

By increasing the amplitude of the high frequencies before modulation, and therefore before addition of noise, and then decreasing the amplitude of both the high frequencies and the noise, preemphasis increases the signal-to-noise ratio (S/N) of the high frequencies

WITHOUT PREEMPHASIS

10-KC Component of FM Wave
(3 Volts)

Noise
(1 Volt)

S/N = 3/1 = 3

10-KC Component After Preemphasis
(12 Volts)

WITH PREEMPHASIS

10-KC Component After Deemphasis
(3 Volts)

Noise
(1 Volt)

Noise After Deemphasis
(0.01 Volt)

S/N = 3/0.01 = 300

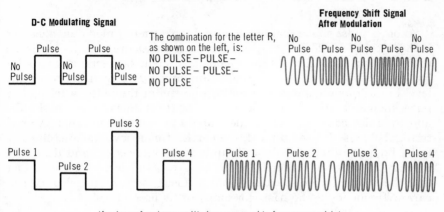

Teletypewriter equipment operates on d-c pulses, whereby each letter of the alphabet has its own combination of pulses

If pulses of various amplitudes were used to frequency modulate a carrier, the modulated signal would have a frequency for each different pulse amplitude, and one for the no-pulse condition

FM with a pulse

Until now, we have considered frequency modulation in which the modulating signal was either continuous, such as a steady tone, or was complex, such as voice or music. Frequently, though, nonsinusoidal pulse-type modulating signals are used with FM. One of the most common types of pulse FM signals is the *frequency shift signal*, which is used with frequency shift keying (FSK), or frequency shift telegraphy. In one method, the modulating signal consists of a series of rectangular d-c pulses, all having *equal* amplitudes. The *sequence* of these pulses represents the intelligence to be transmitted.

Since the modulating signal only has two amplitude values, the modulated wave has only two basic frequencies. One is the unmodulated carrier frequency, and the other is the frequency that corresponds to the presence of a modulating pulse. You can see, then, that a frequency shift signal consists of an FM wave that shifts abruptly between two different frequencies.

Side-band frequencies are produced when a pulse frequency modulates a carrier, just as they are for voice or tone modulation. However, the side-band frequencies produced by a pulse are not symmetrical above and below the carrier as they are for sine-wave modulation. This is because the modulating pulses themselves are not symmetrical above and below their zero reference level. Also, a square wave, as you will learn later, is made up of a large number of odd and even harmonics of the basic square-wave frequency; so that the FM carrier is modulated by a number of higher frequencies in addition to the basic frequency. Therefore, a square wave produces many more side bands than a sine wave. Nevertheless, the number of significant (in amplitude) side-band frequencies still determines the bandwidth of the modulated wave.

FM with a triangular pulse

Another pulse shape that is often used to frequency modulate a carrier is the *triangular pulse*. Typical uses of such pulses are in radio facsimile transmission, and aircraft altimeters. Whereas a rectangular pulse increases *abruptly* to its maximum amplitude and then stays at this level until dropping sharply to zero at the end of the pulse, a triangular pulse increases *gradually*, in a *linear* way, to its maximum amplitude, and then decreases to zero in the same way. This means that when a triangular pulse is used for FM, the carrier frequency increases linearly to its highest value, and then abruptly stops increasing, and decreases linearly back to the center frequency. As you will learn later, the fact that the triangular pulse causes both a linear increase and decrease in carrier frequency is the basis for many of its uses in FM.

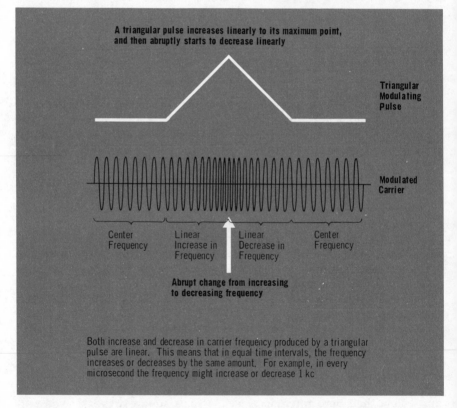

A triangular pulse increases linearly to its maximum point, and then abruptly starts to decrease linearly

Triangular Modulating Pulse

Modulated Carrier

Center Frequency | Linear Increase in Frequency | Linear Decrease in Frequency | Center Frequency

Abrupt change from increasing to decreasing frequency

Both increase and decrease in carrier frequency produced by a triangular pulse are linear. This means that in equal time intervals, the frequency increases or decreases by the same amount. For example, in every microsecond the frequency might increase or decrease 1 kc

The triangular pulse, like the rectangular pulse, consists of many component frequencies, called harmonics, each of which produces side-band frequencies as a result of the modulation process. These side-band frequencies, just like those produced by a rectangular pulse, are not symmetrical about the carrier center frequency, since the pulses themselves are not symmetrical about their zero reference level.

noise and FM

You will recall that a major disadvantage of AM was that noise amplitude modulates an AM signal, and, in effect, rides along with the intelligence of the signal. Noise also *amplitude modulates* FM signals. But, whereas electronic circuits cannot easily distinguish between the noise and the intelligence in an AM signal, this is relatively easy in FM signals. The *intelligence* is in the form of *frequency variations*, while the *noise* is in the form of *amplitude variations*. Therefore, by eliminating the amplitude variations from an FM signal prior to demodulation, any noise that had amplitude modulated the signal is removed.

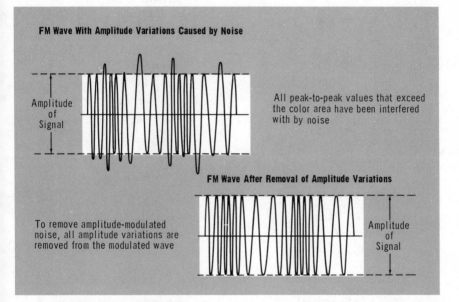

FM Wave With Amplitude Variations Caused by Noise

Amplitude of Signal

All peak-to-peak values that exceed the color area have been interfered with by noise

FM Wave After Removal of Amplitude Variations

To remove amplitude-modulated noise, all amplitude variations are removed from the modulated wave

Amplitude of Signal

Besides producing amplitude variations, noise can also cause *frequency changes* in an FM signal. This happens when the noise pulse falls between sine waves of a carrier, and effectively widens or narrows the sine wave to make it act like a lower or higher frequency. However, the extent of the frequency changes depends not on the relative strengths of the signal and the noise, but rather on the relative values of the signal modulation index and the noise modulation index. The greater the modulation index of the signal is compared to that of the noise, the more the noise will be made ineffective, or suppressed. Thus, by using as large a *carrier deviation* as possible during modulation, the frequency changes caused by noise can be minimized. This is so, since, as you remember, the larger the carrier deviation, the greater is the value of the modulation index. With a large enough maximum carrier deviation, it is possible to almost completely suppress a noise level that is only slightly less than the signal level.

FM demodulation or detection

Demodulation, or *detection* as it is also called, is the process of recovering the original intelligence from a modulated wave. Whereas AM demodulation is accomplished with detectors that remove the carrier, leaving only the audio variations of the envelope, FM demodulation uses the modulated carrier to *reproduce* the audio signal. The circuits used for FM demodulation are sensitive to the *frequency variations* of the modulated wave, and generate a voltage that corresponds to these variations. This generated voltage thus reproduces the original modulating signal, and therefore the intelligence.

Received FM Wave

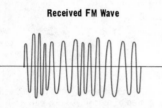

The received FM signal contains noise in the form of amplitude variations

After Noise Limiting

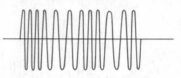

Before demodulation, the noise amplitude variations are removed from the FM wave

After Demodulation

The demodulation process then produces a signal which corresponds to the frequency variations of the modulated wave

After Deemphasis

The high frequencies of the demodulated signal are then reduced so that the resulting signal is the same as the original modulating signal

Two frequently used processes, which although are not actually part of FM demodulation, but are closely related to it, are *noise limiting* and *deemphasis*. Noise limiting takes place before demodulation, and involves the removal of amplitude variations from the modulated wave; this eliminates the noise. Deemphasis takes place after demodulation, and involves the reduction in amplitude of the high-frequency components of the signal that had been emphasized prior to modulation.

Noise limiting is the process that gives FM its big advantage over AM. Since noise occurs as an *amplitude* variation of the carrier, noise in AM is difficult to reduce because AM uses amplitude variations for its modulation. But, since FM does not, its peaks can be leveled off to remove the noise pulses.

summary

□ Preemphasis is a process whereby, before frequency modulation takes place, the higher modulating frequencies are amplified more than the lower ones. □ At the receiver, preemphasis has the result of increasing the signal-to-noise ratio of the higher-frequency components of the signal. □ Deemphasis is the opposite of preemphasis. It takes place in the receiver, and reduces the frequencies back to their normal level. □ In effect, deemphasis reduces the noise accompanying the higher frequencies.

□ Rectangular d-c pulses can be used to frequency modulate a carrier wave and produce a frequency shift signal. Such a signal shifts abruptly between two different frequencies, with the sequence of these shifts representing the intelligence being transmitted. □ Triangular pulses can also be used to frequency modulate a carrier wave. An FM signal of this type increases linearly to its highest frequency, and then abruptly stops increasing and decreases linearly back to the center frequency.

□ Noise that amplitude modulates an FM signal can easily be distinguished from the frequency variations that carry the intelligence. To eliminate the noise, all that is required is that the amplitude variations be removed. This is called noise limiting. □ Noise can also cause frequency changes in an FM signal. These can be minimized by using as large a carrier deviation as possible during modulation. □ Circuits used for the demodulation of FM signals produce a voltage that corresponds to the frequency variations of the signal.

review questions

1. What is *preemphasis*?
2. Why is preemphasis used?
3. What effect does deemphasis have on the signal-to-noise ratio of an FM signal?
4. Draw waveforms that show how a frequency shift signal is produced.
5. When a rectangular pulse frequency modulates a carrier, are the side-band frequencies symmetrical about the carrier?
6. How can noise affect the frequency of an FM signal?
7. Why is an FM signal less susceptible to noise interference than an AM signal?
8. How does FM demodulation differ from AM demodulation?
9. Does deemphasis take place before or after demodulation?
10. Does preemphasis take place before or after modulation?

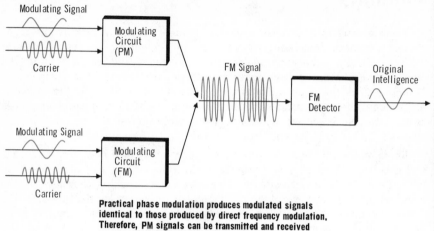

Practical phase modulation produces modulated signals
identical to those produced by direct frequency modulation.
Therefore, PM signals can be transmitted and received
by conventional FM equipment

phase modulation

In FM, it is very important that the center frequency of the carrier stays the *same* throughout the entire demodulation process, because it is the amount of *deviation from the center frequency* that represents the intelligence. These frequency variations are detected to reproduce the original intelligence. If the carrier center frequency were to change, or *drift*, during modulation, the frequency variations would not have a *common reference* point, and the demodulated signal would be distorted.

In many of the electronic circuits used to produce FM signals, the carrier center frequency has a tendency to drift. To overcome this, a form of modulation called *phase modulation* (PM) is often used. You should understand here that phase modulation is a method of modulating a continuous-wave carrier. The *result* of phase modulation is an FM signal that is transmitted, received, and demodulated the same as FM signals you have already studied. In other words, phase modulation is an *indirect* way of producing an FM signal having a high, stable center frequency. The principle on which phase modulation works is that any change in the *phase* of a sinusoidal wave automatically causes a change in the *frequency* of the wave.

In phase modulation, the instantaneous phase of the carrier is varied from its phase at rest by an amount proportional to the amplitude of the modulating signal. The maximum phase deviation, like the maximum frequency deviation of FM, is determined by the maximum positive and negative amplitudes of the modulating signal. As the carrier is shifted in phase by the modulating signal, it also varies in frequency. These frequency variations make up what is called *equivalent FM,* and it is these frequency variations that are eventually used to recover the signal intelligence.

producing the PM signal

A significant difference between PM and direct FM is the effect of the *modulating frequency* on carrier frequency. In FM, the carrier frequency deviation depends only on the amplitude of the modulating signal, not its frequency. Thus, equal-amplitude 1-kc and 10-kc modulating signals will produce identical shifts in carrier frequency.

In PM, on the other hand, carrier frequency deviation is affected by *both* the *amplitude* and *frequency* of the modulating signal. Higher frequencies produce proportionately greater deviations. This means that the shift caused by the 10-kc modulation will be ten times greater than that caused by the 1-kc modulation.

To eliminate this greater carrier shift at higher frequencies, and make the equivalent FM produced by PM the same as directly produced by FM, the modulating signal is passed through a *correction network* prior to modulation. The correction network reduces the amplitudes of the components of the modulating signal by an amount *proportional* to their *frequency*. Thus, the higher the frequency of the component, the more its amplitude is reduced. Of course, this distorts the modulating signal. But it does so in the same, but opposite, way so that the carrier frequency deviation during modulation will be proportional to the modulating frequencies. The overall effect, then, is that all equal-amplitude components of the modulating signal, regardless of their frequency, will cause shifts in carrier frequency.

FM signals produced indirectly by PM have relatively low carrier deviations. As a result, *frequency multipliers* are used to increase the deviation to the level required for a satisfactory modulation index and bandwidth. For example, a 100-to-1 frequency multiplier will raise the maximum deviation of a signal from 150 to 15,000 kc. All frequency components of the signal will similarly be increased in frequency by a factor of 100.

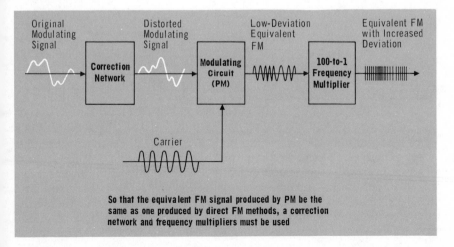

So that the equivalent FM signal produced by PM be the same as one produced by direct FM methods, a correction network and frequency multipliers must be used

signal-to-noise ratio

Since all electronic signals are actually voltages or currents that because of some varying property carry intelligence, any other voltages or currents that interact with signals will tend to *mask* the signal intelligence. These unwanted voltages or currents are grouped together under the terms *noise* and *interference*, and are produced in many ways. The most common sources of electronic noise are atmospheric static; interference generated by electrical equipment, such as motors and automobile ignition systems; and the individual components of electronic circuits. In the processing of electronic signals, some noise is always present; it can never be entirely eliminated. However, as long as the signal is sufficiently *stronger* than the noise, the signal intelligence will be unaffected.

The ratio of the signal voltage to the noise voltage is called the *signal-to-noise* ratio, S/N.

$$\frac{S}{N} = \frac{signal\ voltage}{noise\ voltage}$$

Sometimes, the signal-to-noise ratio of a signal is expressed in terms of *power* instead of voltage. In these cases, the S/N is the ratio of the signal power to the noise power. In addition, depending on the type of signal and noise under consideration, the S/N may be in terms of *peak values* of the signal and noise, or in terms of their *effective values*.

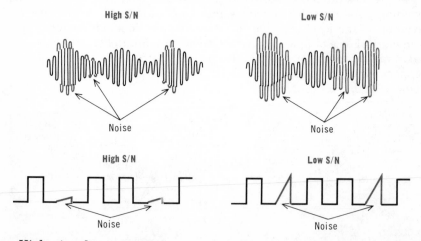

High signal-to-noise ratios are desirable, since they mean that the noise, being much weaker than the signal, will not interfere to any great extent with the signal intelligence. Low signal-to-noise ratios, on the other hand, indicate that both the signal and the noise are relatively close in value, and the intelligibility of the signal, therefore, will be partially or completely destroyed. The concept of signal-to-noise ratio applies to all electronic signals, whether they are FM, AM, dc, or ac.

pulse modulation techniques

In the discussion of the various types of modulation, you have seen how electronic signals can be made up of a series of pulses. In most of these pulse-type signals, the intelligence was carried by having the sequence of pulses correspond to some code, such as the Morse code or teletypewriter code. As a result, only intelligence that can be converted into some simple code can be carried. These pulse methods cannot be used for *complex* or *continuous* intelligence, such as voice signals. There are various other methods of pulse modulation, however, that can be used for carrying practically any type of intelligence. In all of these methods, the pulses make up the carrier, and some characteristic of the pulses is varied in accordance with the modulating signal.

Pulse modulation is an efficient means of transmitting electronic signals, since, as you learned, the power requirements of a pulse modulated signal are considerably less than those of a comparable AM or FM signal. The equipment required for pulse modulation and demodulation, however, is more complex and expensive than conventional AM and FM equipment. So pulse modulation is usually only used where its advantages outweigh the increases in size, weight, and cost of equipment.

Pulse modulation methods get their names from the way in which the pulses are varied to carry the intelligence. The most commonly used types of pulse modulation are: *pulse amplitude* modulation, *pulse width* modulation, *pulse position* modulation, and *pulse code* modulation. Sometimes, either or both pulse width and pulse position modulation are referred to as *pulse time* modulation.

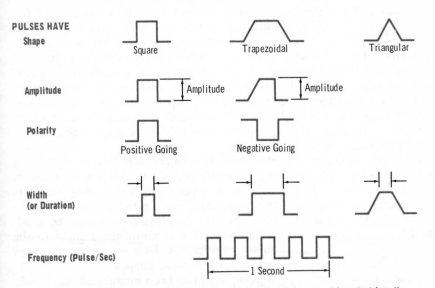

Other characteristics, such as rise and decay time, and period, are most important from the standpoint of how they affect the electronic circuits that process the pulses. They have little to do with the way in which the pulses carry intelligence

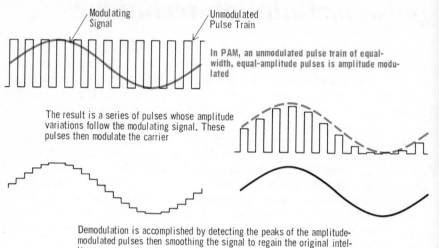

Modulating
Signal

Unmodulated
Pulse Train

In PAM, an unmodulated pulse train of equal-
width, equal-amplitude pulses is amplitude modulated

The result is a series of pulses whose amplitude
variations follow the modulating signal. These
pulses then modulate the carrier

Demodulation is accomplished by detecting the peaks of the amplitude-
modulated pulses then smoothing the signal to regain the original intelligence

pulse amplitude modulation

As explained in the discussion of amplitude modulation, in pulse amplitude modulation (PAM), the amplitudes of the individual pulses in a *pulse train* are determined by the amplitude of the modulating signal. This breaks the modulating signal into a series of pulses whose *peaks* follow the outline of the modulating signal.

As you will learn, a pulse is composed of an *infinite* number of frequency components. A circuit that processes a pulse must be able to respond equally to *all* of the frequencies, or the pulse will be distorted. Of course, it is impossible to have an *infinite bandwidth;* so pulses will always be distorted to some extent. Distortion of a characteristic that does not affect the intelligence is permissible. But if some characteristic that affects intelligence is distorted, the intelligence itself will be distorted. Thus, for practical reasons, the bandwidth of a pulse signal is limited to the range of frequencies that contributes to the information-carrying characteristic of the signal.

In pulse amplitude modulation, the important characteristics of the signal are: (1) the pulse amplitude, since this corresponds to the intelligence; and (2) the time it takes the pulse to drop from its peak value to zero, since this time must be limited to prevent interference between pulses. The minimum bandwidth that can be used, therefore, will include those frequencies that contributed most to the peak amplitude and decay time of the pulses. Of course, this will vary from signal to signal, depending on the pulse shapes.

As was pointed out, once a pulse train has been modulated, the resulting pulse modulated signal can be used to amplitude *or* frequency modulate an r-f carrier.

pulse width modulation

In pulse amplitude modulation, the unmodulated pulse train consisted of equal-width, equal-amplitude pulses whose amplitudes were changed in accordance with the modulating signal. A similar unmodulated pulse train of equal-width, equal-amplitude pulses is used for *pulse width modulation* (PWM). However, in PWM, the *width* of the pulses *is changed* in accordance with the modulating signal. After modulation, all the pulses still have equal amplitude, but their width is proportional to the instantaneous value of the modulating signal. The leading edges of the modulated pulses correspond to the leading edges of the unmodulated pulses. As a result, the amplitude of the modulating signal is limited, since too high an amplitude would cause one pulse to run into the next.

To recover the intelligence from a PWM signal, the signal is put through any circuit whose output amplitude is proportional to the width, or time duration, of the input pulse. Wide pulses will thus produce large-amplitude outputs, and narrow pulses small-amplitude outputs. By smoothing, or averaging, the variations in these output amplitudes, the overall output of the circuit will have the same variations as the modulating signal.

In electronic literature, pulse width modulation is also often called pulse *duration* modulation (PDM) and pulse *length* modulation (PLM). Sometimes, it is also called pulse *time* modulation (PTM), but this is also used for pulse position modulation, discussed next.

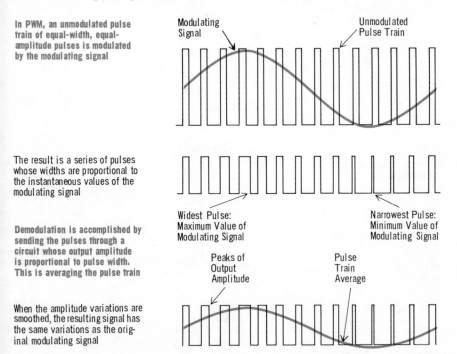

In PWM, an unmodulated pulse train of equal-width, equal-amplitude pulses is modulated by the modulating signal

Modulating Signal

Unmodulated Pulse Train

The result is a series of pulses whose widths are proportional to the instantaneous values of the modulating signal

Widest Pulse: Maximum Value of Modulating Signal

Narrowest Pulse: Minimum Value of Modulating Signal

Demodulation is accomplished by sending the pulses through a circuit whose output amplitude is proportional to pulse width. This is averaging the pulse train

Peaks of Output Amplitude

Pulse Train Average

When the amplitude variations are smoothed, the resulting signal has the same variations as the original modulating signal

pulse position modulation

In PAM and PWM, the pulse characteristics of amplitude and width were used to add intelligence to a pulse train. Another pulse characteristic that can be used is the *position* of each pulse in the train relative to the other pulses. This is *pulse position modulation* (PPM). One way to do this is to use a circuit that *without modulation* generates a train of *equally spaced pulses*. With modulation, though, the time of occurrence of each pulse depends on the value of the modulating signal. Thus, when the modulating signal is *zero*, the pulses are generated at the *same* time as they would be without modulation. But when the modulating signal has a *positive* value, the pulses are generated *sooner*, and when it has a *negative* value, they are generated *later*. The result of the modulating process, then, is a train of *unequally spaced* pulses, with the time between the occurrence of a pulse and the point at which it would occur without modulation being proportional to the value of the modulating signal.

Because of the difficulties involved in detecting the time between the actual occurrence of a pulse and the time that it would have occurred without modulation, it is common practice in PPM to transmit equally spaced *reference pulses* with the modulated pulses. The intelligence-carrying pulses, therefore, vary in distance from the reference pulses according to the values of the modulating signal. In the demodulation process, the distance, which represents time, between each intelligence-carrying pulse and its corresponding reference pulse is detected and converted to a signal voltage.

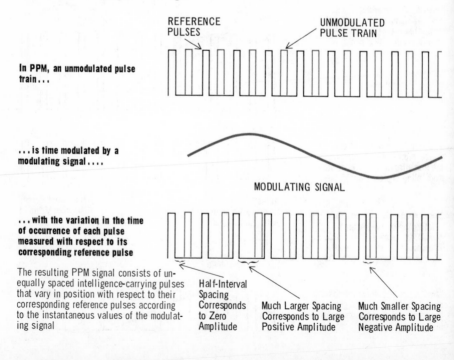

REFERENCE
PULSES

UNMODULATED
PULSE TRAIN

In PPM, an unmodulated pulse train...

...is time modulated by a modulating signal....

MODULATING SIGNAL

...with the variation in the time of occurrence of each pulse measured with respect to its corresponding reference pulse

The resulting PPM signal consists of unequally spaced intelligence-carrying pulses that vary in position with respect to their corresponding reference pulses according to the instantaneous values of the modulating signal

Half-Interval Spacing Corresponds to Zero Amplitude

Much Larger Spacing Corresponds to Large Positive Amplitude

Much Smaller Spacing Corresponds to Large Negative Amplitude

pulse code modulation

In all of the pulse modulation techniques described, some *characteristic* was varied according to the modulation. Once the pulses have been modulated, it is important that the characteristic that represents the intelligence does not change during transmission and processing of the signal. Any change, such as in the amplitude of a PAM pulse or the width of a PWM pulse, would cause distortion of the intelligence. There is one type of pulse modulation that is much more immune to *interference* and *distortion* than the others. It is called *pulse code modulation* (PCM).

In pulse code modulation, the modulating signal is *sampled* at discrete intervals. Each time it is sampled, a *group* of pulses is produced that corresponds to the value of the modulating signal at that instant. Every pulse in the group is *identical* to every other pulse, and it is the *number* and *positions* of the pulses that represent the value of the modulating signal. The system by which the pulses in a group represent a specific value is called a *code*. By using appropriate codes, a limited number of pulses can represent a wide range of values. For example, one code, called the binary code, might be used as follows, where there are four pulse positions in each group, and 1 represents a pulse in a particular position, and 0 no pulse.

Value in Volts	Position				Value in Volts	Position			
	1	2	3	4		1	2	3	4
0	0	0	0	0	8	1	0	0	0
1	0	0	0	1	9	1	0	0	1
2	0	0	1	0	10	1	0	1	0
3	0	0	1	1	11	1	0	1	1
4	0	1	0	0	12	1	1	0	0
5	0	1	0	1	13	1	1	0	1
6	0	1	1	0	14	1	1	1	0
7	0	1	1	1	15	1	1	1	1

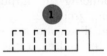

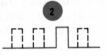

This shows how PULSE – NO PULSE
groups can be used to carry digits
1 through 4

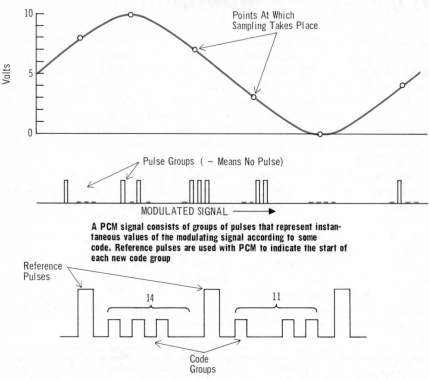

MODULATING SIGNAL

Points At Which
Sampling Takes Place

Pulse Groups (– Means No Pulse)

MODULATED SIGNAL ⟶

A PCM signal consists of groups of pulses that represent instantaneous values of the modulating signal according to some
code. Reference pulses are used with PCM to indicate the start of
each new code group

Reference
Pulses

14   11

Code
Groups

pulse code modulation (cont.)

The use of the binary code with an actual signal is illustrated. Actually, practically any satisfactory coding arrangement can be used. The
important point is that the receiver uses the same code to reverse the
process and recover the intelligence.

When a PCM signal is demodulated, each group of pulses goes through
a circuit that, in effect, decodes the group by producing an output
voltage that corresponds to the level represented by that group.

The relative immunity of PCM to interference and distortion arises
from the fact that it is the *presence* or *absence* of the pulses, rather
than any varying characteristic, that has to be determined to recover
the intelligence. Even if the pulses are distorted, it will have no effect
on their detection, unless of course the distortion is extremely severe.

Reference pulses are used with the pulse code groups to indicate
to the receiving equipment that a new code group is starting. PCM is
especially useful in transmitting numerical data, as is done with telemetering equipment. Also, the codes can be used to represent letters of
the alphabet so that words can be transmitted, as is done with teletype.
Or, as explained previously, the codes can represent relative amplitudes.

time division multiplexing

In a pulse modulated signal, some time is required between pulses. Frequently, however, the intervals are considerably longer than the pulses themselves. Such a signal is said to have a *low duty factor*. These signals can be used to advantage by having one or more pulses that represent *different* intelligence occupy the intervals. This results in a single modulated pulse train that carries *multiple* intelligence. Such a technique is called *time division multiplexing*, and makes possible the simultaneous radio transmission of more than one signal on a single r-f carrier.

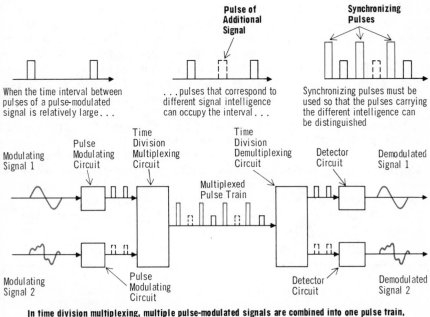

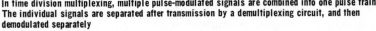

In time division multiplexing, multiple pulse-modulated signals are combined into one pulse train. The individual signals are separated after transmission by a demultiplexing circuit, and then demodulated separately

When time division multiplexing is used, the pulses of the different signals are usually distinguished by reference, or *synchronizing*, pulses. The synchronizing pulses are different from the intelligence-carrying pulses. They may have longer durations or larger amplitudes than the other pulses. The detecting circuits can then separate the pulses of the different signals, and recover the intelligence carried by each signal.

Although two separate signals are shown being multiplexed in the illustration, time division multiplexing commonly involves as many as four or more signals. In addition, synchronizing pulses are not used after every intelligence pulse. Instead, they usually separate groups of pulses that are made up of one pulse of each signal.

summary

☐ Phase modulation (PM) is an indirect way of producing an FM signal having a highly stable center frequency. ☐ In phase modulation, the instantaneous phase of the carrier is varied from its phase at rest in proportion to the amplitude of the modulating signal. This automatically causes corresponding changes in the carrier frequency. ☐ A correction network is required because the carrier deviation is affected by the frequency of the modulating signal, as well as its amplitude. ☐ Phase modulation produces relatively low carrier deviations, and so frequency multipliers are used.

☐ In pulse amplitude modulation (PAM), the amplitudes of the pulses in a pulse train are varied in accordance with the amplitude of the modulating signal. This breaks the modulating signal into a series of pulses whose peaks follow the outline of the modulating signal. ☐ In pulse width modulation (PWM), the widths of the pulses in a pulse train are varied. ☐ Pulse width modulation is also sometimes called pulse duration modulation (PDM) and pulse length modulation (PLM). ☐ In pulse position modulation (PPM), the time of occurrence of the pulses in a pulse train is varied. Reference pulses are usually required with pulse position modulation.

☐ Pulse code modulation (PCM) uses groups of pulses to represent the value of the modulating signal at sampling intervals. The number and positions of the pulses follow some specific code. ☐ Pulse code modulation has good immunity to interference and distortion, since only the presence or absence of the pulses need be determined to recover the intelligence. ☐ Time division multiplexing is a modulation technique in which two or more separate signals are placed on a single pulse train. Synchronizing pulses are used to separate the pulses of the different signals.

---

review questions

1. What is *equivalent FM*?
2. Why are frequency multipliers needed with phase modulation?
3. Why is a *correction network* needed in PM?
4. Why are high signal-to-noise ratios desirable?
5. Draw waveforms to show how a sine-wave modulating signal can pulse-amplitude, pulse-width, and pulse-position modulate a pulse train.
6. What is the major advantage of pulse code modulation?
7. What is *time division multiplexing*?
8. Draw the waveform of a pulse train with a low duty factor.
9. Why is phase modulation used?
10. Is there any way of telling whether a received FM signal was frequency modulated or phase modulated?

complex modulation

You have learned the basic methods of modulation, in which the intelligence contained in one wave (the modulating signal) is transferred onto, or modulates, another wave (the carrier). In the descriptions of these methods, we assumed, for the most part, that the modulating signal contained a *single* intelligence; for example, a single voice signal, a single continuous tone, or maybe an interrupted tone or carrier corresponding to the Morse code. You will find, however, that many types of electronic signals are *not* this simple, because of the nature of the intelligence being carried.

In many actual signals, two or more types of *unrelated* intelligence may be transmitted on the *same* carrier, and they may or may not use the same kind of modulation. In other signals, *related* intelligence might be contained in separate modulating signals, which are used to modulate separate carriers which, again, may or may not employ the same type of modulation. These separate carriers must then be transmitted, received, and demodulated simultaneously, since the overall signal intelligence is the sum of the intelligence carried by each.

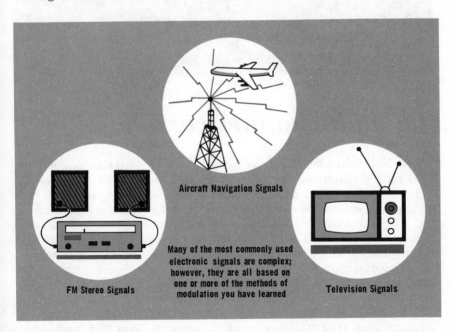

Aircraft Navigation Signals

FM Stereo Signals

Many of the most commonly used electronic signals are complex; however, they are all based on one or more of the methods of modulation you have learned

Television Signals

Some of the more representative types of complex modulated signals are described on the following pages. In addition to those covered, there are many more. However, once you have an understanding of how the basic modulating methods can be used to form some of the common complex signals, you should have no trouble in understanding others that you may encounter.

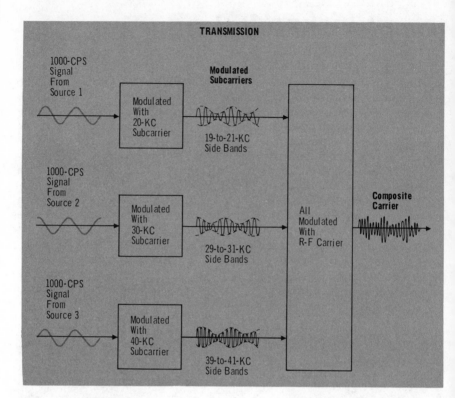

the multichannel carrier

You have already seen how by using pulse modulation combined with time division multiplexing techniques, more than one message, or other modulation, can be transmitted on a *single* carrier. This same principle of sending numerous separate messages on a common carrier can also be realized for *continuous* types of modulation, such as voice signals or tones, by a method called *frequency division multiplexing.*

Frequency division multiplexing is based on the fact that when a signal modulates a carrier, the *intelligence* is unaffected, only the *frequency* at which it is carried is changed. Thus, if two signals having the *same* frequency, or frequencies, simultaneously modulated a carrier, the two would *interact* with each other, and it would be impossible to separate them after transmission. But, if one of them first modulated a *subcarrier*, its frequency would be raised above that of the other signal. Therefore, the products of this modulation together with the other signal could then modulate an r-f carrier, and no interaction would take place between them because of their frequency difference. After transmission, they could be easily filtered out of the composite carrier, and then demodulated separately.

the multichannel carrier (cont.)

The basic principle of the multichannel carrier is, therefore, that various modulating signals each modulate a *different subcarrier*, with the subcarrier frequencies being such that the modulation products (side bands and subcarrier) of each signal occupy a different frequency range. All of these modulated subcarriers then modulate a common r-f carrier to produce a *composite* modulated carrier. Of course, this composite carrier is a very complex wave, consisting of numerous side-band frequencies. Nevertheless, by passing the composite carrier through appropriate filters after transmission, each of the modulated subcarriers can be recovered. These are then demodulated to regain the original intelligence of each of the signals.

Multichannel carriers are used to a great extent for the transmission of data from satellites and space probes. They allow an extensive amount of separate data to be transmitted in a short time from a single transmitter.

RECEPTION

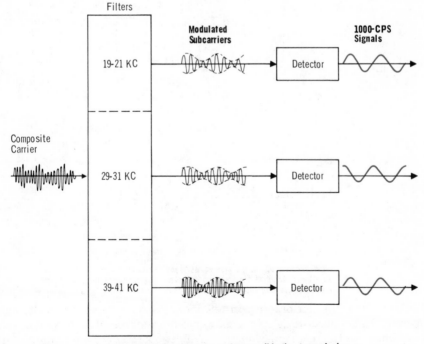

Frequency division multiplexing makes possible the transmission of numerous continuous signals on a common carrier

telephone multichannel carriers

Multichannel carriers can be used for *radio transmission* as well as for transmission by *wire* or *cable*. One of their most common uses is for the transmission of voice signals over telephone lines. By the use of multichannel carriers, many *different* voice signals can be simultaneously carried over the same transmission line without interfering with each other.

The number of channels that can be transmitted simultaneously depends on the bandwidth of the sending and receiving equipment, as well as on the bandwidths of each of the individual signals after they modulate their respective subcarrier. For example, if the equipment has a bandwidth of 200 kc, and each modulated subcarrier has a bandwidth of 40 kc, four channels can be sent on the main carrier. But, if the bandwidth of the modulated subcarrier is reduced, the main carrier can accommodate additional channels. This is why it is common practice to *suppress* one of the side bands of each signal after subcarrier modulation. By the removal of one side band, the bandwidth of the signal is cut in half, without interfering in any way with the intelligence being carried.

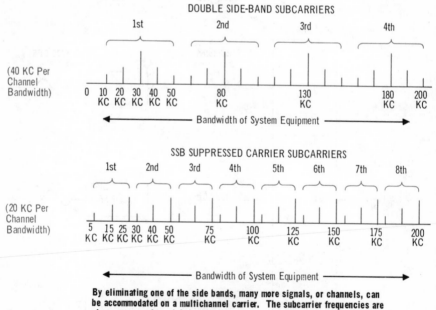

By eliminating one of the side bands, many more signals, or channels, can be accommodated on a multichannel carrier. The subcarrier frequencies are also suppressed to minimize the transmission power requirements

It is also common practice in telephone systems to suppress the subcarrier frequencies to keep the power requirements of the system at a minimum. After transmission, the SSB suppressed carrier signals are removed from the multichannel carrier by filtering, and then the subcarriers are reinserted for demodulation.

the black-and-white television signal

The signal used for the transmission of black-and-white television is a very complex signal in which the overall intelligence is made up of various individual parts or components. Basically, the transmitted television signal consists of *two separate carriers:* one modulated with the *sound,* and the other with the visual, or *video,* portion. A television receiver receives both carriers *simultaneously,* builds up, or amplifies, the level of both, and then separates the two for demodulation. The sound portion of the television signal is a standard *FM* wave.

FM is used rather than AM for the television sound because of its better immunity to noise and interference, and it is more efficient as far as transmitter power requirements are concerned. In addition, FM signals generally have a much better signal-to-noise ratio than do comparable AM signals.

Although the sound portion of a television signal is frequency modulated, the video portion is amplitude modulated onto its separate carrier. AM is used for the video portion mainly because of the possibility of *multipath reception* of the transmitted signal. This occurs when the same signal, because of the reflections from buildings, bridges, etc., reaches a receiving antenna from more than one path. Since the distance traveled by these multipath signals is usually different, different parts of the signal arrive at the antenna at the same time. For AM signals, this causes interference at the television receiver in the form of multiple images, or ghosts, on the screen. For FM signals, the interference would be much more bothersome, since it would be in the form of continuously shimmering bars on the screen.

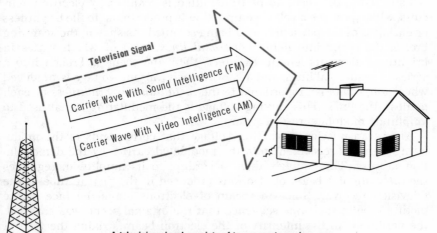

A television signal consists of two separate carriers: one frequency modulated with the sound information, and the other amplitude modulated with the video information

the video portion

The composite television carrier has the sound carrier located 4.5 megacycles above the video carrier. The sound carrier is a normal DSB transmission, but the video portion is a vestigial side-band signal. The frequencies close to the video carrier are the low video frequencies, and those farther away are the highs. Video frequencies of up to 4 megacycles can be sent.

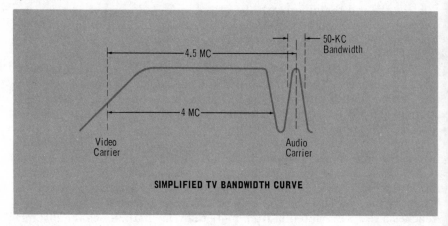

SIMPLIFIED TV BANDWIDTH CURVE

The video portion of a television signal consists of an AM carrier whose *amplitude variations* correspond to the picture or scene being transmitted. To understand how the video signal carries the visual intelligence, you must have an idea of how the signal is produced from the original scene, and then, after transmission, how the demodulated signal is converted to a reproduction of the original scene.

Essentially, the scene to be transmitted is *scanned* by electronic circuits, which produce a voltage output that is proportional to the brightness or darkness of the particular area being scanned. As shown, the scanning breaks the scene into many *horizontal lines,* each of which varies in brightness along its length. In effect, then, the scene is broken into a series of sequential lines, and a continuously varying voltage is produced whose *amplitude* is proportional to the *instantaneous brightness* of each point in the lines. This varying voltage is the modulating signal used to amplitude modulate an r-f carrier.

After transmission, a varying voltage that corresponds to the modulating signal is recovered from the modulated carrier by the demodulation process. This voltage, then, according to its amplitude, regulates the *intensity* of a beam of electrons produced in the picture tube of the television receiver. Since the beam of electrons scans the face of the picture tube in the *same sequence* that the original scene was scanned, the variations in the intensity of the electron beam striking the face of the picture tube follow the variations in brightness and darkness of the original scene.

the video portion (cont.)

Visual reproduction of the original scene occurs as a result of a *phosphorescent coating* on the face of the picture tube. When this coating is struck by the electron beam, it emits light, with the amount of light being proportional to the intensity of the beam. Thus, when the electron beam has a high intensity, which corresponds to a point of extreme brightness in the original scene, a large amount of light is emitted from the point on the picture tube struck by the beam. Similarly, points of low brightness in the original scene will result in a low-intensity electron beam striking the corresponding point on the face of the picture tube, and, hence, little light will be emitted.

The scanning of the original scene at the transmitting end and the reproduced scene at the receiving end must take place *very rapidly* so that the human eye only sees complete pictures on the television screen rather than seeing the pictures being produced line by line. In actual practice, a scene is broken into 525 individual lines, with each line being scanned in 1/15,750 of a second. In one second, therefore, the entire scene is scanned 30 times.

Effectively, then, the television video signal carries 30 complete *still pictures* each second, similar to motion picture projectors. But because of the persistency of vision of the human eye, the rapid sequence of these still pictures gives the impression of continuous action. Also, the picture is actually sent at 60 cps; each picture is broken into two *frames,* each containing alternate lines of a picture. When they combine on the screen, the lines of one frame are interleaved with those of the other frame. This is called *interlacing.* The 60 frames then produce 30 complete pictures per second.

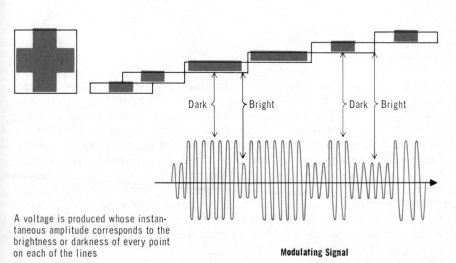

Electronic scanning effectively breaks this scene into horizontal lines

Dark Bright Dark Bright

A voltage is produced whose instantaneous amplitude corresponds to the brightness or darkness of every point on each of the lines

Modulating Signal

television signal fundamentals

The video signal produces the picture by means of 525 horizontal lines of varying instantaneous brightness. The scanning process that produces the picture, though, is not continuous. After each complete line there must be a time lapse before the next line begins to allow the scanning beam to return to its new starting position. In addition, after the 525th line has been scanned, there must be a time lapse to allow the beam to return to its *initial* starting point. These time lapses between lines are called *horizontal* and *vertical retrace times,* and represent periods when no picture information is being transmitted. As you will learn, it is during these times that special pulses are included in the signal to synchronize the operation of transmitting and receiving circuits.

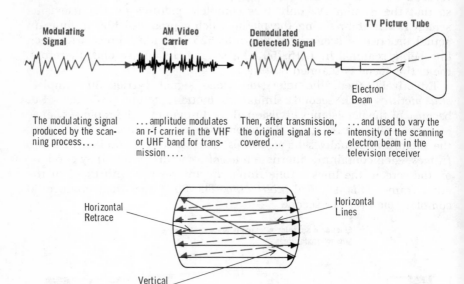

Modulating Signal

AM Video Carrier

Demodulated (Detected) Signal

TV Picture Tube

Electron Beam

The modulating signal produced by the scanning process...

...amplitude modulates an r-f carrier in the VHF or UHF band for transmission....

Then, after transmission, the original signal is recovered...

...and used to vary the intensity of the scanning electron beam in the television receiver

Horizontal Retrace

Horizontal Lines

Vertical Retrace

As you know from your own experience, even without a video signal, a television screen is bright as long as it is turned *on.* This brightness is called the *raster,* and is produced by the electron beam being scanned across the face of the tube by circuits inside of the television receiver. Without a video signal, the beam has a constant intensity, so the screen brightness is uniform across the face of the tube. When a video signal is received, it varies the intensity of the electron beam above and below its *no-signal* intensity, and in this way, produces a picture on the screen.

The circuits that scan the electron beam must be synchronized with those that scan the original scene at the television studio. The synchronizing pulses that are made a part of the video signal perform this function.

nonpicture portions

You have seen how the video signal carries the picture information in the form of amplitude variations that correspond to the brightness and darkness of the scene being transmitted. For proper operation of the television receiver, though, the video signal must carry more than just the picture information. It must provide a means for *cutting off* the electron beam of the receiver scanning circuits during the periods of both horizontal and vertical *retrace*. If this is not done, unwanted white lines would be produced on the TV screen during every retrace. The video signal must also provide for *synchronization* between the transmitting and receiving scanning circuits. Without such synchronization, the picture at the TV receiver would roll vertically and tear horizontally.

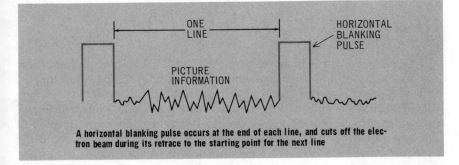

A horizontal blanking pulse occurs at the end of each line, and cuts off the electron beam during its retrace to the starting point for the next line

The electron beam of the receiver is cut off during retrace by portions of the video signal called *blanking pulses*. These pulses are rectangular in shape, and represent a signal voltage level sufficiently high to cut off the electron beam and therefore produce no brightness on the screen. There are horizontal blanking pulses for cutting off the beam during horizontal retrace, and vertical blanking pulses for cutting it off during vertical retrace. As shown, both types of blanking pulses have the same amplitude, but the *vertical* blanking pulses are wider, or of longer duration.

A vertical blanking pulse occurs at the end of the last horizontal line, and cuts off the electron beam during its retrace to the starting point for the first line

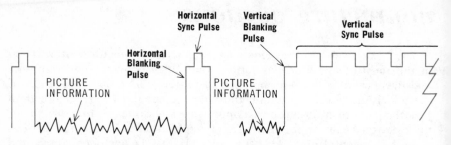

A horizontal sync pulse rides atop each horizontal blanking pulse. The sync pulse triggers the horizontal retrace, insuring that scanning of next line begins at the proper time. 18,750 blanking pulses are sent every second

A vertical sync pulse (a group of pulses) rides atop each vertical blanking pulse. The group triggers the vertical retrace, and also acts as a horizontal pulse. This group is sent 60 times per second

nonpicture portions (cont.)

Just as there are both horizontal and vertical blanking pulses, there are also horizontal and vertical *synchronizing pulses*. These are usually called *sync* pulses, and ride *on top* of the blanking pulses, as shown. The sync pulses occur during retrace, at which times no picture information is being received. This is obviously necessary, since the purpose of the sync pulses is to insure that the scanning of each line starts at the proper instant. Actually the sync pulses do this by starting, or triggering, the retrace at the end of each line. Both the horizontal and vertical sync pulses have the same amplitude, but the vertical pulses are wider. This difference in width is the basis by which the circuits in the TV receiver distinguish between the two types of sync pulses. This will be explained later.

COMPOSITE VIDEO SIGNAL

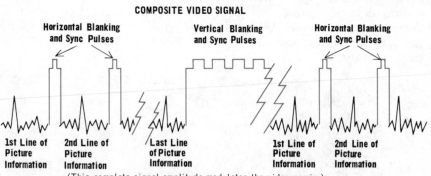

(This complete signal amplitude modulates the video carrier)

The preceding description of the video portion was of a basic nature. A complete description would involve additional elements and refinements beyond the scope of this volume

The vertical sync pulses are contained in a group of 18 special pulses that are used for both horizontal and vertical synchronization. This is explained later

bandwidth

All television signals are assigned a specific 6-megacycle wide frequency channel in the VHF or UHF band by the Federal Communications Commission. There are a total of 82 channels, and they have number designations of 2 through 83. Of the 82 channels, 12 are in the VHF band (channels 2 through 13) and the remainder in the UHF band.

Within the standard channel, the FM sound carrier has a center frequency 0.25 megacycle below the upper edge of the channel. The bandwidth of the sound carrier is approximately 50 kilocycles, which leaves about 5.7 megacycles left in the band for the video carrier. If conventional double side-band modulation was used for the video signal, the highest modulating frequencies that could be transmitted would be around 2.85 megacycles, which is undesirable because most of the picture detail is represented by frequencies higher than 2.85 megacycles. So, instead, vestigial side-band transmission is used.

A television channel contains both the FM sound carrier and the AM video carrier in its 6-mc bandwidth

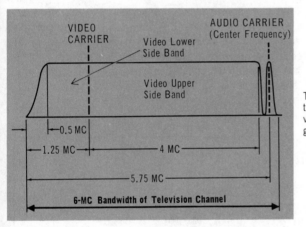

The sound carrier is a conventional FM signal, while the video carrier is of the vestigial side-band type

The bandwidths of the FM and AM portions of the overall signal are such that there is no interference or interaction between the two

The video carrier is placed 1.25 *megacycles* above the lower edge of the channel, and all upper side-band frequencies corresponding to the maximum modulating frequencies of about 4 megacycles are transmitted at their normal amplitude. The lower side-band frequencies are transmitted with varying degrees of attenuation down as far as those that are 1.25 megacycles or more below the video carrier. Those frequencies below this, fall outside of the assigned channel, and therefore must be *completely* eliminated before transmission.

summary

☐ Frequency division multiplexing permits multiple signals to be modulated onto a single carrier wave. Each of the signals first modulates a separate subcarrier, and these modulated subcarriers then modulate the main carrier. ☐ At the receiver, the subcarrier components of a multiplexed signal are removed from the main carrier by filters, and then demodulated separately. ☐ The number of channels that can be accommodated in a frequency multiplexed signal depends on the bandwidths of the modulating signals and the transmitting and receiving equipment.

☐ A black-and-white television signal consists of an FM sound portion and an AM video portion. The sound carrier is located 4.5 megacycles above the video carrier. ☐ The video signal consists of an AM carrier whose amplitude variations correspond to the picture being sent. ☐ Scanning circuits at both the transmitting and receiving ends break the scenes being transmitted into horizontal lines. Each scene consists of 525 lines. ☐ Scanning occurs very rapidly, with each scene being scanned 30 times a second. ☐ Every picture on the television screen is broken into two frames, each containing alternate scanning lines. This is called interlacing.

☐ The brightness on a television screen when no signal is being received is called the raster. The video signal varies the intensity of the electron beam that produces the raster. ☐ The video signal also contains horizontal and vertical blanking pulses, and horizontal and vertical sync pulses. ☐ The blanking pulses cut off the scanning electron beam during horizontal and vertical retrace time. ☐ The sync pulses insure that the scanning of each line starts at the proper instant.

review questions

1. What is the difference between frequency division multiplexing and time division multiplexing?
2. What are *subcarriers*, and why are they used?
3. The video portion of a black-and-white television signal employs what kind of modulation?
4. How many lines are there in a television picture?
5. What is *interlacing*?
6. What is the purpose of blanking pulses?
7. What is the purpose of the sync pulses?
8. How wide is the bandwidth of a commercial television signal?
9. Is the sound carrier above or below the video carrier?
10. What are the highest video frequencies that can be transmitted by a television signal?

the color television signal

In color television, as you know, transmitted images are reproduced at the TV receiver in colors that match quite closely those of the original scene. This *color information* must therefore be transmitted by the color television signal. You are probably aware, however, that color television signals are *compatible* with both black-and-white and color television receivers. This means that a noncolor receiver produces a black-and-white picture from it, and a color receiver produces a color picture. The signal must contain color information, and also black-and-white information about the original scene. Therefore, the color television signal has components that make it quite different from the standard black-and-white signal.

The color signal is similar to the black-and-white signal in that it consists of an FM sound carrier and an AM video carrier, both contained in a 6-mc channel. In addition, the video portion of the color signal, like that of the black-and-white signal, is made up of horizontal lines of picture information, with the individual lines followed by sync and blanking pulses. Here, though the similarity ends.

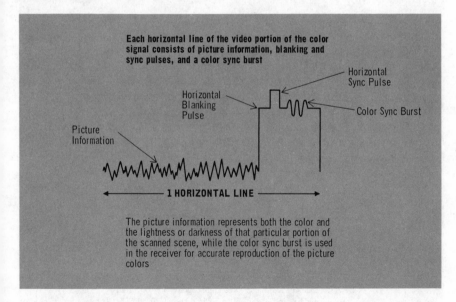

Each horizontal line of the video portion of the color signal consists of picture information, blanking and sync pulses, and a color sync burst

Horizontal Sync Pulse

Horizontal Blanking Pulse

Color Sync Burst

Picture Information

◄——— 1 HORIZONTAL LINE ———►

The picture information represents both the color and the lightness or darkness of that particular portion of the scanned scene, while the color sync burst is used in the receiver for accurate reproduction of the picture colors

In the black-and-white signal, those portions of the signal that correspond to the picture information are merely amplitude variations that represent the brightness or darkness of the original image. But these same portions of a color signal, although still amplitude variations, are a complex representation of both the *colors* and *brightness* of the scene. Furthermore, the color signal has an additional type of sync pulse, called the *color sync burst,* which follows immediately after the horizontal sync pulses.

picture information

The picture information portion of the color video signal is a composite of color information, and brightness or darkness information. The starting point in the generation of this part of the signal is the production of *three* separate *color* signals from the image to be transmitted. Each of these three color signals is produced in the same manner as the modulating signal for black-and-white television.

One of the color signals is for *red*, and consists of a voltage whose amplitude variations follow the variations in the red content of the scene being scanned. The other two signals are for *green* and *blue*, and consist of similar voltage variations for the green and blue content of the televised scene. These three *primary colors* of red, green, and blue are the basis of the color signal, since most other colors, including white, can be obtained by mixing them in the proper ratios.

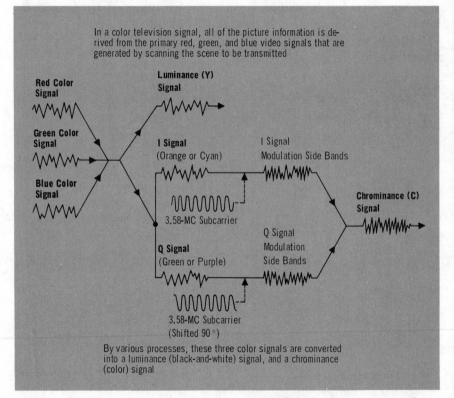

In a color television signal, all of the picture information is derived from the primary red, green, and blue video signals that are generated by scanning the scene to be transmitted

Red Color Signal

Luminance (Y) Signal

Green Color Signal

I Signal (Orange or Cyan)

I Signal Modulation Side Bands

Blue Color Signal

3.58-MC Subcarrier

Chrominance (C) Signal

Q Signal (Green or Purple)

Q Signal Modulation Side Bands

3.58-MC Subcarrier (Shifted 90°)

By various processes, these three color signals are converted into a luminance (black-and-white) signal, and a chrominance (color) signal

Once the three video color signals are produced, they are mixed, or combined, to produce what is called the *luminance*, or *Y*, signal. The signal corresponds to the *lightness* and *darkness* variations of the televised scene, and is similar to the modulating signal used for black-and-white television. The proportions of red, green, and blue in this "white" signal are 30 percent red, 59 percent green, and 11 percent blue.

the colorplexed video signal

The three color signals are also combined to produce two other signals, called the Q and I signals, besides being used to produce the luminance signal. The Q signal corresponds to the *green* or *purple* information in the picture, and the I signal corresponds to the *orange* or *cyan* information. Together, the Q and I signals contain all of the picture color information. Both the Q and I signals then amplitude modulate a 3.58-megacycle carrier wave, which is called a *subcarrier,* since the results of this modulation are used to modulate the main video carrier. Actually, although it is the same 3.58-megacycle subcarrier that is modulated by the Q and I signals, the subcarrier is shifted in phase 90 degrees before modulation by the Q signal. This allows both the Q and I modulation to be carried on the same subcarrier and be distinguishable from each other. The side bands produced by the Q and I modulation are added vectorially to form what is called the *chrominance,* or *C,* signal. The 3.58-megacycle subcarrier is suppressed when the side bands are combined.

The luminance (Y) and chrominance (C) signals, which are produced from the basic red, green, and blue video color signals, contain all of the picture information to be transmitted. They are combined into one signal by being added in such a way that the variations in the *average* value of the resulting signal represent the *luminance* variations, while the *instantaneous* variations represent the *chrominance* information. The composite signal is the picture information portion of the video modulating signal, and together with the blanking, sync, and color burst sync pulses make up what is called the *colorplexed* video signal. This total video signal amplitude modulates the video carrier for transmission to the receiver.

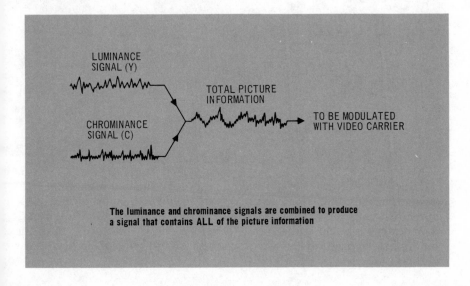

LUMINANCE
SIGNAL (Y)

TOTAL PICTURE
INFORMATION

CHROMINANCE
SIGNAL (C)

TO BE MODULATED
WITH VIDEO CARRIER

The luminance and chrominance signals are combined to produce
a signal that contains ALL of the picture information

the colorplexed video signal (cont.)

Each color sync burst consists of a few cycles of the unmodulated, 3.58-megacycle subcarrier used to produce the Q and I signals. You recall that the subcarrier is *suppressed* after the Q and I signals are generated. This means that the subcarrier must be reinserted in the receiver for detection of the Q and I signals. The color sync burst is used at the receiver to synchronize the phase of the reinserted subcarrier with that of the original subcarrier at the transmitter.

After the colorplexed video signal has been removed from its carrier by detection in the receiver, the way in which the signal is processed depends on whether the receiver is designed for color, or just black and white. In black-and-white receivers, only the luminance (Y) signal is detected from the picture information portion of the video signal. This is then processed, along with the blanking and sync pulses, the same as a standard black-and-white signal.

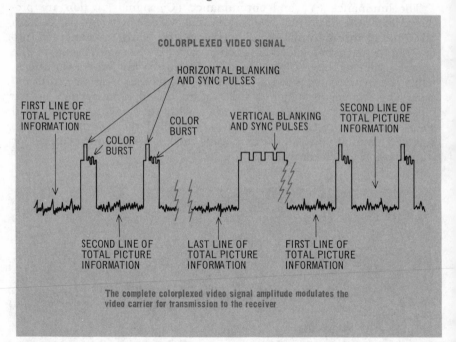

The complete colorplexed video signal amplitude modulates the video carrier for transmission to the receiver

In color receivers, both the luminance (Y) and chrominance (C) signals are detected, and together with the blanking, sync, and color burst sync pulses, are used to reproduce the color picture. The chrominance signal provides the color variations for the picture, while the luminance signal provides the variations in intensity of or brightness of the colors.

the FM stereo multiplex signal

Everyone is familiar to some extent with the stereophonic (*stereo*) reproduction of sound. Basically, it involves the use of two microphones rather than one to pick up the sound being recorded or transmitted. The two microphones are spaced some distance *apart*, and so receive somewhat different sound waves. For example, in the stereo pickup of an orchestra, one microphone might be closer to the violin section than the other microphone. Although the sound waves picked up by both would be similar, the amplitudes of the high-frequency sound components received by the microphone closest to the violin section would be larger than the same frequency components received by the other microphone, since violins are essentially high-frequency instruments.

By having the microphones produce *separate* signals and keeping the signals separate during recording or transmission, it is possible to eventually apply the two signals to separate speakers for reproducing the original sound. In this way, one speaker reproduces sound picked up by one of the microphones, and the other speaker the sound from the second microphone. The sound coming from the two speakers, then, has *depth* or *directional* qualities, somewhat similar to the three-dimensional reproduction of visual scenes.

Despite its popular acceptance, the stereo reproduction of sound was for years limited to use on phonograph and tape recordings. Radio transmission of stereo sound was impractical, since to keep the two sound signals separate, they had to be transmitted separately, as well as processed by radio receivers separately. But, finally, a system was approved by the FCC in which stereo sound can be transmitted on a single FM carrier. This type of transmission is called *FM stereo multiplex,* and is coming into relatively widespread use.

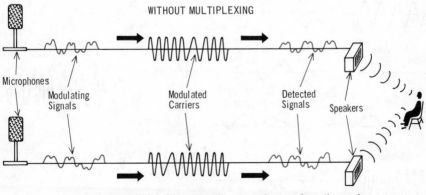

In the transmission of stereo sound, each speaker reproduces the sound picked up by one of the microphones

Without multiplexing, the transmission of stereo sound would require completely separate transmission facilities for each signal

components of the FM stereo multiplex signal

One of the principal advantages of FM stereo multiplexing is that it is compatible with FM receivers that are equipped for stereo, as well as with those that are not. Stereo receivers reproduce the transmitted signal as stereo sound. Conventional (monophonic) receivers, on the other hand, reproduce it as a conventional FM sound signal.

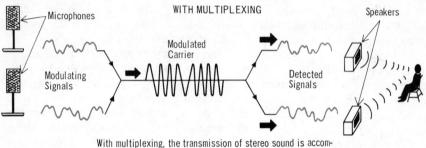

With multiplexing, the transmission of stereo sound is accomplished by placing both signals on a common carrier

The generation of the FM stereo multiplex signal begins with the audio signals produced by the two microphones. These signals are designated L and R, based on the relative positions, left (L) and right (R), of the microphones. The L and R audio signals are applied to a circuit, called a *matrix*, which develops two *new* signals.

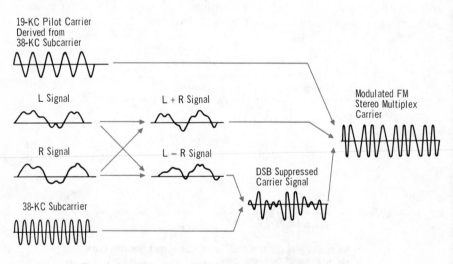

The modulated FM stereo multiplex carrier has many components. At the receiver, these components can be recovered and processed so that the original L and R signals are reproduced

components of the FM stereo multiplex signal (cont.)

One of these new signals corresponds to the instantaneous *sum* of the L and R signals, and is called the *L + R signal*. The other new signal is the *L — R signal*, since it corresponds to the instantaneous *difference* of the L and R signals. The L — R signal then *amplitude* modulates a 38-kilocycle subcarrier to produce side bands above and below 38 kilocycles. The 38-kilocycle subcarrier frequency is *suppressed* after the modulation takes place. Both the L + R signal, and the AM side bands produced by modulating the L — R signal with the subcarrier are then used to frequency modulate an r-f carrier for transmission.

When the original L and R signals are produced, they are limited in bandwidth to 0 to 15 kilocycles. All higher audio frequencies are filtered out. Therefore, the L + R signal that modulates the FM carrier has a bandwidth from 0 to 15 kilocycles, while the lower side band produced by the L — R modulation goes from 23 to 38 kilocycles, and the upper side band from 38 to 53 kilocycles. The intelligence of the L + R and L — R signals are thus separated by 8 kilocycles (15 to 23 kilocycles), making it easy to distinguish them after they are separated from the FM carrier following transmission.

Since the 38-kilocycle subcarrier was suppressed after being used for the L — R modulation, it must be reinserted at the receiver for demodulation. To make this reinsertion possible, a 19-kilocycle *pilot carrier* is also transmitted on the FM carrier. In the receiver, the pilot carrier is frequency doubled to 38 kilocycles, and then used to synchronize the 38-kilocycle demodulation subcarrier with the modulation subcarrier at the transmitter. The pilot carrier is sent at 19 rather than 38 kilocycles, since in this way it falls into the signal frequency spectrum at a point where no signal intelligence is located. This permits it to be easily detected at the receiver.

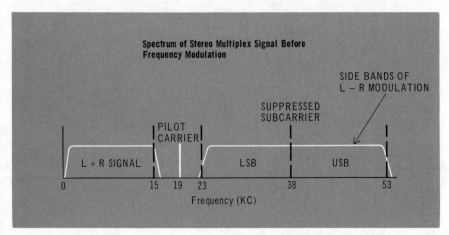

Spectrum of Stereo Multiplex Signal Before Frequency Modulation

SIDE BANDS OF L – R MODULATION

SUPPRESSED SUBCARRIER

PILOT CARRIER

L + R SIGNAL   LSB   USB

0   15   19   23   38   53

Frequency (KC)

recovering the intelligence

When an FM stereo multiplex signal is received by an FM receiver, the intelligence is removed from the carrier by the demodulation process. This intelligence consists of the L + R signal, the side bands of the L — R AM signal, and the 19-kilocycle pilot carrier. If the receiver is not equipped for stereo, it responds *only* to the L + R signal, and processes this as a normal monophonic signal.

In a receiver that is equipped for stereo, the L — R signal is recovered by combining the L — R modulation side bands with a 38-kilocycle carrier, and then removing the original L — R signal. The 38-kilocycle carrier is generated in the receiver, and uses the 19-kilocycle pilot carrier for synchronization. The L — R signal and the L + R signal are then combined in a matrix circuit, similar to the one used at the transmitting end of the system. In the matrix, the L + R and L — R signals are *added* to produce the original L *signal*. Also in the matrix, the L + R and L — R signals are *subtracted* to produce the original R *signal*. These sum and difference signals are then sent to different speakers. Thus, one speaker reproduces the sound picked up by one microphone; the other speaker reproduces the sound picked up by the other microphone.

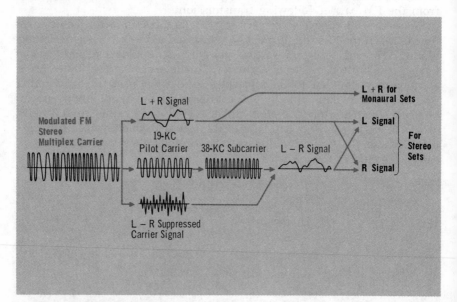

The addition and subtraction of the L + R and L — R signals is a matter of standard algebraic addition and subtraction. The sum of the two signals is

$$\begin{array}{r} L + R \\ +(L - R) \\ \hline 2L + 0 \end{array} \quad \text{or just} \quad 2L$$

recovering
the intelligence (cont.)

When the two signals were added, the R portions cancel each other, while the L portions reinforce each other to produce an L signal with twice the amplitude. The same type of relationship holds for the difference of the L + R and L − R signals, if you remember that in algebraic subtraction, you change the signs of the terms in the subtrahend, and then add. Thus,

$$\begin{array}{r} \text{L} + \text{R} \\ -(\text{L} - \text{R}) \\ \hline \end{array} \quad \text{can be written as} \quad \begin{array}{r} \text{L} + \text{R} \\ +(-\text{L} + \text{R}) \\ \hline 0 + 2\text{R} \end{array} \quad \text{or just} \quad 2\text{R}$$

The effect of algebraic addition and subtraction of signals can be seen by analyzing these simple waveforms

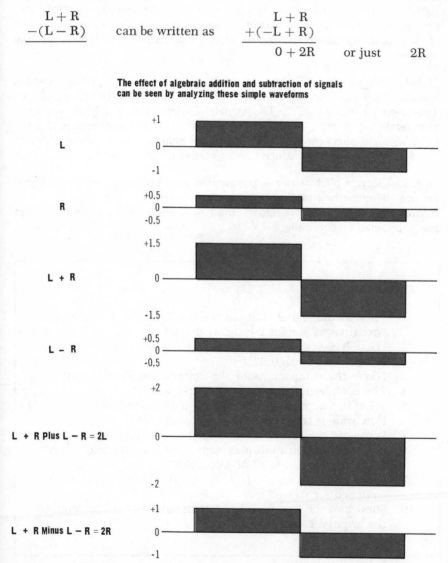

summary

☐ The color television signal is compatible: a noncolor receiver produces a black-and-white picture from it. ☐ Red, blue, and green video signals are produced from the image to be transmitted. These three signals are combined to produce the luminance, or Y, signal, which corresponds to the lightness and darkness variations of the scene being transmitted. ☐ The three color signals are also combined to produce the Q and I signals. ☐ The I signal modulates a 3.58-megacycle subcarrier, and the Q signal modulates the same subcarrier shifted 90 degrees in phase. The resulting side bands are added vectorially to produce the chrominance, or C, signal. ☐ The Y and C signals are combined into one composite signal for transmission. ☐ A color sync burst is transmitted as part of the video signal to synchronize the phase of the 3.58-megacycle subcarrier during subcarrier reinsertion at the receiver.

☐ FM stereo multiplex is compatible with all FM receivers. Stereo receivers reproduce the signal as stereo sound, while conventional receivers reproduce it as monophonic sound. ☐ Two signals, L (left) and R (right), are used to generate L + R and L − R signals. ☐ The L − R signal amplitude modulates a 38-kilocycle subcarrier, and the resulting side bands, together with the L + R signal, frequency modulate an r-f carrier for transmission.

☐ A 19-kilocycle pilot carrier is transmitted with the stereo multiplex signal for use in reinserting of the 38-kilocycle subcarrier at the receiver. ☐ To recover the original L and R signals, the L + R and L − R signals are added and subtracted algebraically.

---

review questions

1. What is the signal that carries the lightness and darkness variations of a color television signal?
2. What is the signal that carries the color information in a color television signal?
3. Name the components of the colorplexed video signal.
4. The color sync burst has what frequency?
5. What is the purpose of the color sync burst?
6. How wide is the color television bandwidth?
7. What are the primary colors of the color television signal?
8. In an FM stereo multiplex signal, why is the pilot carrier 19 kilocycles instead of 38 kilocycles?
9. What happens to the L − R signal inside a receiver not equipped for stereo?
10. Show how the L + R and L − R signals are used to produce the original L and R signals.

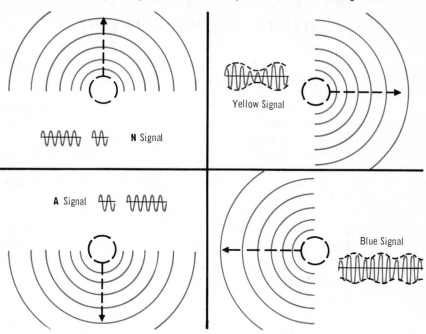

VAR uses four separate signals, each transmitted by its own antenna in a 180-degree arc

Yellow Signal

N Signal

A Signal

Blue Signal

aircraft navigation signals

Ever since aircraft have been designed to fly at heights that make *visual* navigation by means of rivers, roads, and other landmarks impossible, pilots have had to rely almost exclusively on electronic signals and equipment for in-flight navigation. The electronic signals used for aircraft navigation are of many types, with their exact nature depending on the particular type of navigation for which they are used. Some of these signals, and therefore their associated electronic equipment, are quite complex; others are no more than a combination of two relatively simple signals whose relative presence or absence represents the signal intelligence.

One of the earlier aircraft navigation aids is called the *visual-aural range* (VAR). In this system, *four* separate signals are transmitted from directional antennas. Each of the four signals is on a separate carrier, but all of the carriers have the same frequency. This allows the signals to be independent, and yet be received simultaneously. Two of the signals represent the Morse code for the letters N and A, while the other two signals are 90- and 150-cps tones. A receiver in the aircraft demodulates the signal and converts the N and A signals into *audible* tones, listened to by the pilot; while the 90- and 150-cps tones are converted to d-c voltages, which cause an indicating instrument to indicate either blue or yellow.

aircraft
navigation signals (cont.)

The area around the transmitting station in which the transmitted signals are strong enough to be used is called a *range;* and, effectively, the four signals divide the range into four quarters, or *quadrants.* This is done by the *directional* properties of the signals. As shown, each of the signals is only transmitted in a 180-degree arc around the station. As a result, each quadrant contains a *different pair* of signals. Thus, an aircraft can determine which quadrant it is in on the basis of the two signals received. For example, if a pilot heard the code for the letter A in his earphones and his instrument indicated blue, he would know he was in quadrant 4, as shown.

At the intersections of the color quadrants, the 90- and 150-cps tones effectively cancel each other; so anywhere along these two lines the pilot's instrument reads neither blue nor yellow. This zero indication

The four signals divide the area around the transmitting station into four quadrants, with each quadrant containing a unique pair of signals

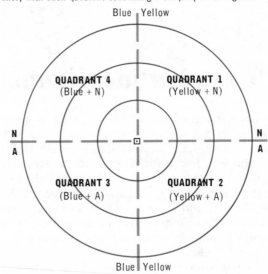

The two audible signals are heard in earphones, and the two visual signals actuate an indicating instrument whose pointer points to either a yellow or blue area

can be used for navigating *directly towards* or *directly away* from the station. Also, at the intersections, the Morse code for the letter A, which is dot–dash, and the code for letter N, which is dash–dot, combine to give a continuous tone.

Of course, with this as with most navigation systems, various charts and maps must be used to properly interpret the signals in terms of geographic directions and areas.

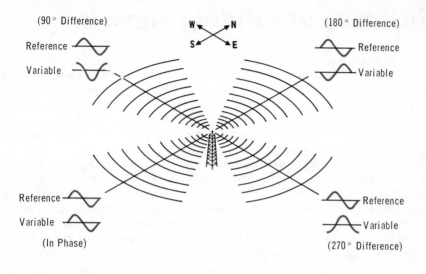

(90° Difference)   W   N   (180° Difference)

Reference   S   E   Reference

Variable   Variable

Reference   Reference

Variable   Variable

(In Phase)   (270° Difference)

In the VOR system, the amount of phase difference between the two signals depends on the direction of transmission

By detecting and measuring the phase difference, the exact bearing of an aircraft from the station can be determined

the visual omnirange

In the VAR navigation system, both *visual* and *audible* signals tell a pilot what *quadrant* he is in. A more sophisticated system, the *visual omnirange* (VOR), permits a pilot to read his *exact bearing* on one instrument. The VOR system uses two signals, one of which has a *fixed phase*, and the other has a phase that depends on the *direction* of transmission. Thus, the first, or *reference phase*, signal has the same phase no matter where it is received in the entire 360-degree arc around the station. The *variable phase* signal, on the other hand, has a different phase for every direction of transmission. It is in phase with the reference signal in the *due south* direction, and becomes increasingly out of phase in a clockwise direction from due south.

Both the reference signal and the variable phase signal are 30-cps tones. The 30-cps reference signal first frequency modulates a 9960 *subcarrier,* and then this FM subcarrier amplitude modulates its r-f carrier for transmission. The 30-cps variable phase signal amplitude modulates its carrier directly. The r-f carrier is somewhere in the frequency range of 112 to 118 megacycles. Putting the reference signal on a 9960 subcarrier makes it possible to easily separate the two signals from the r-f carrier by filtering after transmission. FM demodulation of the reference signal and AM demodulation of the variable phase signal then restores the two original 30-cps tones so they can be compared in phase. The phase difference causes the heading indicator to show the exact bearing of the plane from the airport.

instrument landing signals

Essentially, an instrument landing system is divided into two parts: the *localizer,* and the *glide slope.* The localizer tells the pilot whether he is to the *right* or *left* of the center of the runway as he makes his approach, while the glide slope tells him whether he is *descending* at the proper angle.

The localizer consists of two carriers having the same frequency and transmitted by separate *directional* antennas. One carrier is modulated by a 90-cps tone, and the other by a 150-cps tone. If an aircraft is to the right of the runway center line, the 150-cps signal is stronger; and if the aircraft is to the left, the 90-cps signal is stronger. When the aircraft is directly on line, the signals have equal strength. Equipment in the aircraft demodulates the two tones from their carriers, and develops a voltage from each of them to drive a *visual* instrument that indicates which side of the runway center line the aircraft is on.

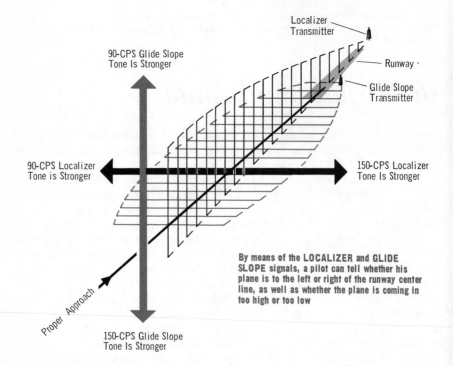

By means of the LOCALIZER and GLIDE SLOPE signals, a pilot can tell whether his plane is to the left or right of the runway center line, as well as whether the plane is coming in too high or too low

The glide slope is similar to the localizer, except that it produces a somewhat horizontal radiation pattern, as shown. When an aircraft is above the proper glide path, the 90-cps signal is stronger; and when it is below, the 150-cps signal predominates. These signals are demodulated in the aircraft and sent to another pointer in the same instrument used for the localizer.

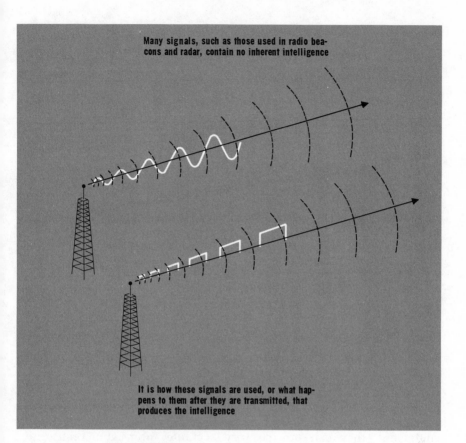

Many signals, such as those used in radio beacons and radar, contain no inherent intelligence

It is how these signals are used, or what happens to them after they are transmitted, that produces the intelligence

other signal intelligence

On the preceding pages, you have seen how electronic signals can modulate other waves for more efficient transmission of the desired intelligence. You have also seen how the complexity of signals can range from a simple continuous tone to a highly complex type having many components, such as the color television signal. In all cases, though, the electronic signals had some varying characteristic that represented intelligence. You will find that there are many applications involving electronic signals in which the signals themselves, as generated, contain *no* intelligence. Instead, intelligence is obtained by the way the signals are *used*, or by *interpreting* variations that occur after transmission. It might be said that these signals are *intelligence-providing* signals rather than intelligence-carrying signals. There are even cases where intelligence-carrying signals are used to provide information that is unrelated to the intelligence they are carrying.

Some examples of intelligence-providing signals are those used in radio direction finding, radio beacons, and radar. These as well as other typical types are described on the following pages.

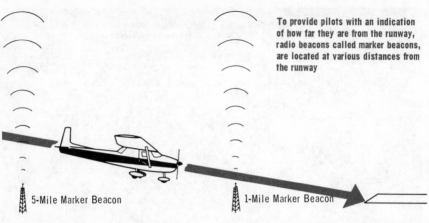

To provide pilots with an indication of how far they are from the runway, radio beacons called marker beacons, are located at various distances from the runway

5-Mile Marker Beacon

1-Mile Marker Beacon

All the beacons use the same carrier frequency, but each is modulated by a different tone. After demodulation by the aircraft's receiver, the various tones cause different colored lights on the instrument panel to glow intermittently

Thus, when a particular color light blinks on and off, the pilot knows he is passing over the corresponding marker beacon

radio beacons

Radio beacons provide signals from *fixed locations* for use as navigational aids. Radio beacons contain no bearing or directional information themselves, but when they are used with *radio direction finding* equipment, they can provide very accurate information concerning bearing or location.

Generally, radio beacons are continuously *repetitive* signals. They may be an uninterrupted tone on a carrier, or either the tone or the modulated carrier may be interrupted to continuously repeat the dots and dashes of a single Morse code letter that identifies the particular radio beacon station. The basic characteristic of a radio beacon is that it is transmitted from a definite, fixed location, marked on appropriate navigation charts and maps. Furthermore, radio beacons are usually transmitted at *low power levels*. Thus, when an aircraft or ship radio picks up a radio beacon signal, it means that it is within some *maximum* distance from the known location of the radio beacon transmitter.

Certain types of radio beacons, especially during time of war, do not transmit unless they first receive a signal from the ship or place wanting their use. This is called *interrogating* the radio beacon. Usually, the interrogating signal is *coded* in some way so that only authorized planes or ships can make use of the radio beacon. When this type of system is used, the radio beacon must be controlled by a device called a *transponder*. This is a combination receiver/transmitter that receives the interrogating signal, and if it recognizes the signal as a legitimate one, triggers the radio beacon.

radio direction finding

Radio direction finding (RDF) is the process of using the radio signals themselves to determine the *relative direction* between the transmitter sending out the signals and the receiver picking them up. RDF should not be confused with the VOR navigation system previously described. VOR uses transmitting stations and signals specifically established for providing bearing information. RDF, on the other hand, makes use of *any* radio signal. For example, if a pilot was lost and tuned his RDF receiver to a station that he recognized as coming from St. Louis, he could easily determine his bearing from St. Louis with good accuracy.

The basic principle on which RDF works is that of the *directional* receiving antenna. This is an antenna whose ability to pick up radio waves varies, depending on its direction relative to the received waves. The characteristics of RDF antennas are such that if they are rotated a full 360 degrees, there are two points in their rotation where they pick up practically *no* radio waves. Both of these points occur when the plane of the antenna is perpendicular to direction in which the radio waves are traveling. This means, therefore, that if such an antenna is rotated until a received signal drops to its lowest or zero level, the plane of the antenna is head on to the direction of the station transmitting the signal.

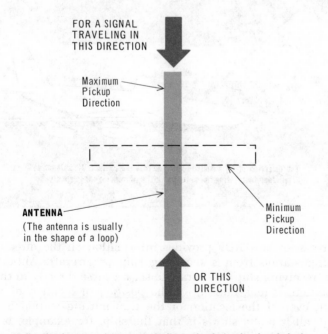

A directional antenna picks up practically no signal when its plane is in the same direction as that in which the signal is traveling

radio direction finding (cont.)

Basically, this is how RDF works: A signal is tuned in, and the antenna is turned until the signal practically or completely disappears. The plane of the antenna is then perpendicular to the direction of the transmitting station, and this direction is shown on some type of indicator. Actually, since the directional antenna picks up minimum signal in either of two opposite positions, the direction of the transmitting station might be in either of two *opposite* directions from the receiving antenna. The user of the RDF equipment can usually determine which of the directions is correct by using other navigation aids, such as a magnetic compass, and his knowledge of his approximate position with respect to the transmitting station. Some RDF equipment uses an auxiliary sensing antenna in conjunction with the rotating antenna. When this is done, only the one correct direction is indicated by the system.

By means of RDF, aircraft and ships can travel an accurate course directly towards any station they can receive; or they can travel in another direction using the station as a guidepost. This station might be a commercial broadcast station, or it might be a radio beacon.

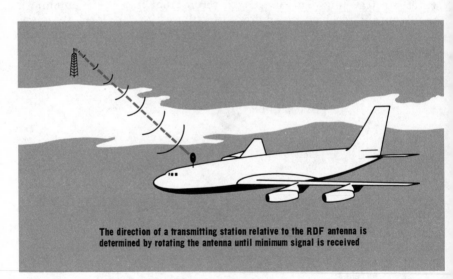

The direction of a transmitting station relative to the RDF antenna is determined by rotating the antenna until minimum signal is received

You have seen how RDF provides information on the direction of a transmitting station from a receiving ship or aircraft. Although this allows the receiving ship or aircraft to set a course directly to the transmitting station, it tells nothing of the *position* or location of the ship or aircraft, even if the location of the transmitting station is known. On a map, all it really shows is that the ship, for example, is located somewhere on a *straight line* that starts at the transmitting station and extends in the direction of the ship.

obtaining
position information by rdf

If the direction of the ship from *two* known transmitting stations is known, the location of the ship can be determined. The result of each RDF measurement can be drawn as a straight line on a map, and the ship must be located where these two lines *cross*. This should be obvious, since the ship has to be somewhere on both lines, and the point of intersection is the only common point that the two lines have.

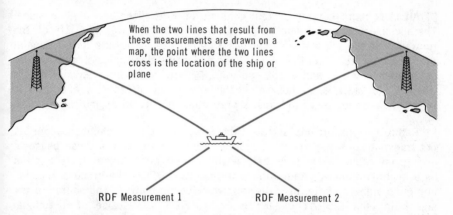

When the two lines that result from these measurements are drawn on a map, the point where the two lines cross is the location of the ship or plane

RDF Measurement 1　　　　RDF Measurement 2

Since there is some degree of error involved in all RDF measurements, the location of the ship, as determined by the crossing lines, is also subject to some error. The degree of error can be reduced by taking RDF measurements on three transmitting stations. The crossing of three resulting lines then produces a small triangular area, and excellent accuracy results by assuming that the ship is at the center of this triangular area.

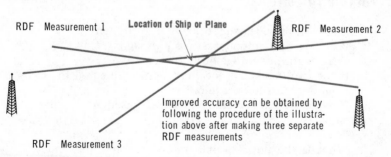

RDF　Measurement 1　　Location of Ship or Plane　　　RDF　Measurement 2

Improved accuracy can be obtained by following the procedure of the illustration above after making three separate RDF measurements

RDF　Measurement 3

RDF measurements for fixing the location of a ship or plane can be taken with respect to any known transmitting station. Commercial broadcast stations, radio beacons, or even a combination of the two can be used.

summary

☐ The visual-aural range (VAR) system uses four separate signals, each transmitted on a separate carrier. Two of these are visual signals, and represent the letters N and A in Morse code. The other two signals are audible tones of 90 and 150 cps. ☐ By means of VAR signals, a pilot can tell which quadrant he is in around the transmitting station. ☐ The visual omnirange (VOR) permits a pilot to read his exact bearing from a station on one instrument. ☐ VOR uses two signals: one is the reference phase and the other is the variable phase. The phase difference between the two indicates the bearing of the aircraft.

☐ An instrument landing system consists of a localizer and a glide slope. The localizer indicates whether an aircraft is to the right or left of the runway, and the glide slope indicates whether the aircraft is descending at the proper angle. ☐ Both the localizer and glide slope consist of a carrier modulated by a 90- and a 150-cps tone. ☐ Both tones have equal strength when the aircraft is on course. If the aircraft is off course, one tone is stronger than the other, and this is presented visually on an indicator.

☐ Radio beacons provide signals from fixed locations. ☐ Some beacons do not transmit until they are interrogated. Transponders control these beacons, and cause them to transmit only if the interrogating signal is recognized as a legitimate one. ☐ Radio direction finding (RDF) is the process of using any radio signal to determine the relative direction between the source of the signal and the receiver picking it up. ☐ RDF makes use of directional antennas, whose ability to pick up radio waves depends on the direction of the antenna relative to the received waves. ☐ RDF can provide position information when two or more RDF measurements are made from separate transmitting stations.

review questions

1. Can VAR provide exact bearing information?
2. What are the components of a VAR signal?
3. What is the advantage of VOR over VAR?
4. If the two tones of a localizer signal are equal in strength, what does this tell the pilot?
5. How many carrier frequencies are used for a glide slope signal?
6. What is a *radio beacon*?
7. What is the purpose of a radio beacon transponder?
8. Why is a directional antenna required for RDF?
9. How can RDF provide position information?
10. Is AM or FM used for radio direction finding?

loran

Loran is a system of extremely accurate, long-range radio navigation for ocean-going ships and transoceanic aircraft. Its name is derived from its basic function: namely, *long range navigation.* From the time of its initial development, various types of loran systems have come into use. One of these is called *standard loran,* and is used for commercial air and sea navigation. In this book, we will describe standard loran.

Loran operates on the basis of radio signals transmitted by a pair of shore-based stations. One of the stations is called the *master station* and the other the *slave station,* according to their function in the system. When a ship or aircraft receives the signals from both stations of the pair, it establishes its position as being somewhere on a line, called a *line of position,* that extends outward from the loran stations. As shown, a line of position is not straight, but shaped like a hyperbola. The exact location of the ship or plane can then be established by using signals from another pair of stations to determine a second line of position. The point where these two lines cross is the location of the ship or aircraft.

A loran line of position is determined on the basis of the *difference* in time required for a radio signal to reach the ship or aircraft from the master station and the slave station.

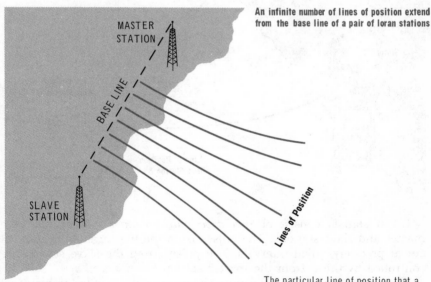

An infinite number of lines of position extend from the base line of a pair of loran stations

The base line is an imaginary line connecting the master and slave stations

The particular line of position that a ship is on depends on the exact difference in time that it takes a radio signal to reach it from the master station and slave station

loran (cont.)

The extreme accuracy of loran results because, for all practical purposes, radio waves travel at a *constant speed* of approximately 186,000 miles per second. This makes it possible to convert the time that a radio wave travels directly into the distance traveled with a high degree of precision, since:

$$\text{Distance traveled} = \text{speed} \times \text{time}$$

So, if the speed of travel and the time traveled are known with accuracy, the distance can easily be found to the same degree of accuracy. As you will see later, this is the basis on which certain types of radar work. It is also fundamental to the operation of loran systems, although in loran it is the difference in the travel times of two waves that is important.

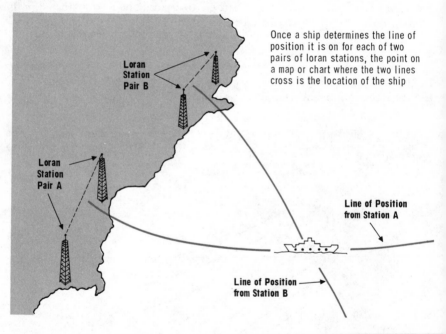

Loran
Station
Pair B

Once a ship determines the line of position it is on for each of two pairs of loran stations, the point on a map or chart where the two lines cross is the location of the ship

Loran
Station
Pair A

Line of Position
from Station A

Line of Position
from Station B

Loran signals consist of *repetitive pulses transmitted* by both the master and slave stations. The pulses from the master station are sent out at precisely timed intervals. The pulses from the slave station are controlled by those from the master station.

Each cycle of a loran transmission begins with a pulse transmitted by the master station. The direction of transmission is such that the pulse travels toward both the slave station and a ship, which we will assume is picking up the loran signals. The pulse arrives first at the slave station, and after a definite time delay causes that station to transmit its own pulse.

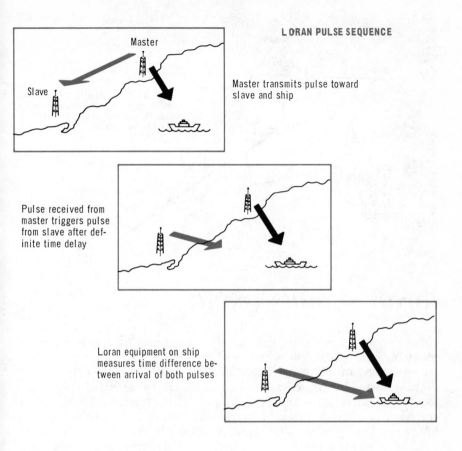

LORAN PULSE SEQUENCE

Master

Slave

Master transmits pulse toward
slave and ship

Pulse received from
master triggers pulse
from slave after def-
inite time delay

Loran equipment on ship
measures time difference between arrival of both pulses

loran signals

The purpose of the time delay is to make the slave pulse always arrive at the ship during the second half of the time interval between master pulses. This is done to simplify the measurement of the time between master and slave pulses at the ship. Since the delay is always the same, it can be easily be compensated for in determining a line of position. Thus, there are *two* pulses traveling toward the ship: one from the slave, and the other from the master. The one from the master arrives at the ship first, followed by that from the slave.

Loran equipment on the ship picks up both pulses and measures the *time interval* between them. There are an *infinite* number of locations within the area served by the loran stations where the time interval between these two particular pulses would be the same. All of these locations, though, lie on *one* hyperbolic line, which is a line of position. Thus, by measuring the time between the slave and master pulses, the loran equipment establishes the line of position on which the ship is located.

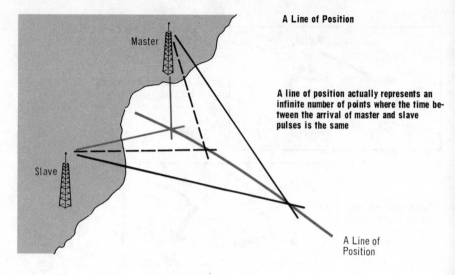

A Line of Position

A line of position actually represents an infinite number of points where the time between the arrival of master and slave pulses is the same

A Line of Position

loran signals (cont.)

Conversion of the time interval data produced by the loran equipment into the geographic location of the line of position can be made on special loran charts, or from tables that allow the line of position to be drawn directly on a navigation chart. To determine the exact location of the ship, pulses from another pair of loran stations can be received, and another line of position established. The crossing point of the two lines then fixes the ship's location.

Loran stations operate continuously. So, the sequence of pulse transmission described is continually repeated.

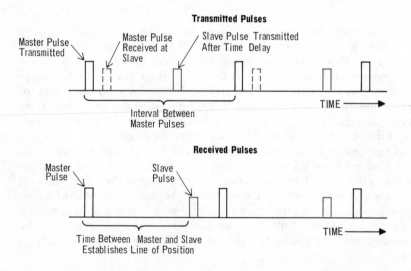

Transmitted Pulses

Master Pulse Transmitted

Master Pulse Received at Slave

Slave Pulse Transmitted After Time Delay

Interval Between Master Pulses

TIME ——▶

Received Pulses

Master Pulse

Slave Pulse

Time Between Master and Slave Establishes Line of Position

TIME ——▶

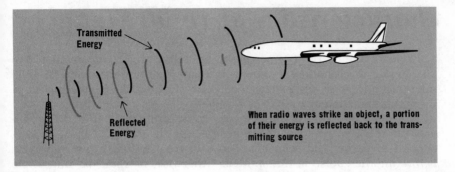

Transmitted Energy

Reflected Energy

When radio waves strike an object, a portion of their energy is reflected back to the transmitting source

radar

Radar uses radio waves for detecting the *presence* and *location* of distant objects. The term "radar" was derived from *radio direction and ranging*. Radar works because when a transmitted radio wave strikes an object, it is reradiated by the object back toward the radar antenna to indicate the presence of the reflecting object. If you can measure the *time lapse* between the pulse transmission and return of its *echo*, the distance of the reflecting object can be determined because the speed of the wave is considered constant at about 186,000 miles per second. So, by multiplying the speed by the total time lapse, the distance traveled is found. And, of course, the distance from the antenna to the reflecting object is one-half of the total distance.

Radar signals consist of narrow *pulses* of high-frequency waves. The intervals between pulses are considerably longer than the pulses themselves, and it is during these intervals that the reflected pulses are received. The radar circuits show the time lapse between a transmitted pulse and any echoes on a screen with visual displays calibrated in distance.

Radar antennas are *directional,* so they must be rotated to cover a 360-degree arc. This means that the *direction* of the reflecting object can also be obtained, since the antenna is facing the object at the instant the echo is received. The radar circuits are synchronized with the antenna, so that its bearing is also indicated on the visual display equipment with the echo.

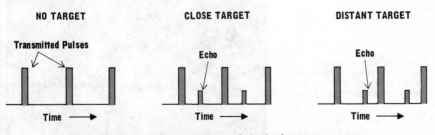

NO TARGET   CLOSE TARGET   DISTANT TARGET

Transmitted Pulses   Echo   Echo

Time ⟶   Time ⟶   Time ⟶

Since radio waves travel at a constant speed, the time lapse between a transmitted pulse and its echo is determined by the range of the reflecting object

characteristics of radar signals

Typical radar carrier frequencies in use today range from about 150 to 30,000 megacycles. Pulse lengths can be anywhere from about 0.25 to 50 microseconds, with the exact value depending on the requirements of the particular system.

The time interval between pulses is determined by the *maximum distance* at which the radar is to be effective. The interval must be long enough to permit the echo of a pulse to return from a distant target *before* another pulse is transmitted. Otherwise, it would be impossible to associate an echo pulse with its corresponding transmitted pulse. And, if this were the case, the signal could not produce information concerning the range of the detected object. If the interval between pulses is too long, though, the rotating antenna might pass over the target during the interval, and fail to detect the target.

The number of pulses transmitted each second is called the pulse repetition rate (PRR) of the signal. The PRR is determined by the pulse width and the time interval between pulses

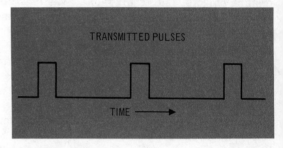

An important characteristic of radar signals is the ratio of their peak to average, or effective, power. Since the power in a reflected echo is a very small percentage of the power in a transmitted pulse, it is necessary that the transmitted pulse contain considerable power. The pulses of actual radar signals, therefore, often contain many millions of watts of power. As you will recall, though, the average power of a pulse signal is much less than the peak power of the individual pulses. As a result, even though radar transmitters put out a great amount of usable power in the pulses, the average power they supply is much lower.

The radar signal is shown as rectangular pulses for convenience Actual signals consist of short bursts of the high-frequency carrier

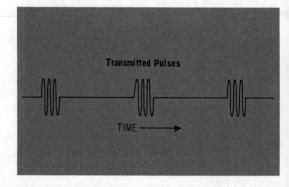

doppler signals

A number of electronic equipment used for detecting objects and measuring their distance and velocity make use of *Doppler signals.* These signals are named after the Austrian physicist Christian Doppler, who discovered the phenomenon of the Doppler effect. The Doppler effect is common to all physical *wave motion,* and you are probably familiar with it, even though you may not be aware of its scientific explanation.

Basically, the Doppler effect means that the *frequency* of a wave emitted by a source is not necessarily the frequency picked up by a receiver, where a receiver here means either a person listening to a sound wave, or an antenna picking up a radio wave. The frequency at the receiver depends on the *relative motion* between the source and receiver. If both the source and receiver are *stationary,* the frequency at both is the *same.* But, if either one, or both, is moving *away* from the other, the frequency at the receiver is *lower* than that emitted by the source. Conversely, if the receiver and source are moving *closer together,* the frequency at the receiver is *higher* than that emitted by the source. A common example of the Doppler effect is the pitch of a train whistle as heard by an observer standing alongside the tracks. As the train approaches, the whistle has a certain pitch. But when the train passes the observer, there is a sudden drop in the pitch of the whistle. This is caused by the change in relative motion between the train and the observer.

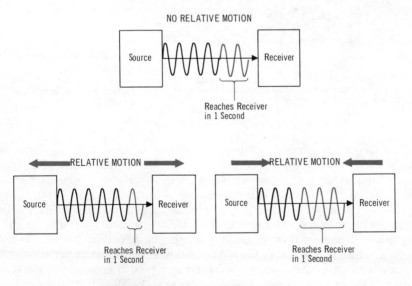

The number of cycles of a wave reaching a receiver in one second, and therefore the frequency of the wave at the receiver, depends on the relative motion between the receiver and the source emitting the wave

doppler radar

The Doppler effect on radio waves is easily understood if you consider the frequency at a radio receiver as the number of cycles of the wave that *reaches* the receiver each second. With both the source and receiver stationary, the radio waves travels toward the receiver at the speed of light. When the distance between the source and receiver is increasing, though, it is as if the wave slowed down with respect to the receiver; so fewer cycles reach the receiver each second. The converse is true when the distance between the source and receiver is decreasing.

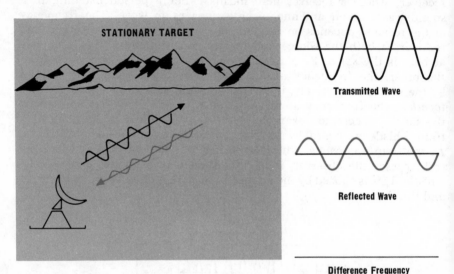

STATIONARY TARGET

Transmitted Wave

Reflected Wave

When the signal from a continuous-wave Doppler radar is reflected from a stationary target, the frequency of the echo is the same as that of the transmitted wave

Difference Frequency
Since the two waves have the same frequency, mixing them produces no signal at the difference frequency

The frequency change that results from relative motion between an emitting source and a receiver is called the *Doppler shift*. The fact that a Doppler shift occurs only when there is relative motion is put to use in a type of radar that detects *moving objects* and ignores *stationary objects*. Such radar is called *Doppler radar*, and is extremely useful in applications where a moving target, such as an aircraft, must be distinguished from fixed objects that might be received by the radar antenna at the same time. There is a definite relationship between the frequency of an emitted wave, the speed at which it travels, the relative motion between source and receiver, and the Doppler shift that occurs. As a result of the relationship, it is possible not only to detect a moving object, but to measure its velocity.

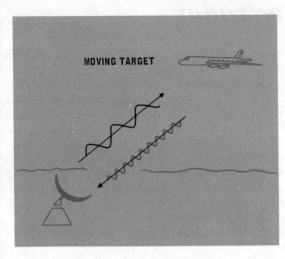

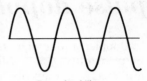

Transmitted Wave

Reflected Wave

Difference Frequency

When the signal is reflected from a moving target, the echo undergoes a Doppler shift. When the target is approaching the antenna, the echo is shifted to a higher frequency

Since the two waves have different frequencies, mixing produces a signal at the difference frequency

doppler radar (cont.)

In one type of Doppler radar, a *continuous wave* is transmitted in a directional beam by a scanning (rotating) antenna. When the wave strikes an object, a portion of the wave is reflected toward a receiving antenna, which picks up the reflected wave and transfers it to receiver circuits. These receiver circuits also continuously receive a portion of the transmitted wave directly from the transmitting circuits.

In the receiving circuits, the reflected wave is mixed with the transmitted wave in a process, which like amplitude modulation, produces sum and difference frequencies. For this application, it is the *difference frequency* that is significant. When the reflected wave is from a stationary object, it has the same frequency as the transmitted wave, so the difference frequency produced by the mixing process is zero. But, when the reflected wave is from a moving object, it undergoes a Doppler shift as a result of the relative motion between the detected object and the receiving antenna. Thus, when this wave is mixed with the transmitted wave, there is a difference frequency produced. The *existence* of the difference frequency indicates the *presence* of the detected object. The exact *magnitude* of the difference indicates the *relative velocity* between the object and the receiving antenna. With this type of Doppler radar signal, though, the *range* of the detected signal cannot be determined.

pulse doppler radar

Doppler radar signals can be made to produce *range* information by transmitting *pulses* instead of a continuous wave. When the echoes are received, they are processed differently from conventional radar. Effectively, each reflected pulse is *subtracted* from an exact *duplicate* of its corresponding transmitted pulse. This subtraction is an algebraic subtraction of the instantaneous pulse amplitudes and its results are different for reflected pulses from stationary and moving objects.

When reflected pulses from a stationary object are subtracted from their corresponding transmitted pulses, the result is pulses all having the same *constant* amplitude. This occurs regardless of the phase of the reflected pulses. Of course, echoes from different objects will have different phases. But all the pulses from any one object will have the same phase, so the pulses that result from the subtraction process will have a constant amplitude.

Reflected pulses from a moving object have *different* phases, with the phase of each succeeding pulse changing as the object moves closer to or farther away from the radar antenna. This difference in phase causes the pulses that result from the subtraction process to *change* in amplitude. The *rate* at which these pulses change in amplitude corresponds to the Doppler shift caused by the motion of the detected object. Thus, a moving target is indicated by varying-amplitude pulses from the subtraction process. The velocity of the detected object is indicated by the rate at which these pulses change in amplitude. And the range of the object is indicated, as in conventional pulse radar, by the time interval between a reflected pulse and its corresponding transmitted pulse. Radar that operates in this way is often called *moving-target-indicator* (MTI) radar.

Pulses Produced By Subtraction Process:

    ⫿   **Stationary Target**

    ⫿   **Moving Target**

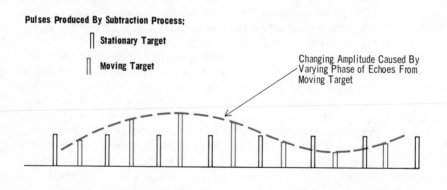

Changing Amplitude Caused By Varying Phase of Echoes From Moving Target

MTI radar differentiates between the stationary and moving targets by subtracting echo pulses from exact replicas of their corresponding transmitted pulses	This subtraction produces constant-amplitude pulses for stationary targets, and varying-amplitude pulses for moving targets

sonar

Sonar is used for detecting objects *under water* and measuring their range, and so is similar to radar. However, radar uses signals having extremely high *radio* frequencies; sonar signals are actually *physical sound waves* in or near the *supersonic band*. The reason for this is that radio waves cannot be sent under water, and high-frequency sound signals are greatly attenuated after traveling only short distances. So, to achieve a satisfactory transmission range, much lower frequencies are used. Sonar means *s*ound *na*vigation and *r*anging.

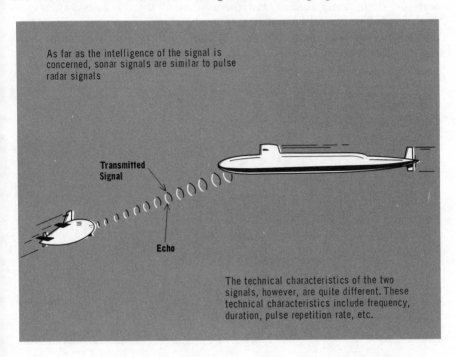

As far as the intelligence of the signal is concerned, sonar signals are similar to pulse radar signals

Transmitted Signal

Echo

The technical characteristics of the two signals, however, are quite different. These technical characteristics include frequency, duration, pulse repetition rate, etc.

Sonar signals consist of *pulses* of a fixed frequency that are transmitted into the water by a powerful device that works similar to a loudspeaker. The pulses are usually a few seconds in duration, and have a frequency somewhere between about 10 and 50 kilocycles. During the interval between transmitted pulses, the sound transmitter functions as a microphone to pick up any echoes. Since the speed of sound in water is a *known quantity*, the time interval between a transmitted pulse and its echo allows the range of the detected object to be determined. The transmitter-microphone is directional, making it possible to determine the direction of the object as well as its range. Sonar signals are also affected by the Doppler effect, so the pitch of the echo will change if the target is moving toward or away from you.

Sonar signals are also used for measuring *depth,* and to locate schools of fish.

radar altimeters

Electronic signals are frequently used for the measurement of height. The most common example is the radio altimeters used in aircraft for determining the altitude of the aircraft above ground. Basically, there are two broad types of radio altimeters: one that employs radar principles, and another that uses FM signals.

Radar altimeters are essentially pulse radars used to determine range, which in this case is the distance between the aircraft and the ground. Pulses are transmitted downward from the aircraft, and the time interval between their transmission and the return of their echoes is directly proportional to the altitude. Circuits in the altimeter convert the measured time intervals into distance indications for visual presentation.

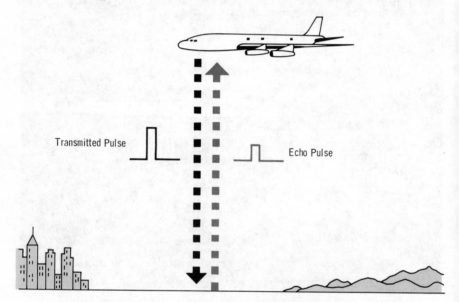

Transmitted Pulse   Echo Pulse

In radar altimeters, the time interval between a transmitted pulse and its echo is converted directly into altitude

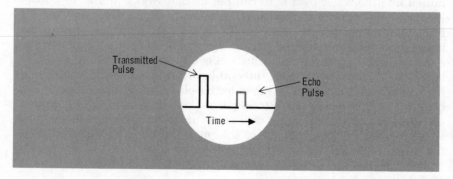

Transmitted Pulse   Echo Pulse

Time ⟶

FM altimeters

FM altimeters also transmit signals toward the ground and use their return echoes to measure the altitude. However, it is the frequency of the returning echoes that is used to determine the altitude. This is possible, since the pulses consist of an FM carrier that has been modulated by a *triangular* pulse. You recall from your reading of FM that in this type of signal the frequency of the carrier increases linearly from its center frequency, and then abruptly starts to decrease linearly until it returns to its center frequency. By the consideration of just the increasing portion of the pulse, this means that in equal time intervals, the frequency increases by equal amounts. Thus, there is a direct relationship between the instantaneous frequency at any point in the signal and the time from the beginning of the pulse to that point.

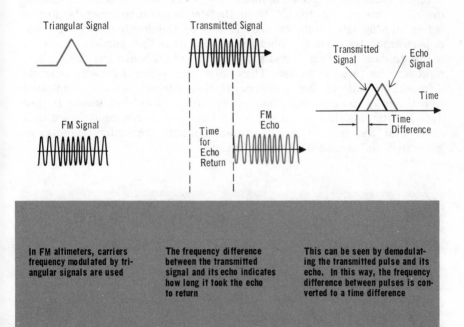

In FM altimeters, carriers frequency modulated by triangular signals are used	The frequency difference between the transmitted signal and its echo indicates how long it took the echo to return	This can be seen by demodulating the transmitted pulse and its echo. In this way, the frequency difference between pulses is converted to a time difference

When the echo of a signal is received, its instantaneous frequency is compared with that of the transmitted signal, which is actually still being transmitted. The difference in their frequencies then indicates the time that has elapsed from the instant transmission of the signal began to the instant its echo began being received. In other words, by measuring the *frequency difference* between the transmitted and reflected signals, the *time* of travel of the signal, and, therefore, the distance traveled is determined.

missile guidance

Electronic signals are widely used in the field of missile guidance. By means of these signals, the missile is controlled by a source *external* to the missile. This is called *command guidance*. Normally, the function of guidance signals is to control the operation of auxiliary rocket motors, control surfaces, or other controlling devices and thereby alter the direction of the missile to put it on the right course. There is an almost limitless variety of command guidance signals, ranging from a simple sequence of pulses or tones, to extremely complex pulse and subcarrier modulation systems. In a simple system, one tone or pulse code can mean "turn right," and another tone or pulse code can mean "turn left." This can be done for "climb," "dive," "go faster," "go slower," "explode," and so on.

Since guidance signals are used to correct the course of a missile, the *deviation* of the missile from the desired course must be known before appropriate guidance signals can be transmitted. This function is performed by what is called the *information link* portion of a command guidance system. Signals are generated on board the missile that represent its present course. These are transmitted by radio over the information link to the guidance station where they are compared, sometimes in an electronic computer, with signals that would be produced if the missile was on the desired course. If this comparison indicates that the missile is off course, suitable correction signals are generated and transmitted to the missile.

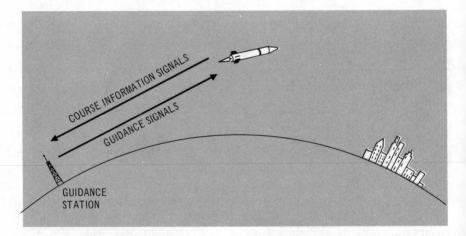

Missile command guidance signals are of two types: those that carry information on the actual course of the missile, and those that carry the correction information used by the missile to change direction to the desired course

Both types of these signals are part of any command guidance system. In some systems, the correction information is generated by the missile itself

missile guidance (cont.)

In another type of command guidance system, the actual course of the missile is determined by *radar tracking stations*. This course is then compared, again usually by an electronic computer, with the desired course, and appropriate course-correction signals are generated and transmitted to the missile by radio.

You should not get the impression from the above discussion that all missiles are guided by *radio signals*. There are various systems of missile guidance in which all of the guidance equipment is located right *on board* the missile. Signals are still generated that indicate the actual course of the missile; and these signals are used to produce guidance signals. However, all of this is done on board the missile.

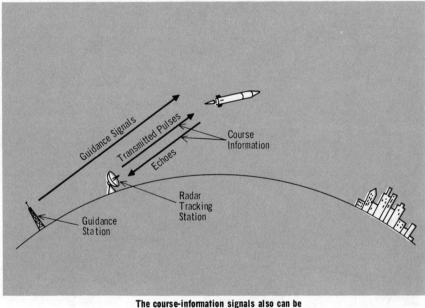

The course-information signals also can be produced by radar tracking stations

Missile homing systems consist of equipment on board a missile that permits the missile to seek a target on its *own,* without the need for external command signals. In these systems, the missile follows, or *homes in* on, a signal emitted by the target. There are three basic types of homing systems, grouped according to the *original* source of the target signal that they home in on. They are *active, semiactive,* and *passive* systems.

Active homing systems generate a signal, transmit it toward the target, and then home in on the reflection, or echo, of this signal. Radar signals are used extensively for such active systems, since they allow both the *distance* and *direction* of the target to be determined.

missile homing

In semiactive systems, the missile also homes in on reflected signals from the target. However, the missile itself does not transmit the original signal to the target. Instead, it is sent to the target from some *other* source, such as a ground station, the aircraft firing the missile, etc.

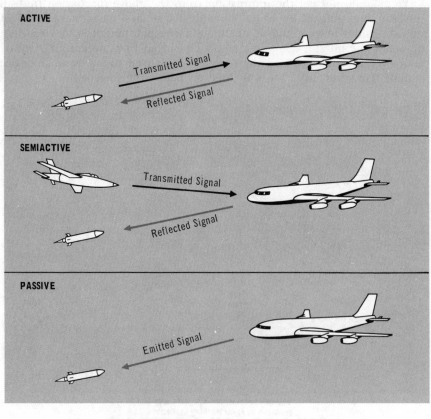

ACTIVE

Transmitted Signal

Reflected Signal

SEMIACTIVE

Transmitted Signal

Reflected Signal

PASSIVE

Emitted Signal

Homing systems are classified according to the original source of the homing signal

In passive systems, the missile homes in on some form of radiation emitted *directly* by the target. Usually, this radiation is not electronic, but in the form of light, heat, or sound waves. There are other even more sophisticated forms of missile guidance, such as beacons and map readers. In beacon guidance, a manned plane can fly over enemy territory and drop a number of radio beacons at many strategic locations, and then the signals from the beacons will provide a homing beam for the missiles. A map-reading missile can make a radar map of its course over land to check its course and keep itself on target.

summary

☐ Loran is a very accurate long-range radio navigation system. ☐ Loran signals received from a master station and a slave station establish the location of a ship or plane somewhere on a line of position. Signals received from two pairs of Loran stations then locate the exact position at the point where the two lines of position cross. ☐ Radar uses radio waves for detecting the presence and location of distant objects. ☐ Radar works by measuring the time lapse between the transmission of a pulse and the return of its echo, or reflection, from a target. ☐ Directional antennas are used to provide information on the direction of the target relative to the radar transmitter.

☐ A Doppler shift occurs when there is relative motion between a source emitting radio waves and a receiver. ☐ Doppler radar makes use of the Doppler shift to detect moving objects. It does so by comparing the frequency of the transmitted wave with the frequency of the reflected wave. ☐ Doppler radar can produce range information, as well as detection, if pulses are transmitted instead of a continuous wave. ☐ Sonar is a method of detecting objects under water and measuring their range. It does this by transmitting sound pulses and detecting the echoes returned from targets.

☐ Radar altimeters are essentially pulse radars that measure the distance between an aircraft and the ground. ☐ FM altimeters make use of triangular pulses that frequency modulate a carrier. Distance is determined by measuring the frequency difference between the transmitted and reflected signals. ☐ Command guidance uses electronic signals from an external source to control the path of a missile. ☐ Missile homing systems can be classified as active, semiactive, or passive, depending on the original source of the signal that they home in on.

---

review questions

1. Why does Loran require both a master and a slave station?
2. What information can radar supply about a target?
3. Why are directional antennas required for radar?
4. In pulse radar, what determines the time interval between pulses?
5. What is the *Doppler shift*?
6. Can Doppler radar detect stationary objects?
7. How can Doppler radar be made to produce range information?
8. Why are radio waves not used for detecting objects under water?
9. How does an FM altimeter determine height?
10. What is *command guidance*?

facsimile

Facsimile is a process by which electronic signals are used to transmit *visual material*, such as still pictures, printed matter, and maps. The material to be transmitted is placed on a *revolving drum* and scanned by a narrow beam of light so that every spot on the material is touched by the light beam in some sequence.

During the scanning, the light striking the picture is reflected to a photocell, which produces a signal voltage proportional to the *intensity of the reflected light*. The signal modulates an r-f carrier for transmission.

Production of Facsimile Signal

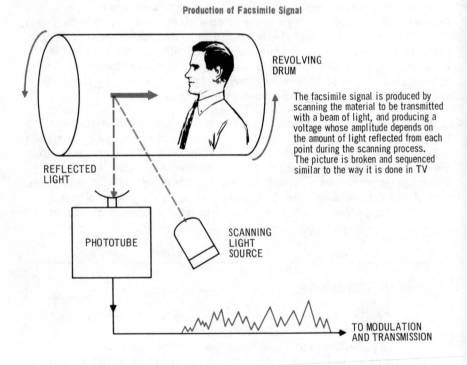

REVOLVING DRUM

The facsimile signal is produced by scanning the material to be transmitted with a beam of light, and producing a voltage whose amplitude depends on the amount of light reflected from each point during the scanning process. The picture is broken and sequenced similar to the way it is done in TV

REFLECTED LIGHT

PHOTOTUBE

SCANNING LIGHT SOURCE

TO MODULATION AND TRANSMISSION

After transmission, the signal is demodulated and reproduced in various ways. One is to use *photographic paper* that is exposed to a special gas-filled lamp whose light intensity can be varied by the signal. So when the photographic paper is developed, an image of the original material appears.

Another method is to use special paper that allows electric current to pass through it, and turns dark at that spot, in proportion to the signal current. A pen-like *stylus* scans the paper to provide the current.

At the transmitter, synchronizing signals are added to the carrier so that the receiving equipment follows the same scanning pattern. This is similar to what is done in television.

FCC frequency bands

As has been stated, the Federal Communications Commission allocates frequency bands for all radio transmission within the United States. The need for government regulation of radio transmission is obvious once you realize the chaos that would result if anyone could transmit radio waves, and do so at any power level and frequency. The intelligence carried by many of the waves would become unintelligible and therefore useless as a result of the interaction and interference that would occur.

To prevent this interference, the FCC divides the radio-frequency spectrum into various bands, and limits the use of these bands to certain types of radio transmissions. The FCC also regulates the use of the particular frequencies in any one band to prevent interference between signals transmitted within the *same* geographic area. In addition to its regulation of frequencies, the FCC also limits the amount of power that can be used to transmit the various types of signals. This prevents signals from carrying beyond their intended area of coverage and interfering with radio reception in distant geographic areas.

Many of the frequency assignments made by the FCC are listed on this and the following page. A complete list can be found in standard handbooks or other reference works, or obtained from the FCC.

FCC FREQUENCY BANDS

Band	Frequency Range	
Standard Broadcast Band (540 to 1600 kc): It is divided into 107 channels, each having a 10-kc bandwidth.	540 kc 550 kc 560 kc 570 kc 580 kc	590 kc 600 kc 610 kc And so on to 1600 kc
Commercial FM Broadcast Band (92.1 to 107.9 mc): It is divided into 80 channels, each having a 200-kc (0.2-mc) bandwidth.	92.1 mc 92.3 mc 92.5 mc 92.7 mc 92.9 mc	93.1 mc 93.3 mc 93.5 mc And so on to 107.9 mc
Television Channels: There are 82 channels, each having a 6-mc bandwidth. What was channel 1 is now, for the most part, taken up by amateur radio operators.	Low VHF Band: 54-60 mc (channel 2) 60-66 mc (channel 3) 66-72 mc (channel 4) 76-82 mc (channel 5) 82-88 mc (channel 6) High VHF Band: 174-180 mc (channel 7) 180-186 mc (channel 8) 186-192 mc (channel 9) 192-198 mc (channel 10) 198-204 mc (channel 11) 204-210 mc (channel 12) 210-216 mc (channel 13) UHF Band: 470-476 mc (channel 14) 476-482 mc (channel 15) And so on to channel 83 at 884-890 mc	

FCC frequency bands (cont.)

Many of the following frequency bands are subject to frequent change by the Federal Communications Commission.

FCC FREQUENCY BANDS

Band	Frequency Range	
Radio Navigation (Nonaeronautical)	10-14 kc 90-110 kc 1800-2000 kc 2900-3300 mc	5250-5650 mc 8500-9800 mc And others
Aeronautical Radio Navigation	200-285 kc 325-405 kc 1605-1800 kc 108-118 mc 328.6-335.4 mc	960-1215 mc 1300-1660 mc 2700-3300 mc And others
Aircraft (Air-to-Ground) Communications	325-405 kc 2850-3155 kc 3400-3500 kc 6525-6765 kc 23.2-23.5 mc	118-132 mc 6425-6575 mc 16,000-18,000 mc And others
For Government Use	24.99-25.01 mc 27.54-28.00 mc 34.00-35.00 mc 132.00-144.00 mc 148.00-152.00 mc	157.05-157.25 mc 4400-5000 mc 13,225-16,000 mc And others
For Land Transportation (Taxicabs, railroads, etc.)	30.64-31.16 mc 43.68-44.60 mc 72.00-76.00 mc 452-453 mc 890-940 mc	2110-2200 mc 6425-6875 mc 11,700-12,700 mc And Others
Amateur Radio	3500-4000 kc 7100-7300 kc 28.00-29.70 mc 50.00-54.00 mc 220-225 mc	2300-2450 mc 5650-5925 mc 10,000-10,500 mc And others

special signal considerations

You have now seen how electronic signals can be made to both carry and produce a wide variety of information. You have also seen how although signals possess various properties, the intelligence being carried is usually only contained in *certain* of these properties. Any changes in these *intelligence-carrying properties* that occur during transmission or processing of the signal cause distortion of the signal intelligence, and are therefore undesirable. Other properties of a signal, though, which do not represent intelligence, can be changed or distorted without affecting the usability of the signal in any way. And, as a matter of fact, in many practical applications certain characteristics of signals are changed without distorting their intelligence so that the signal may be processed in the most effective and efficient manner. Examples of this include changing the frequency of the carrier on which a signal is carried, as well as changing the shape of the individual pulses of certain pulse signals.

Of course, since signals can represent intelligence in so many ways, it is impossible to make general statements about what can and what cannot be done to a signal without distorting it to the point where its usability is impaired. This can only be done by having a good understanding of the nature of the signal, how it carries its intelligence, and the degree of distortion of the intelligence that is permissible.

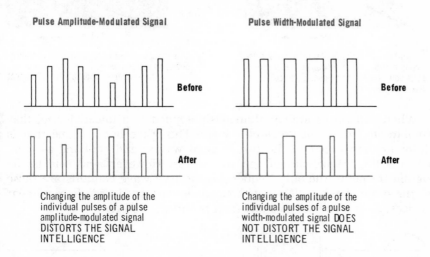

Pulse Amplitude-Modulated Signal   **Pulse Width-Modulated Signal**

Before   Before

After   After

Changing the amplitude of the individual pulses of a pulse amplitude-modulated signal DISTORTS THE SIGNAL INTELLIGENCE

Changing the amplitude of the individual pulses of a pulse width-modulated signal DOES NOT DISTORT THE SIGNAL INTELLIGENCE

On the following pages, two of the most common steps that are done to signals when they are processed are covered. These are: *waveshaping*, or changing the shape of the signal; and *mixing* the signal with other signals or frequencies. In addition, the *frequency components* of certain types of signals are described in some detail, since they are the basis of signal shape both before and after distortion occurs.

mixing frequencies

In the processing of electronic signals, different frequencies are often *mixed* for various reasons. The products, or resulting signals, produced by mixing depend on whether the mixing is done in a *linear* or a *nonlinear* device. In electricity, a device, such as a resistor, is called linear because *equal changes* in applied *voltage* cause *equal changes* in *current*. Thus, the increase in current caused by an increase in applied voltage from 2 to 4 volts is the same as the current increase caused by a voltage increase of 100 to 102 volts. In other words, the *resistance* is essentially *constant* over the resistor's normal operating range.

A nonlinear device, on the other hand, has a *variable impedance*, whose value depends on circuit conditions. Thus, in a nonlinear device, a 2-volt increase in applied voltage from 2 to 4 volts may cause the current to increase 1 ampere; but the same 2-volt increase from 100 to 102 volts may cause the current to increase 2 amperes.

Linear Device	Nonlinear Device
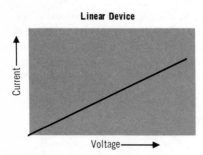	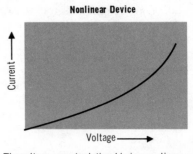
The voltage-current relationship in a linear device is represented by a straight line, since equal voltage changes produce equal current changes	The voltage-current relationship in a nonlinear device is represented by a curved line, since equal voltage changes produce different current changes

When two waves are simultaneously applied to a linear device, they combine to form a new *complex* wave. This wave has a shape that is different than either of the two original waves, and contains as components the frequencies of the two waves. However, and this is the significant point, the only frequencies the new wave contains are those of the original waves. *No* new frequencies are produced. In nonlinear devices, as you will see, the situation is entirely different.

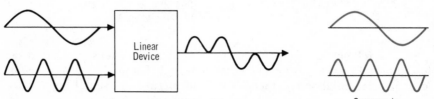

When two waves are mixed in a linear device, the resulting complex wave contains only the two original frequencies

nonlinear mixing

When two waves of different frequencies are mixed in a *nonlinear* device, the result is a complex wave, the same as in linear mixing. However, whereas in linear mixing the resultant wave contains only the frequencies of the original signals, in nonlinear mixing the resultant wave contains *additional* frequencies. These additional frequencies are produced by the mixing process. The total number of additional frequencies produced depends on the specific nonlinearity of the mixing device. Generally, however, devices are used with characteristics such that the resultant wave contains the two original frequencies, plus an additional frequency equal to their *sum* and another equal to their *difference*. Thus, if a 9-kc and a 10-kc wave are mixed in a nonlinear device, the resultant wave has frequency components of 9, 10, 19, and 1 kilocycle.

You probably recognize the similarity between *nonlinear mixing* and *modulation*. Actually, they are essentially the same process, with the difference between them being the frequencies of the input waves, and the components of the output wave that are used. In modulation, a high-frequency carrier is mixed with a relatively low-frequency modulating signal, and the carrier frequency and sum and difference frequencies are used. In what is called mixing, as you will see, two high-frequency waves are mixed, and generally only their *difference frequency* is used. This type of mixing is also called *heterodyning*.

Quite often, if the sum and difference frequencies are strong enough, they can mix to form more sum and difference frequencies that will beat with themselves and the original frequencies to form even new ones. However, the amplitudes of sum and difference frequencies are generally small, so continued heterodyning is usually negligible.

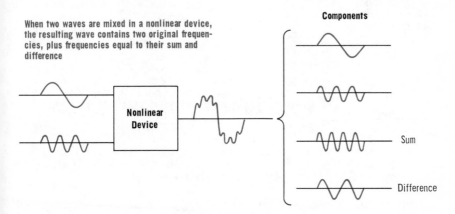

When two waves are mixed in a nonlinear device, the resulting wave contains two original frequencies, plus frequencies equal to their sum and difference

Components

Sum

Difference

In actual circuits, more frequencies than these are usually produced by the mixing process. For most practical purposes, though, these other fre- quencies can be neglected, since the amplitudes of the sum and difference frequencies get smaller and smaller in any continued mixing process

heterodyning

In practically all types of electronic receiving equipment, received signals must be amplified, or built up, before they are demodulated. For reasons that you will learn later, it is highly desirable that this amplification be done at a *single* frequency rather than at the frequencies of the many different carriers that are received. To make this possible, all modulated carriers that are received are first converted to a common frequency, called the *intermediate frequency* (if). The intermediate frequency is produced by the nonlinear mixing of the received signal with a high-frequency sinusoidal wave, called the *oscillator frequency*, produced in the receiver. Either the sum or difference frequency produced by the mixing can then be used for the intermediate frequency. In most cases, it is the *difference frequency* that is used. All the other frequencies are removed by filtering.

For the intermediate frequency to be the same regardless of the carrier frequency of the received signal, the oscillator frequency must be changed each time a new carrier frequency is received. In most receivers, such as a common AM radio, for example, this is done by arranging the controls so that the oscillator frequency is changed by the required amount at the same time that a new carrier is tuned in.

Receiving equipment uses the heterodyning process to convert all modulated carriers to the identical intermediate frequency

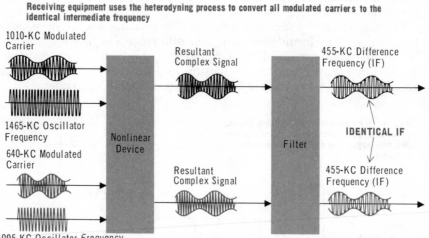

For a 455-kc intermediate frequency, as shown, the oscillator frequency must always be 455 kc higher or lower than the frequency of the modulated carrier. In practically all cases, the oscillator frequency is made higher than the carrier frequency

This mixing of the received signal with an oscillator frequency and then using the sum or difference frequency as the receiver intermediate frequency is called *heterodyning*. The signal intelligence is not affected by heterodyning. It is only put on a carrier of a different frequency. The difference frequency, normally used as the intermediate frequency, is also called the *beat frequency*.

producing the beat frequency

When two waves are heterodyned, they produce a resulting wave that contains the two original frequencies plus their sum and difference. The different, or *beat*, frequency is then selected by filtering and used as the intermediate frequency. As shown, when two waves are mixed, they *reinforce* each other at some points and *oppose* each other at others. This addition and subtraction of the instantaneous amplitudes produces a wave having a *varying amplitude.* The pattern, or *envelope*, of the varying amplitude is exactly equal to the difference between the frequencies of the original waves. Thus, as shown, if a 10-cps wave is mixed with an 8-cps wave, they produce a wave whose amplitude varies at a rate of 2 cps, which is the beat frequency.

As was mentioned, the beat frequency produced by heterodyning a modulated carrier with an oscillator frequency contains all of the intelligence of the modulated carrier. Only the intelligence is carried on the *intermediate frequency* rather than the higher r-f carrier frequency. As you can see, the variations of *peak-to-peak amplitude* of the beat frequency follow the same pattern as those of the AM carrier. And since the carrier variations represent the intelligence, the intelligence has, in effect, been transferred to the beat frequency. In summary, then, heterodyning of an AM carrier causes the amplitude variations of the carrier to be transferred to a lower frequency wave.

10-CPS Wave + 8-CPS Wave

Wave Produced by Addition
of Instantaneous Amplitudes

Envelope Corresponds to
2-CPS Wave

The beat, or difference, frequency is the envelope of the varying-amplitude wave produced by adding the instantaneous amplitudes of the two waves being mixed

Heterodyning of an FM carrier is similar, except that it is *frequency variations* that are transferred to a lower frequency wave. The beat frequency is a *band* having a width corresponding to the signal bandwidth, and a center frequency equal to the desired intermediate frequency.

Beat frequency detection is often used with interrupted CW carriers that do not have tones. The carrier is mixed with an oscillator signal that produces a difference frequency that can be heard. Then, as the carrier goes on and off, the audible difference frequency goes on and off.

the beat frequency and intelligence

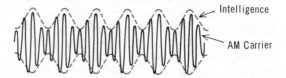

Intelligence

AM Carrier

When this AM carrier...

Oscillator
Frequency

...Is heterodyned with this oscillator frequency...

Beat Frequency
(Envelope)

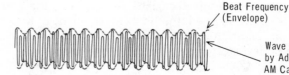

Wave Produced
by Addition of
AM Carrier and
Oscillator Frequency

...This beat frequency is produced...

Intelligence

Beat Frequency

Wave Produced
by Addition of
AM Carrier and
Oscillator Frequency
(This is Removed
by Filtering)

...But since the peak-to-peak amplitude of one of the heterodyning waves varied, so does the peak-to-peak amplitude of the beat frequency

The variations of the peak-to-peak amplitude of the beat frequency are the same as the variations of the peak-to-peak amplitude of the original AM carrier. And it is the variations that represent the intelligence

Intelligence

Beat Frequency

After removing the unwanted frequencies by filtering, the beat frequency alone carries the intelligence

summary

☐ Facsimile is a process that uses electronic signals to transmit visual material. The signals are generated photoelectrically, transmitted, and then converted to images on paper by one of several means. ☐ The Federal Communications Commission allocates frequency bands for all radio transmission within the United States. It also limits the amount of power that can be transmitted by various types of signals.

☐ A nonlinear device has a variable resistance, whose value depends on the applied voltage. ☐ A linear device has a linear resistance. That is, equal changes in applied voltage cause equal changes in current. ☐ When two signals are mixed in a nonlinear device, heterodyning takes place. ☐ A wave produced by heterodyning contains four components. These are the two original frequencies, plus their sum and difference frequencies. ☐ Modulation and heterodyning are essentially the same process. In modulation, one of the original frequencies (the carrier) plus the sum and difference frequencies are used. In heterodyning, only the difference frequency is usually used.

☐ Heterodyning is used in most receivers to convert all incoming modulated carriers to a single intermediate frequency. ☐ The intermediate frequency is produced by heterodyning the incoming signal with a local oscillator frequency, and using the resulting difference frequency. ☐ Signal intelligence is not affected by heterodyning. It is only put on a carrier of a different frequency. ☐ The difference frequency produced by heterodyning is often called the beat frequency. ☐ Beat-frequency detection is frequently used with interrupted CW carriers that do not have tones. This allows an audible difference frequency to be heard as the carrier goes on and off.

review questions

1. Briefly describe how a facsimile signal is developed.
2. The Standard Broadcast Band extends over what frequency range?
3. What is a *nonlinear device*?
4. Is a resistor a linear device?
5. What is the difference between heterodyning and nonlinear mixing?
6. If a 5- and a 10-kilocycle wave are mixed in a nonlinear device, what are the frequency components of the resulting wave?
7. How does modulation differ from heterodyning?
8. What is an *intermediate frequency*? How is it produced?
9. What is a *beat frequency*?
10. Does heterodyning affect signal intelligence?

the basic signal
and its harmonics

Voice signals contain *many different frequencies;* the combination of these frequencies gives the voice signal its shape. Each of these frequencies is a *sine wave,* but when they are combined, the resulting signal is not sinusoidal. This is true of every other signal that can be represented by a waveshape, except for a pure sine wave, which consists of only one frequency. All other waves consist of many frequencies having *different* amplitudes and phase relationships.

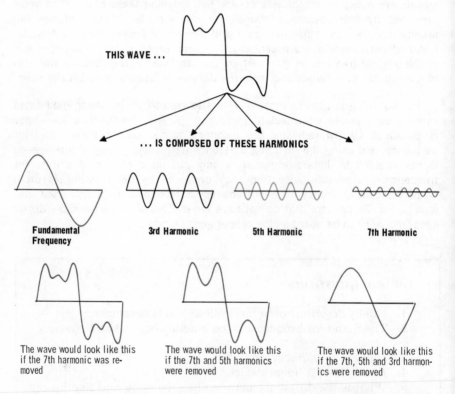

THIS WAVE ...

... IS COMPOSED OF THESE HARMONICS

Fundamental Frequency   3rd Harmonic   5th Harmonic   7th Harmonic

The wave would look like this if the 7th harmonic was removed

The wave would look like this if the 7th and 5th harmonics were removed

The wave would look like this if the 7th, 5th and 3rd harmonics were removed

The *component frequencies* of any wave are all multiples, or *harmonics,* of some *basic frequency,* which is called the *fundamental frequency;* this is the lowest frequency in the wave. Thus, if a wave has a fundamental frequency of 100 cps, its second harmonic is 200 cps, its third harmonic 300 cps, and so on. The first harmonic is actually the fundamental frequency.

All of the odd numbered harmonics of a wave are called the *odd harmonics;* and all the even numbered ones, the *even harmonics.* As you will see later, some waves contain only even harmonics, some contain only odd harmonics, and others contain both.

the harmonic content of pulses

Since the harmonics contained in a wave are responsible for its shape, anything that disturbs the harmonic content *distorts* the *waveshape*. If the shape of a signal is to be preserved exactly, therefore, the circuits that process the signal must *respond equally* to all of the frequencies contained in the signal. In practice this is impossible to do, since many circuit components, such as inductors and capacitors, respond differently to different frequencies. As a result, some distortion of a signal always takes place. This is not too bad, though, as long as the harmonics *most responsible* for the signal's shape are not affected by the circuit components. For some signals, only a few harmonics are necessary to satisfactorily preserve the waveshape. For other signals, especially those in which the waveshape changes rapidly, many more harmonics are required.

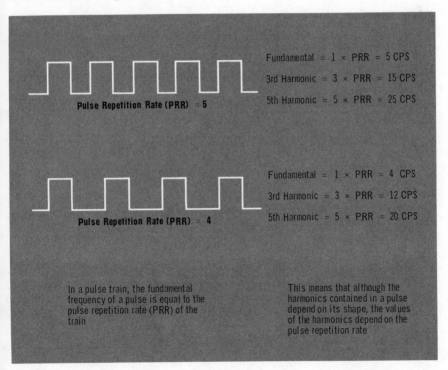

Pulse Repetition Rate (PRR) = 5

Fundamental = 1 × PRR = 5 CPS
3rd Harmonic = 3 × PRR = 15 CPS
5th Harmonic = 5 × PRR = 25 CPS

Pulse Repetition Rate (PRR) = 4

Fundamental = 1 × PRR = 4 CPS
3rd Harmonic = 3 × PRR = 12 CPS
5th Harmonic = 5 × PRR = 20 CPS

In a pulse train, the fundamental frequency of a pulse is equal to the pulse repetition rate (PRR) of the train

This means that although the harmonics contained in a pulse depend on its shape, the values of the harmonics depend on the pulse repetition rate

The harmonic content of pulses is important not only from the standpoint of preserving waveshape, but from the standpoint of *deliberately* changing waveshape as well. Very frequently in electronic circuits, it is desirable for one reason or another to change the shapes of pulses without destroying their basic pulse nature. Many of the circuits that perform this waveshaping effectively do so by changing the harmonic content, and therefore the shape, of the pulses.

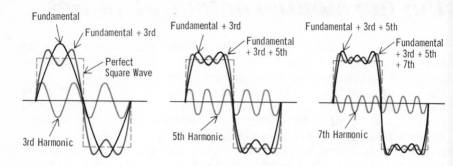

As more and more harmonics are added, a square wave comes closer to its theoretically perfect shape

the square wave

A perfect square wave has straight vertical sides, which indicates *zero* rise and decay times. Such a theoretically perfect wave has an *infinite* number of *odd* harmonics and *no even* harmonics. Since an infinite number of harmonics requires an *infinite bandwidth,* perfect square waves are impossible to achieve in electronic circuits. However, by using the fundamental and the lowest nine odd harmonics (3 through 19), practical square waves can be achieved that closely resemble the perfect square ware.

The effect of limiting the harmonics to a finite rather than an infinite number is to cause a *sloping* of the sides of the square wave. This means that the rise and decay of the pulse takes a certain amount of time, rather than occurring instantly. The more harmonics that are included, the steeper is the slope of the sides, and therefore the shorter are the rise and decay times.

In any pulse, the *higher harmonics* have the most effect on the *rise* and *decay* times of the pulse, while the *lower harmonics* have the most effect on the *duration* of the pulse. Thus, a circuit that does not respond to the higher frequencies will distort a square wave by increasing its rise and decay times. A circuit that does not respond to the lower frequencies, on the other hand, will distort the flat horizontal portions of a square wave.

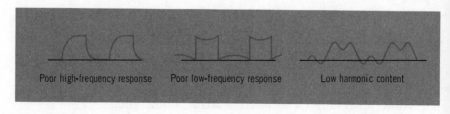

Poor high-frequency response　　　Poor low-frequency response　　　Low harmonic content

the sawtooth wave

The sawtooth wave is one of the most useful waveshapes in electronics. Its gradual rise and then abrupt drop to zero is the basis for many circuits that operate on a linear increase in voltage followed by an instantaneous drop in voltage to zero. A perfect sawtooth wave contains an infinite number of both odd and even harmonics. In other words, it contains all possible harmonics. As you know, in electronic circuits this requires an infinite bandwidth, so perfect sawtooth waves are never realized. Nevertheless, almost perfectly shaped sawtooth waves can be obtained by including a reasonable number of odd and even harmonics.

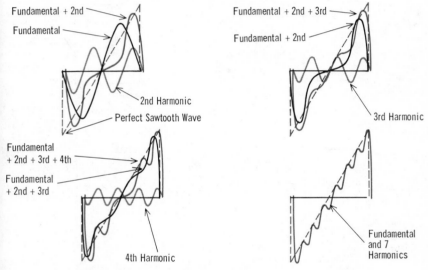

As more and more harmonics are added, a sawtooth wave becomes smoother and smoother, and comes closer to the shape of the perfect sawtooth

In a sawtooth pulse, the lower harmonics affect the rising portion of the pulse, while the higher harmonics affect the decay time. Thus, as shown, a circuit with poor low-frequency response will steepen the slope of the rising portion of the pulse. This has the effect of reducing the rise time. A circuit with poor high-frequency response will cause the pulse to decay more gradually. If the decay is slow enough, it can even run into the rise time of the next pulse.

Poor low-frequency response   Poor high-frequency response   Low harmonic content

waveshaping

A number of electronic circuits have the sole function of *changing* the *shape* of a signal or wave. This is especially true of pulse-type waves, although not limited exclusively to them. The particular way in which a circuit changes the shape of a wave depends on the characteristics of both the *wave* and the *circuit*. Because of this, not only will the same wave be shaped differently by different circuits, but the same circuit will have a different effect on various types of waves. As a result, waveshaping is a complex subject, requiring a knowledge not only of waves and their components, but of circuits and their properties as well.

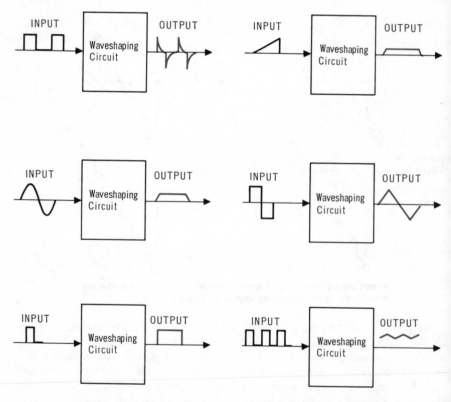

In practically all electronic equipment, waveshaping of some sort takes place. Sometimes the shape of the wave is changed only slightly. In other cases, though, a wave may be changed to a completely different shape

Nevertheless, there are certain types of waveshaping operations that are used extensively, and that involve the same basic principles regardless of the types of waves they are reshaping. Before these operations are described, though, a brief review of RL and RC *time constants* will be given.

the time constant

You should recall that the time constant of an RL or RC circuit is a measure of how *rapidly* the voltages and currents in the circuit can respond to changes in input voltage. A *small* time constant indicates that the circuit can respond *very rapidly*. A *large* time constant indicates that the circuit responds *very slowly*. Mathematically, the time constant of an RL circuit is the time required for the current to build up to *63 percent* of its *maximum* value. It is equal to the value of inductance (L) divided by the value of resistance (R).

$$t = L/R$$

Similarly, in an RC circuit, the time constant is the time required for the capacitor to charge to 63 percent of the applied voltage. It is equal to the value of the resistance (R) times the value of the capacitance (C), or

$$t = RC$$

When a pulse is applied to an RL or RC circuit, the circuit time constant determines three factors. These are (1) *whether* the circuit output voltage rises to the peak voltage of the pulse; (2) *how long* it takes to rise to the peak voltage of the pulse, if it does; and (3) the time required for the circuit voltage to *decay*. All three of these factors have a significant effect on pulse shape. You can see then that when a pulse is applied to an RL or RC circuit, the circuit time constant plays an important role in determining whether the shape of the pulse will be changed, and, if so, in what way.

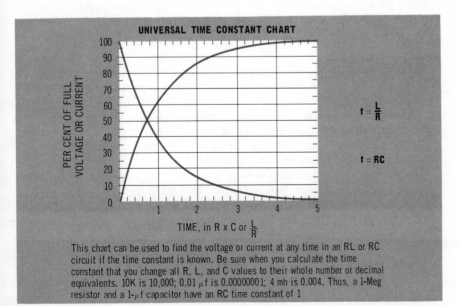

UNIVERSAL TIME CONSTANT CHART

PER CENT OF FULL VOLTAGE OR CURRENT

$t = \dfrac{L}{R}$

$t = RC$

TIME, in R x C or $\dfrac{L}{R}$

This chart can be used to find the voltage or current at any time in an RL or RC circuit if the time constant is known. Be sure when you calculate the time constant that you change all R, L, and C values to their whole number or decimal equivalents. 10K is 10,000; 0.01 μf is 0.00000001; 4 mh is 0.004. Thus, a 1-Meg resistor and a 1-μf capacitor have an RC time constant of 1

time constant and signals

In itself, a time constant is neither *long* nor *short*. It is only when the time constant is referred to some *reference period* that the terms "long" and "short" become meaningful. With a *sine wave*, the time constant is compared to the time *period* of one cycle. In the case of a pulse, other reference periods also of interest are usually the *rise time*, the *duration*, and the *decay time*. With respect to these reference periods, plus the cycle period, a time constant can be considered as being long in one case, and short in another.

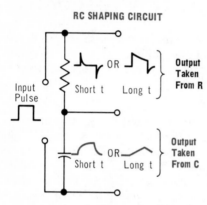

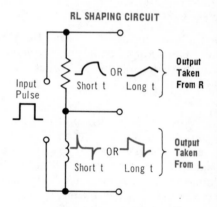

The identical input pulse is shaped different-ly, depending on whether the time constant is long or short with respect to the pulse duration. The resulting pulse shape depends also on whether the output pulse is taken from the resistor or the reactive component of the circuit

The pulse taken from the resistor of the RL circuit is identical to that taken from the capacitor of the RC circuit. Similarly, the pulse taken from the resistor of the RC circuit is identical to that taken from the inductance of the RL circuit

A commonly used rule of thumb is that a time constant is long if it is over *five times* the duration of the reference period. Similarly, if a time constant is less than *one-fifth* the duration of the reference period, it can be considered as short. You can see that it is very possible for a time constant to be long with respect to the rise and decay times of a pulse, and at the same time be short with respect to the duration, or constant-amplitude portion, of the pulse.

Knowing the relative longness or shortness of a time constant with respect to a pulse is still not sufficient to determine the effect that an RL or RC circuit will have on the pulse. This is because the output waveform of such a circuit depends on whether the output is taken from across the *resistor,* or from across the *reactive component* (inductor or capacitor). Completely different waveforms can be produced, depend-ing from where the output pulse is taken.

With sine waves, the time constant determines the phase *shift* of the signal.

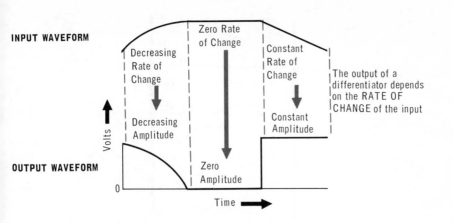

INPUT WAVEFORM

Zero Rate
of Change

Decreasing
Rate of
Change

Constant
Rate of
Change

The output of a
differentiator depends
on the RATE OF
CHANGE of the input

Decreasing
Amplitude

Constant
Amplitude

OUTPUT WAVEFORM

Zero
Amplitude

Volts

0

Time ➡

This output waveform would be produced by a perfect differentiator having an
infinitely small time constant. Practical differentiated waveforms are shown below

the differentiator

A differentiator is a shaping circuit with a short time constant whose output voltage is proportional to the *rate of change* of the input voltage. When the rate of change is zero, the output is zero; when the rate is constant, the output is constant; and when it is increasing or decreasing, the output increases or decreases. Thus, it is the *changes* in the value of the input that produce the output, and not the values themselves.

Any *horizontal* line means a *zero* rate of change, and therefore zero output. Any straight line that is *not horizontal* means a *constant* rate of change, and so a constant output. The closer the line is to being perfectly vertical, the greater is the rate of change. A curved line represents an increasing or decreasing rate of change, and therefore a changing output. These relationships between input and output waveshapes are shown.

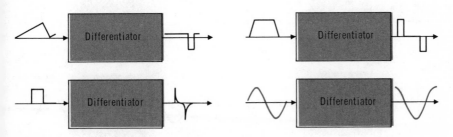

Notice that a differentiator does not change the shape of a sine wave. All
it does is to shift the phase of the sine wave

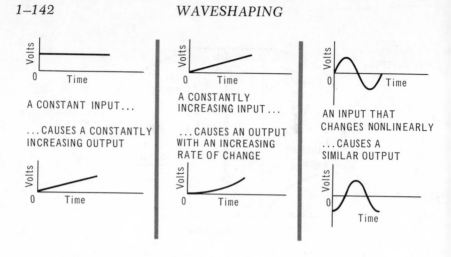

A CONSTANT INPUT...

...CAUSES A CONSTANTLY
INCREASING OUTPUT

A CONSTANTLY
INCREASING INPUT...

...CAUSES AN OUTPUT
WITH AN INCREASING
RATE OF CHANGE

AN INPUT THAT
CHANGES NONLINEARLY

...CAUSES A
SIMILAR OUTPUT

**In an integrator, the rate of change of the output varies
in accordance with the value of the input**

the integrator

Another frequently used waveshaping circuit is the *integrator*. In
many ways, the integrator functions exactly *opposite* to the differentiator. Whereas the *differentiator* is a *short-time-constant* circuit, the
integrator is a *long-time-constant* circuit. In addition, whereas the output of a differentiator varies in accordance with the rate of change of
the input, in an integrator, the rate of change of the output varies in
accordance with the *value* of the input. Thus, if the input voltage to an
integrator is constant, the output *increases* at a constant rate; while if
the input increases or decreases at a constant rate, the output increases
or decreases at an *increasing* rate. Also, if the input increases or
decreases in a nonlinear way, the rate of change of the output varies
accordingly. These input–output relationships are shown.

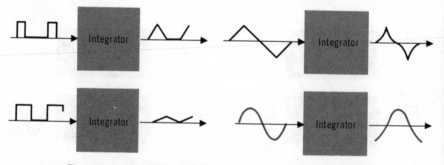

These are some of the changes in waveform shape that can be made by an
integrator. Notice that the integrator, like the differentiator, shifts the
phase of a sine wave, but does not change its shape

integrating and differentiating television pulses

An excellent example of the use of both integration and differentiation is the separation of the horizontal and vertical sync pulses of a television signal. After the sync pulses are removed from the signal, a pulse train is produced. The narrow horizontal sync pulses now have to be sent to the horizontal scanning circuits, and the wide vertical pulses to the vertical scanning circuits. This is done by applying the entire pulse train to both an integrator and a differentiator.

As shown in B, the differentiator converts *every* pulse, both horizontal and vertical, into a positive and negative *spike*. The positive spikes are all *equally spaced,* since they correspond to the *leading edge* of the pulses, which are all the same distance apart. The negative spikes are not equally spaced because of the difference in widths between the horizontal and vertical pulses. This is unimportant, though, since all of the negative spikes are removed before the spike train is sent to the horizontal circuits. Thus, the differentiator provides a pulse train of equally spaced spikes for horizontal synchronization.

At the same time that the differentiator is converting the sync pulses into spikes, the integrator is integrating each and every sync pulse. As shown in C, integration of the horizontal sync pulses produces low-amplitude sawtooth pulses that start at the zero reference and *end* there also. But when the vertical sync pulses are integrated, their greater width produces a somewhat triangular wave that does *not* return to the zero reference. Succeeding pulses, therefore, have *greater amplitudes,* and in this way, a single, high-amplitude vertical pulse is built.

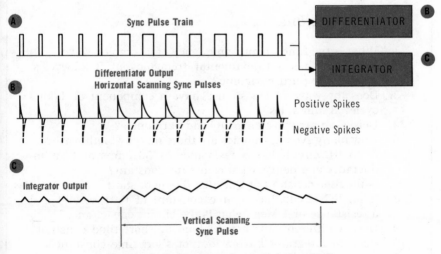

The pulse train shown above is actually only a simplified version of the vertical television pulse train

summary

☐ All complex waves consist of many sine-wave components having different amplitudes and phases. ☐ The lowest component frequency in a complex wave is called the fundamental frequency. All other component frequencies are harmonics of the fundamental frequency. ☐ All of the odd numbered harmonics (1, 3, 5, etc.) of a wave are called the odd harmonics. All of the even numbered harmonics (2, 4, 6, etc.) are called the even harmonics. ☐ The shape of a wave is determined by the harmonics it contains. Changing the harmonics, therefore, changes the waveshape. ☐ A perfect square wave has an infinite number of odd harmonics and no even harmonics. A perfect sawtooth wave contains an infinite number of both odd and even harmonics. These waves require an infinite bandwidth, and so are impossible to achieve exactly.

☐ The time constant of an RL circuit is given by $t = L/R$, and that of an RC circuit by $t = RC$. ☐ A small time constant indicates that the circuit can respond to an input signal very rapidly. A large time constant indicates the circuit responds very slowly. ☐ The time constant of a circuit determines whether the shape of an applied pulse will be changed by the circuit. ☐ Generally, a time constant is considered long if it is over five times longer than the duration of the reference period being used. It is short if it is less than one-fifth the duration of the reference period.

☐ A differentiator is a short-time-constant circuit whose output is proportional to the rate of change of the input voltage. ☐ An integrator is a long-time-constant circuit in which the rate of change of the output varies in accordance with the value of the input.

---

review questions

1. What is the fundamental frequency of a complex wave?
2. If a wave has a fundamental frequency of 2 kilocycles, what is the third harmonic?
3. Does the wave of Question 2 have a component of 1 kilocycle? 3 kilocycles?
4. Does a square wave have any odd harmonics?
5. How many even harmonics are there in a sawtooth wave?
6. If an RL circuit has a resistance of 50 ohms and an inductance of 1 henry, what is its time constant?
7. Is the time constant of Question 6 long or short?
8. If an RC circuit has a time constant of 0.01 second and a resistance of 1 Meg, what is the circuit capacitance?
9. Does a differentiator have a long or short time constant?
10. Does an integrator have a long or short time constant?

electronics
two

electronic circuits

In Volume 1, you learned about the generation and processing of electronic signals. You saw how the various characteristics of the signals are made to carry intelligence, and you became acquainted with many of the electronic systems and equipment that are in widespread use today. The overall emphasis there was on the signals themselves and how their waveshapes and other characteristics can be modified to meet the requirements of specific applications. Little or no information was given on the actual circuits that produce and process these signals. As you will learn in later volumes of this series, these circuits consist of various combinations of electron tubes, transistors, resistors, capacitors, coils, and other components. The components of a particular circuit are arranged, or connected, in such a way that the circuit performs a *specific function*. For example, it might amplify the signal or change its shape, or it might increase the frequency of the signal. In any case, every circuit has as its purpose the performance of a definite function.

In this volume, the various types of electronic circuits will be treated from the standpoint of their function. For the most part, the circuits will be covered on a *block diagram* level. The information given for each circuit will include a description of the input signal, a discussion of what the circuit does to the signal, and a description of the output signal. All of the commonly used circuits will be covered. After the basic circuits have been described, block diagrams will be presented to show how the basic circuits can be combined to produce complete equipments and systems. Thus, the basic circuits will be treated as individual *building blocks* that can be used in a variety of ways to produce practically any desired overall function.

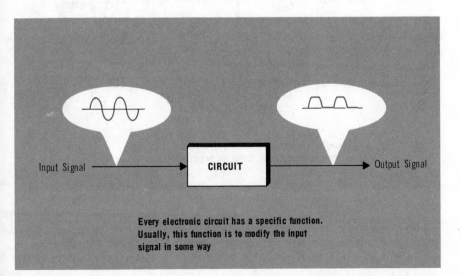

Input Signal → CIRCUIT → Output Signal

Every electronic circuit has a specific function.
Usually, this function is to modify the input
signal in some way

the half-wave rectifier

The primary source of power for most electronic equipment is derived from local commercial power companies or from electrical generators. In most cases, this power is *ac*. And, as you will see in Volumes 3 and 4, tubes and transistors, which are an essential part of electronic circuits, require d-c power for their operation. Before a-c input power can be applied to most circuits, therefore, it must be converted to *d-c power*. This process is called *rectification*, and the circuits that perform the process are *rectifiers*. Usually, a single rectifier is used in an electronic equipment, and it supplies the d-c power for all the equipment circuits.

As shown, a sinusoidal voltage is applied to the input of a rectifier. Usually, this is the 115-volt, 60-cps power supplied by a local power company. The rectifier delivers as its output only the *positive alternation* of the input voltage. It effectively cuts off the negative alternation. The output is thus a *fluctuating d-c voltage* that has the same frequency as the a-c input. This is the way a positive supply rectifier works. For a negative supply, of course, the positive alternation is blocked, and the negative half cycle is passed. Such a rectifier is called a *half-wave rectifier*. This name, of course, comes from the fact that only half the input waveform appears in the output.

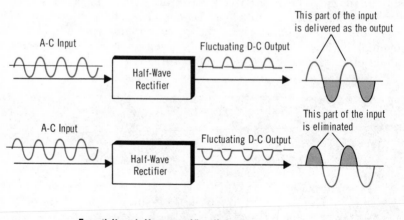

Essentially, a half-wave rectifier eliminates one-half of the a-c input, either the negative or positive half

In the circuit shown, the rectifier converts *a-c electrical power* into *fluctuating d-c power*. This involves a relatively large current. As you will learn, rectifiers are also used to change a-c *signal voltages* into dc. In both cases, the function of the rectifier is the same. Only the voltages and currents involved are different.

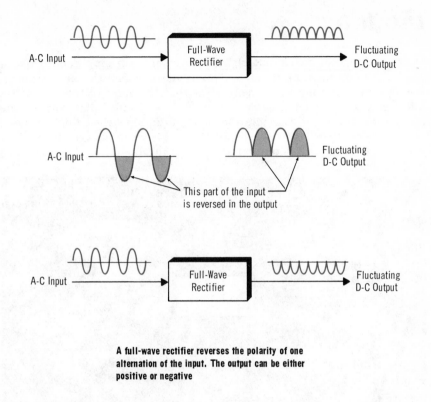

A-C Input → Full-Wave Rectifier → Fluctuating D-C Output

A-C Input → Fluctuating D-C Output

This part of the input is reversed in the output

A-C Input → Full-Wave Rectifier → Fluctuating D-C Output

A full-wave rectifier reverses the polarity of one alternation of the input. The output can be either positive or negative

the full-wave rectifier

Half-wave rectifiers, as shown on the previous page, have certain significant disadvantages. Foremost among these is their *inefficiency,* which results from their output power being considerably less than their input power. This is caused by the elimination of one alternation of the input. A much higher efficiency can be obtained by using what is called a *full-wave rectifier.* In this type of rectifier, none of the input waveform is eliminated from the output. Instead, the circuit effectively reverses the polarity of one alternation of the input sine wave. The output is, therefore, a fluctuating d-c voltage whose frequency is *twice* that of the input sine wave. This is shown for a positive power supply. For a negative supply, the other alternation would be reversed.

With the same input signal, a full-wave rectifier is capable of delivering an average or effective voltage twice as large as that of a comparable half-wave rectifier. The peak output voltage of both, however, is the same. Because of the differences in output level, full-wave rectifiers are used in most electronic equipment. Half-wave rectifiers, for the most part, are limited to applications in which the output power requirements are relatively small.

the filter

The fluctuating d-c output of a rectifier varies in amplitude between zero and some maximum value. This is not satisfactory for the operation of most electronic equipment, since they require a *smooth*, unfluctuating dc such as that provided by batteries. Circuits that convert the fluctuating output of rectifiers into smooth dc are called filter circuits, or just *filters*. The output of a filter is never completely steady, but contains some small fluctuation known as *ripple*.

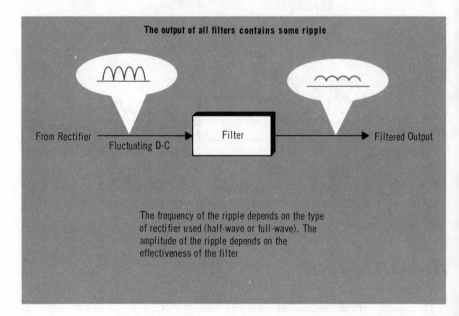

The output of all filters contains some ripple

From Rectifier —— Fluctuating D-C —→ Filter —→ Filtered Output

The frequency of the ripple depends on the type of rectifier used (half-wave or full-wave). The amplitude of the ripple depends on the effectiveness of the filter

Ripple is characterized by frequency and amplitude. With half-wave rectifiers, the ripple frequency at the output of the filter is the *same* as that of the rectifier input. With full-wave rectifiers, the ripple frequency is *twice* that of the rectifier input. The peak-to-peak amplitude of the ripple is the difference between the maximum and minimum output voltages of the filter. The ratio of the effective (rms) value of the ripple voltage to the effective value of the filter output voltage when expressed as a percentage is called the *percentage of ripple*. Thus, if the rms output voltage is 100 volts and the rms ripple voltage is 1 volt, the percentage of the ripple is

$$\text{Percentage ripple} = \frac{E_{\text{RIPPLE}}}{E_{\text{OUT}}} \times 100 = \frac{1}{100} \times 100 = 1\%$$

The percentage of ripple is frequently used to express the quality or effectiveness of a filter circuit. The smaller the percentage of ripple, the closer the filter output is to pure dc.

the regulator

When a rectifier and a filter are used together, they make up a basic *electronic power supply*. Together these two circuits perform the same function as a battery. Actually, in some cases, batteries are used to supply the d-c operating power for equipment. This is not done too often, though, because of the inherent limitations of batteries.

Electronic power supplies have another characteristic of batteries, namely, an *internal resistance* across which a voltage drop is developed when circuit current flows. This voltage drop *subtracts* from the output voltage of the power supply, and is directly proportional to the power being drawn from the supply. Thus, if varying amounts of power are drawn from the supply, the supply output voltage will vary accordingly. In some equipment, this variation cannot be tolerated since it will cause improper equipment operation. In such cases, circuits called *voltage regulators* are used.

As shown, a voltage regulator is connected in series between the power supply filter and the circuits to which power is being supplied. The regulator acts as a *variable resistor* whose resistance changes automatically in accordance with changes in the power drawn from the supply. Because of the action of the regulator, the output voltage of the supply remains essentially *constant* in spite of changes in the power demands on the supply. Often, the output of a power supply can change due to fluctuations in the power line. Although the regulator described helps compensate for this, too, many times a *power line regulator* is also used.

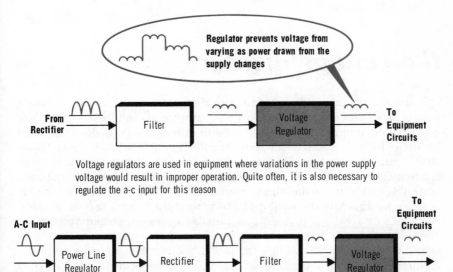

Regulator prevents voltage from varying as power drawn from the supply changes

From Rectifier → Filter → Voltage Regulator → To Equipment Circuits

Voltage regulators are used in equipment where variations in the power supply voltage would result in improper operation. Quite often, it is also necessary to regulate the a-c input for this reason

A-C Input → Power Line Regulator → Rectifier → Filter → Voltage Regulator → To Equipment Circuits

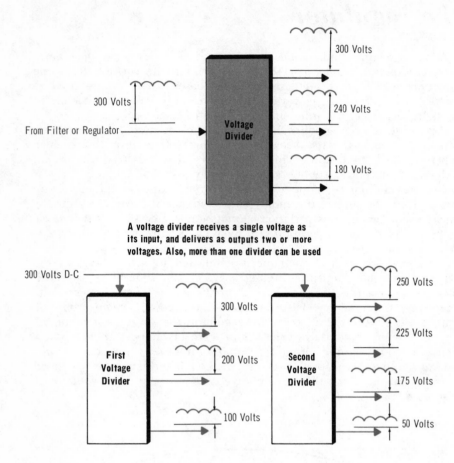

A voltage divider receives a single voltage as
its input, and delivers as outputs two or more
voltages. Also, more than one divider can be used

the voltage divider

Many electronic equipments require d-c power at *more* than a single
voltage level. For example, some of the equipment circuits might require
300 volts dc, others 240 volts dc, and still others 180 volts dc. This could
be done by using three separate rectifiers, each with its own filter
circuit, and each delivering one of the required voltages. But, it is more
economical to use a single rectifier and filter, and derive all the required
output voltages from the single combination. Such an arrangement is
possible by applying the output of the power supply to a *voltage divider*.
By means of a voltage divider, it is possible to obtain output voltages of
almost any specific value between 0 volts and the single output voltage
of the rectifier and filter. For example, if the rectifier and filter produce
a voltage output of 300 volts, various voltages between 0 and 300 volts
can be obtained by the use of an appropriate divider.

the power supply

You have now seen the major components that make up an electronic power supply. These are the *rectifier*, the *filter*, the *regulator*, and the *voltage divider*. Together, these components convert an a-c power input into various steady d-c voltage outputs that remain constant regardless of changes in the power being delivered. Actually, not every power supply contains all four components. A rectifier is always used, and a filter is also generally required. Regulators and voltage dividers, on the other hand, are used only when the requirements of a particular application make them necessary.

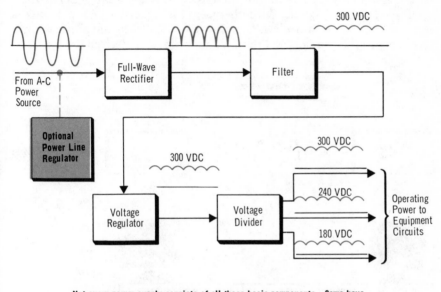

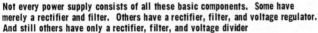

Not every power supply consists of all these basic components. Some have merely a rectifier and filter. Others have a rectifier, filter, and voltage regulator. And still others have only a rectifier, filter, and voltage divider

A complete power supply consisting of all four of the basic components is shown. The rectifier is the full-wave type, and converts the a-c input into fluctuating dc. The ripple contained in the output of the rectifier is almost completely removed by the filter so that the filter output contains a very low percentage of ripple. For practical purposes, the output of the filter can be considered as pure dc. The regulator keeps the total output voltage of the filter constant, in spite of variations in the current being drawn from the supply by the equipment, or load. The voltage divider receives the total filter output voltage, and delivers as an output several separate d-c voltages. One of these is the filter output voltage, and the others are smaller voltages. The outputs of the voltage divider provide operating power for the circuits of the equipment in which the power supply is used.

the oscillator

Very frequently a-c voltages must be generated within a piece of electronic equipment. These voltages are used to process a signal in some way, or they may be used as signals themselves. For convenience, though, we will refer to these a-c voltages as signals. The circuits used to *generate* their own signals are called *oscillators*. Basically, an oscillator converts *d-c power* supplied by a power supply into the desired *a-c signal*. The characteristics of the signal depend on the particular application, and it is on the basis of these characteristics that oscillators are usually classified. The two principal classes of oscillators are those that generate *sinusoidal* output signals, and those that generate *nonsinusoidal* output signals. In both types, the function of the oscillator is to produce a certain continuous output waveform having a definite frequency, and to maintain the frequency within desired limits.

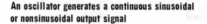

An oscillator generates a continuous sinusoidal
or nonsinusoidal output signal

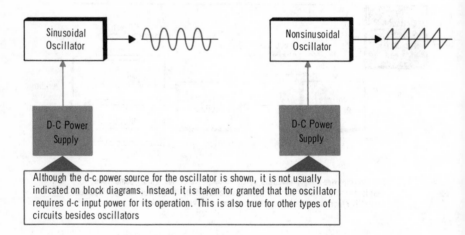

Although the d-c power source for the oscillator is shown, it is not usually indicated on block diagrams. Instead, it is taken for granted that the oscillator requires d-c input power for its operation. This is also true for other types of circuits besides oscillators

If the frequency of the oscillator output varies during operation, the oscillator is said to *drift*, or to be unstable. This condition can occur either as a result of factors within the oscillator circuit itself, or because of interactions between the oscillator and other circuits to which it is connected. In either case, frequency drift in the oscillator output is usually highly undesirable, and, as you will learn later, various methods are used to prevent it.

Frequently, nonsinusoidal oscillators are called *generators*. For example, oscillators that produce sawtooth output waveforms are often called *sawtooth generators*, while those that produce pulses are called *pulse generators*.

summary

☐ Rectification is the process of converting a-c voltages and currents into dc. ☐ A half-wave rectifier delivers as its output either the positive or negative alternations of the a-c input. This output is thus a fluctuating d-c voltage having the same frequency as the a-c input. ☐ A full-wave rectifier delivers as its output both alternations of the a-c input. The frequency of the full-wave rectifier output is twice that of the input sine wave. ☐ A full-wave rectifier can deliver twice the average or effective voltage of a half-wave rectifier.

☐ Filter circuits convert the fluctuating output of rectifiers into smooth dc. ☐ The effectiveness of a filter circuit is expressed as a percentage of ripple, where ripple is the small voltage fluctuation that exists at the filter output. ☐ Percentage ripple is the ratio of the effective value of the ripple voltage to the effective value of the filter output voltage, expressed as a percentage. ☐ A voltage regulator keeps the output voltage of a power supply constant in spite of changes in the power demands on the supply. ☐ Many voltage regulators also compensate for fluctuations in the power line supplying a-c power to the supply.

☐ A voltage divider provides a number of different voltages from a single voltage. Frequently, a voltage divider is used across the output of a power supply. ☐ Oscillators convert d-c power into some desired a-c signal. ☐ Oscillators are classified according to the types of output signals they produce. The two main classes are sinusoidal and nonsinusoidal. ☐ An oscillator is said to drift if its output frequency varies during operation. ☐ Nonsinusoidal oscillators are often called generators.

review questions

1. Draw the input and output waveforms of a negative supply half-wave rectifier.
2. What is the output frequency of a full-wave rectifier that receives 60-cps a-c input power?
3. Name two disadvantages of half-wave power supplies.
4. What is the purpose of a filter circuit?
5. Is a large percentage of ripple normally desired at the output of a filter circuit?
6. What is the purpose of a voltage regulator in a power supply?
7. Why are voltage dividers used in power supplies?
8. Draw a block diagram of a complete power supply.
9. What is an *oscillator*?
10. What is *drift* in an oscillator? Is it desirable?

**An amplifier increases the amplitude of its
input signal without changing the other
signal characteristics**

Input Signal

Amplifier

Output Signal

The amplifier must be supplied
with d-c operating power,
although the source of this power
is not shown

the amplifier

One of the most important characteristics of an electronic signal is
its *amplitude*. A signal may have the desired waveform and frequency,
and yet be unusable if its amplitude is too small. This is because the
circuits or devices that operate in response to signals require definite
levels of signal amplitude for proper operation. A simple example of
this is a radio loudspeaker. If the signal input to the loudspeaker does
not have sufficient amplitude, the sound output produced will be too low
to understand.

Very often signals do not have the necessary amplitude to accomplish
their function. They must, therefore, have their amplitude increased
without affecting any other of their characteristics. This is called *amplification*, and the circuits that accomplish it are called amplifiers.
Basically, therefore, an amplifier is a circuit that receives an input
signal and delivers as an output the *same* signal but with an increased
amplitude.

Amplifiers are classified in a wide variety of ways, as you will see in
subsequent volumes of this series. In this volume, we will classify them
for the most part by *frequency* and *bandwidth*, where the frequency is
that of the input signal, and the bandwidth is the range of frequencies
that can be amplified without excessive distortion.

Two examples of amplifier use are:

**(1) The amplification of the
small signal normally
generated by an oscillator,
and . . .**

**(2) The amplification of a
weak signal picked up by an
antenna after transmission of
the signal**

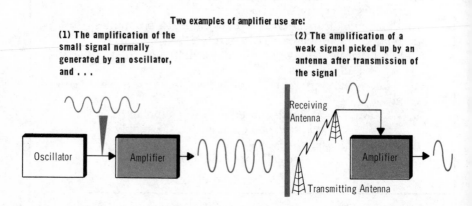

Oscillator

Amplifier

Receiving
Antenna

Amplifier

Transmitting Antenna

gain

Every amplifier has certain characteristics that make it suitable for some applications and unsuitable for others. The most important of these characteristics are the amplifier's *gain, bandwidth,* and *distortion.* Gain is the term used to describe *how much* amplification the amplifier can provide. An amplifier with a gain of 20 will deliver an output signal having an amplitude twenty times larger than that of the input signal. Similarly, a gain of 100 means that the amplifier increases the signal amplitude one hundred times.

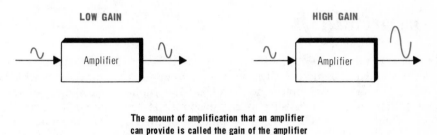

The amount of amplification that an amplifier
can provide is called the gain of the amplifier

Very often, a single amplifier does not have sufficient gain to increase the amplitude of a signal to the required level. A *series* of amplifiers has to be used, each amplifying the output of the previous one. Thus, an overall signal gain of 10,000 can be obtained by using two amplifiers each having a gain of 100, since 100 × 100 = 10,000. The same gain can also be achieved with four amplifiers each having a gain of 10, inasmuch as 10 × 10 × 10 × 10 = 10,000. You can see from this that the higher the gain of the individual amplifiers, the fewer are needed to produce a given overall gain. When amplifiers are arranged in this way so that each adds to the total signal gain, they are said to be *connected in cascade.*

When amplifiers are connected in cascade, each
one adds to the overall signal gain

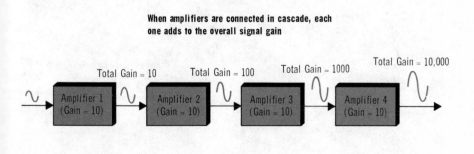

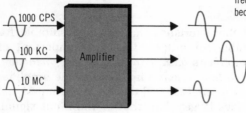

Signals that have equal amplitudes but different frequencies are amplified different amounts because of the amplifier frequency response

bandwidth

The gain of an amplifier is *frequency dependent*. This means that the gain is not the same for all input-signal frequencies. The way in which the gain varies with frequency is called the *frequency response* of the amplifier. Normally, the frequency response is represented by a graph on which the amplifier gain is plotted against signal frequency. In most applications, an amplifier is used that provides maximum gain at the signal frequency, or frequencies, involved. This corresponds to the frequencies represented by the highest portions of the frequency-response curve. Where the curve is less than its maximum height, the gain at the corresponding frequencies is less than the maximum gain.

The *bandwidth* of an amplifier is the range of signal frequencies over which the amplifier gain is *relatively constant*. For practical purposes, this is usually considered to be the range of frequencies between the two points on the frequency-response curve at which the gain is 0.707 times its maximum value. When this range of frequencies is *large*, the amplifier is said to have a *wide bandwidth*. When the range of frequencies is *narrow*, the amplifier is said to have a *narrow bandwidth*. As you will see, certain applications require amplifiers with wide bandwidths, while in other applications, narrow-bandwidth amplifiers are necessary.

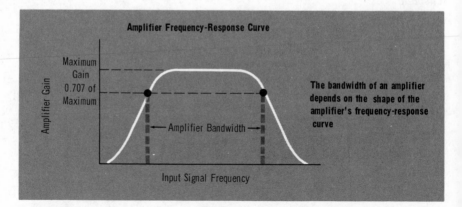

Amplifier Frequency-Response Curve

The bandwidth of an amplifier depends on the shape of the amplifier's frequency-response curve

distortion

It has been stated previously that the output waveform of an amplifier is identical to the input except for an increase in amplitude. Actually, this is only true for an *ideal* amplifier. In practical amplifiers, the output is never exactly the same as the input. Some change in the waveform takes place in addition to the amplitude increase. Such a change is called *distortion*, and is generally undesirable since it can alter the intelligence carried by the signal. In some amplifiers, as you will learn, distortion is introduced *deliberately*. For now, however, we are considering only those amplifiers in which distortion is unwanted.

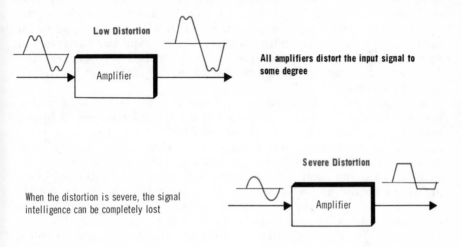

All amplifiers distort the input signal to some degree

When the distortion is severe, the signal intelligence can be completely lost

There are three principal types of amplifier distortion: *frequency* distortion, *phase* distortion, and *amplitude* distortion. Frequency and phase distortion occur when the input signal has a complex (non-sinusoidal) waveform and therefore contains various frequencies. If all of the frequency components are not amplified equally, the output waveform is distorted. This is frequency distortion.

Phase distortion occurs when the input signal is shifted in phase by components within the amplifier circuit. These components do not shift the phase of all frequencies equally. Consequently, the output waveform is distorted.

Amplitude distortion results from certain operating characteristics of an amplifier, which cannot be explained at this point. The result, however, is the same, namely, distortion of the output signal.

The amount and types of distortion that can or cannot be tolerated depend on the particular application of the amplifier. An amplifier that is entirely satisfactory for one application might be unsuitable for another because of the distortion it introduces.

the audio amplifier

An *audio amplifier* is designed to amplify audio-frequency (a-f) signals. These frequencies are generally considered to range from about 20 to 20,000 cps. Since these frequencies are in the range of hearing of the human ear, audio amplifiers are associated with *voice* or other *sound* signals. For example, public address systems and radio receivers always contain one or more audio amplifiers.

There are two basic types of audio amplifiers: audio *voltage* amplifiers, and audio *power* amplifiers. The difference between the two is the amount of *power* contained in the output signal. Voltage amplifiers deliver high-voltage, low-power outputs, while power amplifiers deliver large amounts of power. Frequently, the two are used together, with the voltage amplifier increasing the signal-voltage amplitude to the required level, and the power amplifier then receiving this signal as an input and delivering as an output a signal that contains sufficient current (power) to drive an audio output device such as a loudspeaker. The differences between audio voltage and power amplifiers are covered in detail in Volume 5.

An important feature of audio amplifiers is a relatively *low distortion* over the bandwidth. This is necessary if the sounds represented by the input signals are to be reproduced faithfully. Of course, in certain applications, such as in small AM radio receivers, considerably more distortion can be tolerated from an audio amplifier than is the case in high-fidelity audio equipment. Nevertheless, as a class, audio amplifiers are characterized by low distortion. The reason for this can be clearly seen from the frequency-response curve. The frequency-response curve of an audio amplifier is essentially flat over the entire bandwidth. This means that for practical purposes all audio frequencies are amplified equally. As a result, very little frequency distortion takes place.

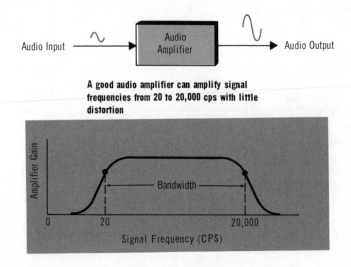

Audio Input ⟶ Audio Amplifier ⟶ Audio Output

A good audio amplifier can amplify signal
frequencies from 20 to 20,000 cps with little
distortion

Amplifier Gain

Bandwidth

0   20   20,000

Signal Frequency (CPS)

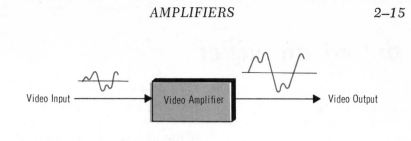

Video Input ────────▶ Video Amplifier ──────▶ Video Output

the video amplifier

Video amplifiers have bandwidths of from about 20 cps to more than 4 megacycles. This means that they can provide equal amplification for all signal frequencies within this range. As you will learn later, significant problems are involved in obtaining such a wide bandwidth. As a result, the actual circuit arrangement of a video amplifier can be considerably different from that of an audio amplifier, which has a much narrower bandwidth. You should understand that it is the *wide range* of frequencies that must be amplified equally that characterizes the video amplifier. The upper frequency of more than 4 megacycles has nothing to do with an amplifier being classified as a video amplifier.

The video amplifier is so called because it is used primarily for amplifying *nonsinusoidal signals* that represent visual intelligence, such as the picture portion of the composite television signal. In addition to its use in television, the video amplifier is also used in radar, telemetering, and communications equipment.

Video signals contain an extremely wide range of frequency components. A video amplifier must be able to amplify all of these components equally

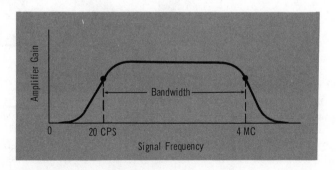

the r-f amplifier

Radio-frequency (r-f) *amplifiers* are used to amplify signal frequencies sent by *radio transmission*. The r-f amplifier does not operate over a broad frequency *range* as do audio and video amplifiers. Instead, it amplifies a *narrow band* of frequencies; and this band can be changed by a process known as *tuning*. For example, a particular r-f amplifier may have a *bandwidth* of 1-kilocycle. By appropriate tuning of the amplifier, the 1-kilocycle bandwidth might consist of frequencies from 150 kilocycles to 151 kilocycles. In this case, frequencies below 150 and above 151 kilocycles are outside of the amplifier's bandwidth, and thus are not amplified.

The same amplifier can be retuned to a different 1-kilocycle range of frequencies. This range might be from 2000 to 2001 kilocycles. Thus, frequencies that were previously outside of the amplifier's bandwidth are now in it, and thus are amplified. The amplifier is capable, therefore, of amplifying any 1-kilocycle range of frequencies in the r-f spectrum. Actually, every r-f amplifier has a limit on both the lowest and highest frequencies to which it can be tuned. The overall tuning range, as well as the upper and lower limits of the range, depend on the design of the particular amplifier. The tuning process described here for r-f amplifiers is similar to the tuning of resonant circuits, with which you are already familiar.

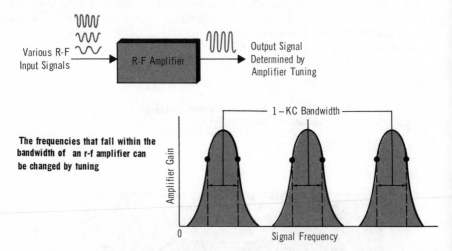

Various R-F Input Signals → R-F Amplifier → Output Signal Determined by Amplifier Tuning

The frequencies that fall within the bandwidth of an r-f amplifier can be changed by tuning

1 – KC Bandwidth

Amplifier Gain

0   Signal Frequency

In most r-f amplifier applications, various signals of different frequencies are applied simultaneously to the amplifier input. An amplified output is delivered only for those frequencies that fall within the amplifier's narrow bandwidth. By properly tuning the amplifier, therefore, certain input signals can be selected for amplification and all others rejected. The r-f amplifier can thus be said to be a *frequency-selecting amplifier*.

the i-f amplifier

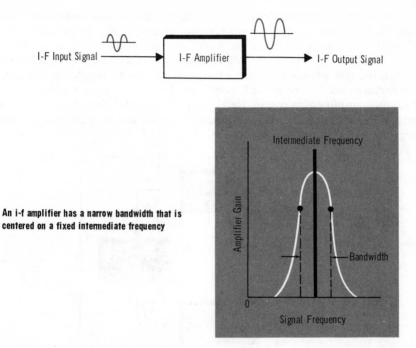

I-F Input Signal ⟶ | I-F Amplifier | ⟶ I-F Output Signal

An i-f amplifier has a narrow bandwidth that is centered on a fixed intermediate frequency

An *intermediate-frequency* (i-f) *amplifier* is essentially an r-f amplifier with a *fixed* frequency range. In other words, an i-f amplifier cannot be tuned to various frequencies. The bandwidth of an i-f amplifier is *narrow*, like that of an r-f amplifier, but whereas an r-f amplifier can be tuned to select the frequencies that fall within its bandwidth, an i-f amplifier always amplifies the *same* band of frequencies.

The i-f amplifier gets its name from the fact that it amplifies *intermediate frequencies*. These are frequencies in a particular piece of electronic equipment that are somewhere between the r-f carrier frequency and the frequency of the signal intelligence. The reasons for using intermediate frequencies will be explained later. For now, it is sufficient to understand that when intermediate frequencies are used, they are amplified by an i-f amplifier.

Often an i-f amplifier is designated according to the intermediate frequency it is used to amplify. Thus, a 455-kilocycle i-f amplifier is used for an intermediate frequency of 455 kilocycles, and a 1-megacycle i-f amplifier is used for an intermediate frequency of 1 megacycle. This does not mean, however, that the amplifier amplifies only a single frequency. It actually amplifies a small band on either side of the intermediate frequency. The intermediate frequency is, therefore, the *center* or *carrier* of the i-f amplifier bandwidth.

the push-pull amplifier

Frequently, two amplifiers are arranged in such a way that they amplify the same signal *simultaneously* and deliver a *common output.* The two amplifiers together are called a *push-pull amplifier.* Although each amplifier in the push-pull arrangement receives the same input signal, the two inputs are *180 degrees out of phase.* This is an essential requirement of the push-pull amplifier. Each of the two parts of the amplifier amplifies its input signal, and delivers its output to a common load. The two separate outputs are combined in the load so that an even larger total output signal results.

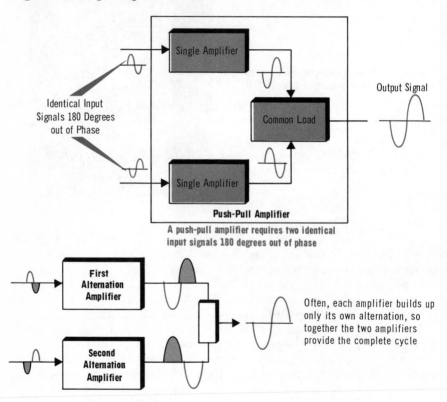

A push-pull amplifier requires two identical
input signals 180 degrees out of phase

Often, each amplifier builds up only its own alternation, so together the two amplifiers provide the complete cycle

Like other amplifiers, push-pull amplifiers are classified according to the signal frequencies with which they are used. The most common type is the audio push-pull amplifier. However, r-f push-pull amplifiers are also used extensively. The advantages of push-pull amplifiers include greater power output, and the significant reduction of certain types of distortion.

As you will learn in a later volume, push-pull amplifiers can be made to operate more efficiently by having each stage amplify only one alternation. Then combined, they amplify the complete cycle.

the phase splitter

You saw on the previous page that a push-pull amplifier requires two 180-degree, out-of-phase input signals. A signal, therefore, has to be converted into two such opposite-phase signals before it can be applied to a push-pull amplifier. Circuits that accomplish this are called *phase splitters*. As shown, a phase splitter receives a *single input* signal. It delivers as output *two* separate signals. One of these is indentical to the input signal, and the other is the input shifted 180 degrees. The two outputs are identical except for the opposite instantaneous polarities.

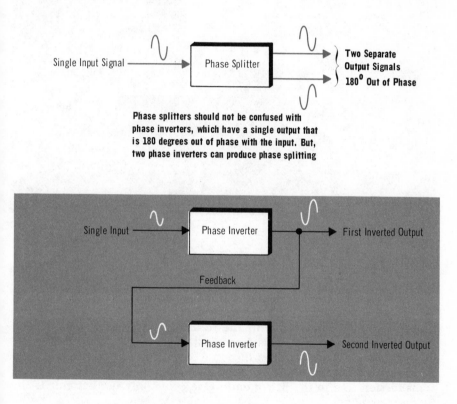

Single Input Signal ⟶ **Phase Splitter** ⟶ { Two Separate Output Signals 180° Out of Phase

Phase splitters should not be confused with phase inverters, which have a single output that is 180 degrees out of phase with the input. But, two phase inverters can produce phase splitting

Single Input ⟶ **Phase Inverter** ⟶ First Inverted Output

Feedback

Phase Inverter ⟶ Second Inverted Output

Phase splitters are also called *paraphase amplifiers*. In some types, a considerable amount of amplification takes place as well as phase splitting. Both output signals have a greater amplitude than the input signal. In other phase splitters, amplification is of minor importance: so little difference exists between the input and output signal amplitudes.

Phase splitting can also be accomplished with two *phase inverters*, which are merely simple amplifiers that produce an 180-degree phase shift. One phase inverter provides one output, which is also fed to another phase inverter to produce the second phase output.

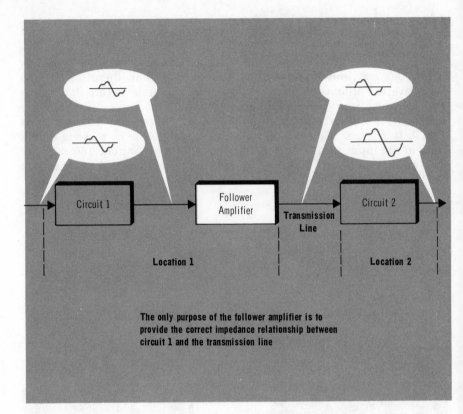

The only purpose of the follower amplifier is to provide the correct impedance relationship between circuit 1 and the transmission line

the follower amplifier

When two electronic circuits are connected over a long distance, a transmission line usually must be used to connect them to prevent interference. The impedance of the transmission line is usually much lower than the circuits. It is important that the two impedances be matched, or the two circuits will not accomplish their function. Therefore, another circuit must be used to match the impedance of the transmission line to the first circuit. One commonly used circuit is the *follower amplifier*.

The input and output impedances of the follower amplifier are such that if the amplifier is connected between the output of one circuit and the input of the transmission line, the correct impedance relationship, or *impedance match*, can be obtained. The follower amplifier also can be used in other ways, but its use as an impedance-matching device is most common. Much more detailed information on circuit impedances and impedance matching is contained in later volumes.

Follower amplifiers are also called *cathode followers* or *emitter followers*, depending on whether they use vacuum tubes or transistors.

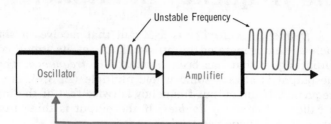

Interaction Between Amplifier and Oscillator

Interaction between an oscillator and the
succeeding circuit can cause the oscillator
frequency to be unstable, or to drift

the buffer amplifier

The signal generated by an oscillator is usually very small, so it is applied to an amplifier for amplification. When this is done, interactions between the amplifier and oscillator can cause the output frequency of the oscillator to change. This *drift* in frequency is highly undesirable since it can result in improper operation of all circuits that depend in any way on the oscillator frequency. To prevent an oscillator from being *pulled* off frequency in this way, a circuit called a *buffer amplifier* is frequently connected between the oscillator and succeeding circuits. The buffer amplifier is designed to *isolate* the oscillator, and so prevent it from being affected by the operation of the following circuits. In some cases, a buffer amplifier also provides amplification. Generally, however, amplification is of secondary importance. When amplification is also important, the isolation characteristics of the stage are generally compromised. In cases such as these, more than one buffer amplifier is used. Often buffer amplifiers are called *buffers*.

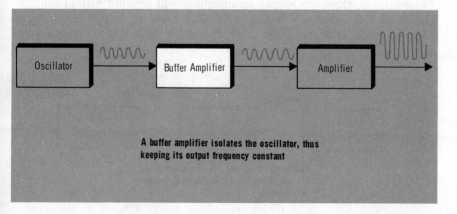

A buffer amplifier isolates the oscillator, thus
keeping its output frequency constant

the frequency multiplier

A *frequency multiplier* is a circuit that receives a *sine-wave signal*, such as that generated by an oscillator, as its input, and delivers an output signal that has been *increased in frequency*. The frequency of the output is always some whole multiple (2, 3, 4, etc.) of the input frequency. If the output frequency is twice that of the input, the circuit is called a *frequency doubler;* if the output is three times that of the input, it is a *frequency tripler;* and so on.

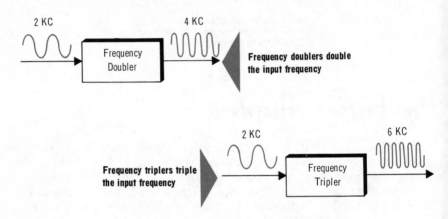

Frequency doublers double the input frequency

Frequency triplers triple the input frequency

Although it is theoretically possible to have a multiplier circuit provide an extremely high degree of multiplication, in actual practice, multiplication by a factor of more than 5 is rarely used. This is because the power contained in the output signal decreases sharply as the degree of multiplication is increased. When a high degree of multiplication is required, a number of individual frequency doublers, triplers, or quadruplers are connected in cascade. The total frequency multiplication is, then, the *product* of that provided by the individual multipliers. For example, three frequency quadruplers will provide a total multiplication of 64, since $4 \times 4 \times 4 = 64$. If the original frequency in this case was 500 kilocycles, the final frequency would be 32 megacycles.

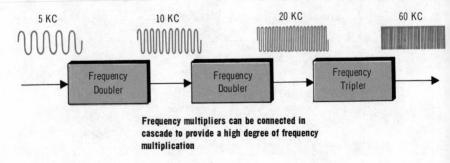

Frequency multipliers can be connected in cascade to provide a high degree of frequency multiplication

the frequency divider

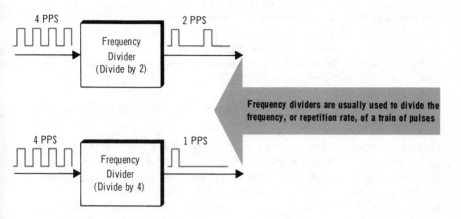

Frequency dividers are usually used to divide the frequency, or repetition rate, of a train of pulses

Just as frequency multipliers multiply their input frequency, *frequency dividers* divide theirs. However, whereas frequency multipliers are used with sinusoidal signals, frequency dividers are generally used with *pulse signals*. As shown, the input to a frequency divider is a continuous pulse train, with the frequency, or repetition rate, of the pulse train equal to the number of pulses that occur each second. The output of the divider is also a series of pulses. The rate of occurrence of the output pulses is some *submultiple* (1/2, 1/10, 1/100, etc.) of the input frequency. For example, if pulses having a repetition rate of 100 pulses per second (pps) are applied to a divider that divides by 10, the output pulse repetition rate is 100/10, or 10 pulses per second.

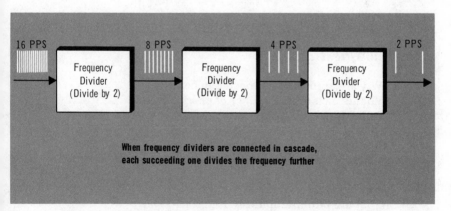

When frequency dividers are connected in cascade, each succeeding one divides the frequency further

Frequency dividers can also be connected in cascade. The total frequency division then is the product of the divisions provided by each individual divider. Three "by-ten" (1/10) dividers will, therefore, divide a signal by 1000, since $1/10 \times 1/10 \times 1/10 = 1/1000$.

summary

☐ Gain is the term used to describe how much amplification an amplifier can provide. When amplifiers are connected so that each adds to the overall gain of a signal, the amplifiers are said to be connected in cascade. ☐ The frequency response of an amplifier describes how the amplifier's gain varies with frequency. ☐ An amplifier's bandwidth is the range of signal frequencies over which the amplifier has a relatively constant gain. ☐ In practical amplifiers, some distortion in signal waveform always accompanies amplification. ☐ The three principal types of distortion are frequency distortion, phase distortion, and amplitude distortion.

☐ Audio amplifiers are used to amplify signal frequencies from about 20 to 20,000 cps. ☐ Video amplifiers have bandwidths of from about 20 cps to more than 4 megacycles. They are used primarily for amplifying non-sinusoidal signals. ☐ Radio-frequency (r-f) amplifiers are used to amplify a narrow band of frequencies. This band can be changed by a process known as tuning. ☐ Intermediate-frequency (i-f) amplifiers are essentially r-f amplifiers that are tuned to a fixed frequency range. ☐ A push-pull amplifier consists of two amplifiers arranged in such a way that they amplify the same signal simultaneously and deliver a common output.

☐ A phase splitter, or paraphase amplifier, converts a signal into two identical but opposite-phase signals. ☐ Follower amplifiers are used to match the impedances of two circuits, or of a circuit and a transmission line. ☐ A buffer amplifier is used to isolate an oscillator so that its frequency is not affected by the operation of succeeding circuits. ☐ A frequency multiplier delivers an output signal whose frequency is some whole multiple of the input frequency. ☐ A frequency divider delivers an output that is some submultiple (1/2, 1/3, etc.) of the input frequency.

review questions

1. Why are amplifiers connected in cascade?
2. What is meant by *amplifier bandwidth*?
3. Name the various types of amplifier distortion.
4. How do audio, video, and r-f amplifiers differ?
5. How does an *i-f* amplifier differ from an *r-f* amplifier?
6. What is a *paraphase amplifier*?
7. Impedance matching is the main function of what type of amplifier?
8. What are buffer amplifiers used for?
9. Two frequency triplers in cascade will raise a 1-kilocycle input signal to what frequency?
10. Why are frequency multipliers used in cascade?

the modulator

You learned in Volume 1 that modulation is a process by which some characteristic of a *continuous wave,* or possibly a train of pulses, is varied in accordance with a *modulating signal.* The modulating signal represents some definite intelligence, and the continuous wave is called the *carrier wave,* since after modulation takes place the intelligence is *carried* by the continuous wave. Circuits in which modulation is performed are called *modulators.* If the modulator causes the *amplitude* of the carrier wave to vary in accordance with the modulating signal, it is called an *AM modulator.* If the modulator causes the *frequency* of the carrier to vary, it is an *FM modulator.* And if the modulator varies some characteristic of a *pulse train,* it is a *pulse modulator.*

A modulator receives two inputs: the modulating signal, and the carrier wave or pulse train to be modulated. The modulator then delivers an output that consists of the carrier, varying according to some characteristic of the modulating signal. The modulated signal is a composite signal that contains not only the frequencies of the carrier and the modulating signal, but also their *sum* and *difference frequencies* as well. These are the side-band frequencies, or side bands.

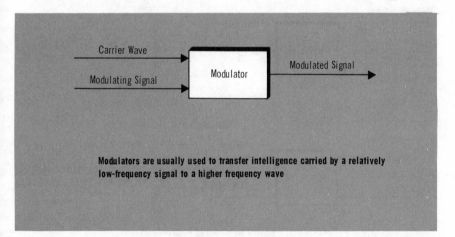

Modulators are usually used to transfer intelligence carried by a relatively low-frequency signal to a higher frequency wave

In certain AM modulators, not all of the modulation products are contained in the output. One or more components of the modulated carrier are completely removed or partially removed (suppressed). This removal is accomplished in special modulators that are broadly classified as *single side-band modulators.* Some of these modulators remove one of the side bands to produce a single side-band output signal. Others remove one side band and the carrier to produce a single side-band, suppressed-carrier output signal. And still others remove only the carrier to produce a double side-band, suppressed-carrier output signal. Sometimes, only a portion of one side band is removed by the modulator. This results in a *vestigial* side-band signal.

types of modulators

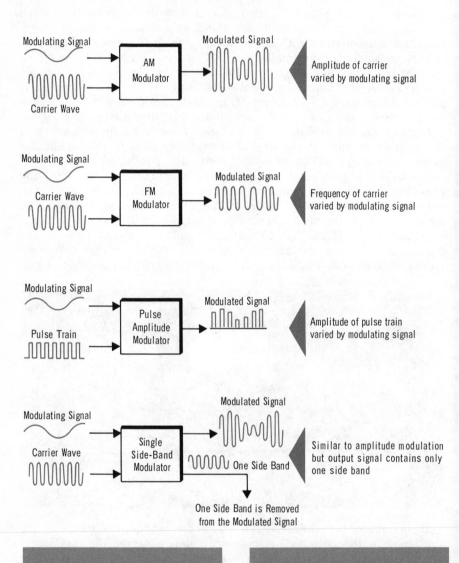

One Side Band is Removed
from the Modulated Signal

Only one type of pulse modulator and one type of single side-band modulator are shown. Other type of pulse modulators include pulse width, pulse position, and pulse code modulators

Other types of single side-band modulators include those that remove only a portion of one side band, and those that remove the carrier as well as one side band

the demodulator

Demodulators are circuits that recover, or extract, the intelligence from a modulated signal. They are more often referred to as *detectors*. Essentially, a detector delivers an output signal that has the same varying characteristics as the modulating signal originally used to produce the modulated wave. Most detectors receive only a single input, namely the modulated signal. However, those that demodulate single or double side-band signals from which the carrier has been removed require an additional input. This input is a continuous wave that has the same characteristics as the original unmodulated carrier. The detector thus *reinserts* the carrier into the signal before it removes the intelligence.

Although all detectors basically perform the same function, there are a great many types, each having its own peculiar characteristics. The types include those used for demodulating AM signals, FM signals, single side-band signals, and the various kinds of pulse modulated signals. The most important charactristics of a detector are: (1) its *linearity*, or freedom from distortion; (2) its *sensitivity*, or ability to amplify as well as demodulate the signal; (3) its *selectivity*, or ability to respond to a given band of frequencies and not respond to frequencies outside of the band; and (4) its *signal-handling capability*, or ability to demodulate large-amplitude input signals without producing excessive distortion.

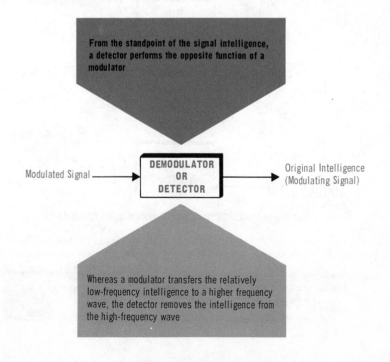

From the standpoint of the signal intelligence, a detector performs the opposite function of a modulator

Modulated Signal ⟶ **DEMODULATOR OR DETECTOR** ⟶ Original Intelligence (Modulating Signal)

Whereas a modulator transfers the relatively low-frequency intelligence to a higher frequency wave, the detector removes the intelligence from the high-frequency wave

types of demodulators

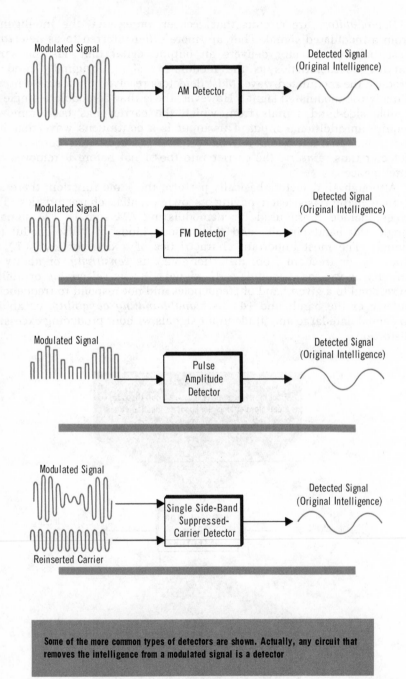

Modulated Signal → **AM Detector** → Detected Signal (Original Intelligence)

Modulated Signal → **FM Detector** → Detected Signal (Original Intelligence)

Modulated Signal → **Pulse Amplitude Detector** → Detected Signal (Original Intelligence)

Modulated Signal / Reinserted Carrier → **Single Side-Band Suppressed-Carrier Detector** → Detected Signal (Original Intelligence)

Some of the more common types of detectors are shown. Actually, any circuit that removes the intelligence from a modulated signal is a detector

the mixer

The mixer makes it possible to convert different carrier-frequency components of various modulated signals into a *single* standard carrier frequency. This conversion is necessary, as you will learn in more detail later, in superheterodyne-type receiver circuits to enable subsequent circuits to process the modulated signals more efficiently. A mixer works by *heterodyning* the incoming carrier with a constant-amplitude CW signal generated by a local oscillator. When the two frequencies are heterodyned, the mixer produces the original frequencies and their sum and difference frequencies.

In most mixers, the oscillator frequency is *higher* than the carrier frequency of the input signal, and the mixer only delivers as an output the *difference* between the oscillator and signal frequencies. This *difference* frequency, however, contains the same variations as the original modulated signal whether they be amplitude, frequency or other variations. Effectively, therefore, the output contains the same intelligence as the input modulated signal but on a lower carrier frequency.

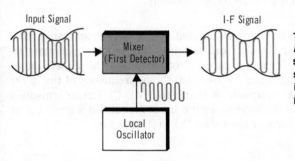

The mixer heterodynes the incoming AM signal with a local oscillator signal to produce a lower frequency signal without altering the signal intelligence in any way. The mixing process is the same for FM signals

The frequency of the output signal from a mixer is called an *intermediate frequency* (if), since it is somewhere between the original carrier frequency and the frequency of the intelligence carried by the signal. You should understand that the output of a mixer is actually a band of frequencies. These are the intermediate-frequency and the intelligence-carrying side bands. It is customary to speak of mixer output as being merely the intermediate frequency. The mixer is also often referred to as the *first detector* since it can be considered as first detecting, or removing, the modulation from one carrier and reinserting it on the intermediate-frequency carrier.

A special type of mixer, called a converter, requires no local oscillator. The oscillator signal needed for heterodyning is generated within the converter

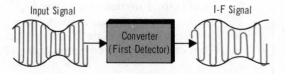

summary

☐ Circuits in which modulation takes place are called modulators. ☐ A modulator receives two inputs: the modulating signal and the carrier wave or pulse train to be modulated. ☐ In an AM modulator, the amplitude of the carrier wave is varied in accordance with the modulating signal. ☐ In an FM modulator, the frequency of the carrier wave is varied in accordance with the modulating signal. ☐ In a pulse modulator, some characteristic of a pulse train is varied in accordance with the modulating signal. ☐ Single side-band modulators are special types of AM modulators. They remove, or suppress, one or more components of the amplitude-modulated signal.

☐ Circuits that recover the intelligence from a modulated signal are called demodulators. Usually, demodulators are referred to as detectors. ☐ Most detectors receive a single input: the modulated signal. Those that demodulate suppressed carrier signals also receive as an input the carrier that is to be reinserted before detection takes place. ☐ The output of a detector is a signal that has the same varying characteristics as the original modulating signal. ☐ The most important characteristics of a detector are its linearity, sensitivity, selectivity, and signal-handling capability.

☐ A mixer heterodynes an incoming modulated carrier with a constant-amplitude CW signal generated by a local oscillator. ☐ Usually the oscillator frequency is higher than the incoming carrier frequency and the mixer output is the difference between these two frequencies. ☐ The frequency of the mixer output signal is called the intermediate frequency (if). ☐ The intermediate frequency carries the same intelligence as the input modulated signal, but at a lower frequency. ☐ A mixer is often called the first detector.

review questions

1. What is the function of a modulator?
2. Draw the input and output waveforms of an AM modulator.
3. Draw the input and output waveforms of a pulse-amplitude modulator.
4. What is the purpose of a detector?
5. Draw the input and output waveforms of a detector for double side-band suppressed carrier signals.
6. Name three important characteristics of a detector.
7. What is the function of a mixer?
8. What is an *intermediate frequency*?
9. How is an intermediate frequency produced?
10. What other name is commonly used for a mixer?

the limiter

In certain circuits, it is necessary that the *instantaneous amplitude* of the signal not exceed a certain level. This limiting of the signal amplitude is frequently accomplished by *limiters*. As shown, some limiters affect only one alternation (either positive or negative) of an a-c signal while others limit both the negative and positive signal amplitudes. Limiters are sometimes called *clippers* since they remove, or clip, the peaks of the signal waveform. The amount of limiting provided by a limiter depends on its particular application. In some applications, the amplitude level at which limiting occurs is relatively high. The limiter, therefore, only affects the signal when its instantaneous amplitude is exceptionally large. At signal levels below this amplitude, the limiter has essentially no effect on the signal. Limiters of this type are frequently used to remove static and other unwanted noise from AM signals. This is possible since noise occurs on an AM signal as large amplitude peaks, or spikes.

In other limiters, the limiting occurs at relatively low amplitudes. As a result, the peaks of every cycle of the input signal are cut off. This type of limiter is used for waveshaping purposes, as well as for removing amplitude variations from an FM signal.

Certain limiters provide signal amplification, as well as limiting. Limiters are also called *clampers,* since they clamp the amplitude to some level.

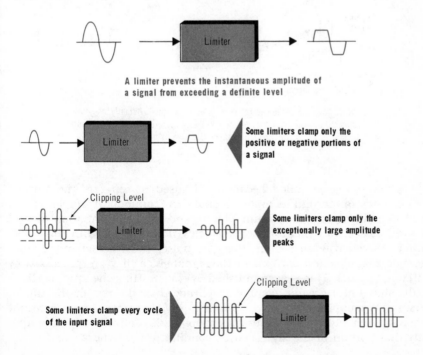

A limiter prevents the instantaneous amplitude of
a signal from exceeding a definite level

Some limiters clamp only the
positive or negative portions of
a signal

Some limiters clamp only the
exceptionally large amplitude
peaks

Some limiters clamp every cycle
of the input signal

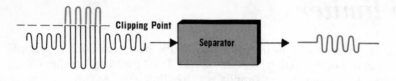

A separator delivers as an output only those
portions of its input signal that exceed a certain
amplitude

the separator

You saw on the previous page that a limiter clamps those portions of a signal waveform that exceed a certain amplitude. All signal amplitudes smaller than the limiting level are unaffected by the limiter. A *separator* is a circuit that functions somewhat the *reverse* of a limiter. In a separator, all portions of a signal below a certain amplitude are *removed* so that only the part of the signal that exceeds this amplitude is delivered as an output. The separator is sometimes also called a *clipper* because the wanted portions of the signal are *clipped off* and sent to the output.

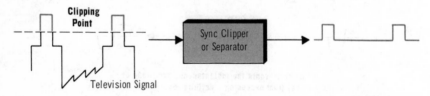

The output waveform of the separator above was sinusoidal. Actually, the
waveshape of a separator output depends on the characteristics of the separator
and the signal. Also, either negative or positive signals can be clipped

A separator is so called because it is used to separate the various components of certain complex signals. A common example is the television signal, which contains picture and sound information as well as sync pulses for synchronizing the television receiver with the transmitter. As you will learn later, the sync pulses must be separated from the picture and sound portions of the signal since they are processed by different circuits. This is accomplished by transmitting the sync portions of the signal at a greater average amplitude than the rest of the signal. When the composite signal is applied to a separator, the separator ignores the pictures and sound portions, and delivers as an output only that portion of the signal corresponding to the sync pulses.

automatic
frequency control circuits

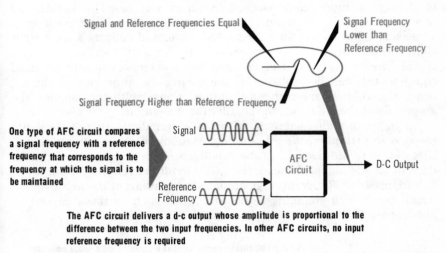

Signal and Reference Frequencies Equal

Signal Frequency Lower than Reference Frequency

Signal Frequency Higher than Reference Frequency

One type of AFC circuit compares a signal frequency with a reference frequency that corresponds to the frequency at which the signal is to be maintained

Signal

Reference Frequency

AFC Circuit

D-C Output

The AFC circuit delivers a d-c output whose amplitude is proportional to the difference between the two input frequencies. In other AFC circuits, no input reference frequency is required

In many equipments, especially those that process FM signals, certain signal voltages and currents must be maintained at essentially a *constant frequency*. Often this is accomplished by the use of *automatic frequency control* (AFC) *circuits*. Essentially, an AFC circuit senses the *difference* between the *actual* frequency of a signal and a *desired* frequency. It then delivers an output signal having some characteristic that varies according to the frequency difference. This signal is, in turn, used to change the frequency of the signal being controlled to the desired constant frequency.

Some AFC circuits compare the frequency of the signal being controlled with the output frequency generated by a stable oscillator. The oscillator frequency represents the desired signal frequency, and the output of the AFC circuit is proportional to the difference between the desired and the actual signal frequencies. Other AFC circuits do not use an oscillator to provide a reference frequency. The only input received is the signal of the frequency being controlled. Nevertheless, the output is proportional to the difference between the actual signal frequency and the frequency at which it is to be maintained.

The output of an AFC circuit is generally a *d-c voltage* with an amplitude proportional to the amount the input signal differs from the desired frequency. For example, when the input signal is right on frequency, the AFC output might be +5 volts. If the signal frequency is too high, the AFC output would be +6, +7, +8 volts, etc., depending on the exact frequency difference. And, if the signal frequency is too low, the AFC output would be +4, +3, +2 volts, etc.

automatic gain control circuits

Automatic gain control (AGC) circuits, as you will learn later, are used in receivers to maintain the output signal level constant regardless of changes in input signal strength, such as are caused by fading and other atmospheric conditions. Essentially, an AGC circuit receives a sinusoidal input signal, such as an AM wave, and delivers a d-c output signal whose amplitude is proportional to the amplitude of the input signal. The d-c output is usually a *negative* voltage, but in transistorized equipment, it can be positive. So, the greater the amplitude of the a-c input signal, the larger the d-c output. Conversely, the smaller the amplitude of the a-c input, the smaller the d-c output.

An important characteristic of an AGC circuit is that it does not respond to *instantaneous* amplitude variations of the a-c input signal. If it did, it would respond to the intelligence-carrying amplitude variations of an AM signal. Instead, the AGC circuit delivers its d-c output in accordance with *slower*, average amplitude variations of the input signal, which occur with changing signal strengths, such as those caused by atmospheric fading.

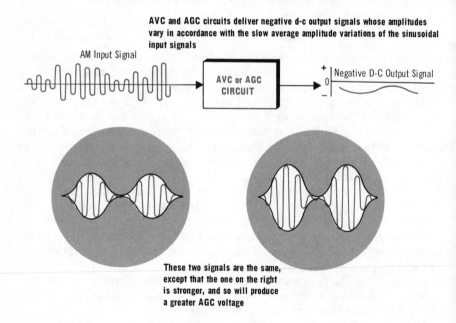

AVC and AGC circuits deliver negative d-c output signals whose amplitudes vary in accordance with the slow average amplitude variations of the sinusoidal input signals

AM Input Signal

AVC or AGC CIRCUIT

Negative D-C Output Signal

These two signals are the same, except that the one on the right is stronger, and so will produce a greater AGC voltage

AGC circuits are also called *automatic volume control* (AVC) *circuits.* Whether these circuits are designated *AVC* or *AGC* usually depends on where and in what equipment they are used. This will be explained more fully later.

traps

In many types of electronic equipment, numerous signals having different frequencies exist at the same point. Usually, only one of these is the desired signal, and it must be selected while the other signals must be rejected. As you will learn later, *frequency-selective circuits* are used to accomplish this selection. These circuits pass, or have no effect on, the desired signal; but they greatly attenuate all other signals. That is, if five signals of different frequencies are applied to the input of a frequency-selective circuit, the desired signal will be delivered as an unchanged output. The four unwanted signals will also appear at the output, but their amplitudes will be so small as to be negligible. Effectively, therefore, the circuit passes the desired signal, and blocks, or rejects, all others.

Certain frequency-selective circuits are often called *traps* since their primary function is to prevent signals of definite frequencies from being passed to subsequent circuits. Some traps pass a single desired signal or a group of signals having relatively close frequencies, and block all others. Other traps pass all signals except those whose frequencies are within some definite frequency range. For example, a trap might pass signals having frequencies below 2 megacycles and above 4 megacycles. All signals with frequencies between 2 and 4 megacycles, then, would be rejected.

Traps are also called *filters*. There are also *lowpass* filters and *highpass* filters.

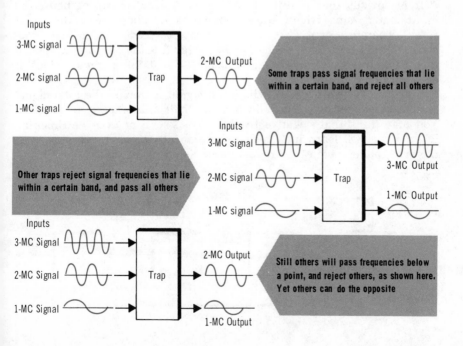

feedback circuits

In many electronic circuits, a portion of the output signal is coupled back to the input. This is called *feedback,* and the signal coupled back is a *feedback signal.* When the feedback signal is *in phase* with the input signal, the feedback is said to be *positive.* And, when the feedback is *180 degrees* out of phase with the input signal, the feedback is *negative.* The phase of the feedback signal depends on how it is derived from the circuit output. This will be covered in later volumes. For now, it is sufficient to know that there is positive and negative feedback, and that each is used for different purposes.

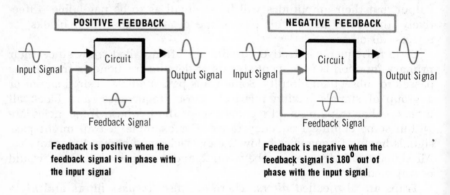

POSITIVE FEEDBACK	NEGATIVE FEEDBACK

Input Signal — Circuit — Output Signal

Feedback Signal

Feedback is positive when the feedback signal is in phase with the input signal

Input Signal — Circuit — Output Signal

Feedback Signal

Feedback is negative when the feedback signal is 180° out of phase with the input signal

It is obvious that positive feedback *reinforces,* or strengthens, the input signal, since the feedback signal is in phase with the input signal. Therefore, it is also called *regenerative* feedback. Positive feedback is used in oscillators. The feedback signal is the only input applied to the circuit; thus, an oscillator is a self-sustaining circuit since it generates its own input.

Negative feedback *opposes* the input signal, reducing the total signal amplitude applied to the circuit. It is also called *degenerative feedback.* You may think that negative feedback is useless, or even detrimental. But, as you will learn later, negative feedback does have various uses, the principal one being the reduction of signal distortion.

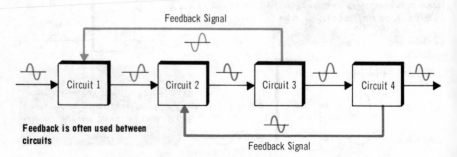

Feedback Signal

Circuit 1 — Circuit 2 — Circuit 3 — Circuit 4

Feedback is often used between circuits

Feedback Signal

counters

A *counter* is a group of individual circuits connected in such a way that a series of pulses applied to the first (or input) circuit is counted. In the basic counter shown below, each of the individual circuits requires two input pulses before it delivers an output pulse. The first circuit does not deliver a pulse to the second circuit until it receives two input pulses. And the second circuit does not deliver a pulse to the third circuit until it receives two pulses from the first circuit. This means that there is no output from the second circuit until four input pulses are applied to the first circuit. Similarly, it takes eight input pulses to the first circuit for the third circuit to deliver an output. Thus, each time the third circuit delivers an output pulse, the counter has actually counted eight pulses.

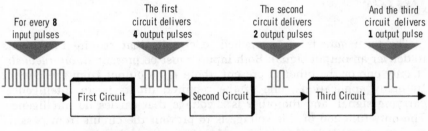

Each individual circuit of this counter requires two input pulses before it delivers an output pulse

The counter above is, of course, a very basic one. Actually, counters are much more complicated since they are normally capable of counting in the millions and include some means of visually indicating the count.

An important counter type is the flip-flop binary counter. Flip-flops are covered in a later volume. With this counter, each input pulse changes the on–off states of the flip-flops to signify binary numerals.

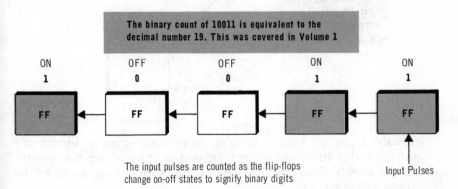

The input pulses are counted as the flip-flops change on-off states to signify binary digits

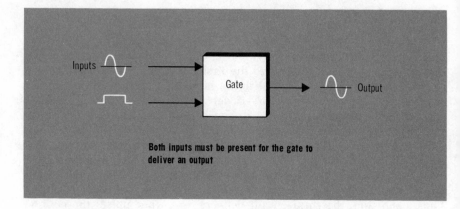

Both inputs must be present for the gate to
deliver an output

gates

The term *gate* is often applied to circuits that require *two inputs* to deliver an output signal. Both inputs must be present *simultaneously*. If only one or the other is present, there is no output from the circuit. In many applications, one of the required inputs is an intelligence-carrying signal, and the other is a voltage that carries no intelligence. The only function of this voltage is to prevent the circuit from passing the signal until the proper time. In effect, the voltage acts as a *gate* for the circuit. When the voltage is not present, the gate is closed, and the circuit cannot process the signal. But, when the voltage is present, the gate is open and the signal is processed by the circuit and delivered as an output.

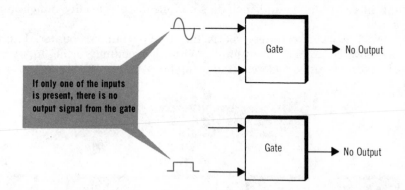

If only one of the inputs
is present, there is no
output signal from the gate

In some types of special circuits, three and/or more inputs are required for the circuit to deliver an output. Except for the greater number of inputs, these multiple-gate circuits function the same as the two-input gating circuit.

summary

□ A limiter prevents the instantaneous amplitude of a signal from exceeding a certain level. □ Limiters are sometimes called clippers or clampers. □ A separator circuit clips off the wanted portion of the signal and delivers this as an output. □ In operation, a separator functions somewhat the reverse of a limiter. □ An automatic frequency control (AFC) circuit is used to maintain some signal voltage or current at a constant frequency. □ The output of an AFC circuit is usually a d-c voltage whose amplitude is proportional to the amount by which the signal being controlled differs from the desired frequency.

□ An automatic gain control (AGC) circuit delivers a d-c output signal whose amplitude is proportional to the amplitude of the sinusoidal input. □ AGC circuits respond to the average and not the instantaneous amplitude variations of the input signal. □ AGC circuits are also called automatic volume control (AVC) circuits. □ Traps are frequency-selective circuits that prevent signals of certain frequencies from being passed to subsequent circuits. □ Traps are also called filters.

□ A portion of an output signal that is coupled back to the input is called a feedback signal. □ Feedback that is in phase with the input is called positive, or regenerative, feedback. Feedback that is 180 degrees out of phase with the input is called negative, or degenerative, feedback. □ A counter is a group of individual circuits connected so that a series of pulses applied to the first circuit is counted. □ A gate is a circuit that has two or more inputs and delivers an output only when all of the inputs are present simultaneously. □ In many applications, one of the inputs to a gate is an intelligence-carrying signal, and the other input ensures that the circuit passes the intelligence only at the proper time.

review questions

1. Draw the input and output waveforms of a negative limiter.
2. How does a separator differ from a limiter?
3. What is the purpose of an AFC circuit?
4. Why doesn't an AGC circuit respond to the instantaneous amplitude variations of the input signal?
5. What is a *trap*? What is a *filter*?
6. What is *regenerative feedback*?
7. What is *degenerative feedback*?
8. Draw a block diagram, with waveforms, that shows how a counter works.
9. What is a *gate circuit*?
10. Can a gate have one input? Five inputs?

building
a basic audio amplifier

The circuits you have learned about on the previous pages form the basis for practically every type of electronic equipment in use today. The remainder of the volume covers the way in which various complex circuits and equipments are made by interconnecting different combinations of the basic circuits.

One of the most common combinations of basic circuits is the audio amplifier, which is the heart of every phonograph and tape recorder. An audio amplifier takes the audio signal, whether supplied by a microphone, record, or magnetic tape, and amplifies it, with as little distortion as possible, to the level necessary to drive a loudspeaker or a set of headphones. A simple audio amplifier is shown below. The audio signal produced by a microphone is applied to an audio voltage amplifier, which increases the voltage amplitude of the signal. The signal is then further amplified by an audio power amplifier, which delivers the relatively large current output required to drive a loudspeaker. Sometimes, a single circuit serves as both the voltage and power amplifier.

A better quality audio amplifier is also shown below. This circuit includes a phase splitter, since the audio voltage and power amplifiers are push-pull circuits, which provide greater overall power output and less distortion. The phase splitter receives the audio signal from the microphone, and delivers two 180-degree, out-of-phase output signals. The two out-of-phase signals are amplified by the respective halves of the voltage and power amplifiers. The total output from the power amplifier is the sum of the outputs of the individual sections, and this total output drives the loudspeaker.

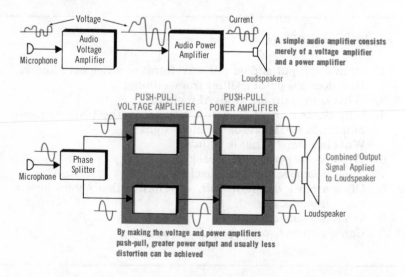

A simple audio amplifier consists merely of a voltage amplifier and a power amplifier

By making the voltage and power amplifiers push-pull, greater power output and usually less distortion can be achieved

building
a basic intercom

Intercommunication systems, or *intercoms* as they are popularly called, are used as a means of voice communication between two or more locations. The audio signals are carried by *wires,* so the distance between the individual units or locations is limited. Normally, such systems are not used for distances greater than a few miles, with the majority being employed in short-range applications such as between rooms or areas in the same building.

Each unit, or *station,* of an intercom system is essentially an audio amplifier with an associated microphone and loudspeaker. A basic two-station intercom system is shown. You will notice that the output of the station 1 amplifier is connected to the station 2 loudspeaker, and vice versa. This is necessary because the purpose of the system is to provide communication between the two stations.

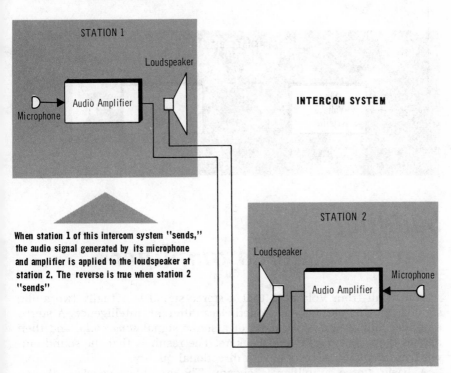

When station 1 of this intercom system "sends," the audio signal generated by its microphone and amplifier is applied to the loudspeaker at station 2. The reverse is true when station 2 "sends"

When an intercom contains more than two stations, which is often the case, the system is considerably more complex than that shown. There has to be additional wiring between stations, as well as various switching arrangements to provide maximum flexibility.

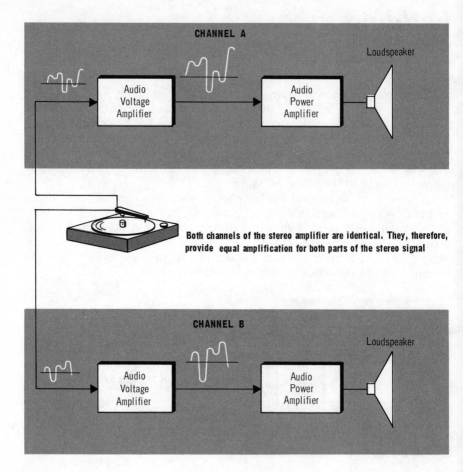

Both channels of the stereo amplifier are identical. They, therefore, provide equal amplification for both parts of the stereo signal

building
a basic stereo amplifier

You recall from Volume 1 that a stereo signal is actually two audio signals carrying similar, but nonetheless different, intelligence. A stereo amplifier amplifies the two parts of a stereo signal *separately*, and then applies them to separate loudspeakers. The result is that the sound output from the loudspeakers have a directional quality.

A basic stereo amplifier is shown. The amplifier consists of two identical *channels,* one for each part of the stereo signal. Each channel is the same as the basic audio amplifier previously described. In effect, the stereo amplifier is two separate audio amplifiers. Many stereo amplifiers employ push-pull stages for both the voltage and power amplifiers to provide greater power output and lower distortion.

building a basic cw transmitter

When electronic signals are to be sent over long distances or to many places, it is usually impractical to send them over wire as is done by intercom systems. When this is the case, the signals are sent by radio. You recall from Volume 1 that low-frequency signals, like those in the audio range, cannot be transmitted efficiently by radio. So they are converted to higher frequencies, called radio frequencies, which can be transmitted effectively over long distances.

The electronic equipment used to produce radio-frequency (r-f) signals for radio transmission is called a *transmitter*. The function of a transmitter is to generate an r-f carrier of proper frequency and sufficient power. The output of a transmitter is applied to an antenna, which radiates the signal into space. Antennas and their operation are covered in Volume 7.

A basic transmitter is shown. It consists of an *oscillator* and an *r-f amplifier*. The oscillator generates a continuous sinusoidal output that serves as the carrier frequency; then, the carrier is amplified to the required power level by the r-f amplifier. An antenna connected to the output of the r-f amplifier radiates the signal into space. This type of transmitter is called a *continuous-wave* (CW) *transmitter*, since it produces an uninterrupted, sinusoidal output.

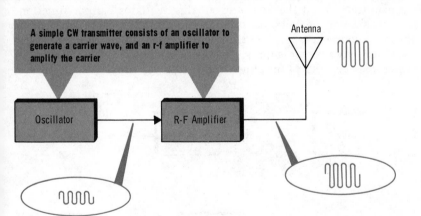

A simple CW transmitter consists of an oscillator to generate a carrier wave, and an r-f amplifier to amplify the carrier

Antenna

Oscillator   R-F Amplifier

Sometimes, although infrequently, a CW transmitter contains only an oscillator, its output connected directly to the antenna. The output power of such a transmitter is very low

the interrupted cw transmitter

The output from the CW transmitter, shown on the previous page, carries no intelligence. This is because the carrier is a continuous sine wave with each cycle identical to all others. To convey intelligence, the carrier must be varied, or *modulated*, in some manner. The simplest way of doing this is to *interrupt* the carrier periodically so that it is effectively broken into a series of pulses. The pulses can then be made to represent some form of intelligible code, like the Morse code, in which a short output pulse represents a dot, and a longer output pulse is a dash. A transmitter used in this way is called an *interrupted CW transmitter*.

A basic interrupted CW transmitter is shown in A of the illustration. It is the same as the CW transmitter, but it also contains a switch between the oscillator and r-f amplifier. This switch is actually a handkey controlled by an operator. When the key is closed, the oscillator output is applied to the amplifier and the transmitter delivers an output. And, when the key is open, the amplifier receives no input; thus, the transmitter does not deliver an output. By means of the key, therefore, an operator can add intelligence to the carrier by breaking it into dots and dashes.

An interrupted CW transmitter, with the handkey connected between the oscillator and the power supply is shown in B of the illustration. The handkey then controls the operating power applied to the oscillator. With the key closed, the circuit is the same as the basic CW transmitter. When the key is open, the oscillator cannot function, so the transmitter delivers no output. The key has the same effect whether it is connected between the oscillator and amplifier, or between the oscillator and power supply. In a similar way, the key could be connected between the r-f amplifier and the power supply.

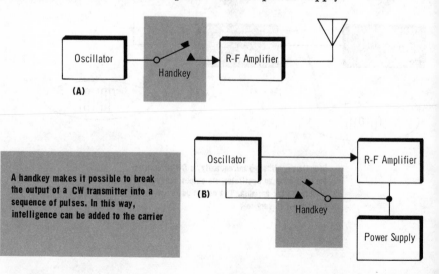

A handkey makes it possible to break the output of a CW transmitter into a sequence of pulses. In this way, intelligence can be added to the carrier

additional transmitter circuits

Most CW transmitters are considerably more complex than the types described because of the large power output that transmitters generally deliver as well as the relatively high carrier frequencies at which they operate. As a result of these requirements, most transmitters contain circuits in addition to the oscillator and power amplifier. These circuits include *buffer amplifiers, frequency multipliers,* and *intermediate power amplifiers.*

A buffer amplifier is often used directly after the transmitter oscillator. Its primary function is to isolate the oscillator from the power amplifier so that there is no electrical interaction between the two. It also insures a constant output frequency from the oscillator and often amplifies the oscillator output as well.

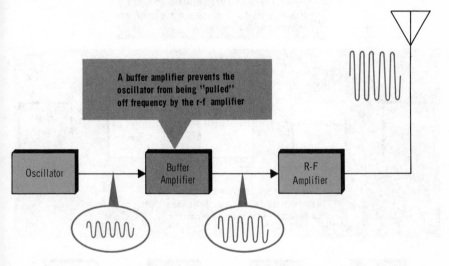

A buffer amplifier prevents the oscillator from being "pulled" off frequency by the r-f amplifier

Oscillator → Buffer Amplifier → R-F Amplifier

An oscillator may be unstable when it delivers a high output frequency. This means that output frequency varies somewhat above and below the desired frequency. To overcome this, the oscillator is often operated at a relatively low frequency, and frequency multipliers are used to raise the carrier to the desired operating frequency. For example, the oscillator might deliver an output signal of 50 kilocycles, which then could be increased to 200 kilocycles by two frequency doublers. A transmitter with frequency multipliers is shown on the following page.

When a single r-f amplifier cannot raise its signal to the high power level that the transmitter must deliver, a series of amplifiers is used, each one providing a portion of the required total power amplification. The *last* amplifier, whose output is coupled to the antenna, is called the *final power amplifier.* All of the others are called *intermediate power amplifiers.* A transmitter having more than one power amplifier is shown on the following page.

additional transmitter circuits (cont.)

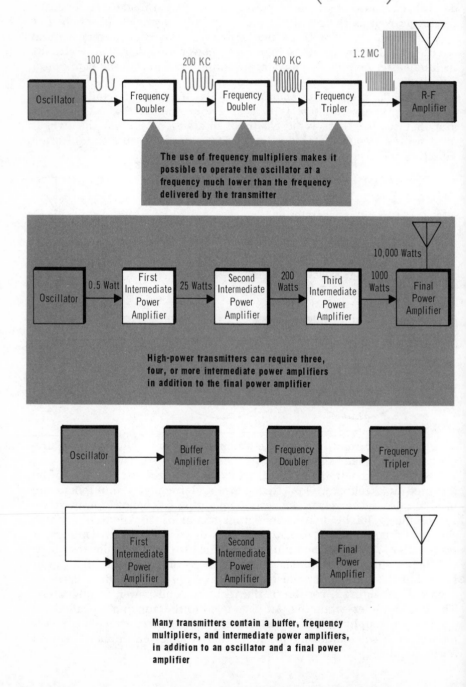

The use of frequency multipliers makes it possible to operate the oscillator at a frequency much lower than the frequency delivered by the transmitter

High-power transmitters can require three, four, or more intermediate power amplifiers in addition to the final power amplifier

Many transmitters contain a buffer, frequency multipliers, and intermediate power amplifiers, in addition to an oscillator and a final power amplifier

summary

☐ An audio amplifier builds up the signal from some audio device such as a microphone, and applies it to a loudspeaker or set of headphones. ☐ A basic audio amplifier consists of two stages: first a voltage amplifier and then a power amplifier. Both amplify the signal with as little distortion as possible. ☐ When push-pull stages are used in an audio amplifier, they are preceded by a phase splitter. ☐ An intercom system provides voice communication, by wire, between two locations. Each station of an intercom system consists of a microphone, an audio amplifier, and a loudspeaker, with the microphone and amplifier of one station feeding the loudspeaker of the other.

☐ A stereo amplifier has two identical channels, each essentially being an audio amplifier. ☐ Each channel amplifies one part of the stereo signal. ☐ A separate loudspeaker is used for each channel. This gives the resulting sound output a directional quality.

☐ A CW transmitter generates an r-f carrier of proper frequency and sufficient power for radio transmission. ☐ The simplest CW transmitter consists of an oscillator, which produces the r-f carrier, and an r-f amplifier, which increases the power level of the carrier. ☐ An antenna is used to radiate the r-f output of a transmitter into space. ☐ The output of a CW transmitter can be made to carry intelligence by being interrupted in accordance with some code, such as the dots and dashes of the Morse code. ☐ Most CW transmitters contain one or more buffer amplifiers, frequency multipliers, and intermediate power amplifiers in addition to the oscillator and power amplifier.

review questions

1. Draw a block diagram of a basic audio amplifier.
2. Why are push-pull circuits often used in audio amplifiers?
3. Draw a block diagram of a simple two-station intercom system.
4. What is the function of a radio transmitter?
5. Draw a block diagram, with waveforms, of a simple CW transmitter.
6. What is the purpose of the handkey in an interrupted CW transmitter?
7. Draw a block diagram of an interrupted CW transmitter and show two places where the handkey can be connected.
8. What is the purpose of a buffer amplifier?
9. Why are frequency multipliers used in CW transmitters?
10. What are intermediate power amplifiers?

the voice-modulated
AM transmitter

CW transmitters are limited by the type of signals they can transmit because they are essentially generators of high-frequency, high-power waves. The only way intelligence can be added to these waves is to interrupt them with some type of code. For the transmission of more complicated signals, other types of transmitters must be used.

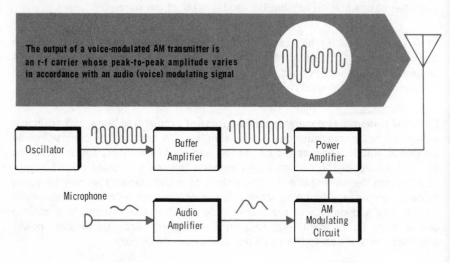

The output of a voice-modulated AM transmitter is an r-f carrier whose peak-to-peak amplitude varies in accordance with an audio (voice) modulating signal

The output is actually a composite signal, containing the r-f carrier and voice frequencies, plus their sum and difference frequencies

These sum and difference frequencies are the side bands, and contain the signal intelligence

The most common of the various transmitters used today is the *voice-modulated AM transmitter*. In this transmitter, complex audio signals are *amplitude modulated* onto an r-f carrier wave, and the resulting modulated signal is transmitted. Such a transmitter is shown. Basically, the transmitter consists of r-f circuits and audio circuits. The r-f circuits are the same as those in a CW transmitter; they produce a high-power, r-f carrier wave. The audio circuits receive a *low-level*, audio input signal, such as that produced by a microphone. This signal is amplified by one or more audio amplifiers and then applied to an AM modulating circuit. The modulating circuit causes the amplified carrier delivered by the power amplifiers to vary in amplitude in accordance with the audio signal.

Although the modulating circuit for this transmitter is shown separately, it is actually made up of a portion of the r-f power amplifier and a portion of the audio amplifier circuits. For analysis purposes, though, it is convenient to consider it a separate circuit.

the tone-modulated AM transmitter

From a receiving standpoint, the dot–dash type signals produced by an interrupted CW transmitter can be improved by combining some of its features with those of the voice-modulated AM transmitter. The resulting transmitter is called a *tone-modulated AM transmitter;* it produces an output corresponding to the dots and dashes of the Morse code. However, instead of using a plain unmodulated carrier, the carrier is amplitude-modulated with an audio tone. The modulated carrier is then broken into long and short pulses for Morse code transmission. As you will learn, this system simplifies the radio receiver reception of a dot–dash type signal.

A basic tone-modulated AM transmitter is shown. Like the voice-modulated AM transmitter, it contains r-f circuits for generating a high-power r-f carrier and audio circuits for processing an audio modulating signal. An audio oscillator is used instead of a microphone to produce the audio signal. The oscillator generates a constant audio frequency, such as 500 or 1000 cps. This audio signal, or tone as it is called, is amplified. Then it is applied to a modulating circuit where it amplitude modulates the power amplifier output.

Operating power for both the r-f and audio oscillators is applied through a handkey. When the key is closed, both oscillators function: the transmitter delivers an output. When the key is open, neither of the oscillators functions: the transmitter delivers no output.

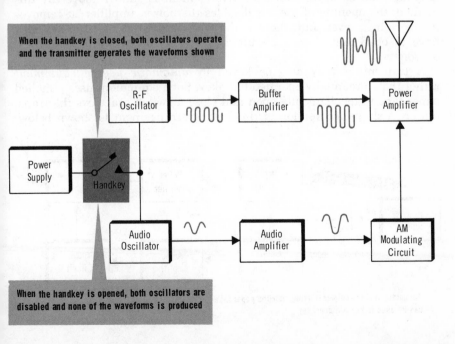

When the handkey is closed, both oscillators operate and the transmitter generates the waveforms shown

When the handkey is opened, both oscillators are disabled and none of the waveforms is produced

variations of the tone-modulated AM transmitter

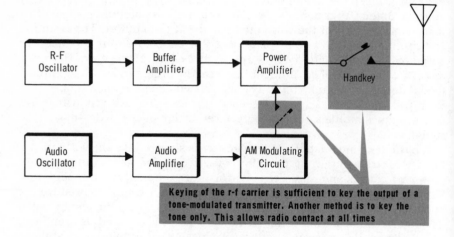

Keying of the r-f carrier is sufficient to key the output of a tone-modulated transmitter. Another method is to key the tone only. This allows radio contact at all times

In the tone-modulated transmitter described on the previous page, the transmitter output is keyed by a handkey that controls the operating power for the r-f and audio oscillators. Other methods can be used to key the transmitter, too. For example, the output circuit of the power amplifier can be keyed. Such an arrangement is shown above. By this method, the opening of the key disables the power amplifier; it removes its operating power. But, there is the disadvantage in that the key may have to open and close a circuit carrying hundreds, even thousands, of volts.

A transmitter may also be keyed by *automatic keying equipment* rather than a manually operated handkey. Such equipment uses punched paper tape to mechanically open and close a switch that keys the transmitter. A simplified version of this keying arrangement is shown below.

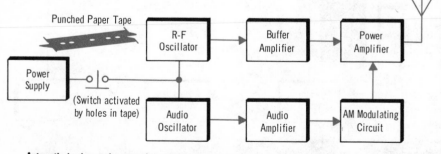

Automatic keying equipment using punched paper tape can be used to key a transmitter

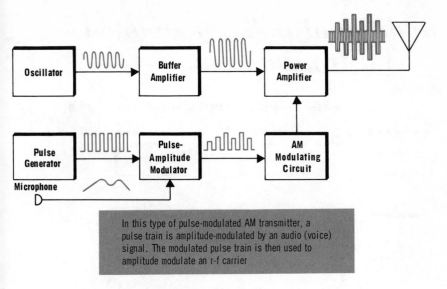

In this type of pulse-modulated AM transmitter, a pulse train is amplitude-modulated by an audio (voice) signal. The modulated pulse train is then used to amplitude modulate an r-f carrier

the pulse-modulated AM transmitter

In pulse modulation, you recall, some characteristic of a pulse train is varied in accordance with a signal that represents a form of intelligence. The modulated pulse train can then be used to modulate an r-f carrier for radio transmission. One type of transmitter used to produce this kind of signal is shown. The transmitter contains r-f circuits for producing the r-f carrier. It also contains pulse circuits that produce and modulate a train of pulses. The first of these pulse circuits is a *pulse generator*. It produces a continuous train of rectangular pulses having both *constant amplitude* and *constant repetition*. The pulse train is applied to a pulse-amplitude modulator, which amplitude modulates the train with an audio signal produced by a microphone.

The modulator's output is a series of pulses that still has a constant repetition rate, but whose amplitudes now vary in accordance with the instantaneous amplitude of the audio signal. The modulated pulse train is then used to modulate the output of the r-f power amplifier. The output of the power amplifier is, therefore, a series of bursts, or pulses, of the modulated carrier: the peak-to-peak amplitude of the individual bursts corresponds to the amplitudes of the pulses in the modulated pulse train.

This type of transmitter is called a *pulse-amplitude-modulated AM transmitter*. Other types of pulse-modulated AM transmitters use *pulse-width, pulse-position,* and *pulse-code modulation.* All of these transmitters are similar, differing only in respect to the type of pulse modulator used.

additional pulse-modulated AM transmitters

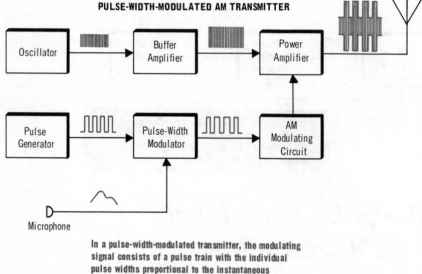

PULSE-WIDTH-MODULATED AM TRANSMITTER

In a pulse-width-modulated transmitter, the modulating signal consists of a pulse train with the individual pulse widths proportional to the instantaneous amplitude of the audio signal

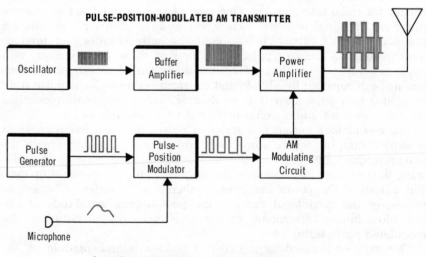

PULSE-POSITION-MODULATED AM TRANSMITTER

In a pulse-position-modulated transmitter, the modulating signal consists of a pulse train with the spacing between adjacent pulses proportional to the instantaneous amplitude of the audio signal

the pulse radar transmitter

A *pulse radar transmitter* produces precisely tuned short bursts, or pulses, of high-frequency energy. The output power represented by each pulse is very great. But, since the *duration* of each pulse is short, sometimes less than 1 microsecond, the average output power from the transmitter is significantly less than that of the individual pulses.

A basic radar transmitter is shown. It consists of a *timing oscillator*, a *buffer amplifier*, a *waveshaping circuit*, and a *magnetron oscillator*. The timing oscillator produces a *sinusoidal* output whose frequency establishes the pulse repetition rate of the transmitter. The buffer amplifier isolates the timing oscillator from the high-power output stages of the transmitter. It also amplifies the oscillator output signal. The sinusoidal output from the buffer amplifier is applied to a wave-shaping circuit, which converts the sine-wave signal into a series of sharp, rectangular pulses. These pulses then trigger the magnetron oscillator, which produces bursts of exceptionally high-power, high-frequency energy. Each input pulse causes the magnetron to deliver an output burst having the same time duration as the input pulse.

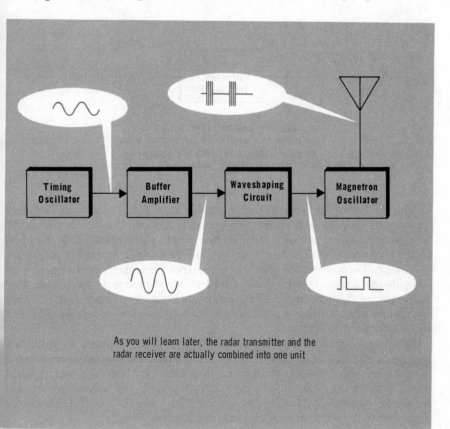

As you will learn later, the radar transmitter and the radar receiver are actually combined into one unit

the single side-band AM transmitter

A *single side-band AM transmitter* that produces a single side-band, suppressed-carrier signal is shown in A on the next page. The transmitter's output is a high-power r-f signal that has amplitude variations corresponding to only *one* modulation side band, instead of to both side bands as in conventional AM transmitters.

In this transmitter, both the carrier, which is generated by a high-frequency oscillator, and an audio signal, which is produced by a microphone, are applied to a single side-band (SSB) modulator. For practical purposes, this modulator can be said to deliver two outputs: one, the *upper side band* produced by the modulation process (carrier frequency *plus* audio frequencies); and the other, the *lower side band* (carrier frequency *minus* audio frequencies). The modulator *suppresses* the carrier frequency. In other words, the carrier does not appear in the output.

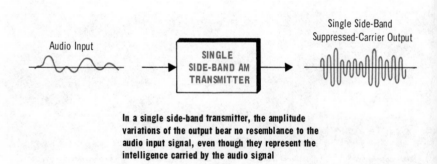

In a single side-band transmitter, the amplitude variations of the output bear no resemblance to the audio input signal, even though they represent the intelligence carried by the audio signal

The output of the modulator is applied to a filter, which passes only one of the side bands, either the upper or lower. The other side band is rejected. After passing through the filter, the desired side band is sent to a mixer, which also receives the sinusoidal output from an r-f oscillator. Through heterodyning, the mixer increases the frequency of the side-band signal to the desired r-f frequency at which the transmitter is to operate. This increase in frequency is necessary because the carrier frequency used for the modulation process is too low to obtain efficient modulation.

After being increased in frequency, the side-band signal is amplified by one or more r-f amplifiers. Since these amplifiers process a modulated signal, they must be *linear:* that is, they must amplify the signal without changing its waveshape. Any alteration of the waveshape would result in distortion of the intelligence. The output of the r-f power amplifier is then sent to the antenna for transmission.

the single side-band
AM transmitter (cont.)

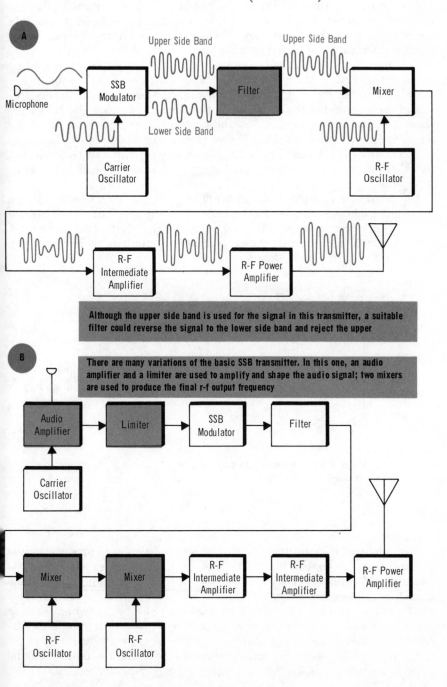

A

Upper Side Band

Upper Side Band

Microphone

SSB Modulator

Filter

Mixer

Lower Side Band

Carrier Oscillator

R-F Oscillator

R-F Intermediate Amplifier

R-F Power Amplifier

Although the upper side band is used for the signal in this transmitter, a suitable filter could reverse the signal to the lower side band and reject the upper

B

There are many variations of the basic SSB transmitter. In this one, an audio amplifier and a limiter are used to amplify and shape the audio signal; two mixers are used to produce the final r-f output frequency

Audio Amplifier

Limiter

SSB Modulator

Filter

Carrier Oscillator

Mixer

Mixer

R-F Intermediate Amplifier

R-F Intermediate Amplifier

R-F Power Amplifier

R-F Oscillator

R-F Oscillator

the multichannel transmitter

All of the transmitters described so far have one thing in common. This is that the output signal, regardless of type, has contained a *single channel* of intelligence. In other words, a single microphone or a single handkey controls the intelligence being transmitted at any one time. Such transmitters are called *single-channel transmitters*.

Other transmitters, called *multichannel transmitters*, are capable of transmitting *two or more* channels of intelligence *simultaneously*. These transmitters deliver a single complex output signal that contains frequency components corresponding to the individual channels. However, these frequency components and the channels they represent are *independent* of each other. As you will see, after transmission of the complex, or composite, signal, the various frequency components can be separated by filter networks, and the intelligence carried by each recovered separately.

By means of multichannel transmitters, outputs from, say, two or more microphones can be modulated independently onto a single r-f carrier. In effect, this permits two or more signals to be transmitted by not much more transmitting equipment and power required for transmission of a single signal.

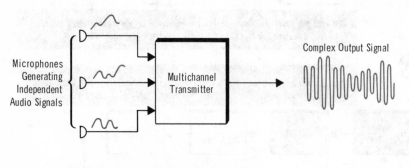

The three audio input signals are each contained in the complex r-f output signal

Multichannel transmitters use *subcarrier modulation* to produce multichannel output signals. This can be seen in the diagram of a basic multichannel AM transmitter on the following page. Each audio modulating signal, or channel, has its own modulator and carrier oscillator. The oscillators are called *subcarrier oscillators*, and the frequencies they generate are called *subcarriers*. The audio signals are amplitude modulated onto their respective subcarriers, and *all* of these modulated signals are applied to another modulator, which we will call the *carrier modulator*. This process is known as *frequency multiplexing*.

the multichannel transmitter (cont.)

The carrier modulator of the multichannel transmitter has its own associated oscillator, called the *carrier oscillator*, which generates the transmitter's output carrier frequency. The carrier modulator delivers an output signal that has the frequency of the carrier oscillator. The amplitude varies in accordance with the algebraic sum of the instantaneous amplitudes of the subcarrier signals. This composite AM signal is then amplified to the required level by a series of linear r-f power amplifiers.

The frequencies of the subcarriers are important considerations in a multichannel transmitter. These frequencies must be different, and they must be far enough apart so that their side bands do not overlap. This is necessary so that at the receiver, each modulated subcarrier can be filtered from the composite signal independently.

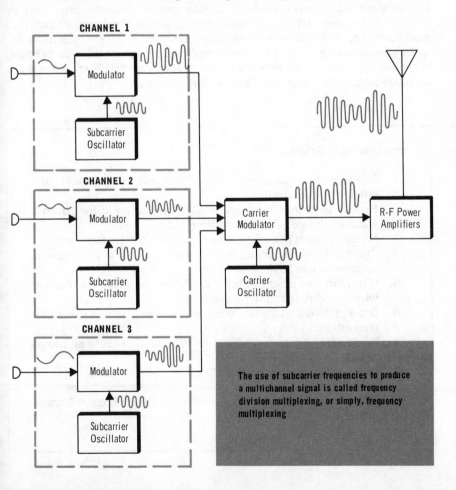

The use of subcarrier frequencies to produce a multichannel signal is called frequency division multiplexing, or simply, frequency multiplexing

summary

☐ In a voice-modulated AM transmitter, the modulating circuit causes the amplified carrier delivered by the power amplifiers to vary in amplitude in accordance with the audio signal. ☐ A tone-modulated AM transmitter combines features of both the interrupted CW transmitter and the voice-modulated AM transmitter. After modulation, the transmitter output is interrupted into dots and dashes by either a handkey or automatic keying equipment.

☐ In a pulse-modulated AM transmitter, some characteristic of a pulse train is modulated in accordance with the modulating signal. ☐ Pulse-amplitude, pulse-width, pulse-position, and pulse-code modulation can be used in pulse-modulated AM transmitters. ☐ Pulse radar transmitters produce short, precisely-timed bursts of high-frequency energy.

☐ The modulator in a single side-band transmitter receives as inputs the modulating signal and a carrier, and delivers as an output only the two side bands. One side band is then removed by a filter. ☐ Multichannel transmitters can transmit two or more channels of intelligence simultaneously. They do this by modulating each audio signal onto a different subcarrier, and then modulating the main carrier with all of the subcarriers. This is known as frequency multiplexing. ☐ In a frequency multiplexed signal, the side bands of the subcarriers must not overlap. This is necessary so that each channel can be filtered from the composite signal at the receiver.

review questions

1. Draw a block diagram, with waveforms, of a voice-modulated AM transmitter.
2. How does a tone-modulated AM transmitter differ from a voice-modulated AM transmitter?
3. Name three types of pulse-modulated AM transmitters.
4. Draw a block diagram, with waveforms of a pulse-amplitude-modulated AM transmitter.
5. What circuits of Question 4 would be the same for a pulse-width-modulated AM transmitter?
6. Draw a block diagram, with waveforms, of a pulse radar transmitter.
7. What are the inputs and ouputs of a single side-band modulator?
8. What is *frequency multiplexing*?
9. What is a *subcarrier*?
10. Is frequency multiplexing used with single-channel transmitters?

the *FM transmitter*

All of the transmitters described so far have been either of the CW or AM type. These transmitters generate a high-frequency, high-power carrier, which is either interrupted or varied in amplitude in accordance with the intelligence being transmitted. A basic characteristic of these transmitters is that their output *carrier* frequency is always the same. The side-band frequencies, and therefore the envelope of the output signal may change, but the carrier does not.

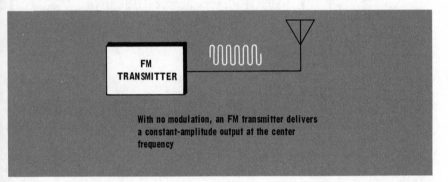

With no modulation, an FM transmitter delivers a constant-amplitude output at the center frequency

Another broad class of transmitters besides the CW and AM types is the *FM transmitter*. The FM transmitter is used to generate high-powered frequency-modulated signals. It delivers a constant-amplitude, sinusoidal output signal, whose *frequency* varies according to the intelligence being transmitted. With no modulation present, the output signal has a constant frequency, called the resting, or *center*, frequency. With modulation present, the output signal frequency varies above and below the center frequency. Regardless of whether or not the output is modulated, though, its amplitude is always constant.

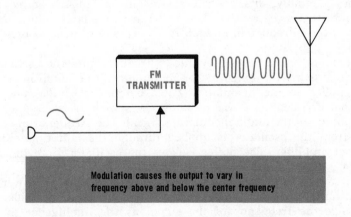

Modulation causes the output to vary in frequency above and below the center frequency

a simple FM transmitter

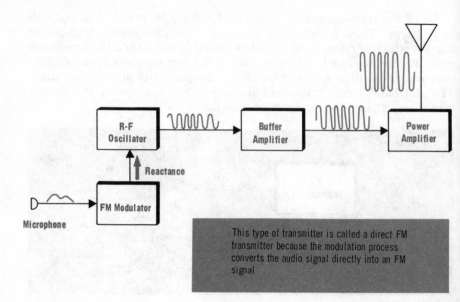

This type of transmitter is called a direct FM transmitter because the modulation process converts the audio signal directly into an FM signal

The number and types of circuits used in an FM transmitter depend on the characteristics desired of the output signal. However, certain circuits are used in practically all FM transmitters. A simple transmitter made up of these basic circuits is shown. Included are an *oscillator,* an FM *modulator,* a *buffer amplifier,* and a *power amplifier.*

The oscillator produces a sinusoidal r-f output, which, with no modulation, serves as the center frequency for the transmitter. The modulator applies a signal to the oscillator that determines the oscillator's output frequency. Actually, this is not a signal but an amount of *reactance,* either inductive or capacitive. You will learn in a later volume of this series how the introduction of such reactance can control an oscillator's frequency.

The amount and type of reactance introduced into the oscillator by the modulator is determined by the *amplitude* of the audio modulating signal applied to the modulator. Thus, by means of the modulator, the output frequency of the oscillator is varied in accordance with the amplitude of the audio modulating signal. The frequency-modulated output from the oscillator is applied through the buffer amplifier to the power amplifier. The buffer isolates the oscillator from the power amplifier and also provides some amplification of the signal.

The power amplifier boosts the FM signal to the high power level required for transmission. Both the buffer and the power amplifier must not change the frequency of the signal as the intelligence is being carried by the frequency variations.

IN A DIRECT FM TRANSMITTER

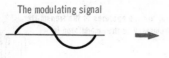

The modulating signal

Is converted directly
into an FM signal

indirect FM transmitters

In a *direct* FM transmitter, as shown on the previous page, the oscillator must be able to change frequency in accordance with the modulating signal. Oscillators capable of doing this are not extremely stable. Their output frequencies are affected by various conditions, such as the surrounding temperature. This is undesirable, since the oscillator frequency should be controlled only by the amplitude of the modulating signal. Certain types of oscillators, called *crystal oscillators,* are extremely stable. However, they cannot be satisfactorily frequency modulated by the introduction of reactance, as is done in direct FM transmitters.

The frequency stability of crystal oscillators is so desirable, though, that they are widely used in FM transmitters. Instead of being frequency modulated, the output of a crystal oscillator is phase modulated by the audio modulating signal. The phase-modulated signal is then converted to a frequency-modulated signal by being *shifted in phase* 90 degrees. This is possible, you recall from Volume 1, since phase and frequency modulated signals are identical, except that they are 90 degrees out of phase.

FM transmitters that use phase modulation and a frequency shift to produce the FM signal are called *indirect FM transmitters.* They are used for applications where frequency stability of the transmitted signal is extremely important.

IN AN INDIRECT FM TRANSMITTER

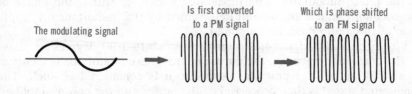

The modulating signal

Is first converted
to a PM signal

Which is phase shifted
to an FM signal

a simple
indirect FM transmitter

In an indirect FM transmitter the oscillator always operates at the transmitter center frequency. The oscillator output frequency is then modulated in accordance with the modulating signal

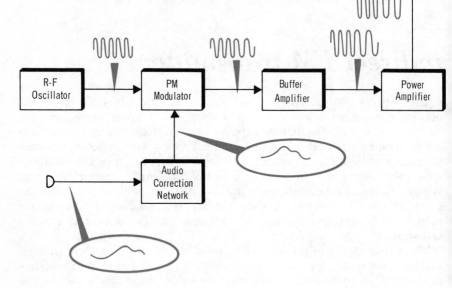

A *simple, indirect FM transmitter* is shown. Like the direct type, it contains an *oscillator*, a *buffer amplifier*, and a *power amplifier*. Instead of an FM modulator, it contains a PM modulator. It also has an additional circuit called an *audio correction network*. The interconnections between the audio signal, the oscillator, and the modulator are also different than those in the direct FM type.

In the indirect FM transmitter, the audio modulating signal is first applied to the audio correction network. This circuit shifts the phase of the entire audio signal 90 degrees. The shifted audio signal is then applied to the phase modulator. The output from the crystal oscillator, which establishes the transmitter's center frequency, is also applied to the phase modulator. The modulator varies, or shifts, the phase of the oscillator signal an amount determined by the instantaneous amplitude of the audio modulating signal.

Since the audio signal has already been shifted 90 degrees in phase by the correction network, the output of the phase modulator is *identical* to an FM signal. For practical purposes, it is considered as such. The modulated signal is then processed by the buffer and the power amplifier, as is done in the direct FM transmitter.

preemphasis

The audio circuits of an FM transmitter are more complex than those shown so far. The audio modulating signal is generally amplified by one or more audio amplifiers before being applied to the modulator in the direct type of FM transmitter or to the audio correction network in the indirect type. This is done to increase the amplitude of the audio signal to that required for proper modulation.

In addition to audio amplifiers, a circuit called a *preemphasis network* is used. The preemphasis network delivers an output that above a certain frequency is proportional to the input signal frequency. When a complex audio frequency is applied to a preemphasis network, the output is a distorted version of the input because the network delivers a greater output for the high-frequency components than for the low ones. Preemphasis networks are used to obtain an *equal signal-to-noise ratio* for all frequency components of the FM signal.

Without preemphasis, the higher frequency components of a voice signal would tend to produce less of a modulation swing. Thus, they would have a lower signal-to-noise ratio than the lower frequency components. The higher frequency components have relatively low amplitudes, while the noise introduced onto the signal during transmission is generally of equal amplitude over the entire signal bandwidth.

After transmission of the signal, a process having the opposite effect of preemphasis is employed in the FM receiver. This process is called *deemphasis,* and it restores the relative amplitudes of all frequency components to their original levels.

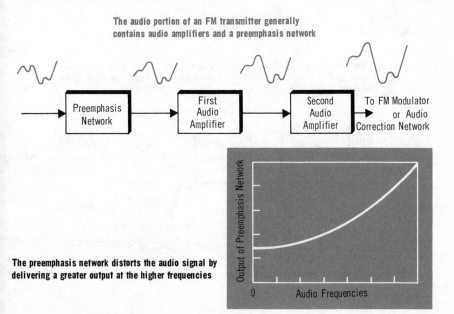

The audio portion of an FM transmitter generally contains audio amplifiers and a preemphasis network

The preemphasis network distorts the audio signal by delivering a greater output at the higher frequencies

frequency multiplication

Practically all FM transmitters use one or more *frequency multiplier* circuits. Frequency multipliers serve two purposes: (1) they make it possible to use an oscillator that operates at a relatively low frequency, and (2) they increase the effective *frequency deviation* of the FM signal. Better frequency *stability* is insured when the oscillator operates at a frequency considerably lower than the r-f transmission frequency. The multiplier then increases the signal frequency to the r-f value desired for transmission.

Since all of the signal frequencies are increased by the multipliers, all deviations from the center frequency are also increased. These deviations represent the signal intelligence. In effect, the frequency multipliers raise the level of the signal intelligence, making it much easier to recover the intelligence after transmission. As an example of this, consider an oscillator that delivers a center frequency of 100 kilocycles, and shifts to 101 kilocycles as a result of a modulating signal. The *deviation* produced by the modulation is therefore 101 minus 100 kilocycles, or 1000 cps.

If the three frequency doublers are used after the oscillator, the situation at the output of the last doubler is quite different than that at the oscillator. All frequencies are increased by 2 × 2 × 2, or 8. The center frequency is thus 100 kilocycles times 8, or 800 kilocycles. The modulated frequency is 101 kilocycles times 8, or 808 kilocycles. The frequency deviation is, therefore, 808 minus 800 kilocycles, or 8 kilocycles. In other words, by increasing *all* frequencies by a factor of 8, the three doublers increase the frequency deviation by the same amount. Since the frequency deviation represents the *amplitude* of the modulating signal, the modulation is easier to detect in the receiver.

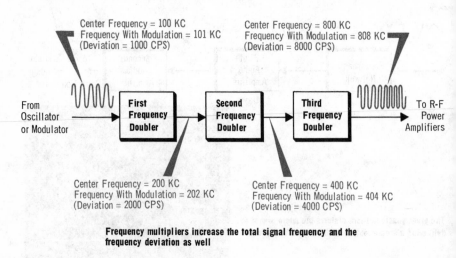

Frequency multipliers increase the total signal frequency and the frequency deviation as well

frequency control

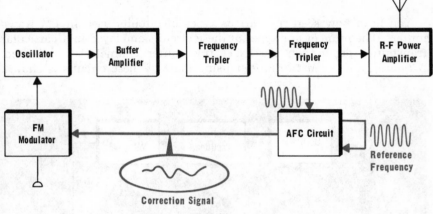

Automatic frequency control is used to maintain a stable transmitter center frequency. It is used with direct FM transmitters because of their inherent frequency instability

Often, direct FM transmitters include a means for *automatically* changing the basic frequency of the oscillator to compensate for unwanted frequency changes, or drift. This feature is called *automatic frequency control* (AFC). Basically, an AFC system constantly compares the transmitter's actual center frequency with a frequency source that represents the desired center frequency. An AFC signal is then generated, which is proportional to the *difference* between the actual and the desired frequency. This signal is applied to the FM modulator, causing it to change the oscillator characteristics and to shift the oscillator back to the desired center frequency.

One type of basic AFC system is shown. The AFC circuit compares the output frequency of the second frequency multiplier with a stable frequency generated *within* the AFC circuit. In this case, the multipliers increase the oscillator frequency by a factor of 9, and the reference frequency generated within the AFC circuit is 9 times higher than the desired oscillator center frequency. Furthermore, although the signal frequency constantly varies because of the modulation, its effective average frequency is the center frequency since it constantly passes through the center frequency while varying equally above and below it.

The overall result is that the AFC circuit compares a frequency that represents the actual center frequency with one that represents the desired center frequncy. If there is any difference between the two, the AFC circuit delivers a correction signal to the FM modulator, which then brings the oscillator back to the center frequency.

a typical
direct FM transmitter

You have now seen the various types of circuits used in FM transmitters. The number and types of these circuits employed in a particular transmitter depend on the exact transmitter characteristics desired. A *typical, direct FM transmitter* using most of these circuits is shown.

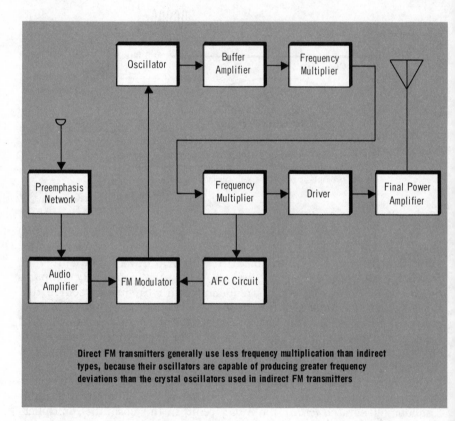

Direct FM transmitters generally use less frequency multiplication than indirect types, because their oscillators are capable of producing greater frequency deviations than the crystal oscillators used in indirect FM transmitters

It consists of an oscillator that generates the basic transmitter frequency; a preemphasis network; an audio amplifier and an FM modulator that processes the audio modulating signal and varies the frequency of the oscillator in accordance with the modulation; a buffer amplifier that electrically isolates the oscillator; two frequency multipliers that increase the signal and deviation frequencies; and two r-f amplifiers that raise the signal to the power level required for transmission. The first r-f amplifier is called a *driver* since it provides the input signal amplitude necessary to drive the output power amplifier. This transmitter also contains an AFC circuit that stabilizes the output frequency.

a typical
indirect FM transmitter

A *typical, indirect FM transmitter* is shown. It contains an oscillator that generates the basic transmitter frequency; a preemphasis network, an audio amplifier, and an audio correction network that processes the audio signal; a PM modulator that varies the oscillator frequency in accordance with the modulating signal; a buffer amplifier that isolates the oscillator; three frequency multipliers that increase the signal and deviation frequencies; and a driver and final power amplifier that raise the signal to the necessary power level.

This indirect FM transmitter does not use an AFC circuit since its crystal oscillator provides a high degree of frequency stability

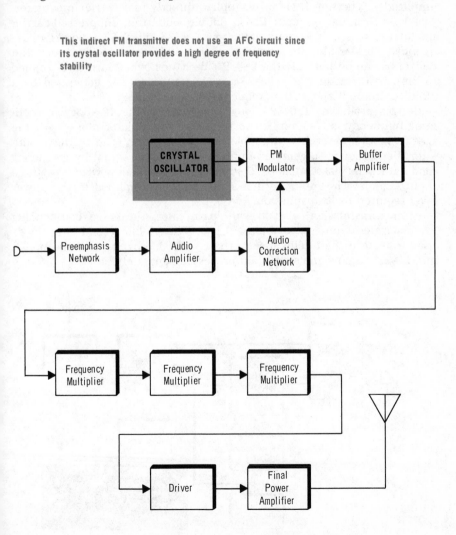

the FM stereo transmitter

In recent years, FM broadcast stations have been transmitting stereo audio signals. They do this by a process known as *FM stereo multiplexing*. The composition of an FM stereo signal was described in Volume 1. The basic transmitter arrangement used for producing these signals is shown.

The audio outputs from the two program microphones, designated *left* (L) and *right* (R), are applied to an adder and subtractor *matrix*. The matrix delivers two outputs: one, called the L + R *signal*, is the *sum* of the instantaneous amplitudes of the individual L and R signals. The other, called the L − R *signal*, is the *difference* of the two signal amplitudes. The L + R signal is applied directly to a *carrier* modulator. The L − R signal is applied to a double side-band, suppressed-carrier modulator where it is modulated with a 38-kilocycle subcarrier frequency. This modulator *suppresses* the 38-kilocycle subcarrier, and delivers as an output only the L − R side bands, which are then applied to the carrier modulator. The 38-kilocycle subcarrier is generated by a 19-kilocycle oscillator and a frequency doubler circuit.

Besides producing the 38-kilocycle subcarrier, the 19-kilocycle oscillator frequency is also applied to the carrier modulator along with the L + R signal and the L − R double side-band signals. The carrier modulator then produces a complex multichannel output signal by frequency modulating its associated carrier oscillator frequency with the three input signals. The multichannel signal is then amplified to the power level required for transmission.

After transmission, as you will learn later, the three components are separated from the complex signal. The 19-kilocycle frequency is used to recover the intelligence in the L − R side bands, and the L + R and L − R audio signals are then processed separately.

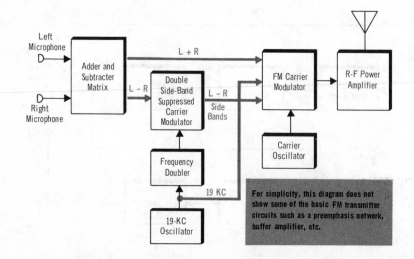

For simplicity, this diagram does not show some of the basic FM transmitter circuits such as a preemphasis network, buffer amplifier, etc.

summary

☐ An FM transmitter delivers a high-powered constant-amplitude sinusoidal output signal whose frequency varies according to the intelligence being transmitted. ☐ There are two basic types of FM transmitters: direct and indirect. ☐ In a direct FM transmitter, the modulation is produced by varying the frequency of the oscillator in accordance with the amplitude of the modulating signal. ☐ In an indirect FM transmitter, the modulation is produced by phase modulating the output of a crystal-controlled oscillator in accordance with the modulating signal. The phase-modulated signal is then converted to a frequency-modulated signal by being shifted 90 degrees in phase.

☐ Preemphasis networks are used in FM transmitters to provide an equal signal-to-noise ratio for all frequency components of the transmitted FM signal. ☐ A preemphasis network delivers an output that above a certain frequency has an amplitude that is proportional to the input frequency. It thus delivers a greater output for the high-frequency components of the input signal than for the low-frequency components. ☐ Frequency multipliers are used in FM transmitters for two reasons: (1) they allow the oscillator to operate at a relatively low frequency, and (2) they increase the effective frequency deviation of the FM signal.

☐ Direct FM transmitters often include an automatic frequency control (AFC) circuit to compensate for drift in the oscillator frequency. ☐ Whenever the oscillator frequency drifts, the AFC circuit generates a correction signal that is proportional to the amount of drift. It applies this signal to the FM modulator, which then brings the oscillator back on frequency. ☐ An FM stereo transmitter multiplexes the two channels of the stereo signal onto a single frequency-modulated carrier.

---

review questions

1. Draw a block diagram of a simple direct FM transmitter.
2. Draw a block diagram of a simple indirect FM transmitter.
3. What is the purpose of an audio correction network?
4. Why are preemphasis networks used in FM transmitters?
5. How does a preemphasis network work?
6. Why are frequency multipliers usually always used in FM transmitters?
7. Describe briefly how an AFC circuit in a direct FM transmitter works.
8. Why aren't AFC circuits used in indirect FM transmitters?
9. Why are most FM transmitters of the indirect type?
10. Draw a block diagram of an FM stereo transmitter.

a simple black-and-white television transmitter

A television transmitter can be considered as *two* separate sections feeding their outputs to a common antenna. In the video section, the VHF or UHF carrier is produced by a crystal oscillator and a series of frequency multipliers, and then amplified by one or more intermediate power amplifiers and a final power amplifier. The video signal is generated by the television camera equipment. This composite signal contains the picture information as well as the sync, blanking, and equalizing pulses. The video signal is applied to a series of video amplifiers in the transmitter, and then to a *video modulator,* which performs the same function as the AM modulator does in a voice-modulated AM transmitter.

The amplitude-modulated video carrier is applied to a *vestigial side-band filter.* This filter completely removes the lower side-band frequencies that are more than 1.25 megacycles below the carrier frequency. The filter also attenuates those lower side-band frequencies that are more than 0.75 megacycle but less than 1.25 megacycles below the carrier frequency. Thus, the output from the filter is an amplitude-modulated, vestigal side-band signal.

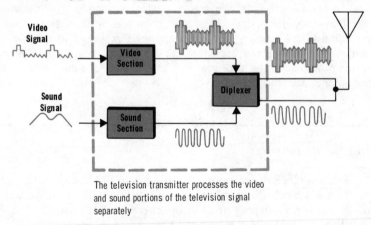

The television transmitter processes the video and sound portions of the television signal separately

The sound portion of the television transmitter is the same as that of a conventional FM transmitter. The indirect type is shown. The audio signal phase modulates the output of a crystal oscillator. The effective FM signal thus produced is raised to a center frequency 4.5 megacycles higher than the video carrier, and then increased in power by a driver and a power amplifier.

Both the AM video signal and the FM sound signal are coupled to an antenna through a circuit called a *diplexer.* The diplexer isolates the video portion of the transmitter from the sound portion, thus preventing undesirable interaction between the two.

a simple black-and-white television transmitter (cont.)

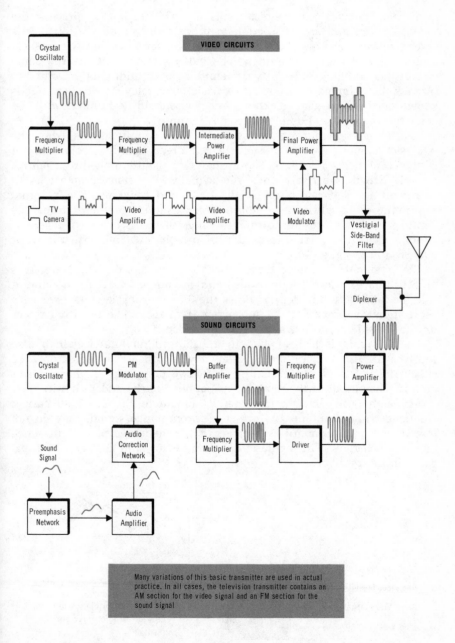

Many variations of this basic transmitter are used in actual practice. In all cases, the television transmitter contains an AM section for the video signal and an FM section for the sound signal

a simple color television transmitter

A color television transmitter has an AM section to process the video portion, and an FM section to process the sound portion of the color television signal. The FM section is the same as that for a black-and-white television transmitter. The video section contains the same circuits as a black-and-white transmitter, plus additional circuits to process the complex color signal. A basic color television transmitter is shown on the next page. At this point, you should be familiar with the color television signal as presented in Volume 1.

The color transmitter receives three video input signals from the television camera. They represent the red, green, and blue color content of the scene being televised. These three signals are applied to a *matrix* circuit, which effectively adds the signals in various proportions to produce three separate outputs: the Y, Q, and I signals. The Y signal represents the brightness, or *luminance*, variations of the picture. The Q and I signals represent a different range of colors. The two together, contain all of the color information of the picture, and form the C, or *chrominance*, signal.

The Y signal is coupled directly to an *adder* circuit. The I signal is applied to a balanced (double side-band, suppressed-carrier) modulator. The modulator amplitude modulates the 3.58-megacycle subcarrier with the I signal, suppressing the subcarrier frequency. The resulting upper and lower side bands are applied to the adder circuit.

The Q signal is also applied to a balanced modulator, which also receives an input from the 3.58-megacycle subcarrier oscillator. The subcarrier's phase, however, is first shifted 90 degrees by a phase shifter circuit. The output of the modulator is applied to the adder circuit.

Although both the Q and I signals modulate the same subcarrier frequency, and combine to form the chrominance signal, they do not lose their separate identities because of the 90-degree phase difference of the subcarriers. The signals produce a vector sum that can be separated in the receivers.

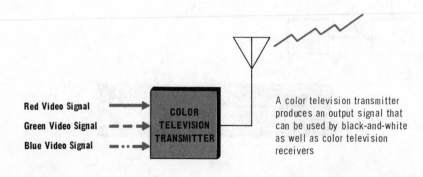

Red Video Signal → **COLOR TELEVISION TRANSMITTER**
Green Video Signal – – →
Blue Video Signal – ·· →

A color television transmitter produces an output signal that can be used by black-and-white as well as color television receivers

a simple color television transmitter (cont.)

The chrominance (C) and luminance (Y) signals are combined into a single video signal in the adder circuit. Horizontal and vertical sync pulses, as well as blanking and equalizing pulses, are generated by a group of timing circuits, and sent to the adder, where they are inserted at the proper intervals in the video signal. One additional sync pulse, called the *color sync burst,* is added to the video signal. Each color sync burst consists of a few cycles of the 3.58-megacycle subcarrier superimposed on each horizontal blanking pulse. The color sync bursts are necessary for proper demodulation of the Q and I signals in the television receiver.

The output of the adder circuit is the complete color video signal, containing all picture and timing information. The rest of the circuits in the color transmitter are the same as those found in a black-and-white transmitter.

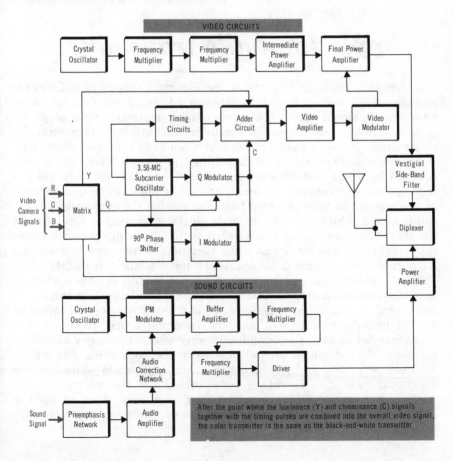

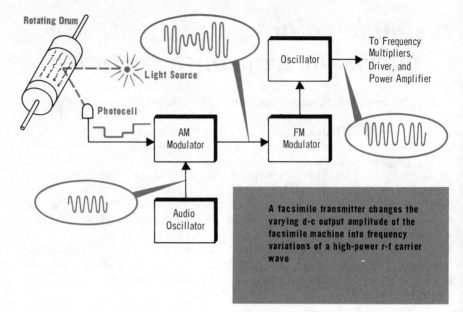

A facsimile transmitter changes the varying d-c output amplitude of the facsimile machine into frequency variations of a high-power r-f carrier wave

a simple facsimile transmitter

A facsimile transmitter receives the electrical output of a facsimile machine and converts it to a high-power r-f signal suitable for transmission. The signal output represents graphic materials, such as photographs, sketches, and maps. The facsimile machine consists, essentially, of a *rotating drum,* a *light source,* and a *photoelectric cell* (photocell).

The graphic material to be transmitted is mounted on the rotating drum. A light source is directed on the copy and light from the copy is reflected to the photocell. The amplitude of the photocell output depends on the amount of light reflected from the spot on the copy at which the cell is aimed, which, in turn, depends on the whiteness or blackness of the spot. The drum slowly rotates so that the photocell *scans* the entire copy, converting the black and white variations of the copy to a varying d-c output. This varying d-c signal is the input to the transmitter.

The facsimile signal is the input to an AM modulator that *amplitude modulates* an audio tone produced by an audio oscillator. The amplitude-modulated audio tone is then converted to a low-frequency *FM signal* by an FM modulator and oscillator. The facsimile signal, therefore, has been changed to a constant-amplitude wave whose frequency variations represent the whiteness and blackness of the copy. This FM signal, however, is in the audio range; for example, it might shift between 2000 and 3000 cps. Therefore, conventional FM transmitter circuits, such as frequency multipliers and power amplifiers, must be used to raise the signal to the frequency and power levels required for radio transmission.

the teletypewriter transmitter

A teletypewriter transmitter receives the signals generated by a tele-typewriter and its associated equipment and converts it to r-f signals suitable for transmission. The teletypewriter, as you know, produces signals that represent the various *letters* of the alphabet. These signals are a continuous series of *pulses* and *no pulses*. A pulse is called a *mark*, and a no pulse is called a *space*. For example, the letter J is repre-sented by the combination mark–mark–space–mark–space.

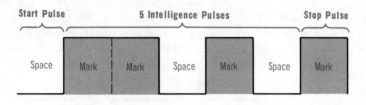

This is the complete teletypewriter signal for the letter J

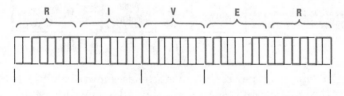

This is the teletypewriter signal for the word RIVER

In one common type of teletypewriter transmission, the total signal duration for each letter is 163 milliseconds. This time span is divided into seven parts. The first part is a space lasting for 22 milliseconds, and serving as a synchronization pulse. This synchronization pulse is called a *start* pulse, even though it is actually a space, or no pulse. The next five parts are each 22 milliseconds, and are any combination of marks and spaces. The particular combination depends on the letter being sent. The last part is a 31-millisecond pulse, or mark, called the *stop* pulse. Like the start pulse, the stop pulse is used for synchroniza-tion. Every letter code starts with a start pulse and ends with a stop pulse, but the pulses in between vary for each letter. Thus, the complete signal for the letter J is *space–mark–mark–space–mark–space–mark*.

The coded signals are sent into a teletypewriter transmitter, two types of which are described on the following page.

a simple
teletypewriter transmitter

It is possible to transmit teletypewriter signals by either AM or an FM system. One type of AM system is shown below. Basically, this is a *tone-modulated* AM transmitter with the keying controlled by the marks and spaces of the input teletypewriter signal. Every marking pulse causes operating power to be applied to the r-f and audio oscillators. Thus, the transmitter delivers a tone-modulated carrier for the duration of each mark. Conversely, every spacing pulse causes operating power to be removed from the oscillators. So for the duration of each space, the transmitter delivers no output. In other words, the transmitter converts the marks and spaces of the teletypewriter signal into the presence and absence of a high-power, tone-modulated r-f carrier.

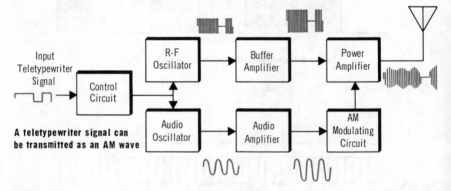

A teletypewriter signal can
be transmitted as an AM wave

An FM type teletypewriter transmitter is shown below. In this transmitter, the marks and spaces of the teletypewriter signal cause a frequency shift of the generated carrier. Marks are represented by one output frequency and spaces by another. This method of transmitting is called *frequency shift keying*. After the modulator, the circuits of the transmitter are the same as those of conventional FM transmitters.

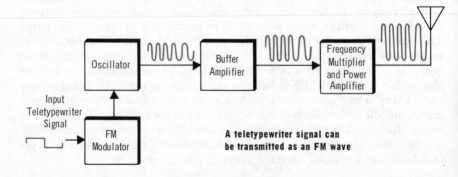

A teletypewriter signal can
be transmitted as an FM wave

time-division multiplexing

A system called *time-division multiplexing* is often used in the transmission of teletypewriter signals. In this system, two or more separate signals are transmitted as a single composite signal by means of a *time-sharing* arrangement. An example of a three-channel, time-division multiplex signal is shown. Each of the three channels represents a signal generated by a different teletype machine.

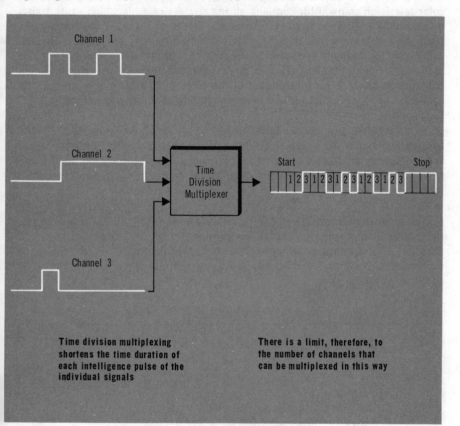

Channel 1

Channel 2

Time Division Multiplexer

Start   Stop

1 2 3 1 2 3 1 2 3 1 2 3 1 2 3

Channel 3

Time division multiplexing shortens the time duration of each intelligence pulse of the individual signals

There is a limit, therefore, to the number of channels that can be multiplexed in this way

The three signals are fed into a time-division multiplexer unit. The multiplexer delivers a single output that has the same *overall* time duration as each of the individual inputs, but it contains the intelligence of all three inputs. It does this by dividing each of the five intelligence-carrying pulse periods into three equal parts. The first third of each pulse period carries the signal of channel 1, the second third the signal of channel 2, and the last third the signal of channel 3. A single start and stop pulse is still used for all channels. The composite signal can be sent either by AM or FM means, the same as an ordinary, single-channel teletypewriter signal.

summary

☐ A black-and-white television transmitter contains a video section and a sound section. ☐ In the video section, the picture information together with various sync pulses is amplitude modulated onto a VHF or UHF carrier. A vestigial side-band filter then removes a portion of the lower side band to produce a vestigial side-band signal. ☐ The sound section is basically a conventional FM transmitter. ☐ Both the AM video signal and the FM sound signal are applied to the antenna through an isolating circuit called a diplexer. ☐ A color television transmitter contains all the circuits of a black-and-white transmitter, plus additional circuits to process the color signal. ☐ Color signals from the camera are applied to a matrix, which produces Y, Q, and I signals. ☐ The Y, or luminance, signal represents the brightness variations of the picture. ☐ The combined Q and I signals form the chrominance signal, which contains all of the color information of the picture. ☐ The color sync burst is added to the video signal for use in demodulation of the Q and I signals.

☐ In a facsimile transmitter both AM and FM modulation are used. ☐ The modulating signal amplitude modulates an audio tone, and this AM signal then frequency modulates a low-frequency carrier. ☐ Frequency multipliers and power amplifiers are used to produce the final frequency and power required for transmission.

☐ Teletypewriter transmitters can be either AM or FM. ☐ In AM transmitters, the marks and spaces of the teletypewriter signal are converted into the presence and absence of a high-power, tone-modulated r-f carrier. ☐ In FM transmitters, the marks and spaces are converted into two different frequency shifts of a carrier.

review questions

1. What is the purpose of the diplexer in a television transmitter?
2. Draw a block diagram of a color television transmitter?
3. What is the purpose of the color sync burst?
4. What is the frequency relationship between the *video* and *sound* portions of a television signal?
5. Is the video portion of a television signal a single side-band signal?
6. Draw a block diagram of a simple facsimile transmitter.
7. Are teletypewriter transmitters AM or FM?
8. What is *frequency shift keying*?
9. What is *time division multiplexing*?
10. Are television transmitters AM or FM?

receivers

You have now seen the various types of *transmitters* that are used for radio transmission of electronic signals. In the descriptions of these transmitters, all of the circuits required for the processing of the signal were usually included as part of the transmitter. You will find that in actual practice some of the circuits that were considered as part of the transmitter are really part of associated or companion equipment. Because of their close relationship with a particular transmitter, however, they were treated as transmitter circuits.

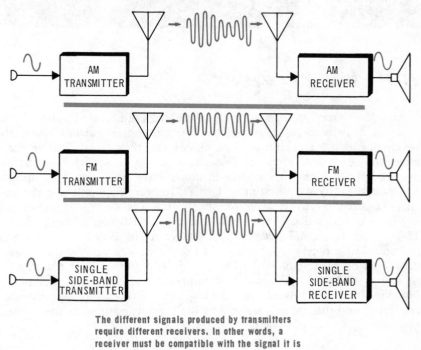

The different signals produced by transmitters require different receivers. In other words, a receiver must be compatible with the signal it is to receive

The next portion of this book describes the various types of radio *receivers* in current use. Essentially, receivers have the opposite function of transmitters. Whereas a transmitter converts a modulating signal to a higher frequency and power level and radiates this signal into space, a receiver picks up, or intercepts, transmitted signals and recovers the original lower frequency intelligence. There are many types of receivers just as there are many types of transmitters. Usually, each receiver is able to receive only certain types of signals. Thus, to receive AM signals, an AM receiver must be used; and for FM signals, an FM receiver is required; etc.

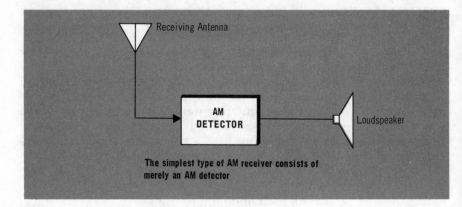

The simplest type of AM receiver consists of
merely an AM detector

the AM receiver

An *AM receiver* processes amplitude-modulated signals received by its antenna, It delivers as an output the original signal that modulated the r-f carrier at the transmitter. The signal can then be applied to some reproducing device, such as a loudspeaker, or a set of headphones. Actual AM receivers vary widely in complexity. Some are very simple, and contain only a few circuits. Others are very sophisticated devices, and contain a relatively large number of circuits.

The most elementary type of AM receiver consists of a single circuit. This circuit is an *AM detector*. It receives as its input the AM signal picked up by a receiving antenna. The detector recovers the intelligence contained on the modulated r-f carrier in two steps: (1) it *rectifies* the r-f signal, and (2) removes the r-f component of the rectified signal by *filtering*. In effect, this leaves only one-half of the original modulation envelope. And this, as you know, has the same variations as the original modulating signal used at the transmitter.

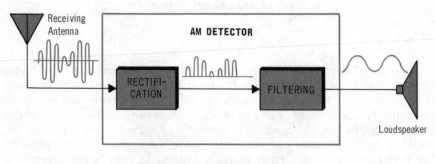

The detector performs both basic receiver
functions: rectification and filtering

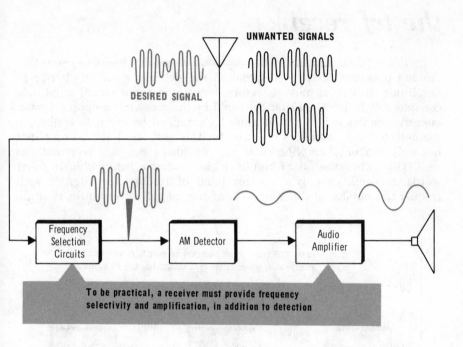

a practical AM receiver

The elementary AM receiver described on the previous page has two serious limitations that make it impractical for actual use. First, there is *lack of amplification*. The signal picked up by a receiving antenna is extremely small, and after rectification and filtering, it is even smaller. Such a weak signal cannot properly energize reproducing devices such as loudspeakers, which require substantial input signal levels. One or more audio amplifiers must be used after the detector to provide the necessary signal level. Some detectors amplify the signal as well as demodulate it. The degree of amplification provided by the detector, though, is insufficient by itself, so audio amplifiers are still needed.

The other shortcoming of the elementary one-stage receiver is that it has *no frequency selectivity*. In other words, all of the r-f signals simultaneously picked up by the antenna are processed by the receiver. The output of the detector would actually be the composite result of all these signals. Such a detected signal would be worthless as it would correspond to none of the individual input signals. There must be some means of selecting the desired r-f signal from all those received by the antenna. This function is accomplished by frequency-selection circuits. These circuits are *tuned* to the frequency of the desired signal. They therefore pass the desired signal to the detector, and block all other r-f signal frequencies.

the trf receiver

In the receiver shown on the previous page, the frequency-selection circuits pass the desired r-f signal to the detector with *no* change in amplitude. However, most detectors, require an input signal amplitude considerably larger than that delivered by the receiving antenna. Consequently, the desired r-f signal must be amplified before it is applied to the detector. R-f amplifiers are used for this purpose. Each r-f amplifier not only produces *amplification*, but provides *frequency selectivity* as well. This is because an r-f amplifier has a *narrow bandwidth*. In other words, it amplifies only a narrow band of frequencies. Signals with frequencies outside of this narrow band are amplified very little, if at all.

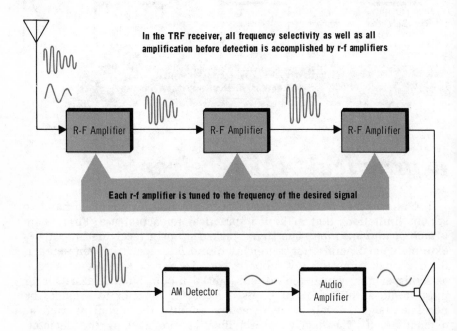

In the TRF receiver, all frequency selectivity as well as all amplification before detection is accomplished by r-f amplifiers

R-F Amplifier   R-F Amplifier   R-F Amplifier

Each r-f amplifier is tuned to the frequency of the desired signal

AM Detector   Audio Amplifier

An r-f amplifier can be tuned so that while the bandwidth remains essentially the same, the frequencies that fall within the bandwidth can be changed. For example, an amplifier may be tuned to a bandwidth of 100 to 105 kilocycles, and then be returned to a bandwidth of 150 to 155 kilocycles. In both cases, the bandwidth is 5 kilocycles, but *different* signal frequencies fall within the bandwidth.

Receivers that use r-f amplifiers to provide the frequency selectivity and amplification required for the r-f signal are called *tuned radio-frequency receivers*, or *TRF receivers*.

disadvantages of the trf receiver

Although TRF receivers were once widely used, they are employed in limited applications today. This drastic reduction in use is due to certain inherent disadvantages of all TRF receivers. These disadvantages arise because all r-f amplification in a TRF receiver is accomplished by tuned r-f amplifier. If a receiver had to always receive the same signal frequency, a TRF type receiver could be designed that was entirely satisfactory. But, if a receiver must be capable of being tuned to any signal frequency over a wide range, the TRF type is generally unsatisfactory. This arises because of the basic characteristics of the r-f amplifiers.

The frequency-response curves of one r-f amplifier
tuned to low, intermediate, and high r-f frequencies

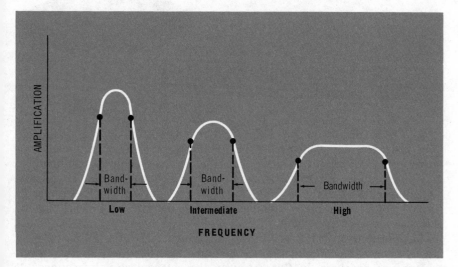

The higher the tuned frequency, the less the
amplification and the wider the bandwidth. A wide
bandwidth means low frequency selectivity

The amplification as well as the frequency selectivity of a practical r-f amplifier depends on the tuned frequency. As the amplifier is tuned to higher and higher frequencies, its ability to amplify and provide frequency selectivity decline. A TRF receiver used for a wide range of input signal frequencies, therefore, has poor performance at the higher frequencies. In some cases, the performance is so poor that the output of the receiver is unusable.

R-F SIGNAL

In the superheterodyne receiver, the desired r-f signal is converted to an i-f signal before amplification and detection

I-F SIGNAL

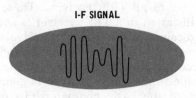

The intermediate frequency is always the same regardless of the r-f signal frequency

DEMODULATED INTELLIGENCE

the superheterodyne receiver

The basic disadvantage of the TRF receiver is its *varying* amplification and selectivity. This problem would not exist if one signal frequency were always received, because then the receiver could be designed to have maximum amplification and good selectivity at that frequency. Of course, this cannot be done for most receivers, since they must be capable of receiving any frequency over a definite band, such as the commercial broadcast band.

The desired features of tuning flexibility and r-f amplification at always the same frequency can be obtained, however, in the *super-heterodyne* receiver. In this receiver, the selected signal frequency is converted to a lower r-f frequency, called the *intermediate frequency* (if). The intermediate frequency carries the same intelligence as the original incoming r-f signal; only the frequency of the carrier is changed. The intermediate-frequency signal is amplified before being applied to the detector for demodulation.

A superheterodyne receiver has a single intermediate frequency. All incoming r-f signals, regardless of frequency, are converted to this single intermediate frequency. Thus, the signal amplification that takes place before detection is always accomplished at the same frequency. This eliminates the varying amplification and frequency selectivity that is characteristic of TRF receivers.

a simple superheterodyne receiver

A simple *superheterodyne receiver* is shown. The incoming r-f signal is applied to a mixer, which also receives the output from an associated local oscillator. The mixer is frequency selective: it accepts the signal frequency to which it is tuned and rejects all other frequencies. The local oscillator is tuned *simultaneously* with the mixer, so that its frequency always *differs* from the desired signal frequency by an amount equal to the receiver's intermediate frequency.

Usually, the oscillator operates at a higher frequency than the signal frequency. For example, if the receiver has an intermediate frequency of 456 kilocycles and the mixer is tuned to a 1600-kilocycle signal, then the local oscillator is simultaneously tuned to 2056 kilocycles, since 2056 − 1600 = 456 kilocycles. And, if the mixer is then retuned to accept a 1000-kilocycle signal, the local oscillator is similarly retuned to 1456 kilocycles. The difference between the two input frequencies to the mixer is still 456 kilocycles.

The mixer *heterodynes* the oscillator frequency and the input signal frequency. It delivers as an output the *difference frequency*, in this case 456 kilocycles, which carries the same amplitude-modulated intelligence as the original r-f signal. The i-f output from the mixer is amplified by a series of i-f amplifiers, then applied to the detector for demodulation. The i-f amplifiers are similar to r-f amplifiers, except that they always operate at the same frequency, namely, the intermediate frequency. After the audio intelligence is removed from the i-f signal in the detector, it is amplified by one or more audio amplifiers, and then delivered to a loudspeaker or other reproducing device.

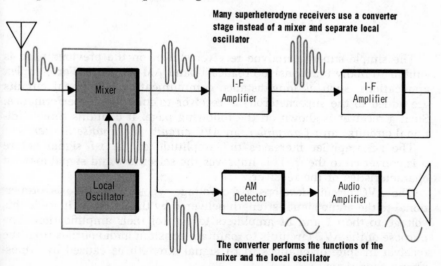

Many superheterodyne receivers use a converter stage instead of a mixer and separate local oscillator

The converter performs the functions of the mixer and the local oscillator

a superheterodyne receiver with auxiliary circuits

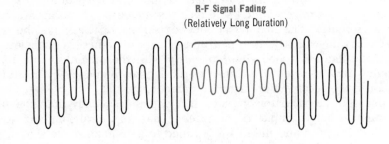

R-F Signal Fading
(Relatively Long Duration)

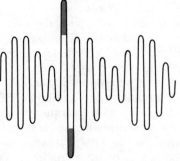

Noise Spike
(Very Short Duration)

The changes in r-f signal strength counteracted by the AVC circuit are of relatively long duration. Noise spikes eliminated by the noise limiter are of extremely short duration

The simple superheterodyne receiver shown on the previous page is similar to many inexpensive broadcast-band AM receivers. For complex applications, such as long-distance communication, additional circuits are added to the superheterodyne receiver to improve its performance. Such a receiver is shown on the following page. It contains three additional circuits: an *r-f amplifier*, an *AVC circuit*, and a *noise limiter*.

The r-f amplifier increases the amplitude of the r-f signal before it is converted to the if. This improves the selectivity and signal-to-noise characteristics of the receiver.

The AVC circuit develops a d-c voltage whose amplitude is proportional to the audio signal strength delivered by the detector. It feeds this voltage to the r-f and i-f amplifiers to control their amplification. The purpose of the AVC circuit is to maintain constant audio output from the receiver in spite of changes in r-f signal strength as caused by atmospheric conditions.

a superheterodyne receiver with auxiliary circuits (cont.)

If the r-f signal strength decreases, the AVC circuit senses this as a decrease in the audio output level from the detector. The AVC voltage fed back to the amplifiers causes them to increase amplification. Conversely, if the r-f signal strength increases, the AVC circuit feeds back a voltage to decrease the amplification of the amplifiers.

The noise limiter prevents excess noise riding on the signal from reaching the receiver output. The noise takes the form of large-amplitude spikes superimposed on the signal. The limiter removes these spikes by preventing the signal amplitude from exceeding a certain level.

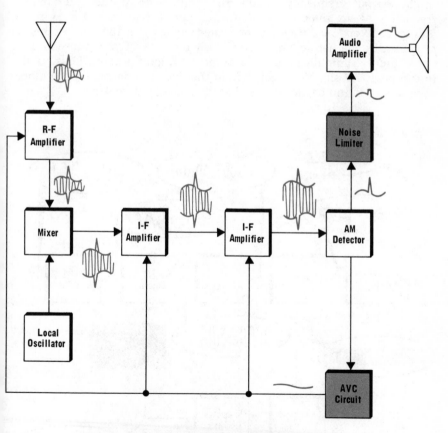

Many kinds of auxiliary circuits are often used with superheterodyne receivers to improve receiver performance. Two of the most common are the noise limiter and the AVC circuit

superheterodyne receivers for cw reception

The detector in an AM superheterodyne receiver recovers the *audio* component from the i-f signal. Continuous-wave (CW) and interrupted CW signals have no audio component, so they cannot be detected by standard AM detectors. Such signals, however, can produce an audio output when a circuit called a *beat-frequency oscillator* (BFO) is added. As shown, the output of the BFO is connected to the detector by a switch. When the switch is open, the receiver operates as a standard AM receiver. When the switch is closed, the BFO output is *heterodyned* with the i-f signal in the detector.

The output frequency of the BFO differs from the intermediate frequency by an amount equal to some audio frequency, for example, 500 or 1000 cps. A difference, or *beat*, frequency in the audio range is produced by the heterodyning action whenever the CW is present. This audio note is amplified, then delivered to a loudspeaker. Thus, if the interrupted CW signal corresponds to the dots and dashes of the Morse code, the dots and dashes can be heard on the loudspeaker.

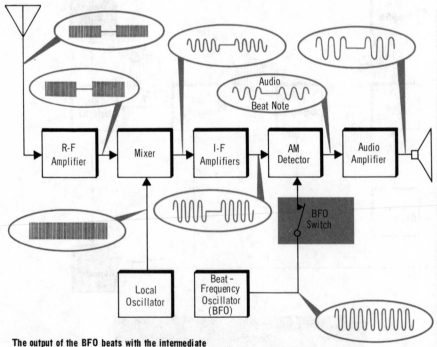

The output of the BFO beats with the intermediate frequency to produce an audio note that can be heard in the loudspeaker

the single side-band receiver

A single side-band receiver is in many respects similar to an AM superheterodyne receiver. The main difference is that *carrier reinsertion* must also be accomplished in a single side-band receiver. This is necessary to compensate for the fact that the r-f carrier used to produce the side-band signal is suppressed at the transmitter.

A basic single side-band receiver is shown. The input side-band signal is amplified by an r-f amplifier, and converted to an i-f signal by a mixer and associated oscillator. The i-f output of the mixer is applied through a *selective filter* to a series of i-f amplifiers. The filter prevents r-f signals that are close in frequency to the intermediate frequency from being passed to the detector. The filter has much better frequency-selection characteristics than conventional i-f amplifiers. After being amplified by the i-f amplifiers, the signal is applied to a side-band detector.

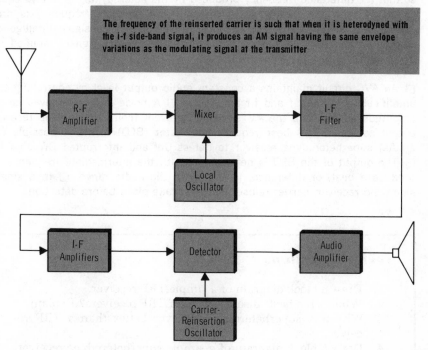

The frequency of the reinserted carrier is such that when it is heterodyned with the i-f side-band signal, it produces an AM signal having the same envelope variations as the modulating signal at the transmitter

The detector also receives an output from a carrier-reinsertion oscillator. The output frequency of this oscillator has the same *frequency relationship* to the i-f side-band signal that the original r-f carrier at the transmitter had to the side bands. Essentially, the detector heterodynes the side-band signal with the oscillator output, then detects the envelope variations of the resulting signal. The output of the detector is an audio signal that corresponds to the intelligence carried by the side-band signal. The detected signal is amplified, then delivered to a loudspeaker.

summary

☐ The basic functions of a receiver are to select, detect, and amplify a desired signal. ☐ In a TRF receiver, r-f amplifiers provide both amplification and frequency selectivity. ☐ The ability of an r-f amplifier to both amplify and provide frequency selectivity varies with frequency, declining as the signal frequency increases. Consequently, although TRF receivers are satisfactory when a narrow range of frequencies are to be received, they are generally unsatisfactory in applications involving a wide range of input frequencies.

☐ Superheterodyne receivers overcome the disadvantage of TRF receivers by converting all incoming frequencies to a single intermediate frequency. ☐ The intermediate frequency is generally lower than the received r-f frequency, but carries the same intelligence. ☐ To produce the intermediate frequency, the incoming r-f frequency is heterodyned in a mixer stage with the output of a local oscillator. The mixer and local oscillator are tuned simultaneously so that the difference frequency produced by the heterodyning is always equal to the intermediate frequency. ☐ After the intermediate frequency is produced, it is amplified by one or more i-f amplifiers. The signal intelligence is then removed by a detector, and the resulting audio signal amplified by audio amplifiers.

☐ An AVC circuit maintains a constant audio output level by controlling the amplification of the r-f and i-f amplifiers. ☐ A noise limiter removes large-amplitude spikes from the AM signal, to prevent their reaching the receiver output as noise. ☐ A beat-frequency oscillator (BFO) makes it possible for an AM superheterodyne receiver to detect CW and interrupted CW signals. ☐ The output of the BFO is heterodyned with the intermediate frequency to produce a beat, or difference, frequency in the audio range. ☐ In a single side-band receiver, carrier reinsertion must take place before detection.

review questions

1. Draw a block diagram of a simple TRF receiver.
2. What is the basic disadvantage of TRF receivers? Explain.
3. Why is a superheterodyne receiver better than a TRF receiver.
4. Draw a block diagram of a simple superheterodyne receiver.
5. Explain how the intermediate frequency is produced.
6. What is *AVC*? Why is it used?
7. How does a noise limiter in an AM receiver work?
8. What is the purpose of a beat-frequency oscillator?
9. Draw a block diagram of a simple single side-band receiver.
10. Why does an SSB receiver need carrier reinsertion?

the FM receiver

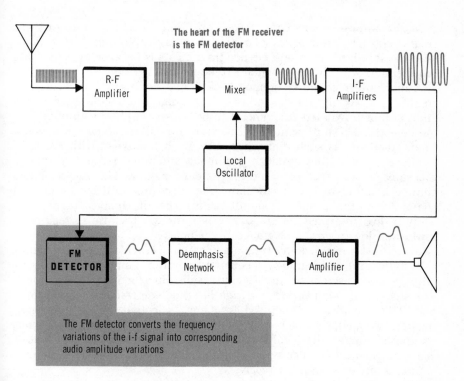

The heart of the FM receiver
is the FM detector

The FM detector converts the frequency
variations of the i-f signal into corresponding
audio amplitude variations

FM receivers are used for the reception and reproduction of frequency-modulated signals. On a block diagram level, they are somewhat similar to AM superheterodyne receivers. This can be seen from the basic FM receiver shown. The FM signal to be received is selected and amplified by an r-f amplifier. It is then converted, with no loss of intelligence, to the receiver's intermediate frequency by a mixer and local oscillator. The i-f signal has a constant amplitude and varies above and below the intermediate frequency in accordance with the modulation. In other words, the center frequency of the FM signal is converted to the receiver's intermediate frequency.

The i-f signal is amplified by a series of i-f amplifiers, then applied to an FM detector. The detector converts the frequency variations of the i-f signal into a corresponding audio signal, then feeds this signal to a *deemphasis network*. The deemphasis process is essentially the reverse of the preemphasis process accomplished at the FM transmitter. The deemphasis network *restores* the relative amplitudes of the signal's frequency components to what they were before preemphasis was carried out. It does this by delivering a greater output at the lower frequencies than it does at the higher ones. After deemphasis, the audio signal is amplified and applied to a loudspeaker.

the double-conversion FM receiver

Most communications FM receivers operate in the VHF band. At these frequencies, it is not always possible to obtain optimum performance with the standard superheterodyne circuit. This is because of conflicting requirements for the intermediate frequency.

A high intermediate frequency is desirable because it provides good frequency selectivity for the receiver. But a high intermediate frequency allows other unwanted frequencies to be passed by the i-f amplifiers to the detector. These unwanted frequencies are called *image frequencies*. Their frequency is such that when they are heterodyned with the local oscillator output, they produce a sum or difference frequency that is the same as the receiver's intermediate frequency. The i-f amplifiers cannot distinguish the intermediate frequency produced by the desired signal from that produced simultaneously by the image frequencies. Thus, a low intermediate frequency is desirable because it results in fewer and lower amplitude image frequencies.

Since one intermediate frequency cannot provide good frequency selectivity and good image frequency rejection, many FM receivers employ a process called *double conversion*. Such a receiver is shown. The signal is first converted to a *high intermediate frequency* and amplified. This provides the required frequency selectivity. The high intermediate frequency is then converted to a *low intermediate frequency* by another mixer and local oscillator. This process provides the necessary image rejection. The remaining circuits are the same as those of a standard single-conversion receiver.

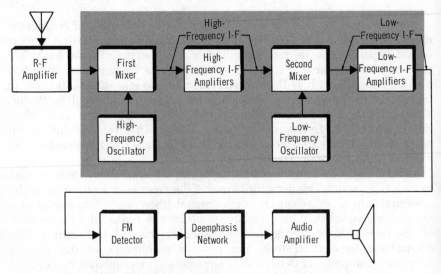

Double-conversion receivers combine the advantages of high and low intermediate-frequency amplifiers

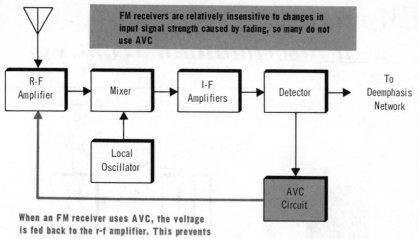

FM receivers are relatively insensitive to changes in input signal strength caused by fading, so many do not use AVC

When an FM receiver uses AVC, the voltage is fed back to the r-f amplifier. This prevents strong signals from overdriving the mixer stage

FM receiver with discriminator

As you will learn in a later volume, there are various types of FM detectors. All of these perform the same function but nevertheless have different characteristics. One type of detector is called a *discriminator*. When it is used, additional circuits are usually added to the basic FM receiver previously described. A receiver using a discriminator is shown on the following page. You can see that, in addition to the basic circuits, it contains a *limiter* and an *AFC circuit*.

The limiter clips the positive and negative peaks of the i-f signal before it is applied to the discriminator. This clipping eliminates any *amplitude variations* (noise) of the FM signal that may have been produced during transmission. Such limiting is necessary, since the FM discriminator is also sensitive to amplitude variations. If these were not removed, the discriminator would deliver a distorted, or noisy, output. Often the limiter provides signal amplification as well as limiting.

The AFC circuit compensates for any frequency drift that occurs in the local oscillator. A change in oscillator frequency would affect receiver performance since it would produce an intermediate frequency different than the frequency to which the i-f amplifiers and discriminator are tuned. If such a condition occurs, the AFC circuit senses the change in the intermediate frequency and produces a d-c voltage proportional to the change. This voltage is fed back to the local oscillator, causing the oscillator to return to the correct frequency.

As shown, AVC is also sometimes used in FM receivers. The type of detector used, though, has nothing to do with whether or not AVC is employed.

FM receiver
with discriminator (cont.)

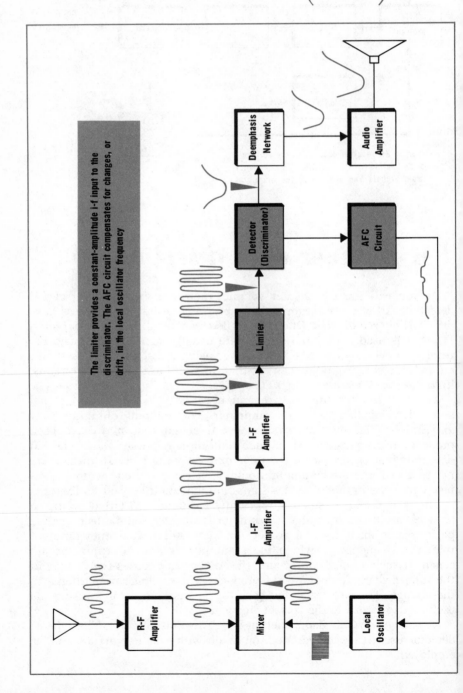

The limiter provides a constant-amplitude i-f input to the discriminator. The AFC circuit compensates for changes, or drift, in the local oscillator frequency

an *FM stereo receiver*

FM stereo receivers are used to receive and reproduce FM stereo multiplex signals. The front-end circuits of this receiver are the same as those of a conventional FM receiver. After the FM detector, though, additional circuits are added to separate the individual components of the complex signal. You recall that these components are an *L + R signal* having a bandwidth of 0–15 kilocycles, an *L − R side-band signal* having a bandwidth of 23–53 kilocycles, and a *19-kilocycle pilot carrier*.

As shown, each of these components is separated from the composite signal by an appropriate filter. The L + R signal is applied directly to a matrix. The L − R side-band signal is applied to an AM detector, as is the pilot carrier after it is doubled in frequency to 38 kilocycles. The detector mixes the side bands and the carrier to produce the original L − R audio signal, which is then applied to the matrix. In the matrix, the L + R and L − R signals are combined in such a way that the original left- and right-channel signals are recovered. Each of these is then processed in a *separate* audio channel containing a deemphasis network and one or more audio amplifiers.

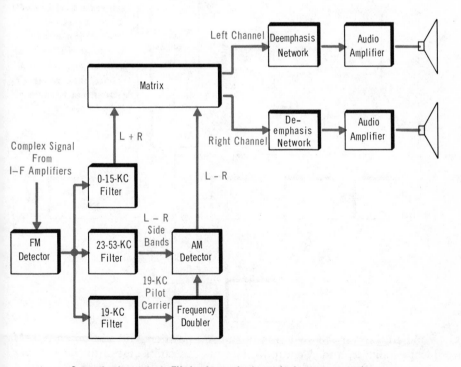

Conventional monophonic FM signals can also be received on a stereo receiver. For such signals, the entire output of the FM detector is passed by the 0-15-KC filter and fed to both audio channels

the AM-FM receiver

An *AM-FM receiver* can receive *either* AM or FM signals. By means of a single switch, reception can be changed from AM to FM, or vice versa. Some circuits in an AM-FM receiver are used for *both* AM and FM reception. Others are used only for AM or only for FM. Still other circuits are partially changed for the two types of operation. In these cases, the basic circuit is used for both AM and FM, but the portion of the circuit that provides frequency-selection characteristics is different for each signal.

An AM-FM receiver is shown. Although various switches are shown, they are all sections of a single, *ganged* switch. When the switch is in the FM position, the FM antenna is connected to the r-f amplifier, and the output of the FM local oscillator is applied to the mixer. Also, frequency-selection (tuning) circuits suitable for FM frequencies are switched into the r-f amplifier, mixer, and i-f amplifier circuits. Also, the FM position of the switch places a second i-f amplifier, an FM detector, and a deemphasis network into the receiver circuit.

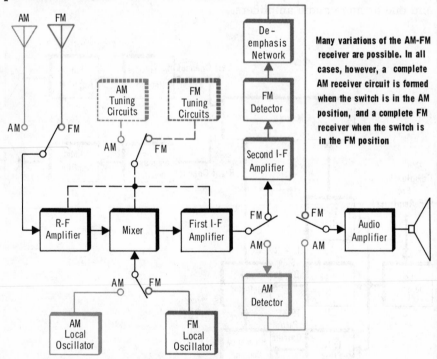

Many variations of the AM-FM receiver are possible. In all cases, however, a complete AM receiver circuit is formed when the switch is in the AM position, and a complete FM receiver when the switch is in the FM position

When the AM-FM switch is in the AM position, the AM antenna, AM local oscillator, and AM tuning circuits are connected into the receiver circuit in place of their FM counterparts. Also, the output of the first i-f amplifier is routed directly to an AM detector, which, in turn, is connected to the audio amplifier.

the uhf receiver

A great amount of radio communications today takes place at signal frequencies in the UHF band. Both amplitude and frequency modulation are used for these signals. Radio receivers that operate at UHF frequencies basically consist of the same circuits as receivers used for lower frequencies. As you will learn in later volumes, the *electrical construction* of the UHF circuits are considerably different than their lower frequency equivalents. Nevertheless, their *functions* are the same. For example, an i-f amplifier in a UHF receiver and that in a broadcast-band receiver amplify a fixed intermediate frequency. But, the internal components and wiring of the two are different.

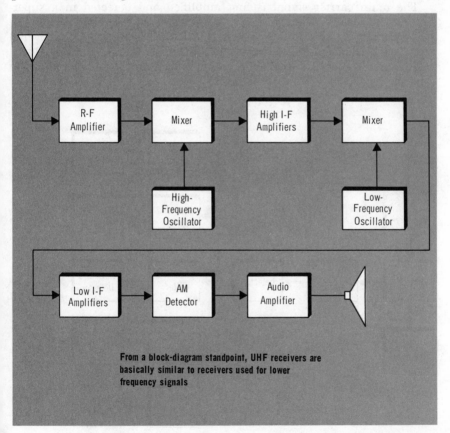

From a block-diagram standpoint, UHF receivers are basically similar to receivers used for lower frequency signals

An AM receiver for UHF signals is shown. The difference between this and a broadcast-band AM receiver is the former's use of double conversion. At the UHF frequencies, amplification at both a high and a low intermediate frequency is necessary to provide the required frequency selectivity and image rejection. You recall that this same arrangement is used in high-quality, communications FM receivers.

the telemetry receiver

Radio telemetry, as you know, involves the *remote* measuring of one or more quantities and the radio transmission of these measurements to some receiving point. The most common use of telemetry is in the testing and operation of missiles and satellites. Because of size and power considerations, a single transmitter usually handles many separate telemetered signals. This is often accomplished by a system of *frequency multiplexing* in which individual subcarriers carry the separate signals, and the subcarriers all modulate a common main carrier to produce a multichannel signal. One possible type of receiver for such a telemetry system is shown.

The main carrier signal is first amplified and detected in a superheterodyne receiver. The subcarrier signals are then separated from the main carrier by appropriate filters. Next, the intelligence is recovered from each subcarrier by a detector. After detection, the individual telemetered signals are applied to an appropriate recording or indicating device.

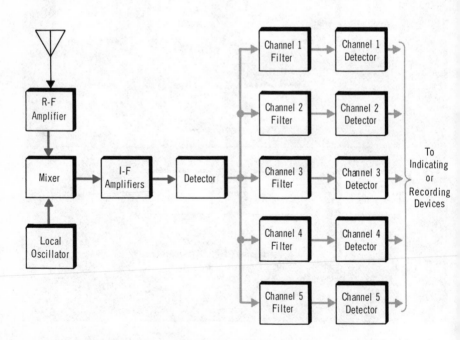

The basic characteristics of most telemetry receivers is the reception and processing of multichannel signals. These signals may be amplitude, frequency, or phase modulated

summary

☐ After r-f amplification, the incoming FM signal is converted to the receiver's intermediate frequency. The i-f signal is amplified by i-f amplifiers, and then the frequency variations are converted to a corresponding audio signal by a detector. ☐ Before audio amplification, the detected audio signal is applied to a deemphasis network. This restores the relative amplitudes of the frequency components to what they were before preemphasis. ☐ Many FM receivers employ double conversion to improve frequency selectivity and image conversion. The high intermediate frequency provides frequency selectivity, and the low intermediate frequency provides image rejection. ☐ When a discriminator is used as the detector in an FM receiver, a limiter is used before the detector to remove amplitude variations from the signal. ☐ AFC circuits are used in FM receivers to compensate for any frequency drift that occurs in the local oscillator.

☐ In addition to conventional FM receiver circuits, stereo FM receivers contain additional circuits to separate the two signal components from the composite signal. After separation, two separate audio channels are used, each containing a deemphasis network. ☐ AM-FM receivers can be switched to receive either AM or FM signals. ☐ In AM-FM receivers, some circuits are used for either AM or FM reception and others for both AM and FM reception.

☐ UHF receivers may be either of the AM or FM type. Although functionally they are the same as lower-frequency receivers, their electrical construction is considerably different. ☐ Double conversion is frequently used in UHF receivers. ☐ Telemetry receivers are often designed to process frequency multiplexed signals. In such receivers, the subcarrier signals are separated from the main carrier by appropriate filters.

review questions

1. Draw a block diagram of a simple FM receiver.
2. Draw an FM receiver with double conversion.
3. What is the purpose of double conversion?
4. What are *image frequencies*?
5. Why is a limiter necessary when a discriminator is used as the FM detector?
6. Why is AFC used in FM receivers?
7. Draw a block diagram of an FM stereo receiver?
8. In an AM-FM receiver, which circuits can be used for *both* AM and FM reception?
9. In an AM-FM receiver, which circuits can be used only for AM *or* FM reception?
10. Draw a receiver for frequency multiplexed signals.

the black-and-white television receiver

A television receiver contains a *loudspeaker,* a *cathode-ray,* or *picture, tube,* and associated circuits. Deflection circuits provide current for a set of coils mounted around the neck of the picture tube to deflect an electron beam produced in the tube so that the beam traces closely spaced horizontal lines on the face of the tube. Because of the phosphorescent coating on the tube face and the persistency of human vision, these lines produce an effect of complete brightness over the face of the tube. This is called the *raster.* It does not depend on a received signal.

When a television signal is tuned in, the entire composite signal is processed by the common signal circuits. The sound component is separated and sent to the sound circuits where it is processed and delivered to the loudspeaker. The video portion of the signal is processed by the video circuits and sent to the picture tube, where it varies the instantaneous intensity of the electron beam as it is swept across the face of the tube. This causes variations in brightness on the tube face, which produce the picture.

The sync pulses are removed from the video signal and sent to the sync circuits. Here the pulses are separated and used to control the operation of the deflection circuits so that the scanning produced by the deflection circuits is synchronized with the scanning of the television camera in the television studio.

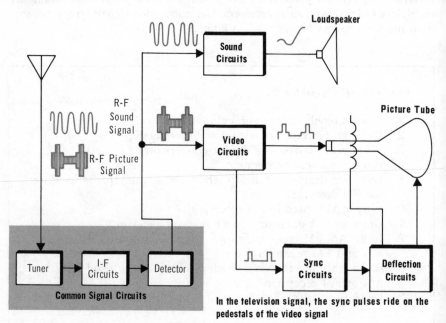

In the television signal, the sync pulses ride on the pedestals of the video signal

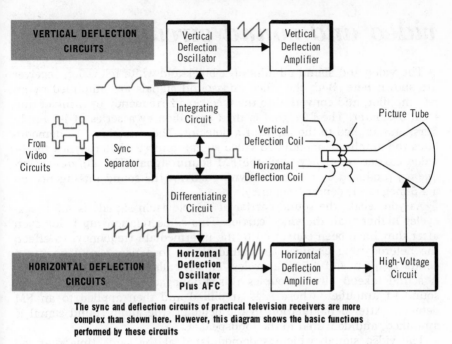

The sync and deflection circuits of practical television receivers are more complex than shown here. However, this diagram shows the basic functions performed by these circuits

sync and deflection circuits

A sync separator removes the sync pulses riding on the video signal and applies them to integrating and differentiating circuits. The integrating circuit converts the vertical sync and equalizing pulses into a series of triangular-shaped pulses, which are applied to a vertical deflection oscillator.

The oscillator produces a sawtooth output signal whose frequency is controlled by the sync pulses, so that the frequency is always identical to the vertical scanning frequency at the transmitter. The output of the oscillator is amplified by a vertical deflection amplifier, then applied as a series of current pulses to the vertical deflection coil. This provides vertical deflection of the electron beam in the picture tube.

The differentiating circuit converts the horizontal sync pulses into a series of sharp pulses, and applies them to a horizontal deflection oscillator and AFC circuit. These pulses control the frequency of the horizontal oscillator, which also delivers a sawtooth output. The input of the horizontal oscillator is amplified by a horizontal deflection amplifier and applied as a series of current pulses to the horizontal deflection coil. Each pulse provides one line of horizontal deflection of the electron beam across the picture tube face.

The output of the horizontal deflection amplifier also drives the high-voltage circuits, which provide between 15,000 to 20,000 volts dc to operate the cathode-ray tube (CRT).

video and sound circuits

The video and sound circuits of a black-and-white television receiver are shown here. Both the video and sound signals are amplified by an r-f amplifier, and converted to the receiver i-f frequency by a mixer and local oscillator. The i-f signal is then amplified by a series of i-f amplifiers, and applied to the input of a detector. The detector: (1) demodulates the amplitude-modulated video signal, and (2) heterodynes the i-f video carrier frequency with the FM sound signal. The *difference frequency* produced by this heterodyning carries the sound intelligence on a 4.5-megacycle center frequency.

As you recall, the sound carrier of all television signals is 4.5 megacycles higher than the video carrier. This same relationship holds even after they have been converted to the intermediate frequency. In effect, the heterodyning changes the sound signal to a new signal having a center frequency of 4.5 megacycles. This is called *intercarrier detection*. A sound takeoff circuit couples this 4.5-megacycle sound signal to a sound i-f amplifier, where it is amplified and then applied to an FM detector. After demodulation in the detector, the audio sound signal is amplified, and delivered to the loudspeaker.

The video signal, which is demodulated at the same time that the 4.5-megacycle sound signal is produced, is amplified by a series of video amplifiers, and then sent to the picture tube. A portion of the detected video signal is also sent to the sync circuits for separation and processing of the sync pulses.

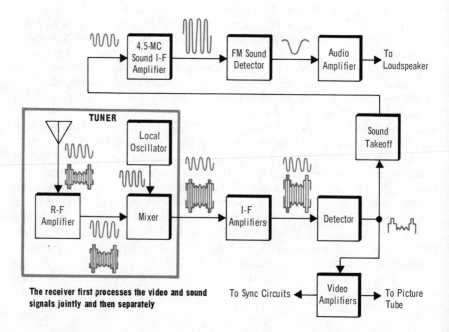

The receiver first processes the video and sound
signals jointly and then separately

the black-and-white
television receiver circuits

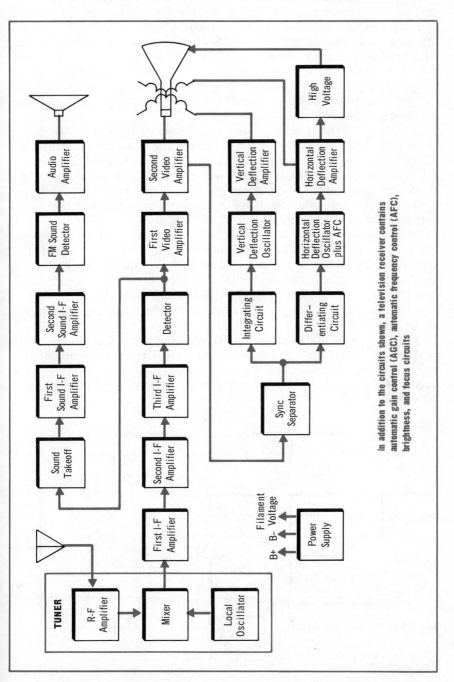

In addition to the circuits shown, a television receiver contains automatic gain control (AGC), automatic frequency control (AFC), brightness, and focus circuits

the color television receiver

A *color television receiver* contains all of the circuits of a black-and-white receiver plus additional circuits for recovering the original red, green, and blue signals from the modulated carrier. After detection, the total video signal (S) is amplified by a video preamplifier stage, and then the various components of the S signal are separated by three filter networks. The Y (luminance) signal is coupled through a delay circuit, amplified, and then sent to a matrix circuit. The delay circuit is needed to insure that the Y signal reaches the matrix at the same time as the chrominance portion of the signal.

After the C (chrominance) signal is separated from the S signal, it is amplified, then applied to both an I and a Q demodulator. Since the C signal consists of the I and Q signals and a 3.58-megacycle *suppressed* carrier, the carrier must be reinserted to demodulate the signals. The 3.58-megacycle carrier is generated by an oscillator, and is kept in phase with the 3.58-megacycle oscillator at the transmitter by the color sync burst signal, which is filtered out of the S signal.

One output of the 3.58-megacycle oscillator is applied directly to the I demodulator, where it is used for demodulation of the I signal. The carrier modulated with the Q signal at the transmitter was *shifted* 90 degrees in phase before it was fed into the modulator. Thus, another output from the oscillator is shifted 90 degrees in phase by a phase-shift circuit, then applied to the Q demodulator for demodulation of the Q signal.

The demodulated I and Q signals are applied to the matrix along with the Y signal. In the matrix, these three signals are combined in the proper proportions to produce the original red (R), blue (B), and green (G) signals. The three color signals are then applied to the picture tube.

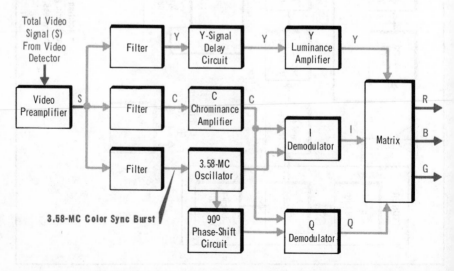

the color
television receiver circuits

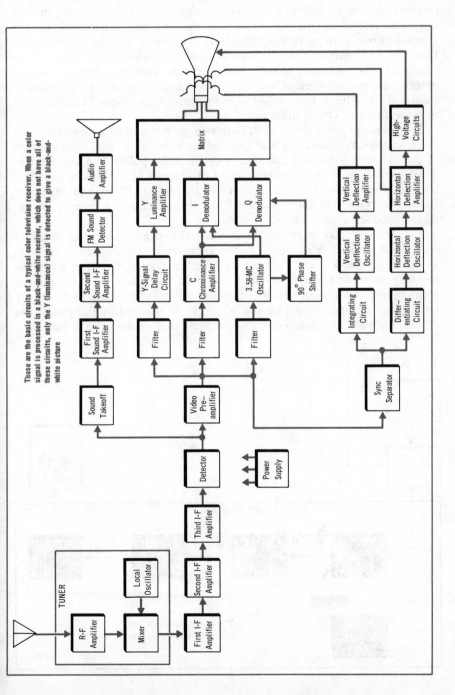

These are the basic circuits of a typical color television receiver. When a color signal is processed in a black-and-white receiver, which does not have all of these circuits, only the Y (luminance) signal is detected to give a black-and-white picture

the radar receiver

A *radar receiver* is, essentially, a special type of *superheterodyne* receiver. As shown below, it receives weak *echoes* of the high-frequency bursts of energy originally emitted by the antenna. These echoes are applied directly to a mixer, which is usually a special crystal-type. Here, they are mixed with the output of a local oscillator to produce an i-f signal. The i-f signal is amplified, and then sent to a detector which detects the *pulse envelope* of the echo signals. The sharp rectangular pulses are amplified by a series of video amplifiers before being applied to some form of visual indicator.

The pulse, or some form of it, is shown on the indicator together with some visible indication of the elapsed time between the transmission of the original pulse and the return of the echo pulse. The indicator is actually calibrated in *distance* instead of elapsed time. This is possible, because radio waves travel at a constant speed. What the indicator shows, therefore, is the distance from the antenna, or range, of the target producing the echo.

As shown, a radar set contains *both* the transmitter and receiver connected through a duplexer to the same antenna. The duplexer acts as an electronic switch, connecting first the transmitter and then the receiver to the antenna. When a pulse is transmitted, the duplexer connects the transmitter to the antenna and prevents the high energy from entering and damaging the receiver. At the end of the pulse, the antenna is switched to the receiver for reception of the echo pulse.

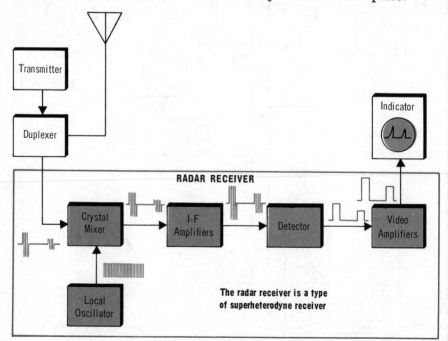

The radar receiver is a type
of superheterodyne receiver

the radar indicator

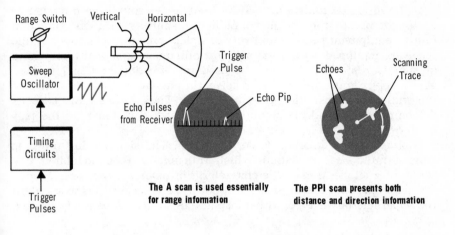

Range Switch   Vertical   Horizontal

Sweep
Oscillator

Trigger
Pulse

Echoes

Scanning
Trace

Echo Pip

Echo Pulses
from Receiver

Timing
Circuits

Trigger
Pulses

The A scan is used essentially for range information

The PPI scan presents both distance and direction information

Radar indicators are essentially cathode-ray tubes (CRT's) that visually present information on the detected target. Two of the most common indicating methods are called the *A scan* and the *PPI scan*. In the A scan, the electron beam is swept across the face of the cathode-ray tube screen in a horizontal line by a sawtooth signal.

The time required for one full sweep corresponds to the maximum distance at which a target can be detected. For example, if the maximum distance is set for 20 miles, one horizontal sweep takes 247.6 microseconds, which is the time required for a radar signal to travel 20 miles and be reflected back to the antenna. The sweep time is controlled by timing circuits that can be set for various maximum ranges by a range switch. Each sweep is started by a trigger pulse every time a radar pulse is transmitted.

When an echo is received, it causes a small vertical deflection of the electron beam as it makes its horizontal sweep. This is called a *pip*. The CRT screen is calibrated so that the distance between the pip and the beginning of the sweep corresponds to the range of the detected target.

The PPI scan indicates both the *distance* and the *direction,* or azimuth, of the target. This is done by rotating the deflection coils around the neck of the CRT in synchronization with the rotation of the antenna. The scanning trace sweeps from the center of the screen to the outer edge, and rotates 360 degrees around the screen. When a received echo pulse is indicated, its distance from the center of the screen corresponds to the target distance. Its angular position from some reference line represents the target direction. The fluorescent coating on PPI screens glows for several seconds, so the echo indication remains on the screen even after the scanning spot has passed. In effect, this produces a radar map of the surrounding area.

radio direction finders

Radio direction finders are widely used to determine the direction of a ship or plane from a known radio transmitting location. Direction finding equipment ranges from very complex units to conventional radio receivers equipped with rotating loop antennas. Practically any kind of signal (AM, CW, etc.) can be used for direction finding purposes. The receiver must be able to receive the signal, and the *location* of the station or transmitter must be known. Thus, either radio beacons or commercial broadcast stations can be used, depending on the particular circumstances.

A simple radio direction finder is shown. The signal being tuned is from a radio beacon station, which transmits a tone-modulated CW signal of a single Morse code character. For example, the radio beacon station might send the letter A continuously. The receiver is the standard AM superheterodyne type, with a loop antenna that can be easily rotated.

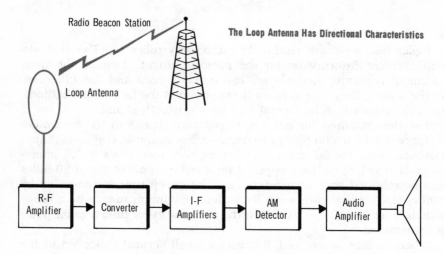

Radio Beacon Station

The Loop Antenna Has Directional Characteristics

Loop Antenna

| R-F Amplifier | Converter | I-F Amplifiers | AM Detector | Audio Amplifier |

The loop antenna picks up minimum signal when its plane is perpendicular to the direction of transmission of the signal

When the signal is tuned in, the station and its location are identified by the code heard in the loudspeaker. The loop antenna is then rotated until the output from the loudspeaker is at a *minimum*. At this point, the plane of the antenna loop is perpendicular to a line drawn between the radio beacon transmitter and the loop antenna. Special techniques are then used to determine the true direction of the radio station. Of course, if two radio stations are used, intersecting line can be drawn to obtain a fix.

radio navigation receivers

Radio direction finding is only one method of navigating by means of radio signals. There are numerous other methods and equipment used for radio navigation. In all of these, one or more signals are transmitted having some characteristic that represents distance, or direction, or both. A receiver picks up the signals, detects the intelligence, and presents it on a visual or aural indicator. It is impossible to describe the wide variety of radio navigation equipments in use today; so only a typical one will be covered here. This is the *runway localizer*. This is used to provide a horizontal reference for aircraft landings.

You recall from Volume 1 that the localizer signal consists of two modulated tones on the same carrier frequency. These are a 90-cps and a 150-cps tone. The signals are transmitted so that to the left of the runway center line, the 90-cps tone is stronger, and to the right, the 150-cps tone is stronger. Directly along the center line, the two tones are equal.

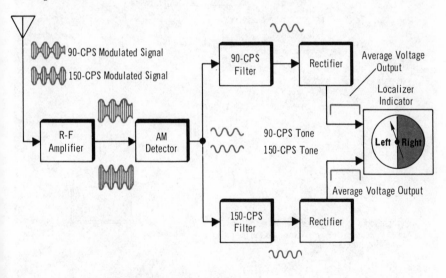

The runway localizer receiver is just one of the many types of radio navigation equipment

A basic localizer receiver is shown. The amplitude-modulated carrier is amplified and detected, and then applied to a 90-cps filter and a 150-cps filter. Each filter passes its corresponding tone to a rectifier. The d-c outputs of the rectifiers then actuate a visual display instrument. If the 90-cps tone is stronger, its rectifier delivers a larger output than the rectifier for the 150-cps tone. As a result, the indicator reads *left*. The converse is true if the 150-cps tone is stronger.

radio control guidance systems

Radio control systems are used in numerous applications. These range from the remote control of model airplanes and boats to the guidance of large missiles. These systems consist of a transmitter to generate the radio signal and modulate it with the desired control information, and a receiver to receive the signal, detect the control information, and apply it in the required form to the controlled item. Practically any type of signal can be used for radio control. The complexity of the signal depends on certain factors, such as the number of things to be controlled.

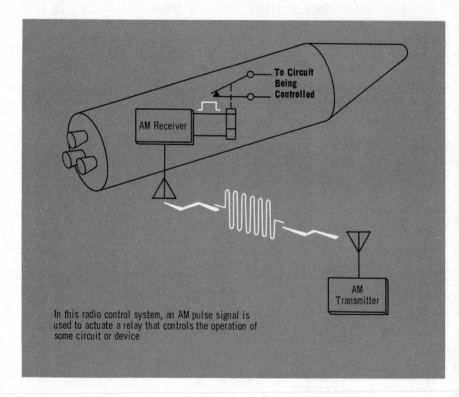

In this radio control system, an AM pulse signal is used to actuate a relay that controls the operation of some circuit or device

The transmitters and receivers used in radio control systems are, for the most part, the same as those that have previously been described. Essentially, the use to which the signals are put is different. For example, rather than provide voice or Morse code information, the output signal from a radio control receiver might actuate a relay. The relay, in turn, might open and close a valve, turn a device or circuit off and on.

In more sophisticated control systems, where many guidance commands can be executed, different pulse codes can be sent for the different commands. Also different tones, or combinations of tones can be sent.

the sonar receiver

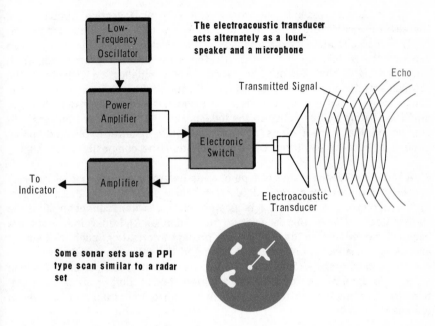

The electroacoustic transducer acts alternately as a loud-speaker and a microphone

Some sonar sets use a PPI type scan similar to a radar set

Sonar equipment is used in *underwater* detection and ranging much the same way radar is used in the atmosphere. However, sonar uses *sound* waves, and the frequencies of sonar signals are in the *ultra audio* range. They are usually somewhere between 20 and 50 kilocycles. High frequencies are not used for these purposes because such frequencies are attenuated rapidly when transmitted in water. A sonar set contains circuits that generate and transmit the sonar signal, and circuits that receive and process the return echo. The functional elements of a sonar set are shown.

A signal of the proper frequency is generated by a low-frequency oscillator and applied to a power amplifier for amplification. The high-powered signal is then applied through an electronic switch to a special *electroacoustic transducer*. The transducer converts the electrical signal into sound waves and transmits them into the surrounding water. After a burst of energy is transmitted, the electronic switch connects the transducer to a receiving amplifier. The transducer now acts as a micro-phone and converts any sound echo that is received into an electrical signal. An echo signal is amplified, and then sent to either a visual or aural indicator, or both.

The indicator converts the time lapse between the transmitted pulse and the echo pulse into an indication of distance between the target and the sonar set. The directional characteristics of the loudspeaker-micro-phone transducer make it possible to also determine the direction of the target.

summary

☐ In a television receiver, horizontal and vertical deflection circuits scan the electron beam across the face of the picture tube to produce the raster. ☐ The video circuits vary the intensity of the electron beam, and in doing so produce the picture on the screen. ☐ The sync pulses are separated from the video signal and are used to synchronize the deflection circuits in the receiver with those in the transmitter. ☐ A sound take-off circuit removes the sound carrier from the video carrier. The sound signal is then detected and amplified before being applied to the loudspeaker. ☐ Color television receivers contain all the same circuits as black-and-white receivers, plus additional circuits to recover the three color signals from the composite video signal.

☐ A radar receiver is a special type of superheterodyne receiver that receives echoes from an antenna and detects the pulse envelope of these echoes. ☐ The duplexer in a radar set acts as an electronic switch, connecting first the transmitter and then the receiver to the antenna. ☐ Radar indicators are basically cathode-ray tubes that visually present information, such as distance and direction, about a target. The A scan and the PPI scan are the two most common indicators. ☐ Radio direction finders consist of a receiver and a loop antenna to determine direction from a known transmitting location. In operation, the loop antenna is rotated until maximum output from the receiver is obtained.

☐ A runway localizer receiver is one type of radio navigation equipment. It receives and detects the two separate localizer tones, and indicates which is the strongest. ☐ A sonar receiver picks up sound-wave echoes reflected by a target. The echoes are received by an electroacoustic transducer, which converts them into an electrical signal. These signals are amplified and then sent to a visual or aural indicator.

review questions

1. What is a *raster*?
2. Draw a black-and-white television receiver.
3. What is the purpose of the sync circuits in a television receiver?
4. What is the purpose of the duplexer in a radar set?
5. Describe how an A-scan radar indicator works.
6. How does a *PPI scan* differ from an *A scan*?
7. What is the purpose of an RDF loop antenna?
8. Draw a simple radio control guidance system.
9. What is an *electroacoustic transducer*?
10. Sonar can provide what types of information about a target?

electronics
three

how electron tubes are used

In Volumes 1 and 2, you learned how electronic signals are used to process and transmit a wide variety of intelligence. Radio, television, radar, and the telephone are just a few of the applications made possible by the ability to produce and control electronic signals. In this volume, you will learn about devices that more than any others are responsible for the advanced state of electronics. These devices are called *electron tubes,* and, until the development of the transistor, were the only devices capable of *amplifying* electronic signals.

Electron tubes are made in a variety of shapes and sizes. The two most general classifications are TRANSMITTING and RECEIVING tubes

**TRANSMITTING
ELECTRON TUBE**

**RECEIVING
ELECTRON TUBE**

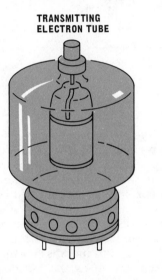

Because of the large amounts of electrical power they must handle, transmitting tubes are generally much larger than receiving tubes

Although they receive their name because they are used in receiving equipment, receiving tubes are actually used in most low-power applications

Besides being able to perform the function of amplification, electron tubes can also perform the equally important functions of *rectification, oscillation, modulation,* and *waveshaping.* Without the capability of carrying out these functions efficiently and economically, there would be no communications, industrial instrumentation, or scientific research as we know them today. All of these, and related fields, grew to their advanced state only after the development and widespread use of the electron tube.

In many applications, transistors are supplementing, and sometimes replacing, electron tubes. Nevertheless, at present, and probably for years to come, electron tubes are the most important class of device used in electronics.

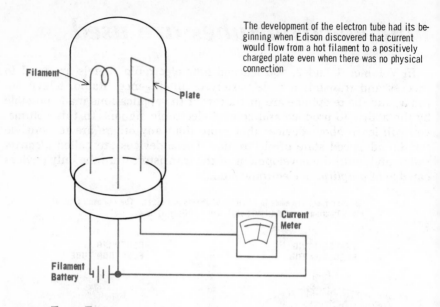

The development of the electron tube had its beginning when Edison discovered that current would flow from a hot filament to a positively charged plate even when there was no physical connection

early history

The first step in the development of the electron tube came near the end of the nineteenth century with experiments by *Thomas Edison* on his newly invented incandescent lamp. Edison observed that when a second electrode, which he called a *plate*, was inserted into a lamp and a voltage was applied to the filament, a current meter connected between the *positive* filament lead and the lead to the plate indicated a current flow. This happened although the plate and the filament were *not* physically connected within the lamp. Edison could offer no explanation for this phenomenon, since it appeared as if current was flowing in an *open circuit*. The phenomenon was then known as the *Edison effect*.

Some years later, British scientist *J. J. Thomson* put forth his electron theory of matter, which offered a plausible explanation for the Edison effect. In essence, the theory stated that electrons were emitted by Edison's filament when it became hot, and these electrons were then attracted to the plate because it had a positive potential.

Based on this early experimental and theoretical work, another British scientist, *J. A. Fleming*, developed a practical electron tube fashioned somewhat after Edison's experimental apparatus. Fleming called his tube a *valve;* a name which is still used for the electron tube in England. The ability of the electron tube to amplify, which is its most significant characteristic, was not realized until some years later, when American inventor *Lee De Forest* developed a tube that included a *third* electrode, in addition to the filament and plate. De Forest called the third electrode the *control grid*, since it controlled the amount of current that flowed from the filament to the plate. Electron tubes are often called *vacuum tubes*, since most of them must be evacuated to work.

electron emission

All electron tubes operate on the basic principle that *electrons emitted* from one electrode in the tube are attracted toward another electrode that is positively charged. Various other electrodes are contained in the tube to control the flow of electrons, and thereby give each tube the desired operating characteristics. Usually, the electrode from which the electrons are emitted is called the *cathode*. Sometimes, as you will see later, in certain types of tubes it is called the *filament*.

You learned that in Edison's experiments electrons were emitted as a result of *heating* the incandescent lamp filament. This is only one method, however, in which a cathode, or filament, can be made to emit electrons. There are various *other* methods, and practically all of them are used to some extent. Each of these methods for producing electron emission is described on the following pages.

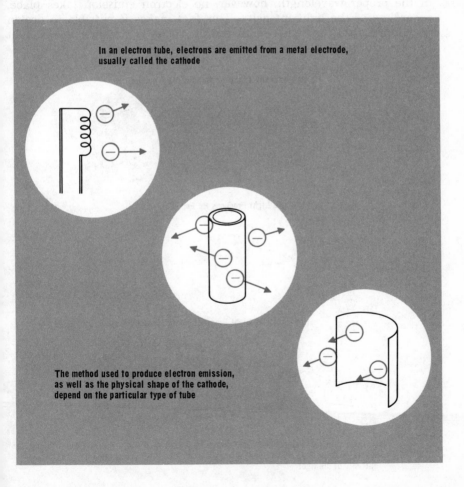

In an electron tube, electrons are emitted from a metal electrode, usually called the cathode

The method used to produce electron emission, as well as the physical shape of the cathode, depend on the particular type of tube

photoelectric emission

Certain materials emit electrons when *light* strikes them. This is called *photoelectric* emission. Materials that exhibit this characteristic are said to be *photosensitive.* Electron tubes that make use of photoelectric emission are called *photoelectric tubes,* or *phototubes,* and are used in numerous detection and control applications.

It is not the purpose of this book to describe the mechanism by which photoelectric emission takes place. In general, however, when light of the proper *wavelength* strikes a photosensitive material, it imparts *energy* to some of the electrons in the material. If this energy is sufficient, the electrons *escape* from the surface of the material into the surrounding space. The number of electrons that are emitted in this way is directly proportional to the *intensity* of the light. Thus, the more intense the light, the greater the number of emitted electrons. If the light is not of the proper wavelength, however, no electron emission takes place, regardless of the light intensity. This fact makes it possible to design phototubes that are sensitive to certain colors or frequencies of light but not to others.

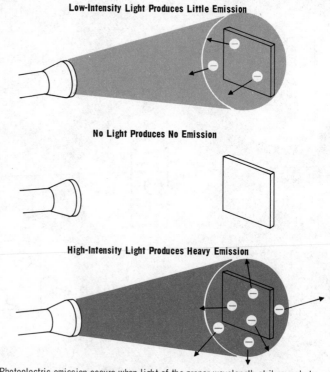

Low-Intensity Light Produces Little Emission

No Light Produces No Emission

High-Intensity Light Produces Heavy Emission

Photoelectric emission occurs when light of the proper wavelength strikes a photosensitive material. The number of electrons emitted is directly proportional to the intensity of the light

secondary emission

When electrons having relatively *high velocities* strike a metallic material, they transfer a portion of their energy to some of the electrons contained in the material. Just as in photoelectric emission, if the amount of energy transferred is sufficient, electrons can *escape* from the material. This type of electron emission is called *secondary emission,* since it is caused by electron bombardment. The electrons emitted as a result of secondary emission are often called *secondary electrons.*

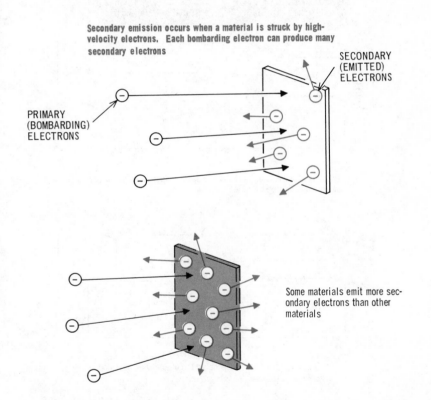

Secondary emission occurs when a material is struck by high-velocity electrons. Each bombarding electron can produce many secondary electrons

SECONDARY (EMITTED) ELECTRONS

PRIMARY (BOMBARDING) ELECTRONS

Some materials emit more secondary electrons than other materials

In actual practice, each bombarding electron may cause *many* secondary electrons to be emitted. This results when the primary, or bombarding, electron has a very high velocity, and therefore a great amount of energy. In effect, the primary electron can collide, billiard-ball fashion, with many electrons in the material, and in the process impart some of its energy to each of them.

In many electron tubes, secondary emission is an *unwanted condition,* and provisions are made to reduce or eliminate it. In certain tubes, however, it is created *purposely* to achieve certain special operating characteristics.

cold-cathode emission

Another method producing electron emission from a material is called *cold-cathode emission,* or *field emission.* In this type of emission, the negatively charged electrons are actually *pulled out* of the material by a *strong positive potential.* The stronger the positive potential, the more electrons are attracted from the material.

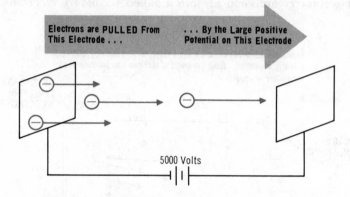

Cold-cathode emission is limited to special applications because of the large voltages that are required

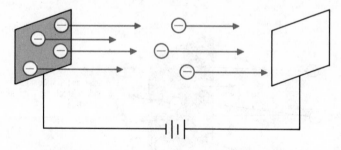

Some materials are more responsive to cold-cathode emission than others

Except for the case of gas-filled electron tubes, which will be covered later, cold-cathode emission has the disadvantage of requiring *extremely high voltages* to produce the necessary large positive potentials. Nevertheless, it has certain advantages that make it highly suitable for special applications. Among the advantages is that it can cause the emission of many electrons almost instantly without a warmup period. In addition, the emitted electrons reach the positively charged plate very rapidly since their velocity is directly proportional to the value of the positive potential.

UNHEATED MATERIAL   HEATED MATERIAL

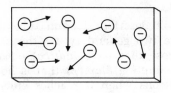 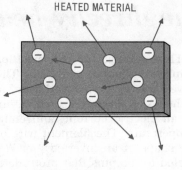

At normal temperatures, the electrons have relatively low energies

When the material is heated, the electrons gain energy and some escape from the material

thermionic emission

Although all of the previously described methods of emission are used to some extent in present-day electron tubes, most tubes use *heat* to provide the required electron emission. This is called *thermionic emission,* and, you recall, is the method used in Edison's original experimental apparatus.

In thermionic emission, the cathode material is heated to a relatively high temperature. The heat energy is transferred to the electrons in the material, and when the electrons near the material's surface attain sufficient energy, they escape from the material. The number of electrons released through thermionic emission depends on the type of *material* from which the cathode is made and the *temperature* to which it is heated. In general, for a given material, more electrons are released the hotter the material becomes. Of course, if the cathode material is heated to too high a temperature, it will melt. To obtain a high level of emission, therefore, it is necessary either to use cathode materials having high melting points and to provide a large amount of heat, or to use materials emitting large numbers of electrons at relatively low temperatures.

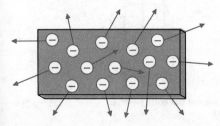

The number of electrons released by thermionic emission depends on the material used

the directly heated cathode

This volume, for the most part, will describe electron tubes that employ *thermionic* emission. There are two general types: those that have *directly heated* cathodes, and those that have *indirectly heated* cathodes. A directly heated cathode is simply a *filament* that is heated by an electric current, and emits electrons when it reaches emission temperature. The filament wire of a directly heated cathode is often in the shape of an inverted V or W as shown. The support wires are connected to the pins that protrude through the base of the tube. The filament voltage that causes the heat-producing current flow through the filament is applied between the two filament pins.

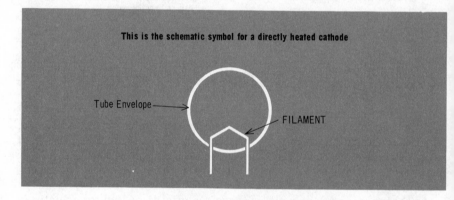

This is the schematic symbol for a directly heated cathode

Tube Envelope

FILAMENT

Directly heated cathodes reach their electron-emitting temperature almost instantly when the filament voltage is applied. If the filament voltage is ac, though, the filament temperature, and therefore the emission, varies with the varying current. In some applications, this variation in the emission would produce undesirable effects. Special circuits, or high-filament-voltage frequencies, must therefore be used to maintain a relatively constant filament temperature.

These are two common types of directly heated cathodes

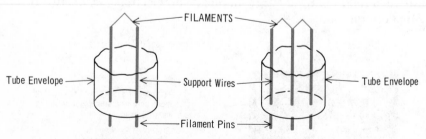

FILAMENTS

Tube Envelope

Support Wires

Tube Envelope

Filament Pins

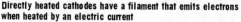

Directly heated cathodes have a filament that emits electrons when heated by an electric current

the indirectly heated cathode

Indirectly heated cathodes consist of two separate elements: a *heater* and a *cathode*. Essentially, the heater is the same as the filament in a directly heated cathode, except that, in itself, it is not designed to emit electrons. Therefore, it is called a heater, and not a filament; however, the two terms are often used interchangeably. The heater is contained *within* the cathode, which is a hollow cylinder. The heater is heated by connecting it to a voltage source, as is done with the filament in a directly heated cathode. However, as noted, the heating itself does not cause any electrons to be emitted. Instead, it heats the cathode to the point where the cathode provides thermionic emission.

Indirectly heated cathodes do not reach emission temperatures as quickly as the directly heated type, since the heat must be transferred across the space between the heater and cathode. At the same time, however, the cathode temperature *cannot follow* the rapid heater temperature variations that occur when an a-c heater voltage is used. This provides a relatively *constant* cathode temperature when the heater is energized by ac, and is the reason that most electron tubes today have indirectly heated cathodes.

As shown, the heater of an indirectly-heated cathode may be in the shape of an inverted U or V, or it may be coiled along its length within the cathode.

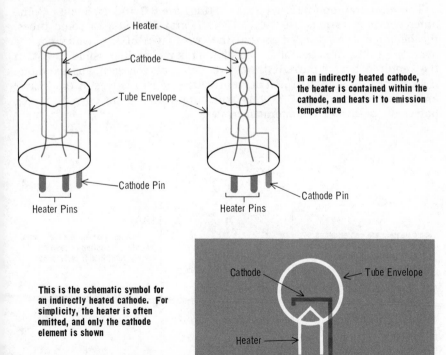

Heater

Cathode

Tube Envelope

In an indirectly heated cathode, the heater is contained within the cathode, and heats it to emission temperature

Cathode Pin

Heater Pins

Heater Pins

Cathode Pin

This is the schematic symbol for an indirectly heated cathode. For simplicity, the heater is often omitted, and only the cathode element is shown

Cathode

Tube Envelope

Heater

heater ratings

The heater of an indirectly heated cathode must raise the temperature of the cathode to the point where it emits electrons abundantly. To do this, the heater itself must be heated to a very high temperature by the current flowing through it. All heaters, therefore, have a certain *current rating* for optimum operation. If the heater current is *less* than the rated value, emission is decreased because of the reduced temperature. And, if the heater current *exceeds* the rated value, the emission will be increased, but the life of the heater will be shortened because of the increased deterioration at the higher temperature.

Normally, the heater current rating of a tube is expressed in terms of the *voltage* which when applied to the heater will produce the rated current. To allow tube heaters to be operated from common voltage sources in electronic equipment, there are relatively few voltage ratings, and the heaters of individual tube types are designed to have the necessary *resistance* to produce the required heater current. For example, two tubes with 6.3-volt heater ratings may require completely different currents for optimum operation. The necessary current in each case is provided by having the suitable heater resistance. Thus, a 6.3-volt heater that requires 1.2 amperes of current would have 5.25 ohms resistance, while a 6.3-volt heater that requires 300 milliamperes of current would have 21 ohms resistance.

The most common heater voltage ratings are 6.3 and 12.6 volts. Some other common ratings are 1.4, 3.15, 4.7, and 25 volts. In some tubes, the heater is *centertapped* so that the two halves of the heater can be operated either in series or in parallel. This makes it possible to obtain the required heater current from two different voltages. For example, if 12.6 volts provide the rated current when the two halves of the heater are operated in series, 6.3 volts will supply the same current if the halves of the heater are operated in parallel.

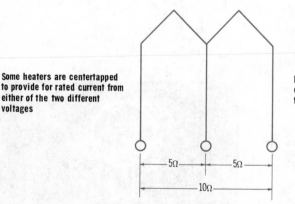

Some heaters are centertapped to provide for rated current from either of the two different voltages

In such heaters, the resistance of each section is one-half of the total heater resistance

SERIES OPERATION

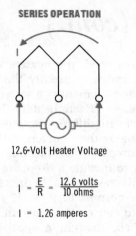

12.6-Volt Heater Voltage

$$I = \frac{E}{R} = \frac{12.6 \text{ volts}}{10 \text{ ohms}}$$

$$I = 1.26 \text{ amperes}$$

PARALLEL OPERATION

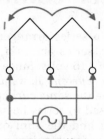

6.3-Volt Heater Voltage

$$I = \frac{6.3 \text{ volts}}{5 \text{ ohms}}$$

$$I = 1.26 \text{ amperes}$$

heater connections

Practically all pieces of electronic equipment have more than one tube. A simple AM radio may have four or five; a television receiver between 10 and 15; and some complex pieces of equipment, 30, 40, or more. The heaters of the tubes in an equipment can be connected either in *series* or in *parallel*. When a parallel arrangement is used, all of the heaters are usually connected to one of the secondary windings of a multiple-secondary transformer. Each heater, therefore, has the *identical voltage* applied across it. Thus, for parallel heaters, each heater must have the same *voltage rating*. For example, if parallel heaters are connected to a 6.3-volt secondary winding, they must all be rated at 6.3 volts. Similarly, if a 12.6-volt winding is used, the heaters must all be rated at 12.6 volts.

Parallel Heaters

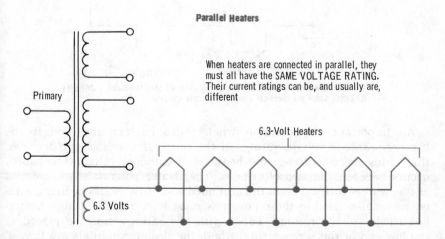

Primary

When heaters are connected in parallel, they must all have the SAME VOLTAGE RATING. Their current ratings can be, and usually are, different

6.3-Volt Heaters

6.3 Volts

heater connections (cont.)

When a series arrangement of heaters is used, the heaters are connected in series across a voltage source, which is usually the a-c line voltage of 115 volts. Since a series heater arrangement is a series circuit, the *same current* flows through each heater. Each heater, therefore, must have the same *current rating*. Heaters with different voltage ratings can be used in series heater circuits as long as their current ratings are the same and the sum of their voltage drops equals the line voltage. To provide for this, it is usually necessary to include a *dropping resistor* in the series circuit. The purpose of this resistor is to increase the resistance of the circuit for rated heater current to flow. If the total resistance of all the heaters is sufficient to cause rated current to flow, a dropping resistor is not required. Often, though, a special surge-limiting resistor is used to limit the initial high current flow that results because cold heaters have much less resistance than hot heaters.

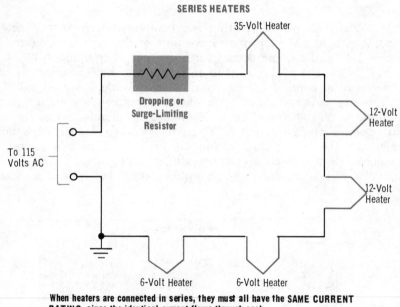

SERIES HEATERS

When heaters are connected in series, they must all have the SAME CURRENT RATING, since the identical current flows through each

An important consideration when series heaters are used is the *heater-to-cathode* voltage ratings of the tubes. If a voltage greater than this rating exists between the heater and cathode, voltage breakdown occurs between the two electrodes. The heater potentials are greatest at the heaters furthest from the grounded end of the series string. Consequently, tubes used in these positions must have relatively high heater-to-cathode voltage ratings. Tubes with low ratings must be placed at the low end of the series string, where the heater potentials are lowest.

producing a space charge

Throughout this volume, unless otherwise necessary for clarity, the emitting electrode of an electron tube will be referred to as the cathode, whether it is of the directly heated or indirectly heated type.

When a cathode is heated to its emission temperature, it emits electrons from its surface in random directions and with various velocities. In the neighborhood of the cathode, the emitted electrons are affected by many forces. For example, they constantly *collide* with each other, and so continually change direction. These collisions occur in spite of the fact that the electrons *repel* one another because of their like negative charges. Another force acting on the emitted electrons is the *positive* charge of the cathode. This charge arises from the electron loss by emission, leaving the cathode with a net positive charge. The cathode, therefore, exerts an *attracting* force on the electrons.

All of the above forces act on the emitted electrons *simultaneously*. Their overall effect is to produce an *electron cloud*, called a *space charge*, near the cathode. The density of the space charge, or the number of electrons in it, is directly proportional to the *temperature* of the cathode. Thus, the higher the cathode temperature, the more electrons there are in the space charge.

For any given cathode temperature, *equilibrium*, or balance, exists between the space charge and the positive cathode potential. For every electron emitted by the cathode once the space charge has been established, one electron from the space charge is attracted back into the cathode as a result of its increased positive potential. At equilibrium, therefore, the space charge has a constant density and the cathode has a constant positive potential. The only way to increase the number of electrons in the space charge is to raise the temperature of the cathode. This causes the emitted electrons to have higher energies, and allows them to resist a larger positive cathode potential.

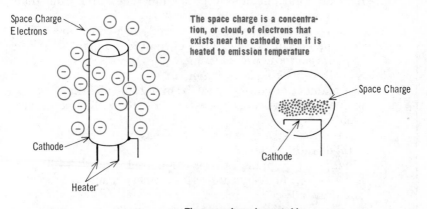

Space Charge Electrons

Cathode

Heater

The space charge is a concentration, or cloud, of electrons that exists near the cathode when it is heated to emission temperature

Space Charge

Cathode

The space charge is created by the various forces acting on the emitted electrons

summary

☐ In an electron tube, electrons usually flow from one element, called a cathode, to a second element, called an anode. ☐ Electrons will be emitted by a cathode if the cathode is heated. ☐ Electrons can also be emitted by photosensitive materials if struck by light of a certain wavelength. Another emission method places a large difference of potential between the cathode and anode. The most common method is the heated cathode.

☐ Directly heated cathodes use a filament that emits electrons. ☐ Indirectly heated cathodes have current passing through a heater, which heats the cathode. ☐ For normal electron emission, the cathode must be heated to the proper temperature. ☐ Vacuum-tube filament circuits are normally rated in terms of filament voltage. This voltage, together with the filament resistance, determines the current. ☐ Filament circuits are designed to operate at standard voltages. Some common filament voltages are 5, 6.3, and 12.6 volts.

☐ For parallel operation, all filament voltage ratings must be the same. ☐ For series operation, all current ratings must be the same, and the voltage ratings must add up to the source voltage. If they do not, a series dropping resistor is used. ☐ The resistance of the dropping resistor is determined by the current rating of the filament circuit and the difference between the source voltage and the sum of the filament voltage ratings. ☐ In a series filament circuit, the heater-to-cathode voltage rating of any tube must not be exceeded.

review questions

1. What is *thermionic emission*?
2. How does current flow in a vacuum tube differ from that in a circuit?
3. What is the disadvantage of a directly heated cathode?
4. What can occur if the cathode current is too high?
5. Explain *photoelectric emission.*
6. Explain *cold cathode emission.*
7. If a filament circuit operates from a 12.6-volt supply, what filament resistance is necessary if 210 milliamperes are required?
8. In a series string, where are tubes with low heater-to-cathode ratings placed?
9. What series-dropping resistor is required if five 6.3-volt and five 12.6-volt filaments are series connected across 110 volts and draw 205 milliamperes?
10. What is a *space charge* or *electron cloud*?

diodes

The space charge around a heated cathode consists of many electrons, which are negatively charged particles. If a *positively charged* electrode is placed near, or around, the cathode, it will *attract* some of the electrons from the space charge. The greater the positive potential on this second electrode, or the closer it is to the cathode, the greater is its attracting force and the more electrons it attracts from the space charge. Tubes that contain a cathode and a positively charged electrode around the cathode are called *diodes*. They are called diodes because they have *two* electrodes: the first is the cathode and the second is the *plate*. The plate is made from metals such as nickel, molybdenum, or monel.

As shown, a diode can be made to conduct continuously by connecting a battery between the plate and cathode, with the *positive* battery terminal connected to the *plate* and the *negative* terminal to the *cathode*. This sets up an electric field between the cathode and plate. The direction of the electrostatic lines of force that make up the field is such that electrons from the space charge are attracted to the plate. Effectively, therefore, a *closed circuit* exists.

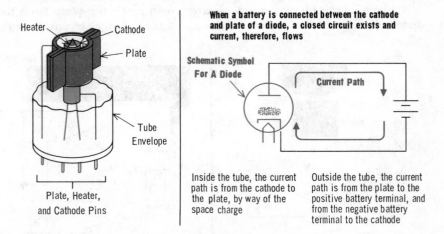

Heater   Cathode   Plate   Tube Envelope

Plate, Heater, and Cathode Pins

When a battery is connected between the cathode and plate of a diode, a closed circuit exists and current, therefore, flows

Schematic Symbol For A Diode

Current Path

Inside the tube, the current path is from the cathode to the plate, by way of the space charge

Outside the tube, the current path is from the plate to the positive battery terminal, and from the negative battery terminal to the cathode

Electrons flow from the space charge to the plate, and then to the positive battery terminal; and from the negative terminal to the cathode, and from there to the space charge. You can see that within the tube, the electrons flow from the cathode into the space charge, and then out of the space charge to the plate. For every electron that leaves the space charge and travels to the plate, one electron is added to the space charge from the cathode. To describe electron flow within an electron tube, it is often convenient to consider the electrons as flowing *directly* from the cathode to the plate. It should always be borne in mind, though, that the space charge is usually present, and that the electron flow is into and out of the space charge.

stopping conduction

You saw on the previous page how a diode can be made to conduct by connecting a battery between the cathode and plate in such a way that the plate is at a positive potential with respect to the cathode. As long as these potentials are maintained, the diode will continue to conduct, provided, of course, that the cathode is kept at its emission temperature. There are various ways in which the conduction can be stopped.

One method is simply to *open the circuit* external to the tube. With the circuit open, no current can flow. Another way of stopping the conduction is to *reverse the battery connections* so that the plate of the tube is negative with respect to the cathode. This reverses the direction of the electrostatic field between the cathode and plate, and causes the emitted electrons to be attracted back into the cathode instead of to the plate.

Conduction can also be stopped by making the potentials on the plate and cathode *equal.* This makes the electrostatic field between the plate and cathode essentially *zero,* with the result that no attracting force is exerted by the plate on the electrons in the space charge. Actually, some of the higher energy electrons will reach the plate from the space charge, but the current produced by these few electrons is negligible.

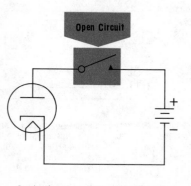

Conduction stops if the diode circuit is opened

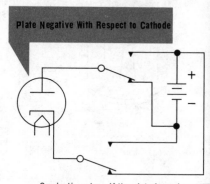

Conduction stops if the plate is made negative with respect to the cathode

Conduction stops if the plate and cathode are placed at the same potential

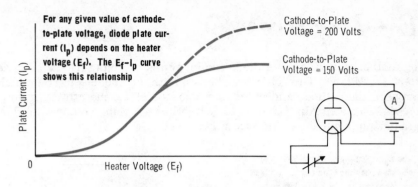

For any given value of cathode-to-plate voltage, diode plate current (I_p) depends on the heater voltage (E_f). The E_f–I_p curve shows this relationship

Cathode-to-Plate Voltage = 200 Volts

Cathode-to-Plate Voltage = 150 Volts

Plate Current (I_p)

0   Heater Voltage (E_f)

For any diode, there are an infinite number of E_f–I_p characteristic curves: one for each possible value of cathode-to-plate voltage

controlling conduction

Diode conduction can be stopped by the methods described on the previous page. The amount of conduction can also be *varied* without being completely stopped. One way of doing this is to apply constant potentials to the plate and cathode, and to vary the heater voltage. Increasing the heater voltage causes more heater current, thereby producing an increase in cathode temperature. More electrons are therefore emitted, and a denser space charge is built up. As a result, a *given* cathode-to-plate voltage will have more electrons attracted to the plate. The converse is true if the heater voltage is reduced. This causes less heater current, a lower cathode temperature, and a less dense space charge. Consequently, less electrons are attracted to the plate for a given cathode-to-plate voltage.

The electrons that reach the plate make up the tube's *plate current*, which is normally abbreviated I_p. In a similar way, the heater voltage is abbreviated E_f. The variation of plate current with changes in heater voltage is shown. Such a curve is called an E_f–I_p *curve*. The solid curve is for a given cathode-to-plate voltage of, say, 150 volts. The broken-line curve is for a higher voltage of, say, 200 volts. Both curves flatten at higher heater voltages. This indicates that for a given cathode-to-plate voltage there is a *limit* to the number of electrons the plate can attract regardless of the density of the space charge. This limit is called the *saturation point.* You can see, though, that the higher the cathode-to-plate voltage, the larger is the value of plate current at which saturation occurs.

E_f–I_p curves are not used very often because electron tubes are operated at standard values of heater voltage in most applications. Other, similar type curves, however, are used extensively to describe the characteristics and performance of tubes. Because of their use, these curves are often called *characteristic curves.*

E_p-I_p curves

Another way of varying diode conduction is by changing the *cathode-to-plate voltage*. This changes the strength of the electrostatic field between the cathode and plate, and also, therefore, the attracting force on the electrons. In general, larger cathode-to-plate voltages produce greater plate currents, and vice versa.

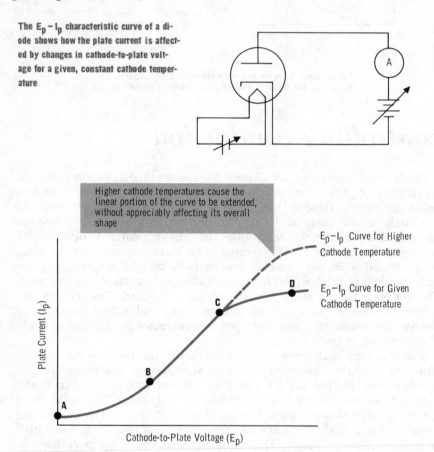

The E_p-I_p characteristic curve of a diode shows how the plate current is affected by changes in cathode-to-plate voltage for a given, constant cathode temperature

Higher cathode temperatures cause the linear portion of the curve to be extended, without appreciably affecting its overall shape

E_p-I_p Curve for Higher Cathode Temperature

E_p-I_p Curve for Given Cathode Temperature

Plate Current (I_p)

Cathode-to-Plate Voltage (E_p)

Probably the most important characteristic curve for an electron tube diode is that which shows the variation of plate current with changes in cathode-to-plate voltage when the emitter temperature is held constant. This more nearly resembles the actual conditions under which diodes are used than does the E_f–I_p curve shown on the previous page. A characteristic curve showing values of plate current for different values of cathode-to-plate voltage is called an E_p–I_p *curve,* with E_p representing the cathode-to-plate voltage, and I_p the plate current. Such a curve for a representative diode is shown.

E_p-I_p curves (cont.)

For low values of cathode-to-plate voltage (from point A to point B), the diode's E_p-vs.-I_p characteristic is *nonlinear*. In other words, *equal changes* in cathode-to-plate voltage produce *different changes* in plate current. Between points B and C, though, the curve is essentially *linear*. In this range, therefore, *equal changes* in cathode-to-plate voltage produce *equal changes* in plate current. Between points C and D, the curve again becomes *nonlinear*, with equal increases in cathode-to-plate voltage producing smaller and smaller changes in plate current. Above point D, the curve essentially flattens, since *saturation* is reached. Further increases in the cathode-to-plate voltage have little or no effect on plate current.

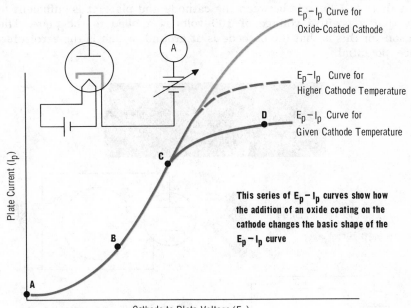

E_p-I_p Curve for
Oxide-Coated Cathode

E_p-I_p Curve for
Higher Cathode Temperature

E_p-I_p Curve for
Given Cathode Temperature

This series of E_p-I_p curves show how the addition of an oxide coating on the cathode changes the basic shape of the E_p-I_p curve

Plate Current (I_p)

Cathode-to-Plate Voltage (E_p)

For diodes having *oxide-coated* cathodes, saturation does not occur until extremely high values of cathode-to-plate voltage are reached. So high are the voltages, in fact, that the tube would be damaged before saturation occurred. For this reason, the E_p-I_p curve of diodes having oxide-coated cathodes does not flatten after point D, but shows a continuous rise.

From the curve, you can see that a small amount of plate current flows even when the value of cathode-to-plate voltage is zero. This is due to some high-energy electrons emitted by the cathode reaching the plate in spite of the fact that the plate exerts no attracting force on them. The current produced by these electrons, however, is very small.

ground

In most electronic circuits, all voltages are with respect to some *common* potential, which serves as the zero reference potential. This zero reference potential is called *ground,* and may be a common wire, a metal chassis or frame, or a rod or pipe that is buried in the earth. In any case, ground is a conductor whose potential effectively never changes regardless of how other potentials throughout a circuit may vary.

In circuits where ground is used, all expressed voltages are given with respect to ground, unless otherwise stated. Thus, if the positive terminal of a 100-volt battery is connected to the plate of a diode, and both the negative battery terminal and the cathode are connected to ground, the circuit will conduct the same as if the battery was connected directly between the cathode and plate. However, instead of saying that there is 100 volts between the cathode and plate, it is sufficient to say that a positive voltage of 100 volts is applied to the plate. The reason for this is that the cathode is at ground, which is the zero reference potential.

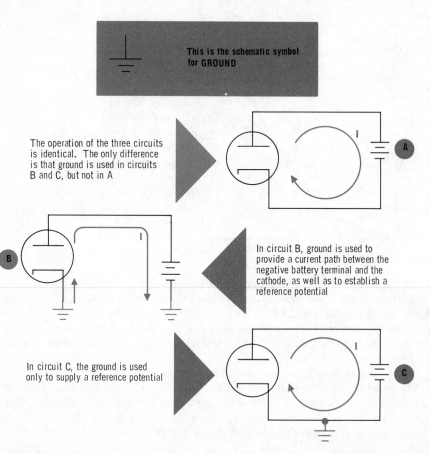

This is the schematic symbol for GROUND

The operation of the three circuits is identical. The only difference is that ground is used in circuits B and C, but not in A

A

B

In circuit B, ground is used to provide a current path between the negative battery terminal and the cathode, as well as to establish a reference potential

In circuit C, the ground is used only to supply a reference potential

C

plate resistance

You have seen how changes in the plate voltage of a diode produce changes in plate current. Since the tube does not act as a short circuit, it must exert some *control* over the amount of current flow. This control is in the form of opposition to current flow, similar to that offered by resistors. It is entirely proper, therefore, to view the diode as the equivalent of a *resistor*, provided, of course, that the plate voltage is positive, so that the tube conducts.

The opposition offered to current flow by a diode arises from many causes, among which are the size of the electrodes and the spacing between them, and the energy wasted by the electrons during emission as well as their interaction within the space charge. Regardless of its causes, the opposition has the same effect as that offered by a resistor, and so it is called the *plate resistance* of the tube, and is expressed in ohms.

Actually, there are two kinds of plate resistance: dc and ac. The d-c plate resistance is designated R_p, and is found by applying a *d-c plate voltage*, measuring the resulting plate current, and then using Ohm's Law to find the equivalent resistance. For example, if a d-c plate voltage of 10 volts resulted in a plate current of 10 milliamperes, the d-c plate resistance would be 1000 ohms.

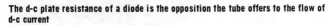

The d-c plate resistance of a diode is the opposition the tube offers to the flow of d-c current

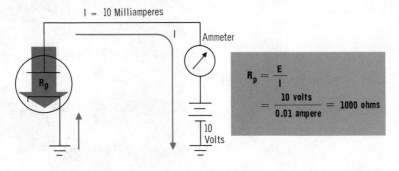

I = 10 Milliamperes

Ammeter

$$R_p = \frac{E}{I}$$
$$= \frac{10 \text{ volts}}{0.01 \text{ ampere}} = 1000 \text{ ohms}$$

10 Volts

Although the d-c plate resistance of a diode has the same opposing effect on current flow as does the resistance of a resistor, there is a significant difference between the two. A resistor has essentially the same resistance value regardless of the value of the applied voltage. It is, therefore, a *linear* device, since equal changes in applied voltage produce equal changes in current. A diode, on the other hand, is *not* a linear device. Its d-c plate resistance is not constant, but *decreases* as the plate voltage is *increased*. This is the reason why the E_p–I_p curve, discussed previously, is not a straight line. Even the portion of the E_p–I_p curve that is considered linear is not really so, but is curved slightly.

plate resistance (cont.)

In summary, then, a value of d-c plate resistance applies only to a *single* value of plate voltage. At other values of plate voltage, the d-c plate resistance is different. The *higher* the *plate voltage,* the *lower* is the *d-c plate resistance.*

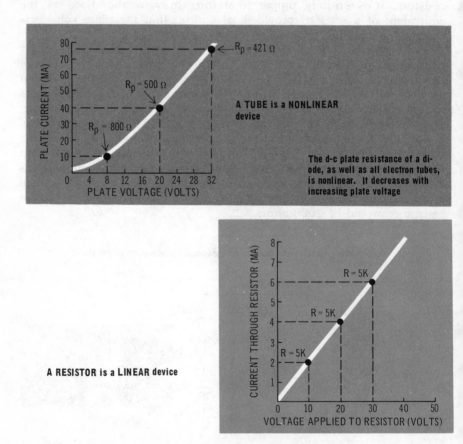

A TUBE is a NONLINEAR device

The d-c plate resistance of a diode, as well as all electron tubes, is nonlinear. It decreases with increasing plate voltage

A RESISTOR is a LINEAR device

Under actual operating conditions, diodes, as well as all other electron tubes, operate on *a-c* voltages, which include *fluctuating dc* because of its similarity to ac. In the case of a diode, this means that an a-c voltage is applied to the plate. Under these conditions, the resistance offered by the tube to current flow is different than it is when a d-c plate voltage is used. This resistance is called the *a-c plate resistance* of the tube, and is designated r_p to distinguish it from the d-c plate resistance, R_p. Generally, whenever the term *plate resistance* is used, it is the a-c plate resistance that is meant, unless specified otherwise.

Like the d-c plate resistance, the a-c plate resistance depends on the plate voltage, and decreases as the plate voltage increases.

plate resistance (cont.)

The value of the a-c resistance is equal to the *ratio* of a small change in plate voltage to the corresponding change in plate current that it produces. As an equation:

$$r_p = \frac{\Delta e_p}{\Delta i_p}$$

where Δ is the Greek letter delta, and represents "a small change," and e_p and i_p are a-c plate voltage and current, respectively.

The a-c plate resistance can be determined from a diode's E_p–I_p curve, as is the d-c plate resistance. For example, the E_p–I_p curve shown is the same as that used for calculating d-c plate resistance. If we take a small change in a-c plate voltage of from 18.4 to 21.6 volts, which is a change ranging 1.6 volts above and below 20 volts, the a-c resistance would be:

$$r_p = \frac{\Delta e_p}{\Delta i_p} = \frac{(21.6 - 18.4)\ \text{volts}}{(0.045 - 0.035)\ \text{amperes}} = 320\ \text{ohms}$$

This means that with an a-c plate voltage of 20 volts, the a-c plate resistance of the tube is 320 ohms. At the same value of d-c plate voltage, you will recall that the d-c resistance of the tube was 500 ohms. This same relationship holds for all other values of plate voltage, with r_p being almost one half less than R_p.

In calculating values of r_p, the accuracy of the results depends on how small Δe_p is. The smaller the current change used, the more accurate is the result.

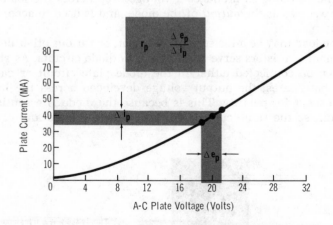

The a-c resistance of a diode is almost one-half smaller than the d-c resistance for all practical values of plate voltage. It is, therefore, nonlinear to the same degree

The useful output of a diode is developed across a load, which may be connected
either in the plate circuit or the cathode circuit

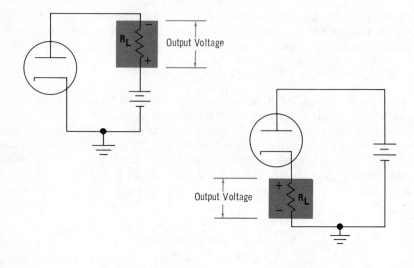

Output Voltage

Output Voltage

adding a load

Until now, you have learned about the diode as a *static* device, capable of conducting when the proper potentials are applied, but performing no useful function. For a diode to be useful, a *load* must be connected to its external circuit. The plate current of the diode then flows through the load, and in doing so produces a voltage drop across the load. This voltage drop serves as the *output* of the diode, and is used to accomplish some function.

The diode load may be a resistor, an inductor, or various other devices. Most commonly, resistors serve as the loads in diode circuits. As shown, the load can be connected either in the diode plate circuit or cathode circuit. In both cases, the output voltage developed across the load is the *same*, except for polarity. This is because the diode is essentially a series circuit, so the same current flows in both the plate and cathode circuits.

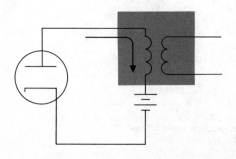

This is the way a transformer
could be used as a diode load

E_p-I_p curve with a load

The diode E_p–I_p curves described previously represent *static* diode characteristics, since they are derived with *no load* in the circuit. The addition of a load changes the diode E_p–I_p curve. Such a modified curve represents the actual conditions under which the tube is used and is called a *dynamic* characteristic curve.

With a load in the diode circuit, the total circuit resistance consists essentially of the plate resistance of the tube plus the resistance of the load. The overall circuit resistance is therefore *greater* than it would be if the load was not present. Consequently, the plate current is less than its value under static conditions. The plate resistance decreases as the plate voltage is increased, but the load resistance, as represented by a resistor, remains constant regardless of changes in plate voltage.

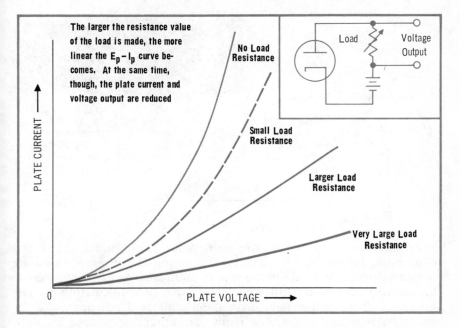

If the load resistance is small, the changes in *total circuit* resistance caused by changes in plate voltage are significant, since the plate resistance is an appreciable part of the total resistance. But, if the load resistance is very large compared to the plate resistance, the total resistance changes very little with changes in plate voltage. This has the effect of making the E_p–I_p curve relatively *linear*. The larger the load resistance is compared to the tube's plate resistance, the more linear the E_p–I_p curve. However, the increase in linearity is gained at the expense of a decrease in plate current, and, therefore, voltage output. The selection of the load resistance value in any particular application thus involves a choice or a compromise between linearity and output voltage.

the diode as a rectifier

You recall from Volume 2 that a rectifier converts a-c voltages into fluctuating dc. Because of their characteristic of conducting in only *one direction,* diodes are considered *unidirectional* devices, and are ideally suited for use as *rectifiers.* A diode rectifier, together with its input and output waveforms, is shown. During the positive half cycles of the input voltage, the plate is positive with respect to the cathode, so the tube conducts. The resulting plate current produces a voltage drop across load resistor R_L, and this voltage serves as the diode output. During the negative half cycles of the input voltage, the plate is negative with respect to the cathode. As a result, the diode does not conduct, so no output voltage is developed across the load resistor. In this condition, the diode is said to be *cut off.*

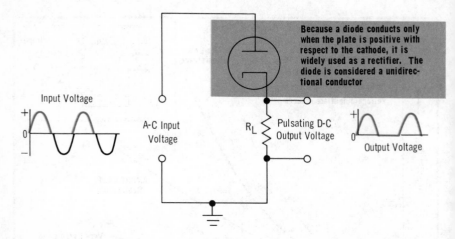

Because a diode conducts only when the plate is positive with respect to the cathode, it is widely used as a rectifier. The diode is considered a unidirectional conductor

Input Voltage

A-C Input Voltage

R_L

Pulsating D-C Output Voltage

Output Voltage

By conducting during positive half cycles of the input signal and cutting off during negative half cycles, the diode delivers a pulsating output voltage that varies between zero and some positive value. Since the output varies in amplitude but not polarity, it is fluctuating dc. The frequency of the output pulsations is the same as the frequency of the a-c input voltage. That is, one output pulsation is produced for each complete cycle of the input voltage.

In the circuit shown, the values of the a-c input voltage and the load resistance are such that the diode is operated essentially on the linear portion of its E_p–I_p curve. The output pulsations, therefore, have basically the same waveform as the positive half cycles of the input signal. The instantaneous value of the output voltage is equal to the instantaneous voltage drop across the load resistor minus the drop across the tube itself, or instantaneous output voltage $= (i_p \times R_L) - (i_p \times r_p)$. If the load resistance is very large compared to the plate resistance, the voltage drop across the diode is very small and can be neglected. The output voltage is then merely $E_{OUTPUT} = i_p \times R_L$.

factors affecting plate current

From the preceding pages, you can see that there are various factors that affect diode plate current under actual operating conditions. One of these, the *cathode temperature,* is always fixed for optimum operation by the use of standard filament voltages. The other factor that affects plate current is the *voltage* applied between the *plate* and *cathode.* This voltage may be ac, such as is used when the diode rectifies ac to fluctuating dc, or it may be a combination of a-c and d-c voltages.

When both an a-c and a d-c voltage are used, each performs a different function. The a-c voltage, the *signal voltage,* is the voltage that is to be processed by the tube. The d-c voltage, the *bias voltage,* determines where on the tube's characteristic curve the signal voltage will cause the tube to operate. For example, if no d-c bias voltage is used and the signal voltage is *small,* the tube will operate on the lower, *nonlinear* portion of its characteristic curve, and will rectify the signal.

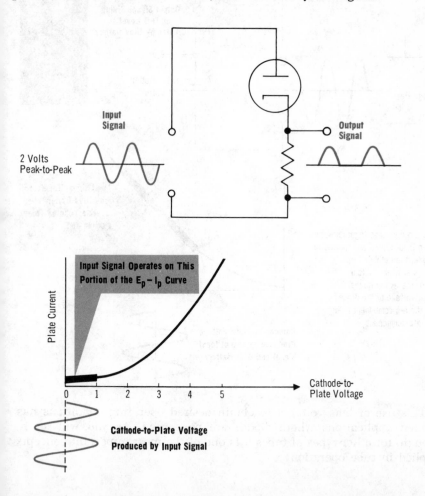

factors affecting
plate current (*cont.*)

If a d-c bias voltage is applied to the diode, the instantaneous cathode-to-plate voltage is the *sum* of the d-c voltage and the signal voltage. If the amplitude of the d-c voltage is sufficient, the sum of the two voltages can be large enough to cause the tube to operate on the central, or *linear,* portion of its characteristic curve. As a matter of fact, by using an appropriate value of d-c bias voltage, operation at any desired point on the E_p–I_p characteristic curve can be achieved.

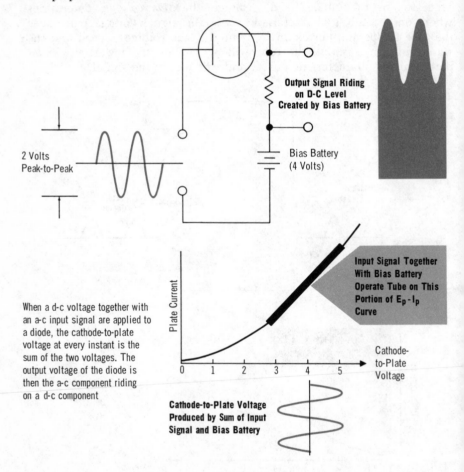

Output Signal Riding
on D-C Level
Created by Bias Battery

2 Volts
Peak-to-Peak

Bias Battery
(4 Volts)

When a d-c voltage together with an a-c input signal are applied to a diode, the cathode-to-plate voltage at every instant is the sum of the two voltages. The output voltage of the diode is then the a-c component riding on a d-c component

Plate Current

Input Signal Together
With Bias Battery
Operate Tube on This
Portion of E_p-I_p
Curve

Cathode-
to-Plate
Voltage

Cathode-to-Plate Voltage
Produced by Sum of Input
Signal and Bias Battery

This use of bias voltages to obtain desired operating conditions has limited applications where diodes are concerned. As you will learn, though, for other types of tubes it is one of the most important concepts applied in tube operation.

summary

☐ A diode consists of a plate and cathode. ☐ Electrons will flow from the cathode to the plate as long as the plate voltage is more positive than the cathode voltage. No electrons will flow if the cathode voltage is equal to or more positive than the plate voltage. This flow of electrons is called plate current. ☐ Plate current can be varied by changing either the heater voltage or the plate voltage. Normally, only the plate voltage is changed. ☐ E_p–I_p curves are normally used to represent the characteristics of a diode. For a given diode, these curves show how the plate current changes because of changes in plate voltage for different values of filament voltage. ☐ Increasing the plate voltage beyond a certain value will not cause a corresponding increase in plate current. This is the saturation point of the diode.

☐ Plate resistance opposes the flow of current in a diode. This resistance is nonlinear and decreases as the plate voltage increases. ☐ The d-c plate resistance, R_p, is determined by the d-c plate voltage and resulting plate current. ☐ Dynamic or a-c plate resistance, r_p, is normally used because diodes operate on a-c voltages. This resistance is determined by changes in plate voltage and corresponding changes in plate current.

☐ For a diode to be useful, a load must be connected in the cathode or plate circuit. This load is always in series with the plate resistance. ☐ The load resistance plus the diode plate resistance determine the plate current for a given plate voltage. ☐ If the load resistance is small with respect to the plate resistance, changes in plate resistance are significant. ☐ If the load resistance is large with respect to the plate resistance, changes in plate resistance are negligible. ☐ Diodes are called unidirectional devices because current flows in only one direction. Because of this feature, diodes are ideally suited for use as rectifiers.

review questions

1. What is a *diode*?
2. How can diode plate current be increased? Decreased?
3. Can current flow in a diode increase indefinitely? Explain.
4. What are E_f–I_p and E_p–I_p curves?
5. Why are E_p–I_p curves used more often than E_f–I_p curves?
6. What is *ground*?
7. How is the d-c plate resistance determined?
8. How is the a-c plate resistance determined?
9. How does a load resistor affect plate current?
10. How do diodes rectify a-c signals?

the need for more control

As you will learn in later volumes, the diode is a relatively versatile device, and is used extensively in various electronic applications. Despite its usefulness, the diode does not possess the ability to *amplify*. That is, it cannot deliver an output voltage having a *greater amplitude* than its input voltage. As a matter of fact, the output voltage is always somewhat *less* than the input voltage because of the losses that occur across the plate resistance of the tube.

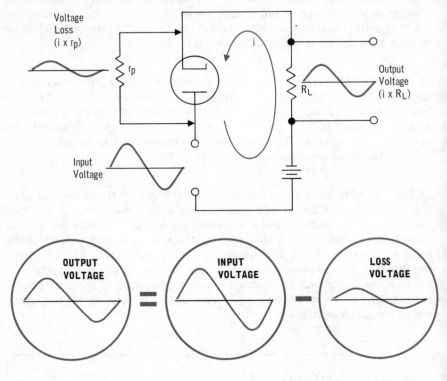

The output voltage of a diode is always somewhat less than the input voltage because of losses introduced by the tube's plate resistance

The inability of the diode to amplify was significant in the lack of development of early radio communications. Prior to 1907, radio signals could be generated and transmitted over distances up to several hundred miles. However, reliable reception and reproduction of these signals was virtually impossible because of their extremely small amplitudes at the point of reception. Only by developing a means of amplifying these weak signals could the field of radio communications grow to the advanced level that we know today. This means came about in 1907 when De Forest added a *third* electrode to the basic diode.

triodes

De Forest added a third electrode, called the *control grid,* to the standard diode. Such tubes are called *triodes.* The control grid is a wire-mesh structure that completely surrounds the cathode and is positioned closer to the cathode than the plate is. The particular shape used depends on the desired characteristics of the tube. As you can see, the control grid is essentially an *open* structure. It does not physically interfere with the electron flow from cathode to plate.

TYPICAL CONTROL GRID SHAPES

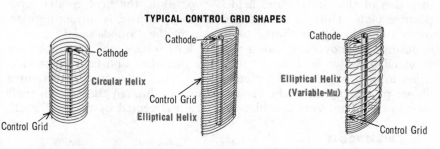

Circular Helix
Cathode
Control Grid

Cathode
Control Grid
Elliptical Helix

Cathode
Elliptical Helix
(Variable-Mu)
Control Grid

The grid controls the cathode-to-plate electron flow in the tube. This is accomplished by applying a voltage between the control grid and the cathode, which sets up an electrostatic field between these two electrodes within the tube. There are thus *two* electrostatic fields within the tube: one between the plate and cathode, and the other between the control grid and cathode.

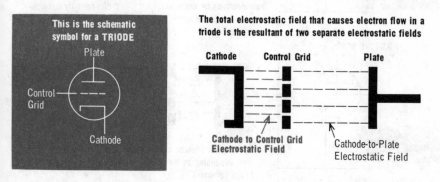

This is the schematic symbol for a TRIODE

Plate
Control Grid
Cathode

The total electrostatic field that causes electron flow in a triode is the resultant of two separate electrostatic fields

Cathode   Control Grid   Plate

Cathode to Control Grid Electrostatic Field

Cathode-to-Plate Electrostatic Field

Various types of voltages can be applied between the control grid and cathode. When a d-c voltage is applied, and its purpose is to set the operating conditions of the tube somewhere on its characteristic curve, it is called a grid-bias voltage, or just *bias.* When a voltage that is to be amplified, or otherwise processed by the tube, is applied between the cathode and grid, it is called the *signal voltage.* Signal voltages can be ac or dc. Under actual operating conditions, both a bias voltage and a signal voltage are usually applied between the cathode and control grid of a triode.

bias voltages

A d-c bias voltage applied between the control grid and the cathode of a triode can make the grid either positive or negative with respect to the cathode, depending on its polarity. If the grid is positive with respect to the cathode, it is *positive bias;* and if the grid is negative with respect to the cathode, it is *negative bias.*

As you know, a voltage between the grid and cathode produces an electrostatic field between them. If the bias voltage is negative, the direction of the electrostatic field is *opposite* to the field created by a positive plate. Thus, while the cathode-to-plate field is attracting electrons from the space charge to the plate, the cathode-to-grid field is opposing this movement. For a positive bias voltage, the conditions are reversed. The two fields are in the *same* direction, and both cause electrons to be attracted to the plate. The spacing between the grid wires allows practically all of the electrons to pass through the grid on their way to the plate. Very few electrons are intercepted by the grid itself.

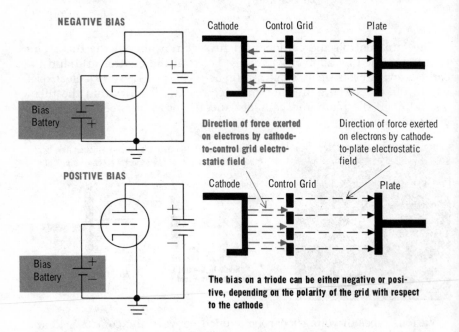

The bias on a triode can be either negative or positive, depending on the polarity of the grid with respect to the cathode

Since the grid is much closer to the cathode than the plate, its field has a greater effect. The strength of an electrostatic field is *inversely proportional* to the *spacing* between the two charged bodies creating the field. This means that for the same voltage between the plate and cathode and the grid and cathode, the grid-to-cathode field in the triode is much stronger than the plate-to-cathode field. As a result, the grid voltage has much *greater* control over conduction within the tube than does the plate voltage.

bias voltages (cont.)

As you will see later, the fact that the grid-to-cathode voltage of a triode has much more control over conduction than does the plate voltage is the reason that the triode is able to amplify. As an example of this difference in degree of control, consider a diode that has 100 milliamperes of plate current when the plate voltage is 50 volts. To increase the plate current to 200 milliamperes, the plate voltage must be raised to 90 volts. Thus, the plate voltage must be increased by 40 volts to obtain a 100-milliampere increase in plate current.

If a control grid is inserted to make the tube a triode, the situation is very different. With a plate voltage of 90 volts and a grid-to-cathode voltage of −3 volts, the plate current is again 100 milliamperes. But, to increase the current to 200 milliamperes, all that is required is to reduce the grid-to-cathode voltage to −1 volt, leaving the plate voltage at 90 volts. Thus, the same plate current change that required a 40-volt increase in plate voltage in the diode can be achieved with only a 2-volt change in grid-to-cathode voltage in the triode.

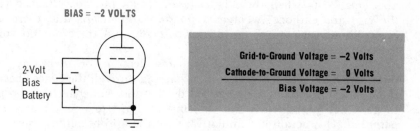

When ground is used as the common reference potential, the bias voltage is the algebraic difference of the grid-to-ground and cathode-to-ground voltages

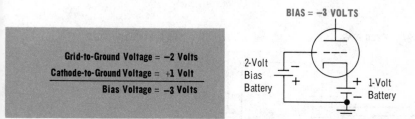

An important point that you should remember about the bias voltage of a triode is that it is the d-c voltage between the *grid* and *cathode*. As shown, if the cathode is at ground potential, the bias voltage is also the voltage between the grid and ground. However, as you will learn, very often the cathode is not at ground potential. The voltage between the grid and ground is then *not* the same as that between the grid and cathode; and, unless otherwise specified, the bias is the voltage between grid and cathode.

the effect of zero bias

When the control grid is at the *same* potential as the cathode, as shown in A, the bias on the triode is zero. In this case, there is no difference of potential between the grid and cathode. The triode, therefore, operates essentially as a diode, since electron flow is influenced only by the plate-to-cathode electrostatic field.

With zero bias, a very small current flows from the space charge to the grid, out of the tube, through the grid circuit, and back to the cathode. This current flows because the grid is positive with respect to the negatively charged space charge, and therefore *attracts* electrons. This is called *grid current*. Grid current that flows with zero bias is very small, and normally has little effect on the operation of the tube. As you will learn later, though, grid current can have an undesirable effect.

When the control grid of a triode is not connected to the cathode, ground, or any other circuit element, it is called a free, or *floating,* grid. This condition is sometimes confused with zero bias, when, actually, its effects are vastly different. A good point to remember, therefore, is that *zero bias* exists when there is a *closed circuit* but no voltage between the grid and cathode; whereas a *floating grid* means that there is an *open circuit* between the grid and cathode, and therefore no voltage between the two.

When a floating grid does exist, some electrons on their way to the plate strike the grid wires instead of passing through the spaces between them. These electrons are *absorbed* by the grid, but then have no place to go. They just accumulate, causing the grid to develop a *negative potential*. This action is cumulative, with the grid becoming more negative as it accumulates more electrons. Under certain conditions, the grid can become so negative that it practically stops the tube from conducting. In general, a floating grid produces erratic tube operation.

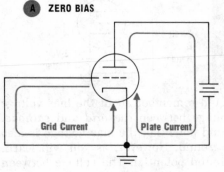

A ZERO BIAS

A small grid current flows under conditions of zero bias

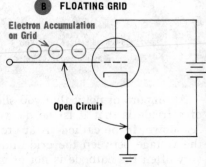

B FLOATING GRID

When the grid is floating, it builds up a negative potential as a result of electrons striking the grid wires on their way to the plate

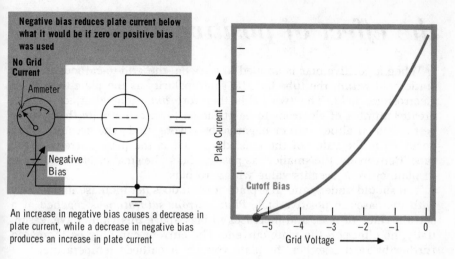

Negative bias reduces plate current below what it would be if zero or positive bias was used

No Grid Current

Ammeter

Negative Bias

An increase in negative bias causes a decrease in plate current, while a decrease in negative bias produces an increase in plate current

Plate Current

Cutoff Bias

Grid Voltage

−5 −4 −3 −2 −1 0

the effect of negative bias

When a negative bias is applied to a triode, the grid-to-cathode electrostatic field within the tube *opposes* the plate-to-cathode field. The electron flow within the tube, or the plate current, is therefore *less* than it would be if the bias was zero or positive. The more negative the bias is made, the stronger is the grid-to-cathode electrostatic field, and so the less the tube conducts.

For every tube, there is a value of negative bias which, for all practical purposes, prevents any electron from reaching the plate. The tube is then said to be *cut off,* and the value of bias that brings this condition about is called *cutoff bias.* There is no one value of cutoff bias for a tube because the negative bias voltage effectively works in opposition to the tube's plate voltage. Consequently, the greater the plate voltage, the larger is the value of negative bias required to cut off the tube.

When dealing with bias voltages, it is common practice to refer to an increase or decrease in bias. For negative bias voltage, an *increase* in bias means that the bias voltage becomes *more negative,* such as from −3 to −5 volts. This results in a reduction in the tube's plate current, assuming, of course, that the plate voltage is held constant, which is the usual case. A *decrease* in bias, when referring to negative voltages, means that the bias voltage becomes *less negative,* such as from −3 to −1 volts. This results in an increase in the tube's plate current.

When a negative bias is used, the grid is maintained at a negative potential. It, therefore, does not attract electrons from the space charge as it does when it has a positive potential with respect to the space charge. This means that no grid current flows when negative bias is used. Since, as you will learn later, grid current is generally undesirable, negative bias is practically always used in actual tube circuits.

the effect of positive bias

When a positive bias is applied to a triode, the grid-to-cathode electrostatic field within the tube has the *same* polarity as the plate-to-cathode electrostatic field. The two fields therefore *aid* each other, causing a greater number of electrons to be attracted toward the plate than would be the case if either zero or negative bias were used. The greater (more positive) is the value of the bias, the larger is the plate current in the tube. Conversely, the smaller the positive bias, the smaller is the increase in plate current over its value with zero bias.

You should understand that plate current does *not* increase indefinitely with increases in positive bias. *Plate current saturation* is reached at a certain value of bias, and increases in bias above this value have, essentially, no effect on the plate current. The current can only be increased further by raising either the plate voltage or cathode temperature.

When positive bias is used, the positive grid results in the flow of *considerable grid current*. The larger the positive bias, the greater is the amount of grid current. Since grid current is generally undesirable, positive bias is rarely used, even though it results in large values of plate current. As a result, the term *bias* is generally understood to mean *negative bias*, unless otherwise specified.

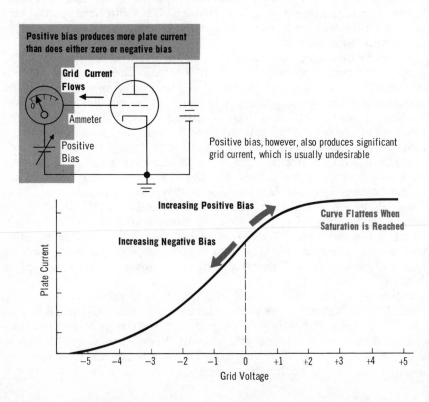

Positive bias produces more plate current than does either zero or negative bias

Grid Current Flows

Ammeter

Positive Bias

Positive bias, however, also produces significant grid current, which is usually undesirable

Increasing Positive Bias

Curve Flattens When Saturation is Reached

Increasing Negative Bias

Plate Current

−5   −4   −3   −2   −1   0   +1   +2   +3   +4   +5

Grid Voltage

summary

☐ Triodes are three-element vacuum tubes containing a plate, a cathode, and a control grid. ☐ The control grid is made of wire mesh and is physically placed between the plate and cathode. ☐ During normal triode operation, there is usually a difference of potential between the grid and cathode. This is called a grid bias voltage, or bias. ☐ Because of the close proximity of the grid to the cathode, bias has a greater control over tube conduction than plate voltage.

☐ Negative bias occurs when the grid is negative with respect to the cathode. This bias produces an electrostatic field that opposes the flow of electrons between cathode and plate. ☐ As negative bias increases (becomes more negative), the plate current is reduced. ☐ Cutoff bias is that bias that effectively stops plate current from flowing. ☐ Positive bias occurs when the grid is positive with respect to the cathode. Positive bias produces an electrostatic field that aids the flow of electrons between the cathode and the plate. ☐ Plate current saturation occurs at some value of positive bias where a further increase in positive bias does not cause a corresponding increase in plate current. ☐ When the grid is positive, electrons are attracted to the grid and appreciable grid current flows. This is undesirable.

☐ In some applications, the grid is externally connected to the cathode. In these applications, there is no difference in grid-to-cathode potential and the bias is zero. The triode then acts as a diode except that a small amount of grid current flows. ☐ A floating grid is not connected to ground, the cathode, or any other circuit element. Some electrons traveling to the plate from the cathode hit the grid wires instead of passing through. ☐ Electrons accumulating on the grid restrict plate current flow. Under certain conditions, this accumulation of electrons can cut off the tube. ☐ A triode with a floating grid results in erratic operation.

review questions

1. What does the triode have that the diode does not?
2. What can the triode do that the diode cannot?
3. What two electrostatic fields affect conduction in a triode?
4. What effect does negative bias have on tube conduction?
5. What occurs when the negative bias becomes excessive?
6. What effect does positive bias have on tube conduction?
7. What occurs when the positive bias becomes excessive?
8. Under what conditions will grid current flow?
9. What is the complete path for grid current flow?
10. Why doesn't a floating grid draw current flow?

adding a load resistor

As was the case with the diode, the operation of a triode without a load represents a *static* condition. In practical operation, the plate current of a diode must flow through a load if the tube is to deliver an output voltage and thus perform some useful function. Most commonly, the load is connected between the plate and the source of plate voltage. Plate current, therefore, flows through a *series circuit* consisting of the tube, the load, and the plate voltage source.

The flow of plate current causes a voltage drop across the load, which, for a given load resistance, is proportional to the value of plate current. If the grid is biased sufficiently negative to cut off the tube, no plate current flows, and therefore no voltage drop is produced across the load. If the bias is reduced to the point where the tube just begins to conduct, a small amount of plate current flows, thereby producing a small voltage drop across the load. And as the bias is reduced closer and closer to zero, more and more plate current flows, with the result that a larger and larger voltage drop is produced across the load.

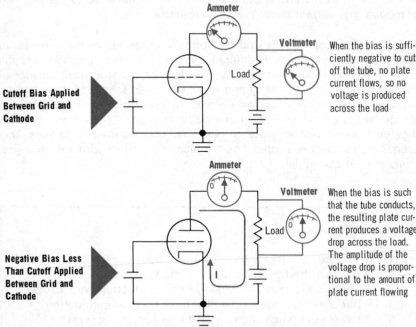

Cutoff Bias Applied Between Grid and Cathode

When the bias is sufficiently negative to cut off the tube, no plate current flows, so no voltage is produced across the load

Negative Bias Less Than Cutoff Applied Between Grid and Cathode

When the bias is such that the tube conducts, the resulting plate current produces a voltage drop across the load. The amplitude of the voltage drop is proportional to the amount of plate current flowing

For any given value of bias, the amount of plate current that flows with a load in the circuit is always *less* than would flow under the same conditions without a load. This should be obvious, since the load is essentially a resistance added in series with the plate circuit. In essence, the load reduces the effectiveness of the plate-to-cathode voltage in producing plate current.

plate circuit voltages

Under static conditions, which occur when no load is used, only one voltage exists in the plate circuit of a triode. This is the applied plate voltage. Actually, a voltage drop also exists, caused by the plate current flowing through the plate resistance of the tube. However, this voltage drop is always equal in amplitude but opposite in polarity to the applied plate voltage. This is in accordance with *Kirchhoff's voltage law*, which states that the algebraic sum of the applied voltages and the voltage drops in a series circuit is equal to zero. When a load is added, the plate circuit voltages still follow Kirchhoff's law, but are drastically changed.

As shown, when a load is used there are *three* voltages in the triode plate circuit. One of these is the applied plate voltage, designated E_{bb}; and the other two are the voltage drop across the plate resistance of the tube, designated E_p; and the voltage drop across the load resistor, designated E_L. Under actual operating conditions, the applied plate voltage (E_{bb}) is *constant*, and changes in plate current are brought about by changes in grid voltage. According to Kirchhoff's law, therefore, the sum of the two voltage drops (E_p and E_L) must always be equal to the applied plate voltage, regardless of the value of plate current:

$$E_{bb} = E_p + E_L$$

Since the two voltage drops are the products of the common plate current, i_p, and the respective plate and load resistances, r_p and R_L, the above equation can also be expressed as:

$$E_{bb} = i_p r_p + i_p R_L$$

You can see from this equation that the plate resistance of a triode, like that of a diode, is *variable,* with its exact value depending on the value of plate current. Effectively, the plate resistance changes with varying plate current in such a way that the sum of the voltage drops $i_p r_p$ and $i_, R_L$ are always equal to E_{bb}.

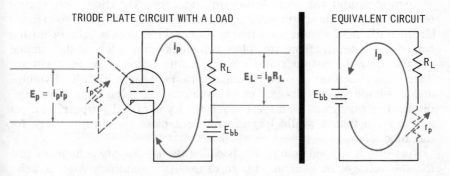

TRIODE PLATE CIRCUIT WITH A LOAD   EQUIVALENT CIRCUIT

The sum of the voltage drops across the plate and load resistances of a triode is always equal to the applied plate voltage

effect of d-c plate current

Whenever plate current flows in a triode, it produces voltage drops across both the load and the plate resistance of the tube. And, as you saw on the previous page, the sum of these voltage drops is equal to the applied plate voltage, E_{bb}. If the plate current has a constant value, or, in other words, is dc, the two voltage drops similarly have constant amplitudes. The voltage across the load is equal to the plate current times the load resistance.

The voltage drop across the tube's plate resistance is called the *plate voltage*, since it exists between the plate and the cathode, which is normally at ground potential. The plate voltage can also be calculated by Ohm's Law by multiplying the plate current by the tube's plate resistance at that particular value of plate current. However, since the sum of the plate voltage (E_p) and the load voltage (E_L) equals the applied voltage, the plate voltage is simply equal to the applied voltage *minus* the output voltage:

$$E_p = E_{bb} - E_L$$

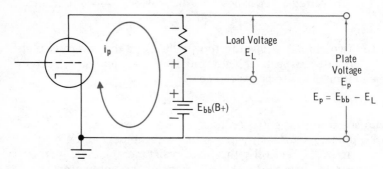

When the tube is cut off, the load voltage is zero and the plate voltage equals the applied voltage

To understand the significance of the above equation, you should realize that it is the plate voltage, E_p, that sets up the plate-to-cathode electrostatic field within the tube, and, therefore, affects tube operating conditions. And, in effect, this plate voltage is what is left of the applied voltage *after* the output voltage is taken into account. As you will see later, tube operation is often a compromise between a high load voltage and a suitable plate voltage. For example, with a given applied voltage, the load voltage must be large enough for its intended purpose, and yet not so large that it would leave insufficient plate operating voltage for the tube.

Very often, applied voltage E_{bb} is called the *B+ supply voltage,* or just the B+ voltage. In general, this term means a relatively *high positive voltage,* regardless of whether it is produced by batteries or electronic power supplies.

effect of varying plate current

The relationships between the applied voltage and the voltage drops across the load resistance and the tube plate resistance are extremely important if you are to understand the operation of a triode in actual circuits. You saw on page 3-39 that whenever the plate current increases, due to a change in grid-to-cathode voltage, the voltage *drop* across the load also increases. This is because the load resistance has a *constant* value, so any increase in current through it produces a larger voltage drop. For the sum of the two voltage drops to still equal the applied voltage, the voltage *drop* across the tube, $i_p r_p$, must decrease by the same amount that the voltage drop across the load, $i_p R_L$, increases. In other words, when plate current increases, the plate resistance effectively decreases to the value required to make $i_p r_p + i_p R_L = E_{bb}$. Similarly, when the plate current decreases, the plate resistance increases to the value required to maintain the Kirchhoff's law relationship between plate circuit voltages.

What the above means is that a change in plate current produces equal voltage changes across the load and the tube. However, the two voltage changes are in *opposite directions;* when one increases, the other decreases, and vice versa. For example, with a given value of plate current flowing and an applied voltage (E_{bb}) of 200 volts, the voltage drops across the load and the tube might both be 100 volts.

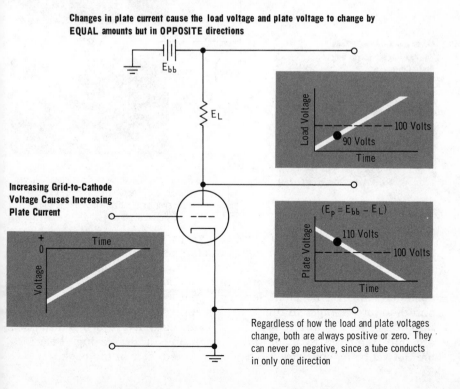

Changes in plate current cause the load voltage and plate voltage to change by EQUAL amounts but in OPPOSITE directions

E_{bb}

E_L

Load Voltage

Time

100 Volts

90 Volts

Increasing Grid-to-Cathode Voltage Causes Increasing Plate Current

Voltage

+
0

Time

$(E_p = E_{bb} - E_L)$

Plate Voltage

110 Volts

100 Volts

Time

Regardless of how the load and plate voltages change, both are always positive or zero. They can never go negative, since a tube conducts in only one direction

effect of
varying plate current (cont.)

If an increase in plate current then causes the voltage drop across the load to increase by 20 volts to a new value of 120 volts, the plate resistance of the tube will effectively decrease so that the new value of plate current will produce a voltage drop of 80 volts. The new voltage drops are thus 120 and 80 volts, and their sum still equals the applied voltage of 200 volts. In a similar way, if a decrease in plate current causes the voltage drop across the load to decrease 10 volts to a new value of 90 volts, the drop across the tube will increase 10 volts to 110 volts. The sum of the two voltage drops thus remains constant at 200 volts.

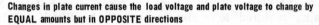

Changes in plate current cause the load voltage and plate voltage to change by EQUAL amounts but in OPPOSITE directions

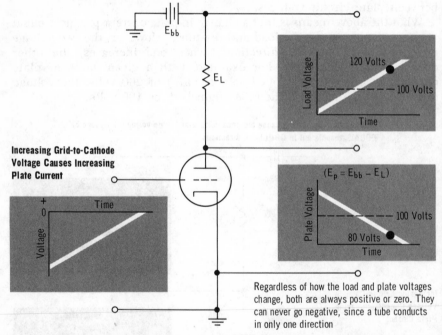

Regardless of how the load and plate voltages change, both are always positive or zero. They can never go negative, since a tube conducts in only one direction

In summary, a change in plate current produces a change in voltage across the *load* that is in the *same direction* as the plate current change. At the same time, the change in plate current produces an equal change in voltage across the *tube* that is in the *opposite direction* to the plate current change. This point is very important, since it is a-c signals and therefore *changes* in tube currents and voltages that are of primary importance in actual circuits. These changes that are being discussed are only referring to *magnitudes* increasing or decreasing. Polarities are not yet being considered. They are covered later in the book.

applying a d-c signal voltage

You have now seen how bias voltages control the amount of plate current that flows in a tube; and how the plate current, in turn, produces a voltage drop across the load as well as a plate voltage from plate to ground. In actual circuits, the bias voltage sets the operating conditions of the tube. This will be covered in detail later. For the tube to accomplish a particular function, a *signal voltage* is applied between the grid and cathode, where it effectively *adds to* or *subtracts from* the bias.

If the bias is negative, which is practically always the case, a negative signal voltage *adds* to the bias, driving the grid more negative with respect to the cathode. This causes a decrease in plate current, which, in turn, results in a decrease in the voltage drop across the load, and a corresponding increase in plate voltage. A positive signal voltage has the opposite effect. It subtracts from the negative bias, making the grid less negative with respect to the cathode. This causes plate current to increase, with the result that the voltage drop across the load increases while the plate voltage decreases a corresponding amount.

As shown on the waveforms, the voltage drop across the load *follows* the signal voltage. The plate voltage, on the other hand, is an *inverted version* of the voltage drop across the load. Both of the changing plate circuit voltages have as a reference or zero signal level a d-c voltage that is set by the bias voltage, applied voltage E_{bb}, and the tube characteristics.

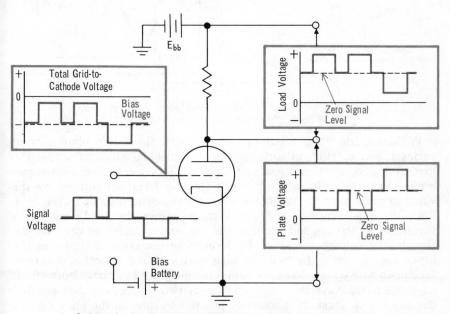

An input signal applied between the grid and cathode of a triode adds to or subtracts from the bias voltage

applying an a-c signal voltage

If an a-c signal voltage is applied between the grid and cathode of a triode, the result is essentially the same as if a d-c signal voltage was applied. The only difference is that an a-c signal is a *constantly changing* voltage. At every instant, the total grid-to-cathode voltage is the combined result of the signal and bias voltages. If the signal voltage is sinusoidal, the total grid-to-cathode voltage varies sinusoidally above and below the bias voltage. For example, if a sine-wave input signal that varies between plus and minus 3 volts is applied, and the bias is minus 5 volts, the total grid-to-cathode voltage varies between minus 2 $[(-5) + (+3)]$ volts and minus 8 $[(-5) + (-3)]$ volts. The reference, or zero signal, level of the grid-to-cathode voltage remains always at the bias value of minus 5 volts.

An a-c signal voltage results in an a-c component in the voltage drops across the load and the tube

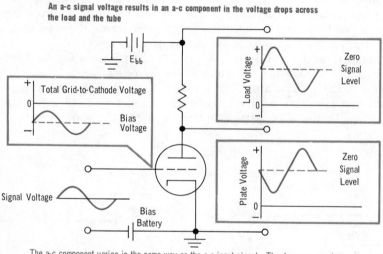

The a-c component varies in the same way as the a-c input signal. The d-c component on which the a-c component "rides" is determined by the level of bias

With the grid voltage varying sinusoidally, the tube's plate current varies likewise. This, in turn, produces sinusoidal voltages across the load and plate. Both of these voltages are really *a-c components* superimposed on d-c voltage levels, with the d-c level determined by the value of plate current that flows when no signal is present at the grid. Both the plate voltage and the voltage across the load follow the variations of the applied input signal. However, as is the case for d-c signals, the voltage across the load varies in the same direction as the input signal, while the plate voltage varies in the opposite direction. Since two sine waves that vary simultaneously but in opposite directions have the same waveshape relationship as two sine waves that are 180 degrees out of phase, it is common practice to refer to the plate voltage of a triode as being *180 degrees out of phase* with the input signal. This is shown on the following page.

waveforms

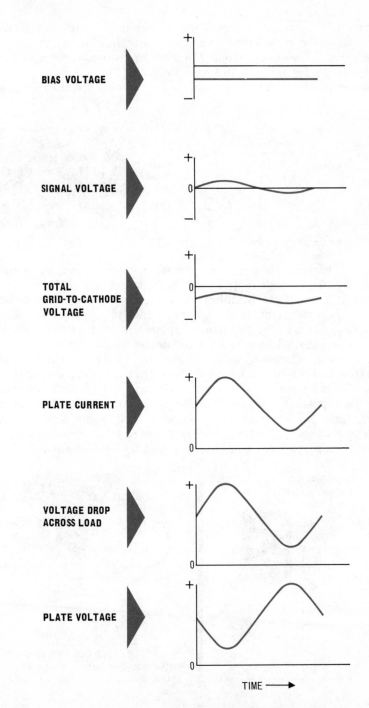

BIAS VOLTAGE

SIGNAL VOLTAGE

TOTAL
GRID-TO-CATHODE
VOLTAGE

PLATE CURRENT

VOLTAGE DROP
ACROSS LOAD

PLATE VOLTAGE

TIME ⟶

the output voltage

You have now seen how a signal voltage applied to a triode produces *two* voltages in the plate circuit, each of which has the same varying characteristics as the input signal. Although the two voltages may have different amplitudes because of the differences in amplitude of their d-c components, the amplitudes of their *a-c components* are the same.

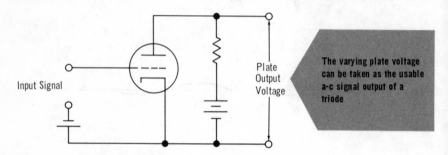

The varying plate voltage can be taken as the usable a-c signal output of a triode

When the varying plate voltage is used as the output, the output signal is 180 degrees out of phase with the input signal. But, as you will learn, this is relatively unimportant, since in many applications the phase of a signal does not matter; while in applications where phase is important, the signal can be applied to another tube and the original phase restored by a second 180-degree phase reversal.

As you will learn, various methods are used to remove the d-c components from the output voltage of a tube so that only the a-c component remains. The most common methods make use of capacitors or transformers that pass the a-c component to other circuits for further processing and, at the same time, block the d-c component. The a-c component of the output voltage is often referred to as the *output signal* to differentiate it from the combined a-c and d-c components.

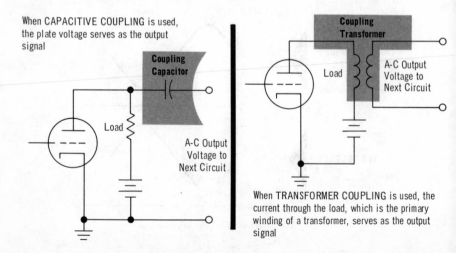

When CAPACITIVE COUPLING is used, the plate voltage serves as the output signal

When TRANSFORMER COUPLING is used, the current through the load, which is the primary winding of a transformer, serves as the output signal

gain

Although a triode can deliver an output signal that has essentially the same waveshape as the input signal, that is not the triode's most significant characteristic. Of more importance is its ability to *amplify* the input signal. This means that, under the proper operating conditions, the output signal, although having the same waveshape as the input signal, has a *greater amplitude*. The basic reason for this, as explained previously, is the high degree of control that the grid has on the plate current because of its relative nearness to the cathode. Small changes in grid voltage, such as 1 or 2 volts, or even much less, can therefore produce considerable changes in plate current. And, when this plate current flows through the load, which can have a high resistance, an output voltage many times greater than the input voltage is developed.

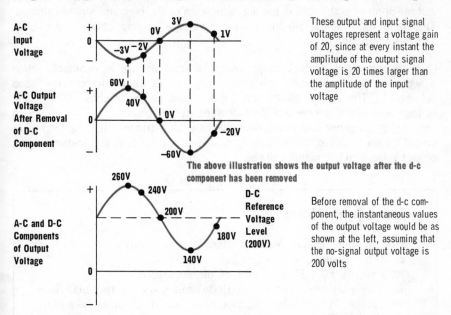

These output and input signal voltages represent a voltage gain of 20, since at every instant the amplitude of the output signal voltage is 20 times larger than the amplitude of the input voltage

The above illustration shows the output voltage after the d-c component has been removed

Before removal of the d-c component, the instantaneous values of the output voltage would be as shown at the left, assuming that the no-signal output voltage is 200 volts

The degree of amplification provided by a triode is also called the *gain*. The *voltage gain*, A, with which we are concerned here, is defined as the ratio of the instantaneous a-c output voltage to the instantaneous input signal voltage, or $A = e_{OUT}/e_{IN}$. You will learn later that in certain triode applications, *power gain* rather than voltage gain is of major significance. In these cases, the power gain is the ratio of the output signal power to the input signal power.

The gain of a particular tube can be determined by actual measurement of the input and output signals, and then the use of the above equation. The gain can also be determined from characteristic curves of the particular triode, which are prepared by the tube manufacturer. These characteristic curves are covered in detail later.

summary

☐ For a triode to perform in an electronic circuit, the plate current must flow through a load, which is usually a resistor. ☐ The applied plate voltage, or B+, is usually constant and is applied to the plate through the load resistor. ☐ When plate current flows, part of the B+ voltage is dropped across the load resistor and part is dropped across the plate resistance. These two voltage drops must always equal the B+ voltage. This is also true when the plate current varies because of varying grid bias.

☐ When the triode is cut off, all the voltage appears across the tube's plate resistance. ☐ As the plate current increases, the voltage dropped across the plate resistance decreases and the voltage dropped across the load resistor increases. ☐ Normally, the grid of a triode receives a negative bias voltage and a varying a-c voltage called a signal voltage. ☐ At any instant, the net voltage applied to the grid is the algebraic sum of the bias and signal voltages. This resulting voltage, which is an a-c voltage varying about a d-c bias, controls the plate current.

☐ When no signal voltage is present, the load voltage is constant. When a signal voltage is present, the load voltage varies about the constant load voltage. ☐ The signal voltage and the bias voltage are in phase. The signal voltage and plate voltage are 180 degrees out of phase. ☐ The ability to amplify is the most important characteristic of a triode. ☐ The degree of amplification is called the voltage gain and is the ratio of the instantaneous output voltage to the signal voltage.

---

review questions

1. How does a load resistor affect plate current?
2. What does $E_p + E_L$ equal?
3. Express $E_p + E_L$ in terms of plate current.
4. The plate current of a triode will vary as the grid bias varies. What tube characteristic must change to satisfy Kirchhoff's voltage law?
5. As plate current varies, how do the voltage drops across the load resistor and plate resistance compare?
6. How do the phases and magnitudes of the two voltages compare?
7. What two voltages are applied to the grid?
8. How is the net voltage at the grid determined?
9. What is meant by an a-c voltage superimposed on a d-c level?
10. What are the phase relationships between the net grid voltage and the plate and load voltages?

establishing
operating conditions

You have seen that a triode can produce an output signal that has the same waveshape as the input signal but a larger amplitude. It should be understood here that although the triode has this capability, it is only realized when the tube is operated under the *proper conditions*. In certain applications, voltage gain is unimportant or even unwanted, while in other applications it is desired that the output waveshape be greatly different than that of the input signal. Either, or both, of these input-vs.-output relationships can also be brought about by using suitable operating conditions for the tube. In general, then, the *gain* and the *linearity* between the input and output signals of a triode are determined by the conditions under which the tube is operated, as well as by the characteristics of the tube itself.

Each type of triode has its own set of static and dynamic characteristic curves, somewhat similar to those previously discussed for diodes. Based on these curves, suitable values of *bias voltage, B+ voltage,* and *load resistance* can be selected to establish the conditions necessary for any one of a wide variety of triode applications. A detailed analysis of how various values of these three fixed quantities, or *parameters,* affect the operation of any specific triode type requires the characteristic curves of that particular triode. A discussion of these curves and their uses is given later. Each of the three parameters, however, has certain general effects on the operation of all types of triodes. These are discussed on the following pages.

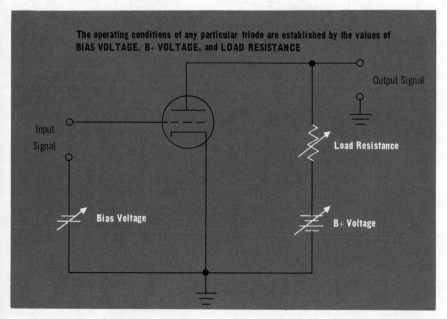

The operating conditions of any particular triode are established by the values of
BIAS VOLTAGE, B+ VOLTAGE, and LOAD RESISTANCE

Output Signal

Input
Signal

Load Resistance

Bias Voltage

B+ Voltage

load resistance

The value of the load resistance affects both the *gain* of a triode and its *linearity*. In general, the larger the load resistance, the more closely the waveshape of the output signal follows that of the input signal, and the greater is the possible voltage gain. This, of course, assumes that suitable values of bias voltage and B+ voltage are used. The increase in linearity with larger load resistance can be seen from the curves of plate current vs. grid voltage shown. Such curves are called *dynamic transfer characteristics*. They show how the value of plate current (i_p) varies with changes in grid voltage (e_g).

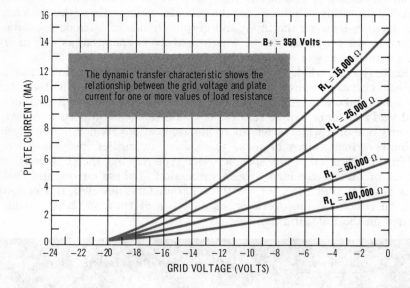

The dynamic transfer characteristic shows the relationship between the grid voltage and plate current for one or more values of load resistance

From the transfer characteristic curves, you can see that the larger the load resistance, the more linear is the e_g–i_p curve. And since the output signal is directly proportional to the plate current, a linear relationship between the grid voltage and plate current produces a linear relationship between the input and output signals.

It is not so obvious from the transfer characteristic that the output signal, and therefore the gain, increases with the value of load resistance. It may appear, because of the lower values of plate current, that the output signal produced by a given change in grid voltage actually decreases with an increase in load resistance. However, the smaller plate current is more than compensated for by the greater load resistance, so that the output signal voltage, which is equal to the load resistance times the change in plate current, increases with increasing load resistance.

B-plus voltage

There is a point beyond which the value of the load resistance cannot be increased. This point depends on the characteristics of the particular tube type and the value of B+ voltage used. At load values beyond this point, little or no increase in gain occurs, and the output signal waveshape becomes distorted. In addition, so much of the B+ voltage is dropped across the load that insufficient plate voltage may be available for proper tube operation.

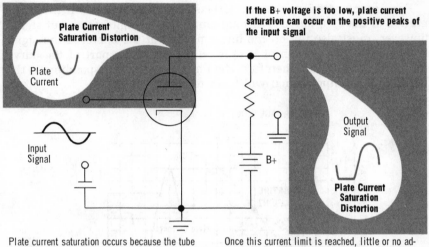

Plate current saturation occurs because the tube can deliver only a limited amount of plate current with a low B+ voltage

Once this current limit is reached, little or no additional current will flow, even though the grid voltage goes further positive

Essentially, the B+ voltage applied to a triode must perform two functions: (1) it must provide the value of plate voltage required for proper tube operation; and (2) it must also provide the voltage drop across the load, thereby producing the output signal. In other words, the B+ voltage must be large enough to provide the desired output signal amplitude, with enough voltage, in effect, left over to operate the tube properly. Too low a B+ voltage can result in both insufficient gain and output signal distortion caused by improper tube operation. Too high a B+ voltage, on the other hand, can also result in distortion of the output signal, as well as damage to the tube itself if the plate voltage exceeds the tube's rated value.

Actually, it is difficult to analyze the effects of the B+ voltage itself on the operation of a triode. This is because of the interacting relationship between the B+ voltage and the grid voltage, as well as between the B+ voltage and the load resistance. In general, though, higher B+ voltages make possible the use of larger load resistances and larger values of grid bias. Larger values of grid bias, in turn, allow a triode to receive larger-amplitude input signals without drawing grid current.

bias voltage

For any particular value of B+ voltage and load resistance, a dynamic transfer characteristic (e_g–i_p curve) can be drawn to show how the plate current will vary with changes in grid voltage. The bias voltage then selects the *operating point* on this curve. Basically, the operating point is the voltage above and below which the input signal will swing with the total grid voltage. The value of bias used depends on the type of operation desired. These types of operations are called *class A, class B, class AB,* and *class C,* and are described on the following pages.

For linear operation, a value of bias is used that falls on the linear portion of the e_g–i_p curve. The total amplitude swing of the input signal, however, must also fall on the linear portion of the curve. If the signal is so large that a portion of it falls on the nonlinear part of the curve, the plate current and, therefore, the output signal corresponding to this portion of the input signal will be distorted.

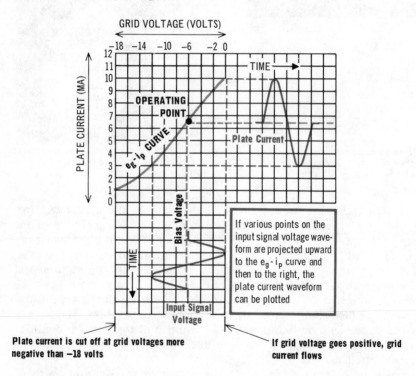

If various points on the input signal voltage waveform are projected upward to the e_g-i_p curve and then to the right, the plate current waveform can be plotted

Plate current is cut off at grid voltages more negative than −18 volts

If grid voltage goes positive, grid current flows

Any portion of the input signal that drives the grid more negative than its plate-current cutoff value does not appear in the output signal, since no plate current flows during the time of its occurrence. In addition, if a bias voltage is used such that the input signal drives the grid positive, grid current will flow during that portion of the input signal when the grid is positive.

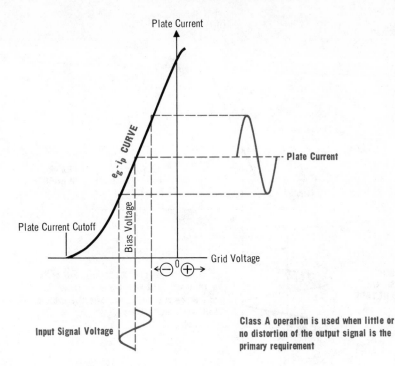

Class A operation is used when little or
no distortion of the output signal is the
primary requirement

class A operation

In class A operation, the tube is biased on the *linear* portion of its dynamic characteristic, and the input signal is small enough so that throughout its full cycle it too remains on the linear portion of the curve. As a result, the plate current waveform closely resembles the input signal. Since the operation is completely on the linear portion of the curve, the input signal never drives the grid sufficiently negative to produce plate current cutoff. As a result, plate current flows during the *complete cycle*. In addition, the amplitude of the input signal is less than the bias voltage, so the grid is *never* driven positive. This insures that grid current, which produces distortion, does not flow.

A term which you will frequently encounter in comparing classes of operation is *plate efficiency*. This is the ratio of the a-c power output developed across the load to the d-c power supplied to the plate. In class A operation, the plate efficiency is low, about 20 percent or less, because plate current flows during the full cycle; this causes a relatively high dissipation of power across the tube's plate resistance, which is supplied by the B+ supply, but not used for any useful purpose. It is, therefore, wasted power.

In summary, class A operation is characterized by little or no distortion, no grid current, plate current flow for the entire input signal cycle, and low plate efficiency.

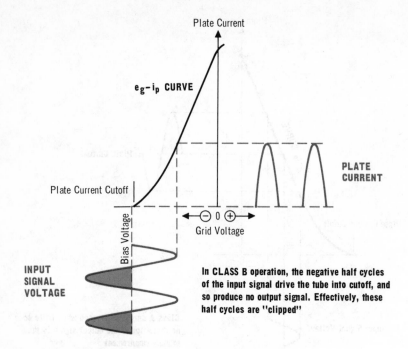

In CLASS B operation, the negative half cycles of the input signal drive the tube into cutoff, and so produce no output signal. Effectively, these half cycles are "clipped"

class B operation

In class B operation, bias is made equal to the value of grid voltage at which *plate current cutoff* occurs. Plate current only flows, therefore, during the *positive* half cycle of the input signal. During the entire negative half cycle, the grid is sufficiently negative to cut off the tube, so no output signal is delivered during this half of the input cycle. The positive half cycle of the input signal causes the tube to operate on the nonlinear portion of its transfer characteristic. If the amplitude of the signal is large enough, it can extend into the linear portion of the curve.

Since in class B operation plate current flows during only one half of the input signal cycle, less power is dissipated across the tube's plate resistance than is the case for class A operation. As a result, the plate efficiency of class B operation is higher than that of class A, being about 40 to 60 percent.

Class B operation produces considerable distortion of the output signal. This is caused by one half of the input signal being cut off, as well as by operation on the nonlinear portion of the transfer characteristic.

In summary, class B operation is characterized by bias equal to the value of plate current cutoff, tube conduction only during the positive half cycles of the input signal, a relatively high degree of distortion, and an intermediate value of plate efficiency.

class AB operation

In class AB operation, plate current flows for *more* than *half* of the input signal cycle, but for *less* than the *full* cycle. Class AB is, therefore, between class A, in which plate current flows during the complete input cycle, and class B, in which plate current flows only during the positive half of the input cycle. As shown, class AB is further subdivided into AB_1 and AB_2. The difference between these two subdivisions is that grid current does not flow in class AB_1 operation but does flow in class AB_2.

For both AB_1 and AB_2 operation, the bias is set somewhere between plate current cutoff and the linear portion of the dynamic transfer characteristic. A portion of the negative half cycle of the input signal drives the tube into cutoff, and is therefore clipped. Generally, a much larger portion of the negative alternation is clipped in class AB_2 than in class AB_1. In AB_1 operation, the amplitude of the input signal is less than the bias voltage, thus preventing grid current. But, in AB_2 operation, the input signal exceeds the bias, and so drives the grid positive during the positive peaks of the input cycle. Grid current flows, therefore, causing distortion of the peaks of the plate current waveform.

Because of its grid voltage swing, class AB_2 operation produces larger outputs than AB_1. The degree of distortion, power output, and plate efficiency of both AB_1 and AB_2 is somewhere between that of class A and class B operation.

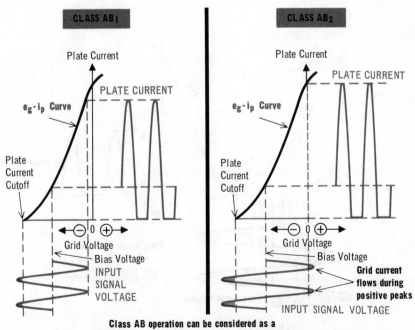

Class AB operation can be considered as a
compromise between class A and class B operation

class C operation

In class C operation, the bias is set well *beyond* the value that produces plate current cutoff. Usually, it is 1-1/2 to 4 times the cutoff value. For instance, if the plate current cuts off with a bias value of −6 volts, class C operation would employ a bias somewhere between −9 and −24 volts. Only the extreme *positive peaks* of the input signal drive the tube above cutoff. As a result, the plate current is in the form of brief pulses that correspond to the positive peaks of the input signal.

Class C operation introduces a large amount of distortion because of the extreme clipping of the input signal. However, it also results in a high degree of plate efficiency, somewhere between 60 and 80 percent, since plate current flows only during a small portion of the input signal cycle.

As shown, the portion of the input signal that causes tube conduction extends from the plate current cutoff point to the linear portion of the transfer characteristic. In some class C applications, the input signal has sufficient amplitude so that its extreme positive peaks drive the grid positive. This results in the flow of grid current.

In summary, class C operation is characterized by a bias value well beyond plate current cutoff, so that plate current flows during only a small portion of the input signal cycle. It produces a large degree of distortion, but results in high plate efficiency.

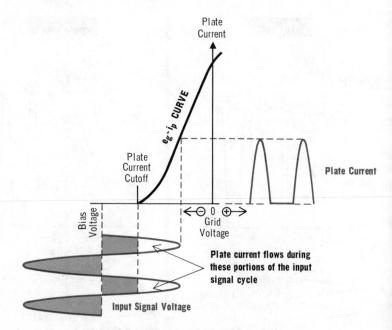

In CLASS C operation, plate current only flows during
a relatively small portion of the input signal cycle

summary

☐ The desired gain and linearity between the input and output signals are determined by the bias voltage, B+ voltage, and load resistance. ☐ Larger load resistors provide more gain and better linearity. ☐ The maximum value of the load resistor depends on the B+ voltage and characteristics of the tube being used. If the load is increased beyond the maximum value, little or no increase in gain occurs.

☐ The B+ voltage must supply proper plate voltage for tube operation and must also provide the voltage drop across the load resistor. ☐ If the B+ is too large, the output signal will be distorted and the tube may be damaged. ☐ For a given load resistance and B+ voltage, the bias voltage selects the operating point on the dynamic transfer characteristic curve and, therefore, the class of operation desired.

☐ For class A operation, the output must be a linear reproduction of the input. The bias is set so that the operating point falls on the linear portion of the e_g-i_p curve. The input signal must be small enough so that the net grid voltage does not drive the triode into saturation or cutoff. ☐ In class AB operation, plate current flows for more than half but less than the full cycle. ☐ Class AB operation is subdivided into class AB_1 and AB_2. In AB_1 operation, part of the negative half cycle of the input drives the tube into cutoff. This also happens in class AB_2 operation and, in addition, part of the positive half cycle causes grid current to flow. ☐ A triode operating class B acts as a rectifier. The triode is biased at cutoff and the entire negative half cycle is clipped. ☐ For class C operation, the bias is set between 1-1/2 and 4 times the cutoff voltage. Only the extreme positive peaks of the input will cause plate current to flow.

review questions

1. Why does a large load resistor provide better linearity?
2. What will happen if the B+ voltage is too small?
3. What does the bias voltage establish?
4. What advantages does a large B+ voltage offer in terms of load resistance, grid bias, and input signals?
5. What occurs in a class A amplifier if the bias is too low?
6. What shape will the output have for class AB_1?
7. How will the waveshape differ if the triode is operating class AB_2?
8. Why will the negative half cycle be clipped if the triode is operating class B?
9. In class C operation, what portion of the input will appear at the output? Why?
10. Compare the efficiency of each class of operation.

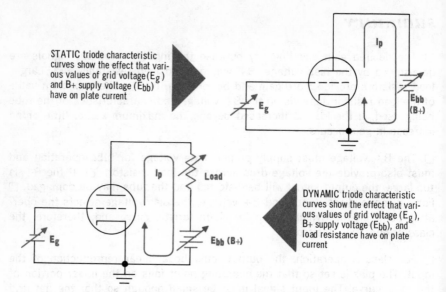

STATIC triode characteristic curves show the effect that various values of grid voltage (E_g) and B+ supply voltage (E_{bb}) have on plate current

DYNAMIC triode characteristic curves show the effect that various values of grid voltage (E_g), B+ supply voltage (E_{bb}), and load resistance have on plate current

triode characteristic curves

The basic operation of triodes has been described on the previous pages. Throughout, it was repeatedly stated that an exact analysis of the operation of any particular triode type can only be made on the basis of the characteristic curves covering that type. And since there are many types of triodes, it is obvious that the characteristics of all types cannot be covered in this book. However, the general form, use, and interpretation of the characteristic curves for all triodes are essentially similar. So by understanding how the curves for a typical triode are prepared and used, you are equipped to analyze and interpret the curves for any specific triode type.

As was the case for the diode characteristic curves previously described, the triode curves describe static and dynamic characteristics. The static curves are for no-load operation, while the dynamic curves show the operating characteristics when a load is connected to the plate circuit. Actually, for our purposes, the most important triode characteristic curve is the dynamic transfer characteristic, which you have already learned to use. However, the other curves are still significant, since they give an insight into the development of the dynamic transfer characteristic.

In the development of all triode characteristic curves, it is assumed that *rated heater voltages* will be used. The variable quantities expressed by the curves are therefore *grid voltage, plate voltage,* and *plate current.* Since the three variables cannot be portrayed on a single curve, two types of curves are used: grid-voltage, plate-current characteristic curves, and plate-voltage, plate-current characteristic curves.

the grid family

A static grid-voltage, plate-current characteristic curve is produced by applying a *constant plate voltage* to the triode and *varying the grid voltage*. The value of the plate current that results from each value of grid voltage is plotted to form a smooth continuous curve. Such a characteristic curve shows how the grid voltage affects plate current at one particular value of plate voltage. If a number of such curves are obtained for different values of plate voltage, the result is called the *grid family* of characteristic curves. You can see on the next page that the value of negative bias required to cut off the plate current increases as the plate voltage increases.

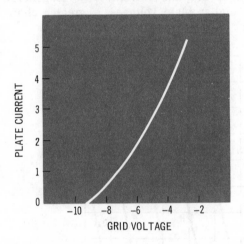

A single grid-voltage, plate-current characteristic curve shows how changes in grid voltage affect the plate current at a given value of plate voltage

The grid family also shows that for the same value of grid voltage, more plate current flows as the plate voltage is increased. For example, with a bias of −9 volts, 0.1 milliampere of plate current flows with a plate voltage of 150 volts (point A). But, with the same bias, 2.1 milliamperes of plate current flow if the plate voltage is 200 volts (point B), and 6.6 milliamperes of plate current with a plate voltage of 250 volts (point C).

You can also determine from the grid family the grid voltage change required to offset a change in plate current caused by a change in plate voltage. This graphically shows how much more control the grid voltage has over the plate current than does the plate voltage. For example, point D corresponds to a plate current of 8.5 milliamperes with a bias of −0.8 volt and a plate voltage of 100 volts. If the plate voltage is increased to 150 volts, the plate current can be held constant at 8.5 milliamperes by increasing the bias to −3.2 volts (point E). This shows that a plate voltage increase of 50 volts can be offset by an increase in bias of 2.4 volts.

the grid family (cont.)

Other information that can be obtained from the grid family includes the change in plate current for a given change in grid voltage at different regions along a particular characteristic curve. For example, on the 250-volt curve, a bias change of 1 volt from −13 to −12 volts (points F and G) produces a plate current increase of 0.9 milliampere (from 0.8 to 1.7 milliamperes). The same 1-volt bias change higher up on the curve from −8 to −7 volts produces a plate current change of 2.8 milliamperes, going from 8.9 to 11.7 milliamperes (points H and I). The grid family also shows that similar 1-volt bias changes (from −13 to −12, and from −8 to −7) on the curve corresponding to larger plate voltages produce greater changes in plate current. This is generally true of all tubes; namely, at higher plate voltages, a greater change in plate current is obtained for a given change in grid voltage.

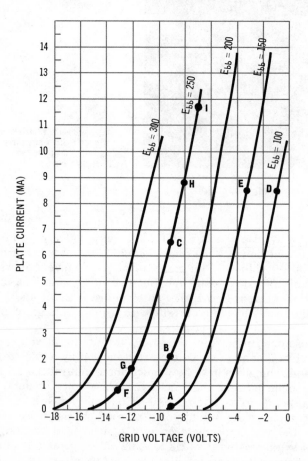

the plate family

A static plate-voltage, plate-current characteristic curve is produced by applying a *constant bias* to the triode and *varying the plate voltage.* A continuous curve showing how plate current varies as the plate voltage is changed is then plotted. This curve is valid only for one value of bias voltage. If a number of such curves are prepared for different values of grid voltage, the result is called the *plate family* of characteristic curves. A typical such plate family is shown.

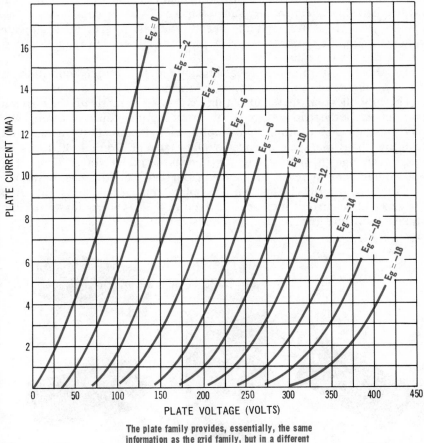

The plate family provides, essentially, the same information as the grid family, but in a different form

This plate family is for the same triode type as the grid family shown on the previous page. Actually, the plate family shows essentially the same information about the tube as does the grid family, only in a different form. Either one of the families can be plotted from the other.

tube constants

The grid and plate families of characteristic curves just described are the results of a definite design meant to give a tube specific operating characteristics. In other words, each triode type is designed to exhibit certain characteristics that are represented by grid and plate families of curves. In designing the desired operating characteristics into a tube, various *geometrical* design factors are important. These include the shape and size of the electrodes, their dimensions, and the spacing between them. Once these geometrical factors have been established by the design, their total effect on the tube can be expressed by numerical ratings called *tube constants*. Tubes that have similar constants exhibit similar properties, although the specific values of grid voltage, plate voltage, and plate current necessary for proper operation may be different for the various tubes.

The three most important tube constants are the *amplification factor,* the *plate resistance,* and the *transconductance.*

The amplification factor of a tube expresses numerically how much *more effective* the grid voltage is in controlling plate current than is the plate voltage. For example, an amplification factor of 40 means that to bring about the same change in plate current requires 40 times as large a change in plate voltage as it does in grid voltage. Thus, if a 100-milliampere increase in plate current can be produced by a +3-volt increase in grid voltage, with the plate voltage held constant, then the same plate-current increase will require a 120-volt increase in plate voltage, with the grid voltage held constant.

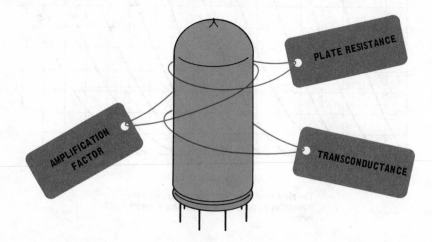

Every electron tube has **THREE TUBE CONSTANTS** specified by the manufacturer. They provide a means for comparing tube types and determining their suitability for various applications

the amplification factor

As an equation, the amplification factor, designated by the Greek letter μ (pronounced *mu*), can be expressed as:

$$\mu = \frac{\text{small change in plate voltage}}{\text{small change in grid voltage}} = \frac{\Delta e_p}{\Delta e_g}$$

where Δ stands for *a small change*, and Δe_p and Δe_g are small changes in plate and grid voltage, respectively, that produce equal changes in plate current i_p.

In this circuit, a rough determination of μ can be made by varying E_g slightly so that the ammeter indicates a different current

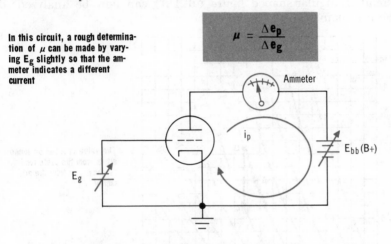

$$\mu = \frac{\Delta e_p}{\Delta e_g}$$

If E_{bb} is then varied until the ammeter indicates the original current reading, the ratio of the change in E_{bb} to the change in E_g will be μ

The amplification factor of every tube is specified by the manufacturer. The value of μ can also be found from either the plate or grid family of characteristics of the tube. The value found from the characteristic curves will usually differ slightly from the manufacturer's specified value. There are two reasons for this. One is that the value of μ is actually *slightly different* for different values of grid and plate voltages because of the *nonlinearity* of the characteristic curves. The other reason is that an exact calculation of μ requires the use of *extremely small changes* in grid and plate voltage. With the type of changes that are practical to read from the characteristic curves, some discrepancy usually results.

The actual values of amplification factor for triodes vary from less than 10 to as high as 100. Triodes that have μ's less than 10 are called *low-μ triodes*, those with μ's between 10 and 30 are called *medium-μ triodes*, and those with μ's greater than 30, *high-μ triodes*. In some special tubes, μ varies widely with the value of grid bias. These are called *variable-μ tubes*.

the amplification factor
from the plate family

Assume that you want to find μ with the tube operating with a plate voltage of 235 volts and a grid voltage of −8 volts. This corresponds to point A. The first step is to move down on the −8-volt curve to some convenient point, which for our example is point B. A horizontal line is then drawn from B to the next grid voltage curve (point C), and from here, a vertical line is drawn up to the −8-volt curve (point D). This small triangular-shaped figure (BCDB) can now be analyzed to find the μ at point A.

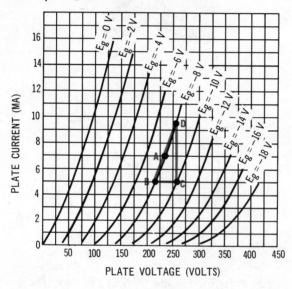

The value of μ can be found either from the plate family, as shown, or from the grid family

Points B and D indicate that if the grid voltage is held constant at −8 volts, the plate current is 5 milliamperes with a plate voltage of 214 volts (point B), and 9.6 milliamperes with a plate voltage of 255 volts (point D). A plate voltage increase of 41 volts (255 − 214) therefore produces a plate current increase of 4.6 milliamperes (9.6 − 5). Points C and D indicate that if the plate voltage is held constant at its new value of 255 volts, the new value of plate current of 9.6 milliamperes (point D) can be reduced to the old value of 5 milliamperes (point C) by increasing the grid voltage to −10 volts. Thus, a grid voltage change of 2 volts produces a plate current change of 4.6 milliamperes (9.6 − 5), which is the same change that is produced by a plate voltage change of 41 volts. Knowing the grid and plate voltage changes that will produce *equal* changes in plate current, the value of μ can be calculated by $\mu = e_p/e_g = 41$ volts/2 volts = 20.5.

The procedure for finding μ from the *grid family* of characteristic curves is similar to that described above.

plate resistance

The plate resistance of a triode is the *internal resistance* of the tube. Like diodes, triodes have two types of plate resistance: dc and ac. The d-c resistance, R_p, is for a *steady* value of plate voltage and depends on the operating voltages applied to the tube. It can easily be found for any conditions of grid and plate voltage from the plate family of characteristic curves, as shown. All that is required is to apply Ohm's Law to the values of plate voltage and current at any desired point on the characteristic curves. For example, point A corresponds to a grid voltage of −8 volts and a plate voltage of 250 volts. The −8-volt curve shows that under these operating conditions, the plate current is 8.6 milliamperes. The d-c plate resistance is, therefore, $R_p = E_p/I_p = 250$ volts/0.0086 ampere $\cong$ 29K.

The a-c plate resistance of a triode is the internal opposition the tube offers to current flow when *a-c voltages* are applied. It is measured by the *change* in plate current that occurs with a small *change* in voltage, while the grid voltage is held constant. The a-c plate resistance, r_p, can be expressed as $r_p = e_p/i_p$ (with E_g held constant). You should note here the use of small letters (r, e, and i) as opposed to capital letters (R, E and I) when the d-c resistance is involved. This is a frequently used convention, with *small* letters representing *a-c quantities,* and *capital* letters *d-c quantities.*

Like the d-c resistance, the a-c plate resistance varies, depending on the operating voltages applied to the tube. However, only a *single* value of a-c plate resistance is specified by the tube manufacturer. This value is for a typical set of operating conditions. Values of r_p for other operating conditions can be determined from the characteristic curves, as described on the next page.

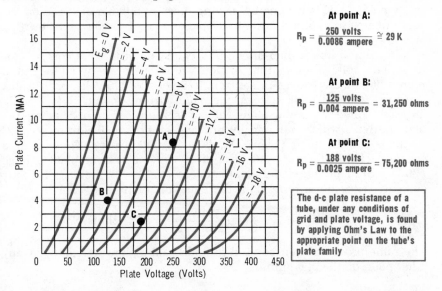

At point A:

$$R_p = \frac{250 \text{ volts}}{0.0086 \text{ ampere}} \cong 29 \text{ K}$$

At point B:

$$R_p = \frac{125 \text{ volts}}{0.004 \text{ ampere}} = 31,250 \text{ ohms}$$

At point C:

$$R_p = \frac{188 \text{ volts}}{0.0025 \text{ ampere}} = 75,200 \text{ ohms}$$

The d-c plate resistance of a tube, under any conditions of grid and plate voltage, is found by applying Ohm's Law to the appropriate point on the tube's plate family

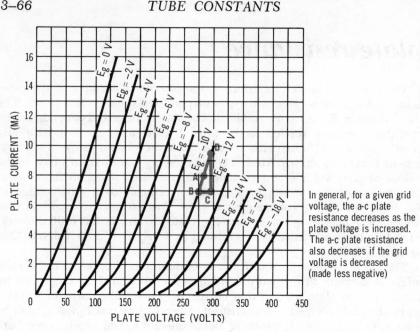

In general, for a given grid voltage, the a-c plate resistance decreases as the plate voltage is increased. The a-c plate resistance also decreases if the grid voltage is decreased (made less negative)

a-c plate resistance from the plate family

In this example, it is desired to find r_p when the grid voltage is −10 volts and the plate voltage is 285 volts. The corresponding point on the plate family is shown as point A. Since the a-c plate resistance involves a *change* in plate voltage, the plate voltage must be varied above and below point A. This is done by moving down a suitable distance on the curve to a point (point B) that corresponds to a plate voltage below that of point A.

A horizontal line is then drawn to a point (point C) that corresponds to a plate voltage above that of point A. The line between B and C represents a plate voltage range from 275 volts to 295 volts, or 20 volts. With the 275-volt plate voltage, the plate current (point B) is 7 milliamperes. And, when the plate voltage is increased to 295 volts, the plate current, which is found by drawing a vertical line from point C to the −10-volt curve (point D), is 9.4 milliamperes. Thus, with a constant grid voltage of −10 volts, a 20-volt increase in plate voltage (295 − 275) produces a 2.4-milliampere (9.4 − 7) increase in plate current. With this information, the equation for r_p can then be used.

$$r_p = \frac{e_p}{i_p} = \frac{20 \text{ volts}}{0.0024 \text{ ampere}} = 8333 \text{ ohms}$$

The same procedure can be used to find the a-c plate resistance at any other point on the plate family.

transconductance

We now come to what is probably the most important of the tube constants. This is the *transconductance,* or the *mutual conductance,* as it is often called. The transconductance is defined as the ratio of a small change in plate current to the small change in grid voltage which produced it, with the plate voltage held constant. As an equation, the transconductance, g_m, is

$$g_m = \frac{i_p}{e_g} \quad \text{(with } E_p \text{ constant)}$$

Since transconductance is the ratio of a current to a voltage, it is a *conductance,* which, you recall, is expressed in units of the *mho* (ohm spelled backwards). The unit of the mho is much too large for vacuum-tube usage, so transconductance is usually expressed in *micromhos.* One micromho equals one-millionth of a mho, and corresponds to a plate current change of 1 microampere for each 1-volt change in grid voltage. Thus, if a tube has a transconductance of 4000 micromhos, its plate current will change 4 milliamperes for every 1-volt change in grid voltage.

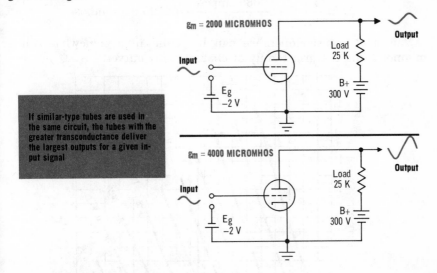

If similar-type tubes are used in the same circuit, the tubes with the greater transconductance deliver the largest outputs for a given input signal

The transconductance is frequently used to compare tubes of the same general class. A tube with a high g_m can deliver a relatively large output signal for a given input, while a low-g_m tube will deliver a smaller output signal with the same input. Of course, such comparisons can only be made between tubes intended for the same general use.

The value of transconductance specified for a tube by the manufacturer is for typical operating conditions. The value can also be found under any condition of grid and plate voltage by using the tube's characteristic curves.

transconductance
from the plate family

An example of how the plate family of characteristic curves can be used to determine transconductance is shown. In this example, the transconductance is to be found with the tube operating with a plate voltage of 235 volts and grid bias of −8 volts. This corresponds to point A.

If a vertical line is drawn upward from A to the next grid voltage curve (point B), as well as downward to the next grid voltage curve (point C), the line represents a change in grid voltage above and below −8 volts, with the plate voltage held constant. At point B, which corresponds to a grid voltage of −6 volts, the plate current is 12 milliamperes. And, at point C, which corresponds to a grid voltage of −10 volts, the plate current is 3.5 milliamperes. Thus, with the plate voltage held constant, a 4-volt change in grid voltage (−10 volts to −6 volts) produces an 8.5-milliampere change in plate current (12 milliamperes − 3.5 milliamperes). From the equation for transconductance, therefore,

$$g_m = \frac{i_p}{e_g} = \frac{0.0085 \text{ ampere}}{4 \text{ volts}} = 2125 \text{ micromhos}$$

Values of transconductance can be found in a somewhat similar manner using the grid family of characteristic curves.

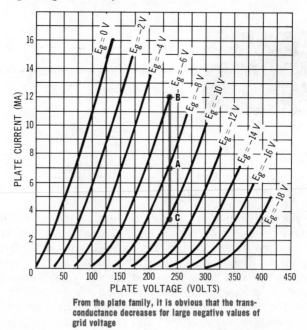

From the plate family, it is obvious that the transconductance decreases for large negative values of
grid voltage

relationship
between tube constants

Since the tube constants (μ, r_p, and g_m) arise from the physical construction of a tube, they bear definite relationships to one another. Mathematically, these relationships can be derived from the equations for the constants. If these derivations are carried out, they yield the basic relationship, $\mu = r_p \times g_m$. This means that at any particular values of grid and plate voltage, the amplification factor is equal to the a-c plate resistance times the transconductance. In this equation, r_p must be in *ohms* and g_m in *mhos*. By rearranging the basic equation, two other relationships can be stated. These are $r_p = \mu/g_m$, and $g_m = \mu/r_p$. You can see that if any two of the tube constants are known, the third can be calculated very easily.

The relationship between the three constants can also be expressed graphically as shown. The three constants for a typical triode are plotted on a common horizontal axis corresponding to plate current. The graph is for a single value of plate voltage, so the increase in plate current on the horizontal axis is the result of the tube's grid voltage becoming less negative. The vertical scale is common for r_p and g_m, but μ is shown separately. The purpose of this arrangement is to show how the three constants change with increasing plate current.

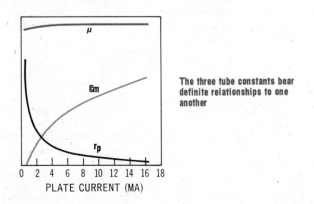

The three tube constants bear definite relationships to one another

The amplification factor increases slightly at low values of plate current, and then remains essentially constant. The a-c plate resistance, on the other hand, decreases rapidly at the lower values of plate current, and then continues to decrease at a slower rate. In a similar, but opposite, way the transconductance increases fairly rapidly at the lower values of plate current, and then continues to increase at a slower rate. At any value of plate current, the value of r_p times the value of g_m is equal to μ.

summary

☐ The grid family of characteristic curves shows the variations in plate current for different values of grid voltage. Separate e_g–i_p curves are plotted for different plate voltages. ☐ Each e_g–i_p curve is generated by applying a fixed plate voltage, varying the grid voltage in small increments, and measuring the plate current.

☐ The plate family of characteristic curves shows the variations in plate current for different values of plate voltage. Separate e_p–i_p curves are plotted for different grid voltages. ☐ Each e_p–i_p curve is plotted by applying a fixed grid voltage, varying the plate voltage, and measuring the plate current. ☐ The operating characteristics of a vacuum tube are described in terms of three constants: (1) amplification factor, (2) plate resistance, and (3) transconductance. ☐ The three tube constants are determined by tube geometry and are specified by the manufacturer. The·constants can also be calculated from either family of characteristic curves.

☐ Amplification factor, μ, indicates the ability of the grid voltage to control plate current. It is expressed as a ratio of a small change in plate voltage to a small change in grid voltage. ☐ Triodes are classified as low-μ, medium-μ, and high-μ triodes according to the numerical value of μ. ☐ Plate resistance, r_p, is the internal opposition the tube offers to plate current when a-c voltages are applied. This constant is expressed as a ratio of a small change in plate voltage to a small change in plate current. ☐ Transconductance, or mutual conductance, g_m, is a measure of how well the grid controls the plate current. It is expressed as a ratio of a small change in plate current to a small change in grid voltage that produced it.

review questions

1. What do the grid family of characteristic curves show?
2. For a given grid voltage, what happens to the plate current as the plate voltage is increased?
3. How is the cutoff voltage affected by plate voltage?
4. What does the plate family of characteristic curves provide?
5. What physical characteristics determine the tube constants?
6. What values of μ describe low-, medium-, and high-μ triodes?
7. What is a variable-μ triode?
8. Do any of the tube constants vary? Explain.
9. Can any of the tube constants be purposely changed during operation? Explain.
10. What is the relationship between the tube constants?

the load line

Although the static characteristic curves of a triode provide useful information, they tell nothing about how the addition of a *load* will affect tube operation. The addition of a load does not change the basic characteristics of a tube, but it does greatly affect the *operating conditions*. For example, with or without a load a tube will behave the same if it has, say, a grid voltage of −4 volts and a plate voltage of 300 volts. In static operation, these conditions are easily met. But, with a load, what value of B+ voltage is required to result in a plate voltage of 300 volts? A portion of the B+ voltage will be dropped across the load, and will not be available as plate voltage. But the exact amount dropped will depend on the values of grid voltage, B+ voltage, and load resistance. What is needed, therefore, is some way of predicting how the B+ voltage will be distributed across the load and the tube's plate resistance under all possible conditions of operation. This is possible by means of a *load line*.

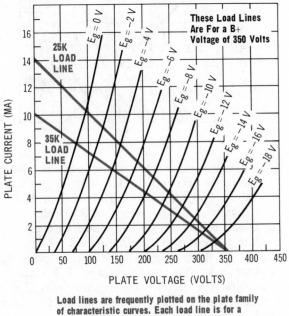

Load lines are frequently plotted on the plate family
of characteristic curves. Each load line is for a
single value of load resistance and B+ voltage

Essentially, a load line is a straight line drawn on the static family of characteristic curves. The load line represents a *single* value of load resistance, and shows how, with the value of load, the B+ voltage will be distributed across the load and the tube's plate resistance. The construction of load lines, although relatively simple, is not within the scope of this book. A description of the use of load lines is given on the following page.

using the load line

There are various ways to use a load line. Some are shown for a load line representing a 25K load and a 350-volt B+ supply. Primarily, the load line is used to show the division of the B+ voltage across the load and the tube. In the example, the tube is to be operated with a bias of −6 volts. The operating point on the load line is then the point where the load line crosses the −6-volt curve (point A). A horizontal line drawn to the plate current axis shows the value of plate current under these conditions. The value is 6.5 milliamperes. Similarly, a vertical line drawn from point A to the plate voltage axis shows the value of plate voltage. It is 190 volts.

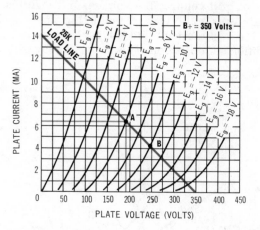

If desired, the voltage dropped across the load can also now be found, since it is the difference between the B+ voltage and the plate voltage. Its value is, therefore, 350 volts minus 190 volts, or 160 volts. The load line thus shows that with a B+ voltage of 350 volts, a bias voltage of −6 volts, and a load resistance of 25K, the tube's plate voltage is 190 volts and the plate current is 6.5 milliamperes.

Another use of the load line is to determine what bias voltage is needed to produce a certain plate voltage. For example, if a plate voltage of 250 volts is required, reading up from the 250-volt point on the plate voltage axis to the load line (point B) shows that a bias of approximately −10 volts is needed.

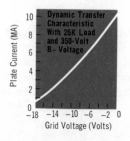

If the effect of the load shown above on the plate family is transferred to the grid family, the result is the dynamic transfer characteristic

methods of bias

From the previous discussion on triode characteristic curves and classes of operation, you saw that with a given value of B+ voltage and load resistance, a tube's potential operation is described by a single dynamic transfer characteristic. This curve shows how the plate current will change as a function of varying grid voltages. By properly analyzing the curve, you can determine other things. Among these are the range of grid voltages that will operate the tube on the *nonlinear* portion of the curve and so produce distortion of the output signal; the range of grid voltage that will operate the tube on the *linear* portion of the curve and so produce little or no distortion; and the value of grid voltage that will *cut off* the tube.

The dynamic transfer characteristic, therefore, provides a means of analyzing the operation of the tube for many possible values of bias voltage and grid input signal. The bias sets the *operating point* on the curve, and the input signal then causes the total grid voltage to vary *above* and *below* the value of bias.

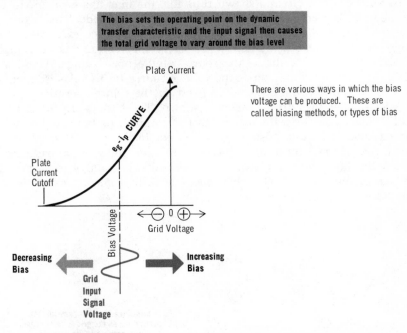

The bias sets the operating point on the dynamic transfer characteristic and the input signal then causes the total grid voltage to vary around the bias level

Plate Current

e_g-i_p CURVE

Plate Current Cutoff

Bias Voltage

0

Grid Voltage

Decreasing Bias

Increasing Bias

Grid Input Signal Voltage

There are various ways in which the bias voltage can be produced. These are called biasing methods, or types of bias

The transfer characteristic presents a *graphical picture* of tube operation. It tells nothing about the actual *circuit* or *components* that bring about this operation. For example, the bias voltage might be supplied by any one of a variety of methods. Although the effects of the various biasing methods are the same, the manner in which they produce the effect is quite different. Each biasing method is, therefore, described separately on the following pages.

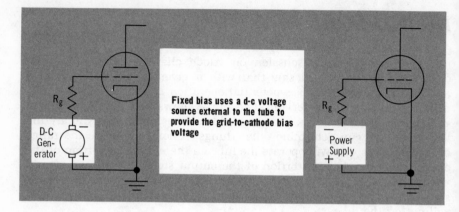

Fixed bias uses a d-c voltage source external to the tube to provide the grid-to-cathode bias voltage

fixed bias

In all the triode circuits shown thus far, the bias has been produced by a battery, E_g, connected between the grid and cathode. This arrangement, by which the bias is provided by a voltage source *external* to the tube, is called *fixed bias*. Instead of a battery, an electronic power supply or a d-c generator might be the source of the bias voltage. These are still sources of fixed bias, since the voltage source for the bias is external to the tube circuit and does not depend on the tube's operation.

A basic fixed-bias arrangement is shown. The battery, E_g, makes the grid 3 volts negative with respect to the cathode, or put another way, the cathode is 3 volts positive with respect to the grid. Resistor R_g is called the grid resistor and, as you will see later, serves as a load across which the input signal voltage is developed. The total grid-to-cathode voltage is thus the −3 volts bias plus the instantaneous value of the input signal voltage developed across R_g.

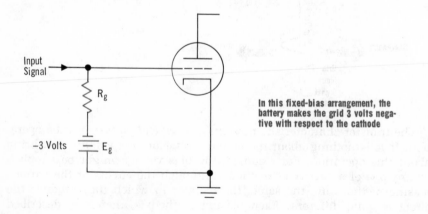

In this fixed-bias arrangement, the battery makes the grid 3 volts negative with respect to the cathode

cathode bias

In *cathode bias*, the tube develops its *own* bias voltage. For this reason, it is a form of *self bias*. Cathode bias makes use of a resistor connected between the cathode and the negative, or return, side of the B+ supply. The plate current of the tube must, therefore, flow through this resistor on its way through the tube. The resistor is called the *cathode resistor*, since it is connected in the cathode circuit of the tube.

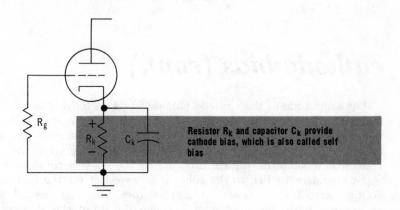

Resistor R_k and capacitor C_k provide cathode bias, which is also called self bias

With no input signal applied to the tube, the flow of plate current through the cathode resistor produces a voltage drop across it. As shown, the polarity of the voltage drop is such that the top, or cathode side, of the cathode resistor is positive with respect to the bottom, which is usually at ground potential. And, since without an input signal, the grid is at the same potential (ground) as the bottom of the cathode resistor, the voltage drop across the cathode resistor makes the cathode positive with respect to the grid. This means that the grid is negative with respect to the cathode, which, of course, is the function of a bias voltage. The flow of plate current through the cathode resistor, therefore, produces bias for the tube.

Capacitor C_k performs its bypass function by charging when the input signal (and therefore the plate current) increases in amplitude, and discharging when the input signal decreases in amplitude. This keeps the cathode voltage relatively constant

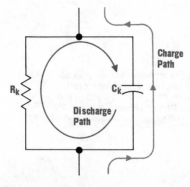

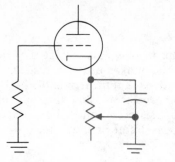

This schematic shows how a variable resistor can be used in the cathode to make the cathode bias adjustable

cathode bias (cont.)

The amplitude of the cathode bias depends on the values of the plate current and the cathode resistor. For a given tube and value of B+ voltage, therefore, the bias is set by the resistance of the cathode resistor. The purpose of the capacitor in parallel with the cathode resistor is to keep the voltage drop across the resistor *constant* when an input signal is applied to the tube. If it were not for the capacitor, the voltage across the resistor, and therefore the bias, would vary in accordance with the input signal. When the input signal increased in amplitude, the plate current would also increase, resulting in a larger voltage across the cathode resistor, and hence an increase in bias. The opposite would occur when the input signal fell in amplitude. Less plate current would flow, resulting in a decrease in bias. The capacitor is called a *bypass capacitor* because it effectively bypasses the plate current *variations* produced by the input signal around the cathode resistor.

The bypass capacitor is chosen so that its reactance at the frequency of the input signal is small compared to the resistance of the cathode resistor. It therefore acts as a short circuit for the current variations (ac), keeping the voltage drop across the resistor at a steady d-c level. In actual practice, the reactance of the bypass capacitor at the lowest signal frequency is one-tenth, or less, the value of the cathode resistor.

This is another method to obtain adjustable bias. Part of the cathode voltage is applied to the grid so that the difference between the grid and the cathode can be changed

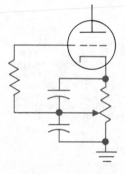

grid-leak bias

Another biasing method in which the tube develops its own bias voltage is *grid-leak bias*. This bias depends on *grid current* flow when the grid is driven positive by the input signal. As a result, when there is *no input signal,* the bias is *zero.*

One type of circuit arrangement for producing grid-leak bias is shown. When a sinusoidal input signal is applied, it is coupled through capacitor C_g and developed across resistor R_g. The way this works will be covered later. The sinusoidal signal voltage input across R_g alternately makes this grid positive and negative with respect to the cathode.

When the grid is positive, it draws grid current, which charges capacitor C_g. As shown, the path of the grid current is from the grid, effectively through C_g, through the input signal source, and back to the cathode. As a result of the grid current, C_g charges to the *peak* value of the input signal, with a polarity such that the capacitor plate connected to the grid is negative.

When the input signal reverses and drives the grid negative with respect to the cathode, the flow of grid current stops. In addition, capacitor C_g begins to *discharge* through resistor R_g, as shown. However, the resistance value of R_g is very large, so that the RC time constant of the $R_g C_g$ combination is long compared to the time for one cycle of the input signal. As a result of the long time constant, C_g has discharged only a small amount by the time the input signal again reverses polarity and drives the grid positive. With the grid again positive, grid current flows and replenishes the small amount of charge on C_g that was lost during the negative half cycle of the input.

The bias for the tube is produced by the voltage developed across R_g each time capacitor C_g discharges. The discharge current is always in the same direction, and the voltage it produces across R_g has a polarity such that the grid is negative with respect to the cathode. Since C_g only discharges when the input signal goes negative, the voltage it produces across R_g is actually slightly varying dc.

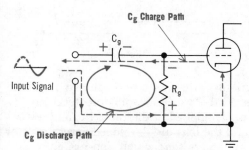

Grid-leak bias requires the flow of grid current. It can, therefore, only be used when the signal distortion that results from grid current can be tolerated

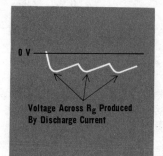

grid-leak bias (cont.)

The discussion on the previous page neglected the input signal for the most part. This was to simplify the explanation of how the bias is developed. Actually, however, there is considerable interaction between the bias and the input signal, since they are both developed across grid resistor R_g. This will become more obvious to you later when coupling methods are described.

Another circuit arrangement for developing grid-leak bias is shown. This circuit also depends on the flow of *grid current* to develop bias. However, whereas C_g and R_g were effectively in series in the previously discussed circuit, in this arrangement they are in *parallel*. When the input signal drives the grid positive, the resulting grid current charges capacitor C_g to the peak value of the input voltage. The path of the C_g charging current is the same as that of the circuit on the previous page.

When the input signal goes negative, C_g discharges through resistor R_g as shown. Again, the value of R_g is large, so only a small portion of the charge on C_g is lost while the input signal is negative. When the input goes positive, grid current again flows and replenishes the charge on C_g. Thus, C_g alternately charges and discharges, with the discharge path being through R_g. The d-c voltage produced across R_g by the C_g discharge current has a polarity that makes the grid negative with respect to the cathode.

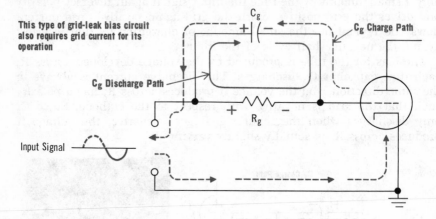

This type of grid-leak bias circuit also requires grid current for its operation

C_g Charge Path

C_g Discharge Path

R_g

Input Signal

A further difference between the grid-bias circuit shown and that described on the previous page is the way in which the total grid-to-cathode voltage (signal plus bias) is applied to the tube. In the previous circuit, both the signal voltage and the bias are developed across resistor R_g, so the total grid-to-cathode voltage is that which appears across R_g. In the circuit shown, however, only the bias voltage is developed across R_g. The bias is then applied between the grid and cathode in *series* with the signal voltage.

contact bias

A method of bias that depends on the flow of grid current and yet does *not* require that the input signal drive the grid positive is *contact potential bias,* or just *contact bias.* This bias makes use of the fact that the space charge within the tube has a negative charge since it is composed of electrons.

With no input signal present, the cathode is at a slight positive potential, since it has emitted, or lost, electrons to the space charge. The grid is, therefore, at the same slightly positive potential compared to the space charge, and so attracts some electrons from the space charge. As shown, these electrons make up a small grid current that flows from the grid, through resistor R_g, and back to the cathode. This grid current is *extremely small,* and in most circuits produces an insignificant voltage drop across R_g. However, for contact bias, the value of R_g is made very *very large,* usually 10 megohms or more. Consequently, the grid current produces a voltage drop that, although small, provides a usable bias for many applications.

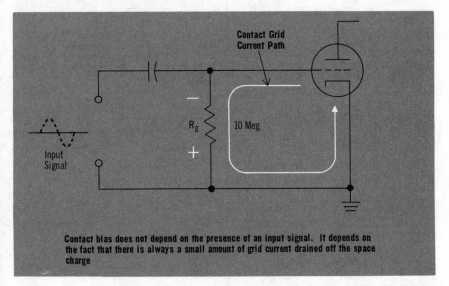

Contact bias does not depend on the presence of an input signal. It depends on the fact that there is always a small amount of grid current drained off the space charge

You can see from the illustration that the circuit arrangement for contact bias can be very similar to that used for the first type of grid-leak bias previously discussed. However, by noting the value of the grid resistor, R_g, you can practically always determine the type of bias being used. The grid resistor for contact bias is always considerably *larger* than that for grid-leak bias. Also, because the grid resistor is so large, often up to 10 megohms, the coupling capacitor must be smaller; otherwise, the RC time constant would also be great enough to produce grid-leak bias when a signal is applied. As a result, a contact-bias circuit can also be identified by a smaller value capacitor.

combination bias

Sometimes, a single type of bias cannot satisfy the requirements of a particular application. In these cases, two types of bias are used simultaneously, with the total bias being the *sum* of the separate bias voltages. The use of two biasing methods is called *combination bias*. Usually, combination bias means the use of both fixed and self bias.

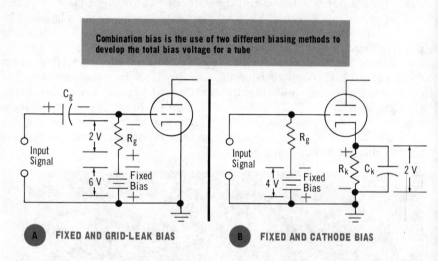

Combination bias is the use of two different biasing methods to develop the total bias voltage for a tube

A FIXED AND GRID-LEAK BIAS   **B** FIXED AND CATHODE BIAS

A frequently used combination is grid-leak bias and cathode bias. The cathode bias serves to provide *protection* for the tube in the event the input signal is lost. Without an input signal, the grid-leak bias is zero, and under these conditions excessive current might flow through the tube and damage it.

As shown in D, fixed bias can also be obtained by making the cathode resistor, R_k, part of a voltage divider network. Since R_k also develops cathode bias, the two voltages add across R_k to produce the bias voltage.

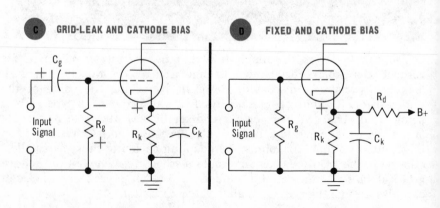

C GRID-LEAK AND CATHODE BIAS   **D** FIXED AND CATHODE BIAS

summary

☐ The load line, which represents a single value of load resistance, shows the plate current and plate voltage for a particular bias voltage. ☐ The voltage drop across the load resistor can also be determined by subtracting the B+ voltage from the plate voltage. ☐ The dynamic transfer characteristic of a triode describes the effect that a changing grid voltage has on plate current for a specific load resistance and B+ voltage.

☐ Grid bias provided by a d-c source external to the triode and not depending on triode operation, is called fixed bias. ☐ Cathode bias is provided by a cathode resistor and a cathode bypass capacitor. Without the cathode capacitor, the voltage or bias at the cathode would vary according to fluctuations in the input signal. The cathode bypass capacitor bypasses these fluctuations and provides a constant positive voltage at the cathode. This form of bias is also called self bias. ☐ Grid-leak bias is present only when grid current flows. It is developed by a capacitor and resistor connected in the grid circuit. The time constant of these two components must be large in respect to the frequency of the input signal.

☐ Contact bias is developed across a resistor in the grid circuit as a result of grid current flow. Contact bias differs from grid-leak bias because the grid need not be positive. Instead, contact bias depends on the small amount of grid current drained off the space charge. ☐ In many applications, more than one method of bias is used. This is called combination bias. Often, fixed bias is used with grid-leak bias to protect the triode.

review questions

1. What is a *load line* and what does it show?
2. How are the plate and load voltages determined from a load line?
3. What is *cathode bias*?
4. Why is cathode bias called *self bias*?
5. How would cathode bias react if no bypass capacitor were used?
6. Why must the time constant of the grid resistor and coupling capacitor be very large when developing grid-leak bias?
7. Will grid-leak bias be developed if the net voltage at the grid is always negative? Explain.
8. How is contact bias developed?
9. From the triode circuit, how can you determine whether grid-leak or contact bias is being used?
10. How does the combination of grid-leak and cathode bias protect the tube?

coupling

Actual electronic equipments usually contain many tubes, each of which receives an input signal, processes it in some way, and then passes it to another tube for further processing. The components used to apply a signal to the input of a tube or to pass the output of one tube to the input of another make up what are called *coupling circuits*.

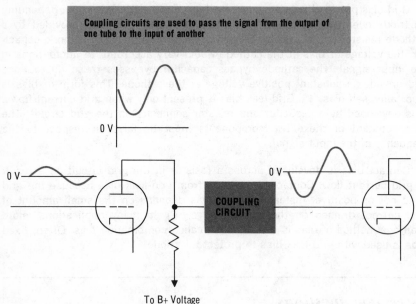

Coupling circuits are used to pass the signal from the output of one tube to the input of another

To B+ Voltage
Source

In most cases, the coupling circuit is connected so that its input is the plate voltage of a tube, which you recall is 180° out of phase with the grid voltage of that tube. As shown, most coupling circuits pass only the signal voltage, which is the a-c component of the tube's plate voltage

A wide variety of coupling circuits is used in actual practice, with each type having characteristics that make it suitable for certain applications and unsuitable for others. As you will learn in later volumes, the gain, frequency response, and distortion of electron-tube circuits are to a large extent determined by the type of coupling used.

The various coupling methods can be divided into four general types, which will be described separately on the following pages:

1. *Direct* coupling.

2. *Resistance-capacitance* (RC) coupling.

3. *Impedance* coupling.

4. *Transformer* coupling.

direct coupling

With *direct coupling,* the plate of one tube is connected *directly* to the *grid* of another. The *entire* plate voltage of V_1 is applied between the grid of V_2 and ground. As with any triode, the plate of each tube must be at a higher potential than its cathode. However, the cathode of V_2 must be at a higher potential than the plate of V_1 at all times. If it is not, the grid of V_2 will be positive with respect to its cathode.

With a varying input signal applied to V_1, the plate voltage of the tube will vary around some d-c level. In the circuit, this d-c level will always be less than 50 volts, since the plate voltage cannot exceed the B+ supply voltage. As shown, the bias of V_1 might cause the no-signal, or *quiescent,* plate voltage to be 40 volts. This makes the grid of V_2 also 40 volts positive with respect to ground. However, since the cathode of V_2 is held at a constant 60 volts *positive* with respect to ground, the grid actually has a 20-volt negative bias wth respect to the cathode.

When the input signal to V_1 causes the plate voltage to vary, say, between 35 and 45 volts, the same voltage variation appears at the grid of V_2. As a result, the grid-to-cathode voltage of V_2 varies between −25 and −15 volts. Thus, the grid-to-cathode voltage of V_2 varies in the same a-c way as the plate voltage of V_1.

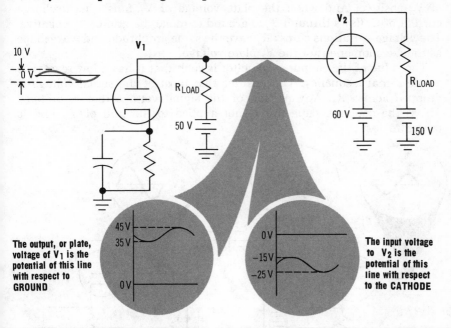

The output, or plate, voltage of V_1 is the potential of this line with respect to GROUND

The input voltage to V_2 is the potential of this line with respect to the CATHODE

Direct coupling is used with d-c or very-low-frequency signals. The disadvantage of direct coupling is that a different level of B+ voltage is needed for each tube. Also, if the voltage levels tend to vary slightly, they effect the tubes' operation. This condition is referred to as d-c *drift.*

resistance-capacitance coupling

In resistance-capacitance coupling, a *resistor* and a *capacitor* are used to couple the a-c component of an output signal while at the same time *blocking* the d-c component. This is frequently referred to as RC coupling.

Two RC coupled stages are shown. The components which accomplish the signal coupling are capacitor C_c, which is called a *coupling capacitor*, and resistor R_g, which is the grid resistor for tube V_2. Essentially, C_c and R_g make up an a-c *voltage divider* connected between the plate of V_1 and ground. With no input signal, V_1 conducts and has a certain value of quiescent plate voltage. Capacitor C_c charges to this voltage, with the path for the charging current being from ground, through resistor R_g, capacitor C_c, load resistor R_L, and the B+ supply.

When a signal is applied to V_1, its plate voltage varies above and below the quiescent value. On an increase in plate voltage, capacitor C_c *charges* further. And when the plate voltage decreases, C_c *discharges* through R_g, and then through V_1 back to the other plate of the capacitor. The capacitor thus charges and discharges in accordance with *changes* in the plate voltage of V_1. When the plate voltage of V_1 increases, the charging current of C_c flows *from* ground up through R_g to make the grid of V_2 positive. And when the plate voltage of V_1 falls, the discharge current of C_c flows through R_g *to* ground to make the grid of V_2 negative. The voltage variations across R_g have the same amplitude and waveshape as the a-c component of the V_1 plate voltage.

The value of the coupling capacitor is such that it has a low reactance at the signal frequency. This insures that most of the signal voltage is dropped across R_g. Any portion of the signal voltage that is dropped across the coupling capacitor is not applied to the grid of V_2, and is therefore lost.

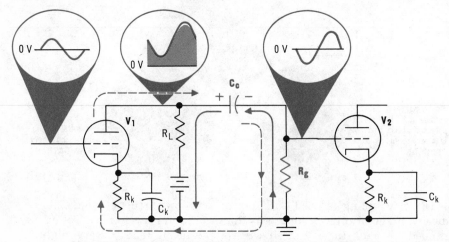

RC coupling passes an a-c signal. The d-c component is blocked by the coupling capacitor

impedance coupling

The basic difference between impedance and RC coupling is that an *inductor coil* instead of a resistor is used as the plate load as shown. The variations in the plate voltage of tube V_1 are coupled to the grid of V_2 by capacitor C_c and resistor R_g, the same as in RC coupling. However, the use of coil L_L in place of a resistor has a significant effect on the signal voltage developed at the plate of V_1. For example, a *lower* value of B+ voltage can be used when a coil serves as the plate load. The reason for this is that the *d-c resistance* of the coil is very *low*, while its *impedance* is usually relatively *high*. The d-c component of the plate current, therefore, produces only a small voltage drop across the coil resistance, leaving practically all of the B+ voltage as plate voltage to operate the tube. The a-c component of the plate current, on the other hand, produces a large voltage drop across the coil *impedance*. This makes it possible to achieve a large signal voltage across the coil, while maintaining a low d-c voltage drop.

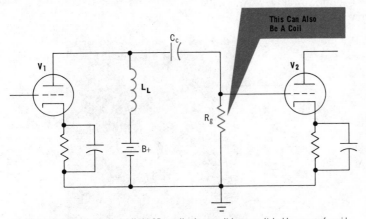

Impedance coupling is also called LCR coupling because it is accomplished by means of a grid resistor (R_g), a coil (L_L), and a coupling capacitor (C_c). When resistors are not used, it can be referred to as LC coupling

Another result of using a coil as the load is that it causes the *gain* of the stage to *vary* with the frequency of the signal. This is because the voltage drop across the load coil depends on the impedance of the coil, which, in turn, depends on its inductive reactance. And, as you know, the reactance is directly proportional to the frequency, as shown by the equation:

$$X_L = 2\pi f L$$

Thus, the higher the signal frequency, the larger is the output voltage, so the greater is the gain. Similarly, the lower the signal frequency, the less is the gain.

Often, with impedance coupling, an inductor is also used in place of grid resistor R_g.

transformer coupling

Transformer coupling makes use of a transformer to couple the output signal variations of one tube to the input of another. Two transformer-coupled triodes are shown. The transformer primary is connected in series with the plate of V_1 and the B+ supply. The secondary of the transformer is connected between the grid of V_2 and ground. When an input signal is applied to V_1, it causes a varying plate current to flow through the primary of the transformer. The varying current produces a varying magnetic field across the primary that induces a signal voltage in the secondary winding. This voltage is applied between the grid of V_2 and ground, and serves as the V_2 input signal.

An important advantage of transformer coupling is that the transformer itself can provide *voltage gain* over and above that produced by V_1. The gain in voltage is accomplished by using a coupling transformer having a *step-up turns ratio*. In the circuit, the transformer has a 2-to-1 step-up ratio. This means that the voltage induced in the secondary is always twice as large as that developed across the primary by the V_1 plate current.

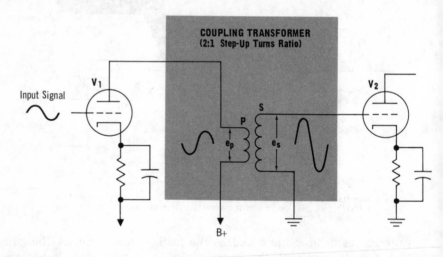

COUPLING TRANSFORMER
(2:1 Step-Up Turns Ratio)

Input Signal

V_1

V_2

P

S

e_p

e_s

B+

As shown, the transformer secondary voltage is 180° out of phase with the primary voltage. This is the standard phase reversal that takes place in a transformer

In practice, however, the leads of the transformer secondary can be reversed so that the secondary voltage applied to the grid of V_2 is in phase with the primary voltage

Besides providing additional voltage gain, transformer coupling permits the use of lower B+ voltages, the same as in impedance coupling. This is because of the low d-c resistance of the transformer primary. Another advantage of transformer coupling is that it has excellent *impedance-matching* properties. This will be covered later. Disadvantages of transformer coupling include the relatively large size and weight of the transformer, as well as its high cost.

tuned coupling

Tuned coupling is used in applications where many signal frequencies are present, and it is desired that only a *narrow band* of these frequencies be coupled from one circuit to another. The tuned coupling circuit must, therefore, respond to these desired signal frequencies but not to others. In one type of tuned coupling, capacitors are added in parallel with the primary and secondary windings of a transformer coupling network. This is called *double-tuned transformer coupling*, and is shown.

Each winding and its respective capacitor is tuned to the desired signal frequency, or band of frequencies. At these frequencies, the primary tuned circuit (L_1C_1) is resonant, and so presents maximum impedance. As a result, maximum voltage is developed across the primary and coupled to the secondary. The secondary tuned circuit (L_2C_2) is also resonant at these frequencies, and applies maximum input signal to the grid of V_2. At signal frequencies off resonance, the impedances of the two resonant circuits are such that little or no signal voltage is coupled to the grid of V_2 by the transformer.

Frequently, only the primary of the coupling transformer is tuned. This is called *single-tuned transformer coupling*. Both single- and double-tuned transformer coupling are covered in detail in Volume 5.

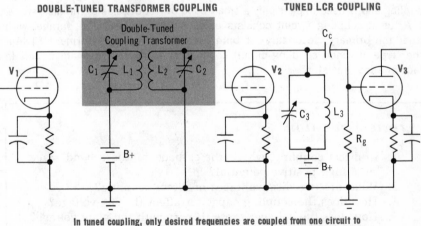

DOUBLE-TUNED TRANSFORMER COUPLING   **TUNED LCR COUPLING**

In tuned coupling, only desired frequencies are coupled from one circuit to another. All other frequencies are greatly attenuated by the coupling circuit

Another kind of tuned coupling is shown in the third stage. In this type, a parallel resonant circuit serves as the load for V_2, and the output signal is coupled to V_3 by capacitor C_c and resistor R_g. To signals above and below its resonant frequency, the parallel resonant load presents a low impedance. Very little signal voltage is developed, therefore, at these frequencies. This type of coupling is called *tuned LCR coupling*. The grid resistor R_g can also be replaced with a tuned circuit.

summary

☐ In direct coupling, the plate of one tube is applied directly between the grid and cathode of the next tube. This makes the grid highly positive. To compensate for this, the cathode of the second tube must always be at a higher potential than the maximum plate voltage of the first tube.

☐ Resistance-capacitance (RC) coupling uses a grid resistor and a coupling capacitor to couple the signal from one stage to the next. ☐ The coupling capacitor charges and discharges in accordance with plate voltage variations of the preceding tube. The charging path is from ground through the grid resistor, making the grid positive. The discharge path is through the grid resistor to ground, making the grid negative. ☐ Impedance coupling is essentially the same as RC coupling except that an inductor coil is used as the plate load instead of a resistor. ☐ The inductor coil permits the use of a lower B+ voltage while still providing a high output voltage. Also, as the frequency increases, the gain also increases.

☐ Transformer coupling uses transformer action to couple a signal from one stage to another. ☐ The primary of the transformer is in the plate circuit of the first tube. The secondary of the transformer is in the grid circuit of the second tube. ☐ The advantage of transformer coupling over other forms of coupling is that it can provide a voltage gain over and above the gain provided by the first tube. ☐ A modification of transformer coupling is tuned coupling and is used to pass only a small band of frequencies to the next stage. ☐ A tuned coupling circuit consists of a variable capacitor in parallel with either the primary, secondary, or both windings of the transformer. ☐ Another type of tuned coupling circuit consists of a parallel resonant circuit in place of a load resistor.

review questions

1. In direct coupling, why is the cathode of the second stage at a high positive potential?
2. What are two disadvantages of direct coupling?
3. How does the coupling capacitor affect the B+ voltage?
4. How does the voltage across R_g vary with the plate voltage?
5. What characteristics of a coil permit the use of a low B+ voltage, but still provide high gain?
6. Why does the gain of an impedance-coupled tube vary with frequency?
7. What are two disadvantages of transformer coupling?
8. How can extra gain be provided by transformer coupling?
9. Name three types of tuned coupling circuits and explain.
10. How does a tuned coupling circuit work?

impedance matching

In the coupling of signals between tubes as well as between tubes and other devices such as microphones, loudspeakers, etc., *impedance* plays an important role. The significant impedances are the *output impedance* of the device supplying the signal, and the *input impedance* of the device receiving the signal. In the case of a signal coupled between two tubes, this means the impedance of the plate circuit of the tube delivering the signal, and the impedance of the grid circuit of the tube receiving the signal. The relationship between these two impedances has an important bearing on the usability of the coupled signal.

There are two general statements that can be made concerning the impedance relationship between any source and the load to which it delivers its output. One of these is that *maximum power* is delivered to the load when the source and load impedances are *equal*. Neither the voltage nor the current transferred to the load under these conditions is necessarily maximum, but the power, which is equal to EI, is.

The other relationship between the source and load impedances is that the *voltage* delivered to the load is proportional to the *ratio* of the load impedance to the source impedance. In other words, the larger the load impedance is compared to the source impedance, the greater is the voltage delivered to the load. The reason for this is that the current that flows through the load impedance also flows through the source impedance and produces voltage drops across each. So when the load impedance is much larger than the source impedance, most of the voltage is dropped across the load, resulting in a large voltage transfer. When the load impedance has a value such that a considerable amount of the total voltage is dropped across the source, the load is said to *load down* the source.

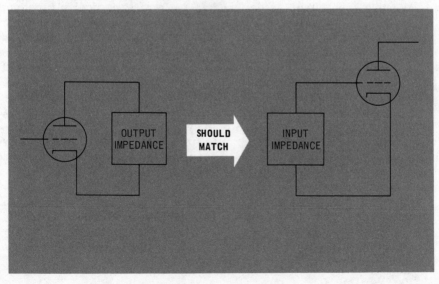

impedance matching (cont.)

From the discussion on the previous page, you can see that maximum power transfer and maximum voltage transfer are mutually incompatible. By using proper impedances, one or the other can be accomplished, but not both simultaneously. The desired relationship between source and load impedances, therefore, depends on the particular application.

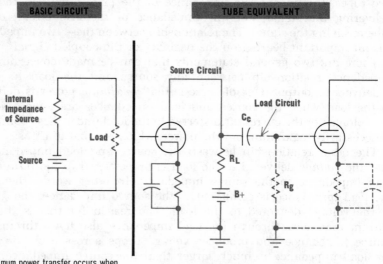

BASIC CIRCUIT

TUBE EQUIVALENT

Maximum power transfer occurs when the source and load impedances are equal. The voltage delivered to the load increases as the ratio of load-to-source impedance is increased

In signal coupling between tube circuits, the plate-cathode circuit acts as a source, and the grid-cathode circuit as the load. The impedances of these circuits are known as the output and input impedances of a tube, respectively

When a tube circuit is designed to perform a particular function, its input and output impedances are usually determined to a large extent by the desired operating characteristics. At the same time, it is often necessary that the input impedance of the tube have a definite relationship to the source or device supplying the input signal, as well as that the tube's output impedance bear a definite relationship to the circuit or device to which the tube delivers its output signal. These relationships may be such that equal impedances are required so that maximum power is transferred; or they may require impedance ratios that will prevent one of the circuits from being *loaded down*. In any case, some method must be used to provide the required impedance relationships. This is called *impedance matching* and can be accomplished in a variety of ways.

One of the most common ways of matching impedances is to use an *impedance-matching transformer*. The transformer is connected between the circuits whose impedances are being matched. Its primary–secondary *turns ratio* is such that each circuit is presented with the impedance required to obtain the desired match.

impedance matching (cont.)

A simple example will illustrate the use of an impedance-matching transformer. Assume that a tube is to deliver its output signal to a loudspeaker having an impedance of 8 ohms. Further, assume that the tube requires a plate load of 5000 ohms for proper operation. As you will learn, a loudspeaker operates on power, so the important consideration here is the transfer of *maximum* power from the tube to the loudspeaker. To accomplish this, 5000 ohms must be matched to 8 ohms.

Such an impedance match is made by using a transformer having a primary winding impedance of 5000 ohms and a secondary winding impedance of 8 ohms at the signal frequency. The primary serves as the plate load for the tube, and the secondary is connected across the loudspeaker. What this means is that the tube delivers maximum power to the transformer primary, while the secondary winding delivers maximum power to the loudspeaker. Since the power in the primary and the power in the secondary of a transformer are equal, maximum power is delivered from the tube to the load. The required transformer turns ratio in the example can be calculated from the standard transformer equation:

$$N_s/N_p = \sqrt{Z_s/Z_p} = \sqrt{8/5000} = 1/25$$

The transformer should, therefore, have a 1:25 step-down turns ratio.

In addition to transformers, there are numerous other methods for matching impedances. One of these involves the use of special tube circuits called *cathode followers*. These circuits have very high input impedances and low output impedances. They are widely used for matching high-impedance sources to low-impedance loads. Like impedance-matching transformers, they are connected between the source and the load, and present each with its required impedance.

In later volumes covering specific circuits, you will learn about many other methods for accomplishing impedance matching.

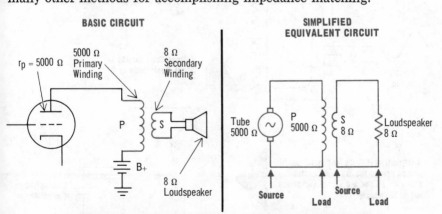

The impedance-matching transformer acts as a load for the tube and as the source for the loudspeaker. In both cases, it presents the proper impedance for maximum power transfer

decoupling

In all the circuits shown thus far, each tube has had its own individual B+ supply. This is done for convenience and simplification. In actual electronic equipment, a *single* B+ supply usually provides plate voltage for *all* or *most* of the tubes. As a result, the plate currents of all the tubes effectively flow through the common B+ supply. This can often produce undesirable effects because of the *fluctuations* in B+ voltage that result. To see why this is so, consider the case of a single tube having a battery as its B+ supply.

When the tube conducts, its plate current flows through the B+ supply, producing a voltage drop across the supply. With an input signal present, the plate current varies, and so also does the voltage drop it produces across the B+ supply. The amplitude of the supply voltage, therefore, varies at the signal frequency, since the voltage drop produced by the plate current subtracts from the total supply voltage. This fluctuation of the B+ supply voltage is small, and has little effect on the tube producing it.

If other tubes derive their plate voltage from the same B+ supply, however, the effect on them can be significant. For this reason capacitors, called *decoupling capacitors*, are usually connected across the B+ supply. These decoupling capacitors have essentially zero reactance at the signal frequency. So, they effectively *shunt* the signal variations of the plate current around the B+ supply, and thus maintain the output of the supply at a steady d-c level. A cathode bypass capacitor is a decoupling capacitor.

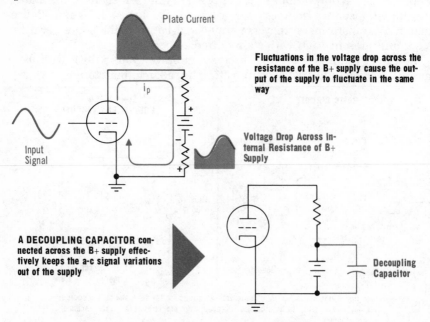

Plate Current

Fluctuations in the voltage drop across the resistance of the B+ supply cause the output of the supply to fluctuate in the same way

Voltage Drop Across Internal Resistance of B+ Supply

Input Signal

A DECOUPLING CAPACITOR connected across the B+ supply effectively keeps the a-c signal variations out of the supply

Decoupling Capacitor

frequency response

The frequency response of any circuit describes the way certain circuits respond to various input *frequencies*. For tube circuits, frequency response is usually expressed in the form of a graph showing how the output level or gain changes as the input frequency is varied. The frequency response of a tube itself is generally meaningless. It is only when the tube is connected into a circuit that frequency response is significant. This is because the response depends not only on the *physical construction* of the tube, but on the *components* used to establish tube operating conditions as well as the method of *coupling* employed.

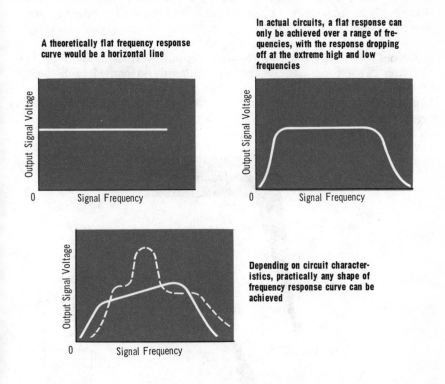

A theoretically flat frequency response curve would be a horizontal line

In actual circuits, a flat response can only be achieved over a range of frequencies, with the response dropping off at the extreme high and low frequencies

Depending on circuit characteristics, practically any shape of frequency response curve can be achieved

If the gain of a tube circuit is relatively unaffected by changes in the input frequency, the circuit is said to have a *flat response*. And, if the gain is significantly higher at a certain frequency, or range of frequencies, than it is at other frequencies, the response of the circuit is said to *peak* at that particular frequency.

The principal reason for a circuit not having a flat response is the presence of *reactive components*, which, by their very nature, react differently at different frequencies. For example, a tube that uses a coil instead of a resistor as a load will not have a flat frequency response.

frequency response (cont.)

Since the output signal is produced as a result of the voltage drop across the reactance of the load coil, a given coil will yield a greater output as the signal frequency is increased. This is because, as you know, the inductive reactance of a coil increases with frequency according to the equation $X_L = 2\pi fL$. In a similar way, the reactance of the windings of a coupling transformer result in greater signal voltages at higher frequencies, and so produce a frequency response that is not flat.

Capacitors also affect the frequency response of a circuit, since their reactance decreases with frequency according to the equation $X_C = 1/(2\pi fC)$. An example of this is a stage that uses RC coupling. Normally, the reactance of the coupling capacitor is negligible at the signal frequency, so practically the entire output signal is coupled through the capacitor and developed across the grid resistor of the following stage. At low signal frequencies, however, the reactance of the coupling capacitor is significant. Consequently, a considerable portion of the signal voltage is dropped across the capacitor. This reduces the amount developed across the grid resistor, and causes a reduction in the signal at these frequencies. As a result, the frequency response falls off at the lower frequencies.

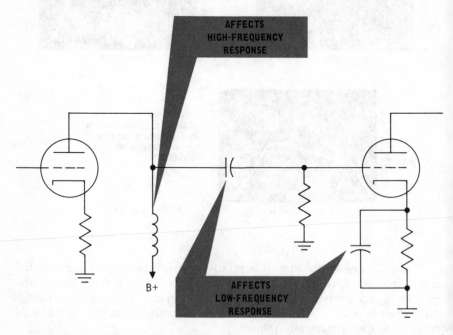

AFFECTS
HIGH-FREQUENCY
RESPONSE

B+

AFFECTS
LOW-FREQUENCY
RESPONSE

The desired frequency response of a particular circuit and the ways of producing it are directly related to the specific function of the circuit. Frequency response is, therefore, covered in detail in later volumes that deal with actual electronic circuits.

signal phases

Until now the triode has been described in what is called the *grounded-cathode configuration*. That is, the cathode has always been connected, either directly or through a resistor, to the negative side of the B+ voltage supply. Usually, the negative side of the B+ supply is at *ground* potential, and hence the term *grounded-cathode configuration*.

When a triode is connected in the grounded-cathode configuration, the input signal is applied between the grid and ground, so that the grid-to-ground voltage varies in accordance with the input signal. And, since the cathode is connected to ground, either directly or through a bias resistor, the input signal varies the grid-to-cathode tube voltage. When the grid voltage increases in a positive direction, plate current increases; and when it goes in a negative direction, plate current decreases. Thus, the *plate current* varies *in phase* with the *input signal*.

The *output signal voltage,* however, which is usually taken from between the plate and ground, is *180 degrees out of phase* with the input signal. This is because the plate voltage is equal to the B+ supply voltage minus the instantaneous value of the voltage drop across the load. In summary, then, the output signal voltage of the grounded-cathode configuration is 180 degrees out of phase with the input signal voltage, while the plate current is in phase with the input signal.

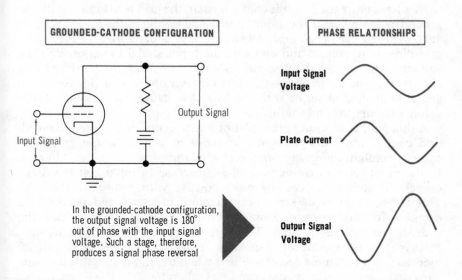

GROUNDED-CATHODE CONFIGURATION

Output Signal

Input Signal

In the grounded-cathode configuration, the output signal voltage is 180° out of phase with the input signal voltage. Such a stage, therefore, produces a signal phase reversal

PHASE RELATIONSHIPS

Input Signal Voltage

Plate Current

Output Signal Voltage

Although in most applications triodes are connected in the grounded-cathode configuration, they are also frequently connected in other ways. These other types of connections, as you will see, have significant effects on the phase relationships between the input signal, the plate current, and the output signal.

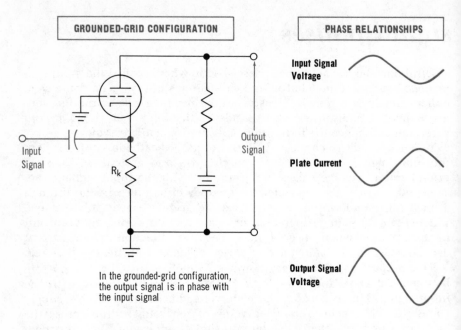

GROUNDED-GRID CONFIGURATION

PHASE RELATIONSHIPS

Input Signal

Output Signal

Input Signal Voltage

Plate Current

Output Signal Voltage

R_k

In the grounded-grid configuration, the output signal is in phase with the input signal

grounded-grid configuration

In a frequently used circuit configuration, the grid is held at a constant ground potential, and the input signal causes the cathode potential to vary with respect to the grid. As shown, this is done by connecting the grid directly to ground and applying the input signal in series with the cathode. This is called the *grounded-grid configuration*. In the circuit shown, resistor R_k provides cathode bias for the stage. So, the input signal is applied *in series* with the bias, and causes the grid-to-cathode voltage to vary around the bias level.

Although the operating principles of a tube connected in the grounded-grid configuration are the same as those of a tube in the grounded-cathode configuration, the *signal phase relationships* are quite different. In the grounded-grid configuration, an increase in input signal voltage causes the cathode to become more positive with respect to the grid. This is the same as making the grid more negative, and results in a decrease in plate current. Similarly, when the input signal falls, the cathode becomes less positive. This is the same as making the grid more positive, so plate current increases. Thus, when the input signal increases, plate current decreases; and when the input signal falls, plate current increases. The plate current is, therefore, 180 degrees out of phase with the input signal.

The output signal voltage in the grounded-grid configuration is developed in the same way as it is in the grounded-cathode configuration. It is, therefore, 180 degrees out of phase with the plate current, so the output signal voltage is *in phase* with the input signal voltage.

grounded-plate configuration

In addition to the grounded-cathode and grounded-grid configurations, triodes can also be connected in a *grounded-plate configuration*. In the grounded-plate configuration, the input signal is applied between the grid and cathode, the same as for the grounded-cathode configuration. The output signal, however, is taken from directly across the load, which is connected in the *cathode circuit* of the tube.

The plate current of a grounded-plate stage is in phase with the input signal, as is the case for a grounded-cathode stage. The voltage drop across the load resistor, R_L, is also in phase with the input signal, since it is directly proportional to the plate current. And, inasmuch as this voltage drop is the output signal, the output signal of a grounded-plate stage is *in phase* with the input signal. A grounded-plate stage is also called a *cathode follower*. This is because the output signal is developed in the cathode circuit, and is in phase with, or *follows*, the input signal.

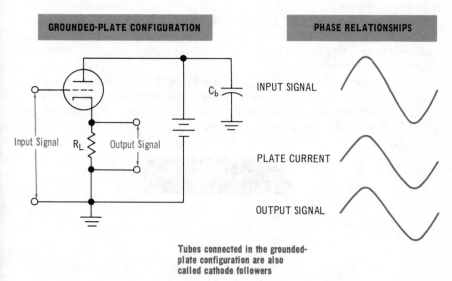

GROUNDED-PLATE CONFIGURATION

C_b

Input Signal R_L Output Signal

PHASE RELATIONSHIPS

INPUT SIGNAL

PLATE CURRENT

OUTPUT SIGNAL

Tubes connected in the grounded-plate configuration are also called cathode followers

The grounded-plate, or cathode-follower, circuit has several characteristics that make it different from other tube configurations. One of these is that the output signal voltage is always *slightly less* than the input signal voltage. In other words, no voltage amplification takes place. This arises from the fact that the output voltage developed across resistor R_L also acts to bias the tube. So, if this voltage equaled the input signal voltage, no output at all would be developed. A hypothetical situation will serve to illustrate this. Suppose that under quiescent (no-signal) conditions a steady voltage drop of 5 volts was developed across R_L. In effect, this would supply the tube with a bias of −5 volts.

grounded-plate configuration (cont.)

Now, suppose an input signal drove the grid 2 volts positive with respect to ground. This would cause an increase in plate current, which, in turn, would produce a greater voltage drop across R_L. If this increase in the voltage drop, which is the output signal, equaled the input signal (2 volts), it would completely nullify the 2-volt signal on the grid. This is because making the cathode 2 volts more positive is the same as making the grid 2 volts more negative. The net result is that the signal would produce no change in the grid-to-cathode voltage, and therefore no change in plate current. You should understand that this situation is purely hypothetical, since the output voltage can never equal or exceed the input voltage. Although voltage amplification is impossible in a cathode follower, power amplification can be achieved.

Another important characteristic of the cathode follower is its *low output impedance*. This is due to the low-valued load resistors used in the cathode circuit. The input impedance, as with most tube circuits, is very high. And the combination of high input impedance and low output impedance makes the cathode follower very useful for impedance-matching purposes.

You should note that the term *grounded-plate* refers to *a-c ground*, not d-c ground. Thus, the cathode follower shown on the previous page has its plate kept at a-c ground by bypass capacitor C_b. The plate could also be kept at d-c ground if a B-minus supply were used at the cathode and grid.

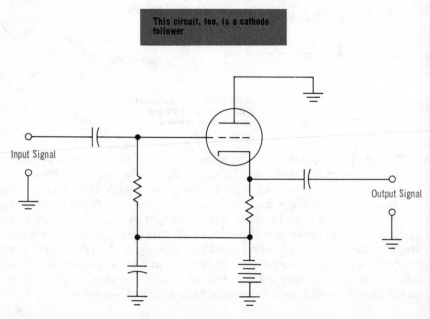

This circuit, too, is a cathode follower

Input Signal

Output Signal

interelectrode capacitance

You know that two electrical conductors separated by a dielectric have capacitance. This situation exists between the metal electrodes *within* a triode. Definite values of capacitance exist between the *grid* and *cathode*, *grid* and *plate*, and *plate* and *cathode*. These are called *interelectrode capacitances*, and are usually designated as C_{gk}, C_{gp}, and C_{pk}, with the subscripts indicating the electrodes between which the capacitance exists. The interelectrode capacitances are relatively small, being on the order of a few picofarads. Their effect on a tube is as if actual capacitors were connected between the tube electrodes.

The reactance of the interelectrode capacitances, like that of any capacitance, is inversely proportional to the capacitance value and the frequency. At the lower frequencies, therefore, the reactances of C_{gk}, C_{gp}, and C_{pk} are large, and the capacitances have little effect on circuit operation. At higher frequencies, though, the effects of the interelectrode capacitances become significant. For example, the grid-to-cathode capacitance is directly across the tube's input circuit. At high signal frequencies, its reactance can be low enough so that it shunts a considerable portion of the input signal directly to ground. This, of course, reduces the level of the input signal applied to the tube. In a similar way, the plate-to-cathode interelectrode capacitance can shunt a portion of the output signal to ground at high frequencies. This would reduce the output signal level available.

The interelectrode capacitances of a triode have the same effect as actual capacitors connected between the electrodes

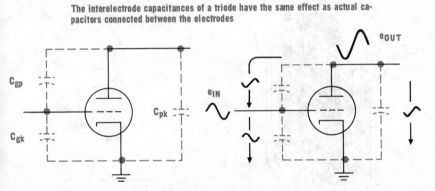

At high signal frequencies, C_{gk} shunts a portion of the input signal to ground, C_{pk} shunts a portion of the output signal to ground, and C_{gp} couples a portion of the output signal back to the grid

Of the three interelectrode capacitances, that between the grid and plate is the most troublesome. At higher frequencies, it provides a path for undesirable interaction between the input and output circuits of the tube. It can be *neutralized* and this is generally necessary if triodes are to be used at high signal frequencies. This is covered in later volumes.

tetrodes

Neutralization of a triode to cancel the effects of the plate-to-grid feedback through the interelectrode capacitance has many disadvantages. Additional circuits are required, and their adjustment is often critical. In addition, it is frequently impossible to neutralize a stage over a wide range of input signal frequencies. These problems are eliminated by adding a fourth electrode to a triode. This electrode is called the *screen grid,* and is inserted between the grid and plate.

The screen grid acts as an *electrostatic shield* between the grid and plate, reducing the grid-to-plate interelectrode capacitance to values as low as 0.01 picofarads or less. The mesh-like structure of the screen grid allows it to perform its shielding function without appreciably interfering with the flow of electrons from cathode to plate. A tube that contains a screen grid in addition to a cathode, plate, and control grid is called a *tetrode,* because it has *four* elements.

On schematic diagrams, the screen grid is sometimes referred to as g_2, or the *second grid,* to distinguish it from the control grid, which is referred to as g_1, or the first grid. In addition, very frequently the screen grid is referred to simply as the *screen.* This is especially true when discussing various properties and characteristics, such as "screen voltage" or "screen current."

The Tetrode Has Four Elements

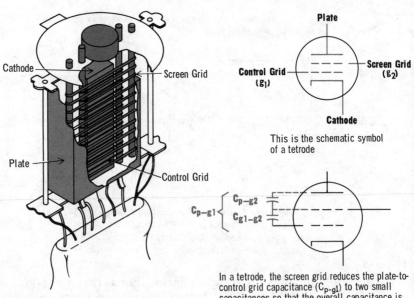

This shows the physical construction of a typical tetrode

This is the schematic symbol of a tetrode

In a tetrode, the screen grid reduces the plate-to-control grid capacitance ($C_{p\text{-}g1}$) to two small capacitances so that the overall capacitance is much less

operation of the screen grid

A simple tetrode circuit is shown below. The arrangement of the grid, cathode, and plate is the same as for a triode. The screen grid is kept at a *positive* potential, which although relatively large, is usually below that of the plate. When current flows in the tube, most of it passes *through* the screen grid and reaches the plate. The plate current then flows through the external plate circuit and back to the cathode.

Not all of the tube current reaches the plate, though. Some of the electrons that make up the current strike the screen. These electrons then flow through the external screen circuit back to the cathode, and make up what is called the *screen current*. The total tube or cathode current is therefore equal to the sum of the plate and screen currents. The screen current usually represents wasted current, so is kept to as low a value as possible.

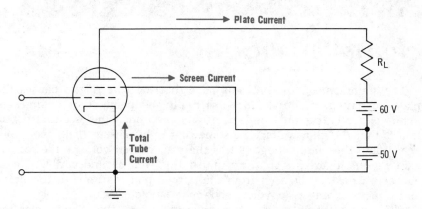

Besides reducing the grid-to-plate interelectrode capacitance, the screen grid has another significant effect on tube operation. This is that it causes changes in plate voltage to have *very little effect* on plate current. The reason for this is that the screen is closer to the space charge than is the plate, and the positive screen potential is practically constant. As a result, the screen grid maintains an almost constant attracting force on the space charge electrons, regardless of changes in plate voltage.

A practical tetrode circuit is shown on the next page. Here, both the plate and screen voltages are obtained from the same B+ supply. The lower value of screen voltage is obtained by applying the B+ voltage to the screen through a large resistor R_s. The small screen current produces a considerable voltage drop across this large screen resistor, and the effective screen voltage is then the B+ voltage minus the drop across the screen resistor. Capacitor C_s is a decoupling capacitor. It shunts the variations in screen current around both the screen resistor and the B+ supply, thus keeping the screen grid at a constant potential.

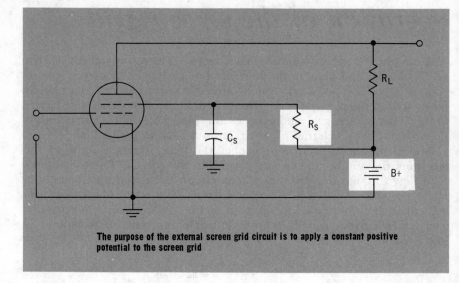

The purpose of the external screen grid circuit is to apply a constant positive potential to the screen grid

characteristics

The statement on the previous page that the screen grid causes the plate current of a tetrode to be virtually independent of changes in plate voltage is true only under certain conditions. The essential condition is that the plate voltage be somewhat *greater* than the screen voltage. When the plate voltage is less than the screen voltage, the tetrode exhibits characteristics that are unusual as well as undesirable. These characteristics can be seen from the tetrode plate-current, plate-voltage and screen-current, plate-voltage characteristic curves.

The curves shown on the next page are for a typical tube operated with a screen voltage of 75 volts. With zero plate voltage, a small amount of plate current and a considerably larger amount of screen current flow. The screen current is due to the screen grid directly attracting electrons, while the small plate current results from some electrons passing through the screen and having sufficient energy to reach the plate even though it exerts no attracting force. For a small plate voltage increase, more electrons have sufficient energy to reach the plate after passing through the screen grid, so plate current increases and screen current decreases a corresponding amount.

A further increase in plate voltage (point A) produces a strange phenomenon. The plate current begins to decrease as the plate voltage is raised. This is exactly *opposite* to the normal plate-voltage, plate-current relationship. The explanation for this phenomenon lies in the *secondary emission* that occurs at the plate when the electrons strike the plate. The secondary electrons emitted by the plate, instead of being attracted back into the plate as they are with high plate voltages, are attracted to the screen, since it is much more positive than the plate.

characteristics (cont.)

As the plate voltage is increased from point A to point B, the total attraction on the electrons of the space charge increases, so those electrons that pass through the screen and strike the plate have more energy. They, therefore, produce more secondary electrons when they strike the plate. As a result, more electrons are actually emitted from the plate and attracted to the screen than reach the plate from the space charge. This causes a further decrease in plate current, and actually constitutes a *negative current*, since more electrons are flowing from the plate than are flowing to it. As a result, this characteristic is called *negative transconductance*, or *negative resistance*.

When the plate voltage is increased past point B, the plate is sufficiently positive to recapture more secondary electrons than it loses to the screen. Plate current, therefore, begins to increase and screen current to decrease. This trend continues as the plate voltage is increased further, with the plate recapturing more and more of the secondary electrons as a result of its increasing positive potential.

When the plate voltage reaches point C, which is *greater* than the screen voltage, it recaptures essentially all of the secondary electrons. This means that all electrons that pass through the screen go into the plate current. Increasing the plate voltage further has practically no effect on the plate current, since at this point, as previously mentioned, it is the screen voltage that primarily affects plate current.

Normal operation of a tetrode is at plate voltages where secondary emission does not affect plate current. This corresponds to plate voltages above point C.

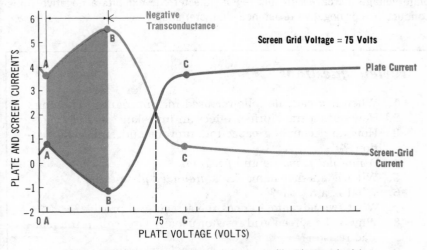

Over the plate-voltage range where current decreases with an increase in plate voltage (point A to Point B), a tetrode is said to exhibit NEGATIVE RESISTANCE, or NEGATIVE TRANSCONDUCTANCE

summary

☐ When coupling a signal between two devices, the output impedance of the first device and the input impedance of the second device should be equal for maximum power transfer. ☐ Transformers are most commonly used for impedance matching. Another impedance-matching device is the cathode follower. ☐ In most electronic equipment, one B+ supply provides plate voltage for many tubes. ☐ Decoupling capacitors are connected across the B+ supply to prevent undesirable fluctuations in the B+ supply. ☐ Frequency response describes how circuits react to various input frequencies and depends upon tube construction, the components used, and the method of coupling.

☐ Triodes can be connected in grounded-cathode, grounded-grid, or grounded-plate configurations. ☐ In the grounded-cathode configuration, the input is applied between grid and cathode and the plate current is in phase with the input. ☐ In the grounded-grid configuration, the signal is applied in series with the cathode and the plate current is 180 degrees out of phase with the input. ☐ In the grounded-plate configuration, the input is applied between grid and cathode but the output is taken off the cathode. Here, the plate current is in phase with the input.

☐ Grid-to-plate interelectrode capacitance in a triode is undesirable. One method of counteracting this is to use a four-element tube called a tetrode. ☐ The fourth element of a tetrode is a screen grid, which is placed between the grid and plate to act as an electrostatic shield. ☐ The screen grid is kept at a high positive potential, which is usually less than the plate voltage. ☐ Secondary emission occurs if the screen voltage is larger than the plate voltage. This is indicated by a small region where plate current decreases as plate voltage increases. In this region, the tetrode exhibits a negative transconductance or negative resistance characteristic.

review questions

1. When is a cathode follower used for impedance matching?
2. How does a transformer effect an impedance match?
3. How do decoupling capacitors prevent undesirable fluctuations?
4. Define *flat response* and *peaking*.
5. What is another name for a *grounded-plate tube*?
6. What is a *tetrode*?
7. What two advantages does the screen grid provide?
8. Why is the screen grid resistor usually larger than the plate load resistor?
9. What is *secondary emission*? When does it occur?
10. Describe *negative current*.

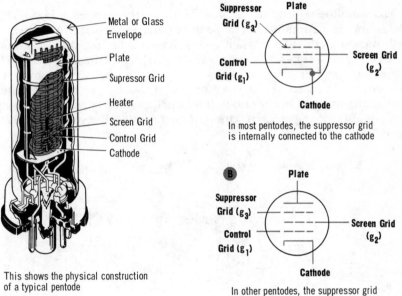

The Pentode Has Five Elements

Metal or Glass Envelope
Plate
Supressor Grid
Heater
Screen Grid
Control Grid
Cathode

This shows the physical construction of a typical pentode

A The schematic symbols below show that there are two types of pentodes:

Suppressor Grid (g_3)
Plate
Control Grid (g_1)
Screen Grid (g_2)
Cathode

In most pentodes, the suppressor grid is internally connected to the cathode

B
Plate
Suppressor Grid (g_3)
Control Grid (g_1)
Screen Grid (g_2)
Cathode

In other pentodes, the suppressor grid is connected to its own external pin

pentodes

Although tetrodes provide a significant reduction in grid-to-plate inter-electrode capacitance and produce greater amplification than triodes, they have definite disadvantages. Most of the disadvantages arise from their negative resistance characteristic at lower values of plate voltage. Therefore, tetrodes are used in a very limited number of applications, involving for the most part radio transmitting equipment. To use the advantages of the tetrode and at the same time avoid its disadvantages, another type of tube, called a *pentode,* is used.

Basically, a pentode is a tetrode to which an additional electrode has been added. This fifth electrode is called the *suppressor grid,* and is connected between the screen grid and the plate. The suppressor grid gets its name because it prevents, or suppresses, the effects of secondary emission that occur in triodes and tetrodes. Like the screen and control grids, the suppressor grid is a mesh-like structure that allows free passage for the electrons on their way to the plate.

The suppressor grid is often designated as the *third grid,* or g_3, on schematic diagrams. Thus, the control grid, which is the closest grid to the cathode, is the first grid; the screen grid, which is next closest to the cathode, is the second grid; and the suppressor grid, which is farthest from the cathode, is the third grid.

the suppressor grid

The suppressor grid is located between the screen grid and the plate, and is maintained at a potential that is considerably *negative* with respect to the plate. When secondary emission occurs at the plate, therefore, the secondary electrons are *repelled* back to the plate by the suppressor grid instead of being attracted to the screen grid. The required potential for the suppressor grid is usually provided by directly connecting the suppressor grid to the cathode, which is usually at ground or a slight positive potential. Often, though, the suppressor is connected directly to ground.

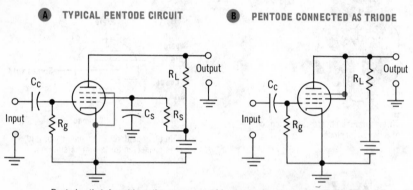

A TYPICAL PENTODE CIRCUIT   **B PENTODE CONNECTED AS TRIODE**

Pentodes that do not have the suppressor grid connected to the cathode within the tube can be used in pentode circuits (see A), or in triode circuits (see B) by connecting the screen and suppressor grids directly to the plate

Most types of pentodes have the suppressor grid connected to the cathode *inside* of the tube envelope. No external connection is required. In some types of pentodes, though, no internal connection is provided. So the appropriate suppressor grid-to-cathode wiring must be made outside of the tube. These types of pentodes can be operated as triodes, if desired, by connecting both the screen and suppressor grids directly to the plate.

In addition to eliminating the unwanted effects of secondary emission, the suppressor grid reduces the grid-to-plate interelectrode capacitance to an even lower value than in the tetrode.

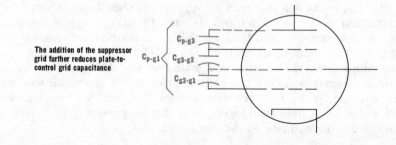

The addition of the suppressor grid further reduces plate-to-control grid capacitance

static characteristic curves

For the plate family of curves for a typical pentode shown, you will notice that the curves are for operation with specific values of screen and suppressor grid voltage. Different values for these grid voltages will produce a different, although similar, family of curves. Notice the difference between the pentode and tetrode curves. Because of the suppressor, at no time does the plate current dip with an increase in plate voltage.

Each of the plate family curves has a region where the plate current increases rapidly with increasing plate voltage. Above this region, though, the curves are relatively flat, which means that changes in plate voltage have very little effect on plate current. This is the usable portion of the curves, since in actual operation, it is desirable that the plate current be immune to plate voltage variations caused by a varying signal voltage.

The curves also show that at any given value of plate voltage, the distances between the various curves are different. This means that *equal* changes in *control-grid voltage* produce *different* changes in *plate current*. For example, at a plate voltage of 300 volts, a 1-volt change in control-grid voltage of from −1 to −2 volts (point A to B) produces a 2.2-milliampere decrease in plate current. But, at the same plate voltage, a 1-volt change in control-grid voltage of from −4 to −5 volts (point C to D) produces only a 1-milliampere decrease in plate current. This implies a *nonlinear* relationship between control-grid voltage changes and plate-current changes, which means the introduction of *distortion* in the output signal. Generally, such is the case; the pentode produces more distortion than does the triode. However, by using proper operating conditions, this distortion can be reduced to tolerable levels.

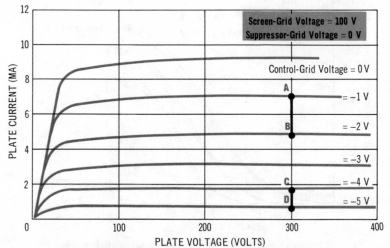

Static characteristic curves, such as this plate family, show the operating characteristics of pentodes with no load connected into the plate circuit

tube constants

Pentodes, like other tubes, are characterized by the three tube constants: amplification factor (μ), plate resistance (r_p), and transconductance (g_m). The amplification factor (mu), you recall, is the ratio of the plate and control-grid voltage changes that produces the same change in plate current. From the usable (flat) portions of the pentode characteristic curves shown on the previous page, you can see that even large changes in plate voltage produce only small changes in plate current. Changes in the control-grid voltage, on the other hand, produce significant changes in plate current. It is obvious, therefore, that pentodes have very large values of μ. A typical pentode can have a μ of 1500, which is about 100 times larger than that of an average triode, and 3 or 4 times greater than a tetrode.

The a-c plate resistance of pentodes is also very high; values on the order of a megohm are not uncommon. This is over 100 times greater than the plate resistance of the average triode. The great difference between the plate resistances of pentodes and triodes is an important consideration in determining what type of tube to use in particular applications.

In spite of their large values of amplification factor, pentodes have transconductances similar to those of triodes. This is because of their high values of plate resistance, as can be seen from the equation:

$$g_m = \mu/r_p$$

As shown, the transconductance is greatest at high values of plate and screen-grid voltage and low values of control-grid voltage.

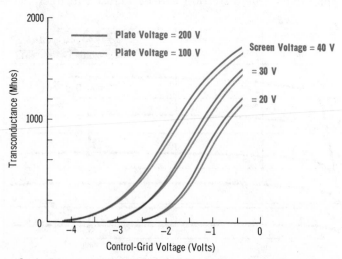

As shown here for a typical pentode, the transconductance is greatest at high values of plate and screen-grid voltage and low values of control-grid voltage

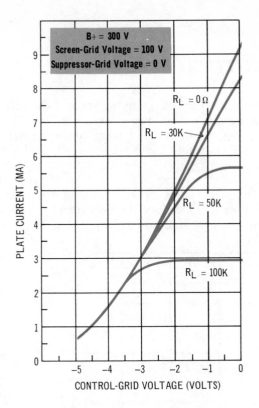

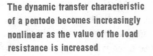

B+ = 300 V
Screen-Grid Voltage = 100 V
Suppressor-Grid Voltage = 0 V

The dynamic transfer characteristic of a pentode becomes increasingly nonlinear as the value of the load resistance is increased

dynamic transfer characteristic

The dynamic transfer characteristic of a pentode describes how the plate current of a tube will vary with changes in control-grid voltage. Such transfer characteristic curves are shown for a pentode having the same operating voltages but different values of load resistance. Although the transfer characteristic of a triode becomes more linear as the value of the load is increased, the *opposite* is true of a pentode. *Increasing* the value of the pentode load resistance causes the transfer characteristic to become more and more *nonlinear.*

The pentode dynamic transfer characteristic can be made essentially linear and relatively large values of load resistance can still be used by *reducing* the screen-grid voltage. This can be seen by comparing the curves shown with those on the following page. On the curves shown above a load resistance of 100K results in an extremely nonlinear transfer characteristic when the screen-grid voltage is 100 volts. But, by reducing the screen-grid voltage to 40 volts, as shown on the next page, the same 100K load produces a reasonably linear characteristic. Reducing the screen voltage, however, has the effect of causing the tube to *cut off* at a much lower value of negative control-grid voltage.

dynamic
transfer characteristic (cont.)

If the input signal is too large, its negative swing will cut off the tube, resulting in distortion of the output signal. Very often, therefore, the establishing of pentode operating conditions is a compromise between the desired screen voltage, the allowable input signal level, and the amount of distortion that can be tolerated. High screen voltages provide increased transconductance, and therefore higher gain, and permit larger input signals. They also, however, result in increased distortion. Low screen voltages, on the other hand, reduce the distortion. But they also reduce the gain and limit the amplitude of the input signals.

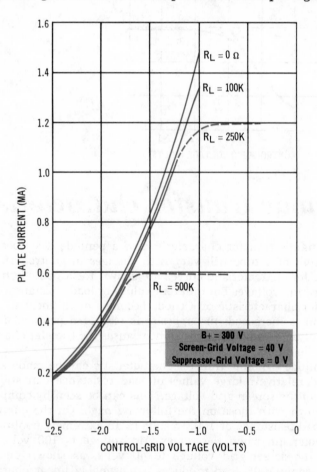

Decreasing the screen-grid voltage increases the linearity of the dynamic transfer characteristic

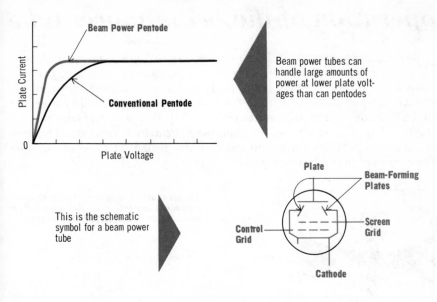

Beam Power Pentode

Conventional Pentode

Plate Current

Plate Voltage

0

Beam power tubes can handle large amounts of power at lower plate voltages than can pentodes

This is the schematic symbol for a beam power tube

Plate

Beam-Forming Plates

Control Grid

Screen Grid

Cathode

beam power tubes

For many applications, the ordinary pentode cannot handle the *power* that is needed. In these cases, *beam power* tubes are generally used. The external appearance of these tubes is similar to normal pentodes, except that they are slightly larger since they must handle more power. The internal construction of a beam power tube, however, is considerably different from that of an ordinary pentode. It is this construction that is responsible for the additional power handling capability.

Various factors are responsible for the characteristics of beam power tubes. Foremost of these is that the electrons are formed into concentrated *beams,* or streams, as they travel toward the plate. In addition, the tubes have large effective plate areas, as well as large cathode areas. All of these factors combined give beam power tubes the capability of producing large amounts of current with less distortion and at lower plate voltages than is possible in a conventional pentode.

The relative power-handling ability with minimum distortion of a beam power tube and a pentode can be seen from the plate-voltage, plate-current characteristic curves. For both curves, signal distortion is minimum over the range in which the curve is *flat.* In other words, when the plate current is virtually independent of changes in plate voltage. For the beam power tube, the plate current increases very rapidly to the minimum distortion level. But for the pentode, the rise is much more gradual, which means that the minimum distortion level is not reached until a higher value of plate voltage is attained. You can see, therefore, that the beam power tube can handle large amounts of power at a lower plate voltage than the pentode.

operation of the beam power tube

Beam power tubes contain a cathode, control grid, screen grid, and plate, the same as a pentode. Instead of a suppressor grid, though, they have *beam-forming plates* on opposite sides of the tube between the screen grid and plate. The beam-forming plates are internally connected to the cathode, and so are maintained at a negative potential with respect to the plate, the same as the suppressor grid in a pentode. The two beam-forming plates set up an electrostatic field that concentrates the plate current into a beamed path.

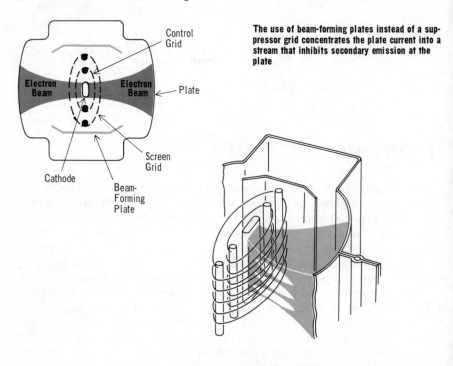

The use of beam-forming plates instead of a suppressor grid concentrates the plate current into a stream that inhibits secondary emission at the plate

The characteristics of the beam power tube are the result of the electrons being formed into concentrated beams

The control and screen grids in a beam power tube are wound so that the turns of the screen-grid windings are *directly in line* with the turns of the control-grid winding with respect to the direction of electron travel. This has a significant effect on the electrostatic field that influences the electrons and causes them to travel toward the plate. The total electrostatic field is further modified by the field produced by the beam-forming plates. The overall result is that the electrons are formed into concentrated beams or streams as they move toward the plate. And these concentrated beams inhibit secondary emission at the plate.

variable-mu pentodes

The amplification factor, or μ (mu), of a tube, you recall, depends on the physical geometry of the tube, and for all practical purposes is usually *constant*. Some variation occurs under different operating conditions, but these variations are generally small. One important tube characteristic determined by the value of mu is the negative control-grid voltage that will cut off the tube at a given plate voltage.

Low values of mu mean that large negative voltages can be applied to the control grid before plate current is cut off. A high mu, on the other hand, indicates that plate current is cut off by a relatively small negative voltage on the control grid. This is the situation, you recall, that exists for pentodes, with their high values of mu. Consequently, pentodes are generally limited to applications where the input signal is relatively small, and therefore does not swing the control grid too far negative.

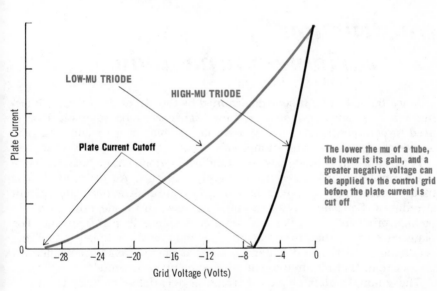

The lower the mu of a tube, the lower is its gain, and a greater negative voltage can be applied to the control grid before the plate current is cut off

Sometimes, though, it is desirable to operate a pentode with a large negative bias, so that the tube can accommodate a large input signal. This cannot be done with conventional pentodes, since it would result in the plate current being cut off during a portion of the input signal cycle, with resulting signal distortion. It is possible, however, with specially constructed pentodes, called *variable-mu pentodes*. The mu of these tubes depends on the value of the negative control-grid voltage. When the voltage is small, the mu of the tube is high, as in a conventional pentode. But, when the grid voltage is large, the effective value of mu decreases considerably.

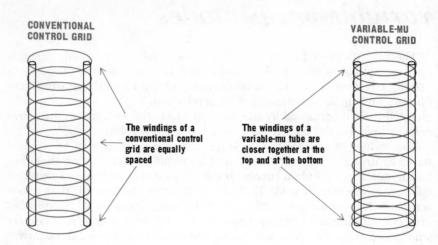

construction of a variable-mu pentode

Since the gain of a tube is determined by the mu of the tube, variable-mu tubes are also *variable-gain* tubes. This is a characteristic that is used in *gain control* circuits. When the grid bias in a variable-mu tube is increased, gain goes down and vice versa.

A variable-mu pentode has the standard pentode characteristics when the control-grid voltage is only slightly negative. As the grid bias is made increasingly negative, though, grid control over the plate current is reduced. Consequently, each equal increase in the negative grid-bias voltage produces a smaller and smaller decrease in plate current. The plate current is, therefore, cut off *gradually,* with complete cutoff not occurring until the grid voltage reaches a negative value considerably greater than that required to cut off a conventional pentode.

The gradual cutoff of plate current in a variable-mu tube is caused by the *physical construction of the control grid.* In conventional pentodes, the windings of the control grid are *equally spaced* along the entire length of the grid. So, a voltage applied to the grid has the same effect on the electrons no matter where they pass through the grid. But, in the variable-mu type of pentode, the control-grid windings are closer together at the top and bottom of the grid than they are in the middle.

At low values of control-grid voltage, the variable-mu grid acts in the normal manner. As the grid voltage becomes more negative, its repelling effect on the flow of electrons increases. But this effect is greatest at the top and bottom of the grid, since here the windings are closer together.

construction of
a variable-mu pentode (cont.)

The flow of electrons from the space charge near the ends of the grid is cut off first, with some electrons still passing through the center portion of the grid. As the grid is made more and more negative, the center portion of the grid that still allows passage of electrons becomes smaller and smaller, until eventually all electron flow is cut off. In this way plate-current cutoff is reached gradually.

The plate-current, grid-voltage characteristics of a typical conventional pentode and a typical variable-mu pentode are shown for comparison. You will notice that the variable-mu tube is extremely nonlinear because of the variable-mu characteristic. Therefore, these tubes are generally used with very *small signals*. A small signal will work only over a very small section of the curve, and so will be little affected by its nonlinearity. A large signal must be operated on the upper, or linear part, of the curve or it will be distorted.

You can see by the curves why a variable-mu tube is called a *remote cutoff tube,* and a conventional tube is called a *sharp cutoff* tube.

Because of their plate-current cutoff characteristics, conventional pentodes are often called sharp-cutoff pentodes, while variable-mu pentodes are called remote-cutoff pentodes

Because the remote-cutoff curve is so nonlinear, the variable-mu tube is used often for controlling the gain of very small signals

summary

☐ The pentode contains the elements of a tetrode plus an additional one called the suppressor grid. ☐ The suppressor grid is located between the grid and plate and is held at a high negative potential with respect to the plate. ☐ Because of the suppressor's relatively negative potential, secondary electrons emitted by the plate are repelled back to the plate instead of being attracted to the screen grid.

☐ Although amplification factor and plate resistance are much greater in a pentode than in a triode, transconductance is about the same. ☐ The output of a pentode becomes more nonlinear as the load resistance is increased. This nonlinearity can be reduced by reducing the screen voltage. However, the overall gain is then reduced as is the maximum signal handling capacity. ☐ When large amounts of power are required, beam power tubes are generally used.

☐ Beam power tubes use two beam-forming plates instead of a suppressor grid. The control grid and screen grid are wound directly in line with one another with respect to electron flow. They, with the beam-forming plates, modify the electrostatic field so that the electrons are formed into concentrated beams, which, in turn, prevent secondary emission at the plate. ☐ The amplification factor, or μ, of a pentode can be made to vary by changing the spacing of the wires in the control grid. This type of tube is called a variable-μ pentode. ☐ Variable-μ pentodes permit the use of large input signals because the grid bias can be made highly negative before the tube cuts off. ☐ The variable-μ pentode is extremely nonlinear and is generally used with very small signals.

review questions

1. What is a *pentode*?
2. Name two advantages of the suppressor grid.
3. How does the pentode overcome the negative resistance of a tetrode?
4. How is the suppressor grid normally connected?
5. How do the μ, r_p, and g_m of a pentode compare with those of a triode?
6. What is the relationship between linearity, screen voltage, and load resistance in a pentode?
7. What is a beam power pentode?
8. Compare the power handling capabilities and distortion of a beam pentode to that of a standard pentode.
9. How are amplification factor and gain related?
10. How is plate current in a variable-μ pentode affected by grid bias?

multiunit
and multielement tubes

All of the tubes described so far have been contained in their own envelope. This is not always the case. Frequently, two or more tubes are contained in a single envelope. This provides compactness and economy, and, in certain applications, improvement in tube performances. When two or more tubes are contained in one envelope the physical structure is called a *multiunit* tube. Electrically, though, it is more than a single tube, because the individual tubes can be used independently. In many multiunit tubes, a single cathode is used, and it supplies electrons for the individual tubes.

The most commonly used multiunit tubes are the dual-diode and dual-triode tubes. These contain two diodes and two triodes, respectively, in a single envelope. Very often, the prefix *duo* is used instead of the word *dual*. Thus, a dual diode is called a duodiode.

A *multielement* tube is one tube that has *more than five* elements, and so can be used to act as more than one tube. An example of such a tube is the *heptode* or *pentagrid* tube. These are used in special converter circuits that are described in a later volume.

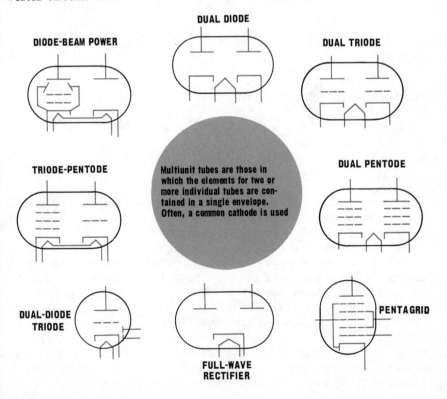

DUAL DIODE

DIODE-BEAM POWER

DUAL TRIODE

TRIODE-PENTODE

Multiunit tubes are those in which the elements for two or more individual tubes are contained in a single envelope. Often, a common cathode is used

DUAL PENTODE

DUAL-DIODE TRIODE

FULL-WAVE RECTIFIER

PENTAGRID

gas-filled tubes

In the tubes discussed previously, the chance of an electron colliding with an air molecule in the tube is relatively small. This is because most of the air is *evacuated* from the tube when it is manufactured. Such tubes are, therefore, called *vacuum tubes*. There is another class of tubes in which a gas is sealed into the tube, so that conduction takes place through this relatively dense gas. These tubes are called gas-filled tubes, or just *gas tubes*. Actually, the gas is only dense in relation to the air density in a vacuum tube. In relation to normal atmospheric air density, the gas is really very thin, being about one ten-thousandth of normal atmospheric pressure.

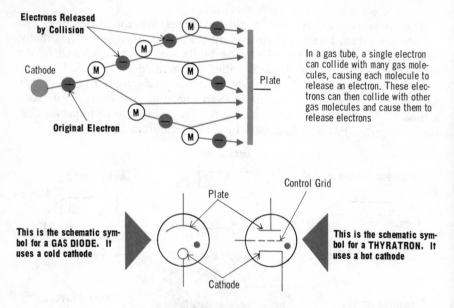

In a gas tube, a single electron can collide with many gas molecules, causing each molecule to release an electron. These electrons can then collide with other gas molecules and cause them to release electrons

This is the schematic symbol for a GAS DIODE. It uses a cold cathode

This is the schematic symbol for a THYRATRON. It uses a hot cathode

Like vacuum tubes, gas tubes contain electrodes for the application of operating voltages and the connection of load devices. Gas tubes operate on the principle that when a gas molecule is struck by a rapidly moving electron, the collision causes the molecule to release one of its own electrons. This electron can then collide with other gas molecules, causing them to release additional electrons. The action is thus *cumulative,* and if the proper operating voltage is applied to the tube, an extremely high output current can be produced.

Because of the nature of gas conduction, gas tubes can be *cold-cathode tubes;* that is, they can have no heater. Gas tubes are broadly classified by the number of electrodes they contain. Those that have only a cathode and plate are called *gas diodes*, while those that contain a cathode, a plate, and a control grid are called *thyratrons.*

voltage–current relationships

Even with no operating voltage, some ions and therefore free electrons, always exist as a result of interaction between the gas molecules and cosmic radiation, light, etc. If two electrodes are placed in the gas to form a gas diode and a voltage is applied between the electrodes, the ions, which are positive, will travel to the cathode and the electrons to the plate. This will cause current to flow in the external circuit even though there is no thermionic emission. The ions that move to the cathode draw out electrons to again become neutral gas molecules, until, of course, they are struck by another rapidly moving electron. The current caused by a relatively small plate-to-cathode voltage is called *dark current*, since the gas gives off no light at this low level of ionization (A to B on the curve).

As the voltage is increased, a point is reached (points B and C) at which the current rises abruptly and the voltage drop across the tube decreases. This is called the *breakdown*, or *ionization point*, and is caused by the electrons in the tube having sufficient velocity to ionize the gas molecules by collision. The drop in voltage is caused by the decrease in the resistance of the tube that occurs because of the ionization.

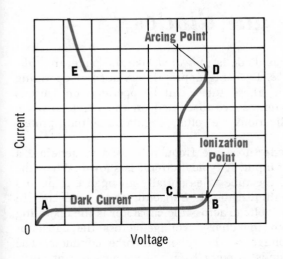

All gas tubes operate on some portion of this basic voltage-current curve

If the plate voltage is increased further, the current continues to rise, and the cathode becomes heated as a result of being bombarded by ions. If the cathode becomes hot enough, it emits electrons by thermionic emission, and this, in turn, causes greater tube current, more ionization, and further heating of the cathode. This cumulative action results in a sudden decrease in the voltage drop across the tube (points D and E) and an increase in tube current to an extremely high value. This is called the *arcing point*.

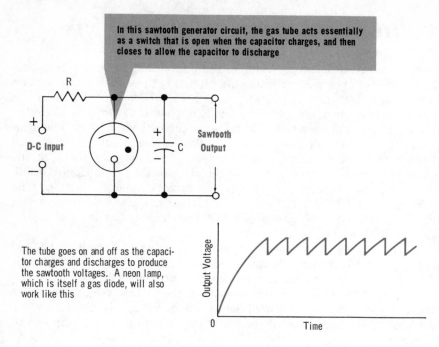

In this sawtooth generator circuit, the gas tube acts essentially as a switch that is open when the capacitor charges, and then closes to allow the capacitor to discharge

The tube goes on and off as the capacitor charges and discharges to produce the sawtooth voltages. A neon lamp, which is itself a gas diode, will also work like this

cold-cathode gas diodes

When the cathode of a gas diode is *unheated*, like the plate, the tube is called a *cold-cathode tube.* By using appropriate values of operating voltage and load resistance, these tubes can be operated on various portions of the voltage-current curve discussed on the previous page. Some of their common applications are voltage regulation, circuit protection, and oscillation.

As oscillators, cold-cathode tubes are frequently used to generate a sawtooth output from a d-c input. A typical circuit is shown. When the d-c voltage is first applied, the tube is essentially an open circuit and capacitor C charges through resistor R. Capacitor C is connected in parallel with the tube, so the voltage across the capacitor is the operating voltage for the tube. When the charge voltage across the capacitor reaches the breakdown voltage of the tube, the tube conducts. The breakdown voltage corresponds to point B on the voltage-current curve previously shown. The tube is then essentially a low resistance across the capacitor, so C discharges quickly through the tube.

When the charge voltage across the capacitor drops below the value required to maintain ionization within the tube, the tube stops conducting, and capacitor C again begins charging to repeat the action. Ionization in the tube essentially stops somewhere below point C on the voltage-current curve. The tube, therefore, operates back and forth over approximately the BC portion of the voltage-current curve.

hot-cathode gas diodes

In hot-cathode gas diodes, the cathode is *heated* by an external source, as is the cathode of a vacuum tube. Electrons are therefore supplied in these tubes by two sources: the gas molecules when they become ionized, and the cathode. The principal use of hot-cathode gas tubes is to *rectify* ac to dc, particularly when large amounts of power are involved. One widely used type of hot-cathode gas tube is called the *mercury-vapor tube*.

In the mercury-vapor tube, a small amount of liquid mercury is contained within the tube envelope. When the cathode, which is actually a directly heated filament, is heated by an a-c current, it performs two functions: (1) it *vaporizes* the liquid mercury to provide gas for the tube; and (2) it *emits* electrons, which collide with the gas molecules to produce ionization. Mercury-vapor tubes are characterized by a low plate-to-cathode voltage drop; and, as a result, they have very high plate efficiencies. In other words, very little of the d-c input power is dissipated, or wasted, by the tube.

MERCURY-VAPOR TUBE

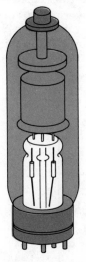

For power rectification purposes, mercury-vapor tubes can handle much higher voltages and currents than can comparable vacuum tubes

Another type of hot-cathode gas tube uses a pool of mercury as the cathode. These are called *pool-cathode tubes*. In these tubes, the ionization is started by creating an arc between a subsidiary electrode, called the *igniter,* and the cathode. Pool-cathode tubes are capable of supplying extremely high output currents continuously.

thyratrons

Thyratrons are gas tubes that have a *control grid* as well as a cathode and plate. They are, therefore, the gas-tube equivalent of vacuum-tube triodes. Thyratrons may be of the cold-cathode or hot-cathode type. The operation of a thyratron is based on two characteristics of a gas tube when operated in certain regions of the voltage-current characteristic. These are: (1) that the breakdown, or firing, voltage is greater than the voltage required to maintain conduction once it has started; and (2) the voltage required to extinguish the tube is considerably less than that needed to fire it.

Under normal operating conditions, the plate voltage of a thyratron is somewhat lower than the breakdown voltage, and the grid is at zero or a negative voltage. The tube is made to fire by raising the grid voltage to the point where ionization occurs between the grid and cathode. The electrons produced by this limited ionization then produce ionization throughout the entire tube. The grid voltage required to fire the tube in this way is considerably less than the plate-to-cathode voltage needed to produce ionization.

Once the grid fires the tube, it *loses control* over conduction, and can neither reduce nor stop the tube current. Making the grid negative would merely cause it to attract, and be surrounded by, positive ions. This would effectively shield it from the rest of the tube. The only way to extinguish the thyratron is to reduce the plate voltage below the level required for ionization. Usually, this is close to zero or a negative potential.

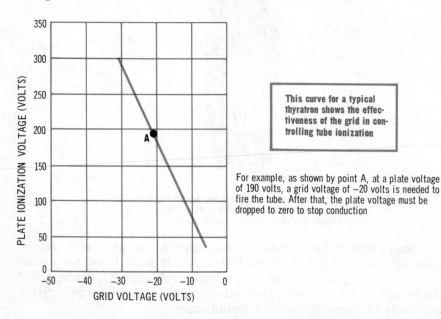

This curve for a typical thyratron shows the effectiveness of the grid in controlling tube ionization

For example, as shown by point A, at a plate voltage of 190 volts, a grid voltage of −20 volts is needed to fire the tube. After that, the plate voltage must be dropped to zero to stop conduction

This is the schematic symbol for a phototube

phototubes

Besides the vacuum and gas types of electron tubes, there are various other types that are widely used in the field of electronics. One of these is the *photoelectric tube,* also called the *phototube.* In this tube, the output current is controlled by *light* falling on the tube. Such tubes make use of the photoelectric effect, which, you recall, is the emission of electrons by certain photosensitive metals when they are struck by light.

Essentially, a phototube consists of a piece of photosensitive material that serves as the cathode, and an electrode that is maintained at a positive potential to serve as the plate. Both are contained in a glass envelope from which most of the air has been removed. The number of electrons emitted by the cathode depends on the intensity of the incident light and the area of the photosensitive cathode. The cathode is, therefore, usually made to have as large an area as possible.

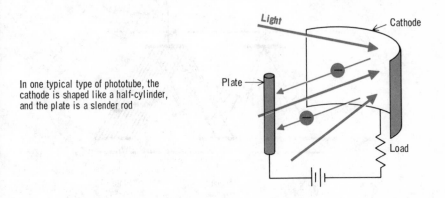

In one typical type of phototube, the cathode is shaped like a half-cylinder, and the plate is a slender rod

The sensitivity of a photosensitive material, or the number of electrons it emits for a given intensity of light also depends on the frequency, or color, of the light. Different tubes are therefore primarily sensitive to different light frequencies. For this reason, the sensitivity rating of a phototube is always specified in terms of specific frequencies.

photomultipliers

Photomultipliers are phototubes which incorporate some feature for converting, or *multiplying*, the number of electrons photoemitted by the cathode into a greater number of electrons. In one type of tube, this multiplication is accomplished by including a small amount of *gas* within the tube envelope. Electrons emitted by the cathode cause ionization of the gas, with the result that more electrons are available to take part in the current flow. The tube, therefore, delivers a larger output.

Another type of photomultiplier uses *secondary emission* to increase the output level. Such a tube is shown. The tube contains a series of multiplier electrodes, or plates. Each of these multiplier plates is treated so that it emits a number of secondary electrons when struck by an incoming electron. The plates are shaped and positioned so that the secondary electrons from each travel to the next succeeding one. Thus, each electron emitted by the cathode produces several secondary electrons when it strikes the first multiplier plate. Each of these electrons then produces several secondary electrons at the second multiplier plate. This sequence continues, until, at the final multiplier plate, an enormous number of secondary electrons is emitted for every electron originally emitted by the cathode.

The multiplier plates are frequently referred to as *dynodes*. Although the illustration shows only three dynodes, as many as nine or more are used in actual photomultiplier tubes.

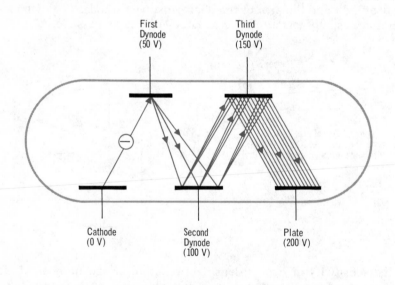

First Dynode (50 V)

Third Dynode (150 V)

Cathode (0 V)

Second Dynode (100 V)

Plate (200 V)

As a result of secondary emission, for every electron emitted by the cathode, a great number of electrons reach the plate

summary

☐ Multiunit tubes are those in which the elements for two or more independent tubes are contained in the same envelope. Typical multiunit tubes are dual diodes and dual triodes. ☐ Tubes that contain more than five elements, such as heptodes or pentagrid tubes, are called multielement tubes. ☐ In addition to vacuum tubes, certain tubes have gas sealed in the envelope. They are called gas-filled tubes.

☐ Gas-filled tubes are classified according to the number of elements they contain. A gas-filled diode contains a plate and a cathode; a gas-filled tube containing a cathode, control grid, and plate is called a thyratron. ☐ In all gas tubes, a small amount of current always flows. ☐ When the plate-to-cathode voltage is increased sufficiently, the gas is ionized. This is characterized by an abrupt increase in current and a decrease in voltage drop across the tube. ☐ If the plate-to-cathode voltage is increased further, the arcing point is reached. At this point, the voltage drop across the tube suddenly decreases. ☐ Gas-filled diodes can be operated with or without having the cathode heated and are designated as hot-cathode gas diodes and cold-cathode gas diodes, respectively. ☐ In a thyratron, the plate voltage is maintained below the breakdown voltage but above the maintaining voltage. The grid voltage is then increased until ionization occurs between the grid and cathode. At this point, the grid loses control and can neither increase nor decrease current flow.

☐ In the photoelectric tube, or phototube, the output current is controlled by light striking a photosensitive material. ☐ The current delivered by a phototube is dependent on the incident light intensity and the area of the photosensitive material. ☐ In photomultipliers or phototubes, the number of electrons leaving the cathode is greatly increased either by adding gas in the envelope or by using the effects of secondary emission.

review questions

1. What are some of the advantages of multiunit tubes?
2. Are multiunit tubes containing more than five elements, multielement tubes? Explain.
3. What is the principle of operation of a gas tube?
4. Define the *breakdown voltage* of a gas-filled tube.
5. How can you tell if the gas in a gas-filled tube is ionized?
6. Name one use of a cold-cathode gas diode.
7. Name one typical hot-cathode gas diode.
8. How can a thyratron be extinguished?
9. How is the sensitivity of a phototube specified?
10. How does a photomultiplier work?

electron-ray indicators

Electron-ray indicators are tubes that provide a *visual* indication of small voltage changes. They are frequently used in FM radio receivers to permit accurate tuning of an incoming signal. Most of these indicator tubes contain two sets of elements: one is a conventional triode amplifier, and the other is a cathode-ray indicator. The amplifier is used to boost the signal voltage to the level required to drive the indicator.

The indicator portion of one type of tube, as shown, has three elements somewhat similar to a triode. These elements are a *cathode,* a *control electrode,* and a *conical-shaped target* that serves as the plate. The cathode is heated, and emits electrons in all directions. The target, or plate, is kept at a positive potential with respect to the cathode, so the electrons are attracted to it. A special *fluorescent coating* on the target causes it to glow wherever it is struck by electrons.

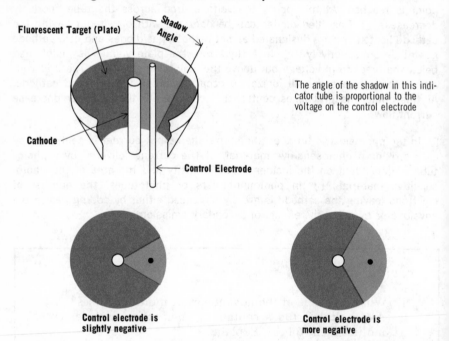

The angle of the shadow in this indicator tube is proportional to the voltage on the control electrode

Control electrode is slightly negative

Control electrode is more negative

The control electrode is in the form a wire that is parallel to the cathode as well as close to it. The potential of the control electrode is determined by the signal voltage to be indicated. When the electrode is negative it repels electrons on their way to the plate. It thus causes a *shadow* to be cast on the fluorescent target. The more negative the electrode is, the greater repelling effect it has, and the wider is the shadow on the target. When the control electrode is at the same potential as the target, the shadow closes, and effectively disappears.

cathode-ray tubes

Electron-ray indicator tubes, just described, give a visual indication of the relative amplitude, or change in amplitude, of a signal voltage. Another type of tube, called a cathode-ray tube (CRT), gives a visual indication not only of the amplitude of a signal voltage, but the *waveform* of the voltage as well. The cathode-ray tube does this by generating a thin *beam* of electrons that strikes a fluorescent screen, causing it to glow at the point of electron impact. A signal voltage then causes this beam to be *deflected* across the face of the fluorescent screen in such a way that the beam traces out the waveform of the signal.

In the electrostatic cathode-ray tube shown, the electron beam is generated and aimed at various points on the screen by an assembly called an *electron gun*. The electron gun is located inside the tube, or envelope, from which most of the air has been removed. The inside of the front of the tube is coated with a phosphor to make it phosphorescent. Electrical connections to the tube are made by means of pins that protrude through the end of the tube's neck. These pins are internally connected to the various tube elements.

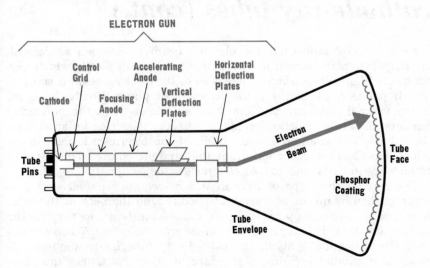

Electrostatic CRT's are usually used where small screens are needed, because electrostatic deflection requires a longer tube

The cathode of the electron gun is heated and emits electrons by thermionic emission. The control grid determines the number of electrons that can pass, so it controls the intensity of the electron beam, and, therefore, the brightness of the screen. After passing through the control grid, the electrons are focused into a thin beam by an electrode called the *focusing anode*. The velocity of the electrons in the beam is then increased by the *accelerating anode*.

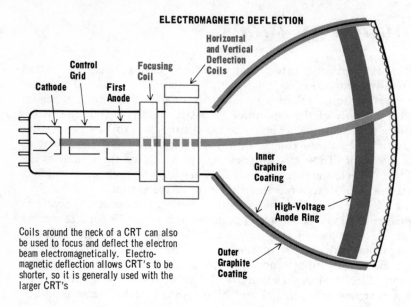

ELECTROMAGNETIC DEFLECTION

Coils around the neck of a CRT can also be used to focus and deflect the electron beam electromagnetically. Electromagnetic deflection allows CRT's to be shorter, so it is generally used with the larger CRT's

cathode-ray tubes (cont.)

In the electrostatic CRT, the electron beam is directed, as desired, at any point on the screen by two pairs of *deflection plates,* which also act as the high-voltage anode. The speed of the electron beam is so great that it passes between the plates. One set of plates directs the beam in the vertical direction, and the other set directs it in the horizontal direction. Each set of deflection plates operates by setting up an electrostatic field. The strength and direction of the electrostatic field determines the electron deflection from the straight course. This type of cathode-ray tube is said to use *electrostatic deflection.*

There is another type of tube in which *electron-beam* deflection is accomplished by means of coils positioned around the neck of the tube. A magnetic field set up by the coils causes the beam to vary in the desired direction. This is called *electromagnetic deflection.* When electromagnetic deflection is used, the cathode-ray tube has a high-voltage anode ring around the rim of the face of the tube. Often, the high-voltage anode is in the form of a graphite coating around the inner body of the tube. Also, a focusing coil can be used for electromagnetic focusing when electromagnetic deflection is used. However, some CRT's use the electrostatic focusing anode even when electromagnetic deflection is employed.

Cathode-ray tubes also have other refinements, such as an aluminum backing for the phosphorescent coating to prevent high-energy ions from damaging the phosphor face of the tube; other CRT's use a magnetic ion trap around the electron gun to deflect the ion beam off course. The outer body of CRT's is usually coated with a graphite composition to shield the electron beam from stray fields.

uhf and microwave tubes

When electron tubes are operated at extremely high signal frequencies, such as UHF or microwave frequencies, various considerations that are relatively unimportant at lower frequencies become extremely significant. These considerations include the capacitance between the tube electrodes, the small but ever-present inductance of the wires that connect the tube electrodes to the tube base, and the inductance of the electrodes themselves. The reactances of these inductances and capacitances change so greatly at high frequencies that they completely alter the operating characteristics of a tube.

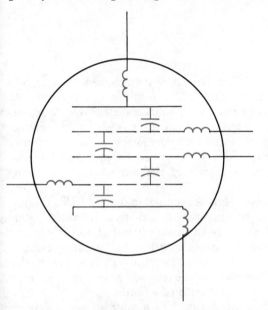

Here are some of the inductances and reactances that have a significant effect on the operation of a tube at high frequencies

Another high-frequency consideration is the time required for the electrons to travel from the cathode to the plate. This is called electron *transit time*. At low frequencies, the transit time is short compared to the time of one cycle of the input signal. Therefore, it has no appreciable effect on tube operation. But, at frequencies above about 200 megacycles, the transit time becomes appreciable with respect to the input frequency. As a result, the normal *phase relationships* between the grid and plate voltages no longer hold, and unstable operation and distortion result.

The above problems are overcome by using specially constructed tubes at high frequencies. These tubes use construction features such as short internal leads or metal rings instead of leads, elimination of the tube base, small electrodes, and close spacing between electrodes. The use of small, closely spaced electrodes results in *miniature construction* being characteristic of high-frequency receiving tubes.

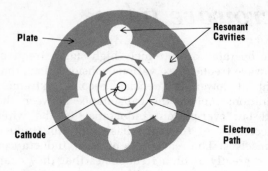

Plate

Resonant Cavities

Cathode

Electron Path

As shown in this simplified top view of the magnetron, the electrons follow a spiral path on their way to the plate

magnetrons

The generation of power at UHF and microwave frequencies over 300 megacycles poses considerable problems. The miniature, receiving-type high-frequency tubes cannot deliver large amounts of power. Furthermore, when tuned circuits are required, as is the case for tuned amplifiers or oscillators, the tuned circuits often cannot be made from combinations of coils and capacitors, as is done at low frequencies. Instead, the tuned circuits must be made a part of the amplifier or oscillator tube itself.

Various types of tubes have been developed that can deliver large amounts of power and provide the necessary tuned-circuit characteristics at high frequencies. One of these is the *magnetron*. It uses *resonant cavities* as its tuned elements. These are cavities that produce electromagnetic oscillations when a stream of electrons passes the cavity opening. This is somewhat similar to the sound waves that can be produced by blowing across the open mouth of a bottle.

A magnetron is essentially a diode that has a very strong magnetic field whose direction is parallel to the axis of the cathode. The interaction between the magnetic field and the electrons emitted by the cathode is such that the electrons follow a *spiral path* around the cathode on their way to the plate. They thus pass the openings in the resonant cavities before they finally reach the plate. As the electrons pass the cavity openings, they produce electromagnetic oscillations in the cavities. The electrical power contained in these oscillations can be very large, and is coupled out of the cavities by suitable coupling circuits and used as the magnetron output.

The frequency of the cavity oscillations is determined primarily by the physical dimensions of the tube, the magnetic field, and the cavities. A magnetron is, therefore, not very flexible as far as frequency is concerned. A magnetron is pulsed to produce oscillations, and so is only used where *intermittent* bursts of high frequencies are needed, as in radar.

klystrons

The klystron is more flexible than the magnetron, since it can be used as an *oscillator* or an *amplifier,* and can be tuned over a small range of frequencies. In a klystron, a stream of electrons is generated and passes through grids controlled by two resonant cavities on its way to the plate. An r-f electromagnetic field applied to the first cavity alternately slows down and speeds up the electron stream. The result is that the stream is broken up into groups, or *bunches,* of electrons that coincide with the signal frequency.

As the electron bunches travel in the drift area between the two cavities, faster-moving bunches overtake and combine with slower ones. The result is that the electron concentration in the bunches has been increased when the bunches pass the grids of the second, or output, cavity. As a result, the power contained in the electron bunches is induced in the output cavity, and is considerably greater than the original power input to the first cavity. Amplification, therefore, takes place between the input and output cavities. When the klystron is used as an oscillator, some of the output power is coupled back to the input cavity in the proper phase. Unlike the ordinary magnetron, the klystron can provide continuous signals. Some klystrons also use an intermediate cavity, and when klystrons are used as high-frequency oscillators, a special *reflex* klystron is used. Ordinary klystrons are for low-wattage use, but there are some high-power klystrons.

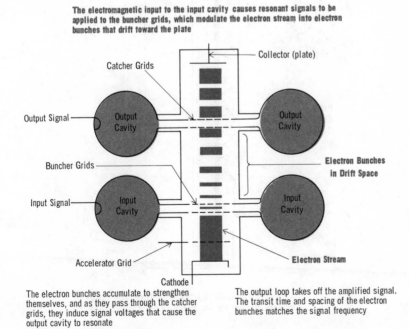

The electromagnetic input to the input cavity causes resonant signals to be applied to the buncher grids, which modulate the electron stream into electron bunches that drift toward the plate

Collector (plate)

Catcher Grids

Output Signal — Output Cavity

Output Cavity

Buncher Grids

Electron Bunches in Drift Space

Input Signal — Input Cavity

Input Cavity

Accelerator Grid

Electron Stream

Cathode

The electron bunches accumulate to strengthen themselves, and as they pass through the catcher grids, they induce signal voltages that cause the output cavity to resonate

The output loop takes off the amplified signal. The transit time and spacing of the electron bunches matches the signal frequency

the traveling-wave tube

Another type of tube that can be used either as an amplifier or an oscillator at extremely high frequencies is called the *traveling-wave* tube. The detailed operation of the traveling-wave tube is beyond the scope of this book. Basically, however, the tube operates because of an interaction between an *electromagnetic wave* and an *electron stream*, both traveling concurrently down a transmission line.

As shown, the transmission line is in the form of a *wire helix*. If a high-frequency signal is applied to one end of the helix, it sets up an electromagnetic wave that travels down the helix. If a beam of electrons is generated and is made to travel down the center of the helix, an interaction takes place between the electron stream and the wave. The exact nature of the interaction depends on the relative velocities of the electron stream and wave.

Normally, the electrons are made to travel faster than the wave. The two then interact in such a way that the wave extracts energy from the stream, and in doing so slows down the electrons. The energy gained by the wave, however, has the effect of increasing the amplitude of the signal represented by the wave. Therefore, the signal at the end of the helix is an amplified version of the original input signal.

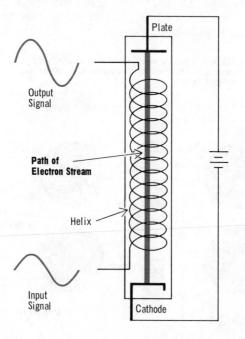

As a wave travels through the helix, it extracts energy
from the electron stream, and in so doing is amplified

KEYED POST

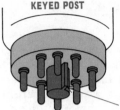

These are the two commonly used methods for ensuring that a tube can be inserted in its socket in only one way

EXTRA PIN SPACING

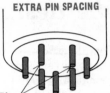

Extra Space Between Two Pins

This Key Must Fit In This Slot

As viewed from the bottom of the tube, the pins are numbered consecutively in a clockwise direction

tube sockets

As has been pointed out, electron tubes are equipped with pins for applying operating voltages and making other external connections. In some tubes, the pins are built into a *base* made of bakelite or other insulating material, and each pin is connected to its respective tube element by wires that pass through the tube envelope. In other tubes, particularly the miniature glass types, no tube base is used, and the pins protrude directly through the tube envelope. Except for some special tube types, connections are usually not made directly to the tube pins. Instead, devices called *tube sockets* are used.

External electrical connections are made to the tube socket, and the tube is inserted into the socket by pressing the tube pins into the socket holes. It is important, therefore, that each tube pin be in the *proper* socket hole. Otherwise, incorrect connections are made to the tube electrodes. In earlier tubes, one or more of the pins were larger than the others, as were one or more of the socket holes. This insured that the tube could be fitted into the socket in only one way. In most modern tubes, all of the pins are the same size, and other methods are used to insure that the tube cannot be inserted into the socket incorrectly. The most common of these methods is the use of extra spacing between two of the pins, or the use of a keyed insulating post at the bottom of the tube base.

A standard numbering system is used for identifying the pins of the common tube types. The pins are numbered consecutively in a *clockwise* direction when looking *up* at the tube base or tube socket. In the tube types that use the keyed part at the bottom of the tube, pin 1 is the pin directly clockwise of the keying ridge on the post. In tubes having extra spacing between two pins, pin 1 is the clockwise pin of the two widely spaced pins.

tube designations

For identification purposes, all tubes are given a designation. Many methods have been devised for having the designations describe useful information about the tubes, but no one method has been completely accepted by all tube manufacturers and users. As a result, there are *three* systems in use today which are used for the majority of tubes.

The first of these is an *alphanumeric system* used for receiving-type tubes. Each designation consists of four parts. The first is a number that represents the rated heater voltage. The second is a letter, or letters, that, in most cases, denotes the type or function of the tube. The third is a number that signifies the number of elements for which terminals have been provided. And the fourth is a letter, or letters, which designate the size, construction, or improved electrical rating of the tube. Very often, this fourth part is not included in the tube designation; it is usually used in tubes that can be made with different physical characteristics, such as glass or metal envelopes. An example of this system is shown.

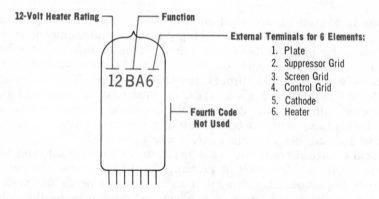

12-Volt Heater Rating ⌐   ⌐ Function

12 BA6

External Terminals for 6 Elements:
1. Plate
2. Suppressor Grid
3. Screen Grid
4. Control Grid
5. Cathode
6. Heater

├─ Fourth Code
Not Used

Additional descriptions of tube numbering systems can be found in a standard tube manual

The second designation system is used for *cathode-ray* and *television picture tubes*. Each designation consists of four parts. The first is a number that indicates either the screen diameter or diagonal length in inches. The second is a letter, or letters, assigned by the tube manufacturers. The third is the letter P followed by a number denoting the type of phosphor coating used on the screen. And the fourth is a letter indicating improved versions of the particular tube. For example, *B* would indicate a later version than *A*.

The third designation system covers tubes that for one reason or another cannot be classified under the other systems. Numbers are used in this system, starting from 5500 and going upward.

using the tube manual

A *tube manual* is a composite listing of the physical, electrical, and operating characteristics of a large number of tubes. This discussion will be limited to receiving-type tubes. Similar type tube manuals do exist for transmitting tubes as well as other tube types.

The tubes in a tube manual are listed according to their *alphanumeric designations*. For each tube, its schematic symbol, showing the pin connections to each element, is given. This is usually followed by the physical specifications and electrical ratings. The physical specifications cover information such as the envelope dimensions and the type of base. The electrical ratings include the maximum as well as rated operating voltages for the various electrodes, and the values of the interelectrode capacitances.

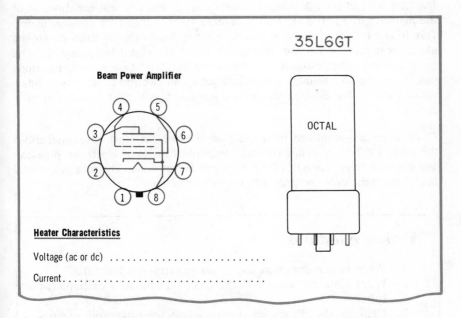

A thorough grasp of the contents and use of a good tube manual is a prime requirement for anyone engaged in the testing, troubleshooting, modification, etc. of electronic equipment and circuits

If the tube has additional modes of operation, such as a pentode operated as a triode, additional ratings are frequently given for the various modes. Next, tube characteristics and typical operating conditions are usually given. The characteristics include the values of μ, r_p, and g_m; while the typical operating conditions specify operating voltages and load values for different types of operation. Finally, one or more families of characteristic curves are usually given. In some tube manuals, average dynamic transfer characteristics are also shown.

summary

☐ Electron-ray indicators provide visual indications of small voltage changes. As electrons strike the fluorescent target, the target glows. ☐ Cathode-ray tubes provide visual indications of the acual voltage waveform. Electrons are emitted by the electron gun and directed toward the front of the tube, which has a phosphor coating. Horizontal and vertical deflection plates or coils deflect this beam according to the signal voltage.

☐ At UHF or microwave frequencies, vacuum tubes are unreliable because of interelectrode capacitance, the inductances of the elements, and the transit time relative to the signal frequencies. At these high frequencies, specially constructed tubes are required. ☐ Magnetrons are used as high-frequency, high-power oscillators. Electrons are emitted from the cathode in a spiral path, setting up electromagnetic oscillations as they pass resonant cavities. The frequency of the oscillation is established by the physical construction of the magnetron. ☐ The klystron is another form of high-frequency oscillator. This tube can also amplify. Resonant cavities inside the klystron cause the electrons to move in bunches that coincide with the signal frequency. ☐ The traveling-wave tube is also a high-frequency oscillator or amplifier. Electrons pass down the tube through a helix and set up an electromagnetic field. Interaction between the electron stream and electromagneic field provides amplification.

☐ All tubes are identified by a designation which, in most cases, describes the tube. ☐ Tube manuals contain composite listings of electrical, physical and operating characteristics for a large number of tubes. The tubes are listed in alphanumeric order according to their designation.

review questions

1. What is one common use of an electron-ray indicator?
2. What elements comprise the electron gun in a cathode-ray tube?
3. Explain the difference between *electrostatic* and *electromagnetic deflection*.
4. What is *transit time*?
5. How do the construction features of a high-frequency vacuum tube differ from those of a conventional tube?
6. When are magnetrons used?
7. Why is a klystron more flexible than a magnetron?
8. How are pins in the base of the tube normally numbered?
9. How are the pins keyed in an octal base tube as opposed to a miniature glass tube?
10. Describe the alphanumeric system for identifying receiving tubes. Use 6SN7GT as an example.

electronics
four

transistors
and semiconductor diodes

Transistors and semiconductor diodes perform essentially the same jobs that electron tubes do in electronic equipment. They have become very important in electronics because of their many advantages over electron tubes. Transistors are much smaller and lighter than tubes. As a result, transistorized equipment is small and weighs very little. Equipment that was heavy, bulky, and permanently mounted can now be portable and miniaturized.

Transistors do not have to be heated as do electron tubes. Thus, equipment power supplies and circuit components can be made smaller, simpler, and cheaper. Transistorized equipment operates much cooler than electron-tube equipment, so that the cooling system for a complex piece of equipment is not needed or is simple. The solid transistor is much more rugged than the relatively delicate electron tube, so that shock and vibration is less of a problem. Transistors are easier to store and last longer on the shelf. One of the biggest advantages of the transistor over the electron tube is that the transistor has a long equipment life, whereas the electron tube accounts for more than half of all electronic equipment failures.

Transistors, though, do have some disadvantages. Ordinary transistors cannot handle as much power as ordinary tubes. There are high-power transistors, but they are specially made. Also transistors are very sensitive to temperature changes and radiation, and it is more difficult to manufacture transistors with consistent characteristics; because of this, the unit cost of a transistor is more than that of a tube. By and large, however, the transistor's advantages outweigh its disadvantages; transistors are continually being improved and used more and more in commercial, industrial, and military electronics.

Transistors are small and light

Transistors do not have to be
heated and run cooler

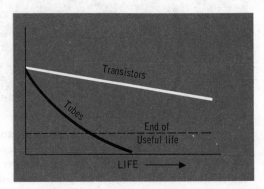

Transistors last much longer than tubes

early history

Semiconductors, and particularly semiconductor diodes, are not really new to electronics. The old crystal detector that was used in the early days of radio was a semiconductor diode; and the old copper oxide and selenium rectifiers, which are still in use today, are also semiconductor diodes. Even transistors can no longer be considered new. They were first developed in 1948 at Bell Telephone Laboratories by John Bardeen, William Shockley, and W. H. Brittain. They were looking for a *solid-state* device whose resistance could be changed in a manner similar to that of the electron tube. The original term used to describe the device they developed was *trans*fer re*sistor*, which was then shortened to transistor.

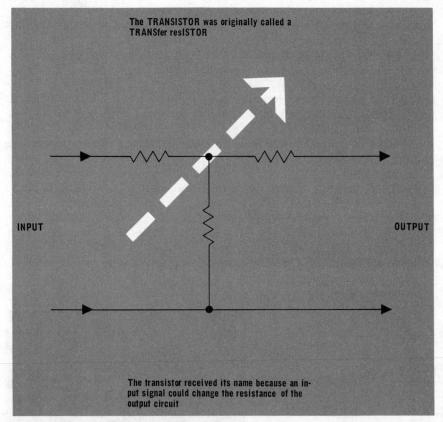

The TRANSISTOR was originally called a TRANSfer resISTOR

INPUT   OUTPUT

The transistor received its name because an input signal could change the resistance of the output circuit

The first transistors were expensive and difficult to control. Because of this, they were at first used mostly experimentally; but as time went on, they were improved and reduced in cost. During the late 1950's, transistors became practical, and were being used in many applications that had used the electron tube. Today, transistors are continually being improved and are being put to more and more uses.

atomic and electron theories

To understand how transistors and other semiconductors work, you should have a good knowledge of atomic and electron theories. The following is a review of their principles. As you know, all matter is composed of *compounds* or *elements*. The elements are the *basic* materials found in nature. When elements are combined to form a new material, we have a compound. The smallest particle that a compound can be reduced to and still retain its properties is a *molecule*. The smallest particle that an element can be reduced to and still retain its properties is called an *atom*. When elements are combined to form compounds, the atoms of the elements join to form the compound molecules. There are thousands of compounds, but there are only slightly more than 100 elements, from which all matter is made. The elements are listed in the table with their atomic number.

THE NATURAL ELEMENTS

Atomic Number	Name	Symbol	Atomic Number	Name	Symbol	Atomic Number	Name	Symbol
1	Hydrogen	H	32	Germanium	Ge	62	Samarium	Sm
2	Helium	He	33	Arsenic	As	63	Europium	Eu
3	Lithium	Li	34	Selenium	Se	64	Gadolinium	Gd
4	Beryllium	Be	35	Bromine	Br	65	Terbium	Tb
5	Boron	B	36	Krypton	Kr	66	Dysprosium	Dy
6	Carbon	C	37	Rubidium	Rb	67	Holmium	Ho
7	Nitrogen	N	38	Strontium	Sr	68	Erbium	Er
8	Oxygen	O	39	Yttrium	Y	69	Thulium	Tm
9	Fluorine	F	40	Zirconium	Zr	70	Ytterbium	Yb
10	Neon	Ne	41	Niobium	Nb	71	Lutetium	Lu
11	Sodium	Na		(Columbium)		72	Hafnium	Hf
12	Magnesium	Mg	42	Molybdenum	Mo	73	Tantalum	Ta
13	Aluminum	Al	43	Technetium	Tc	74	Tungsten	W
14	Silicon	Si	44	Ruthenium	Ru	75	Rhenium	Re
15	Phosphorus	P	45	Rhodium	Rh	76	Osmium	Os
16	Sulfur	S	46	Palladium	Pd	77	Iridium	Ir
17	Chlorine	Cl	47	Silver	Ag	78	Platinum	Pt
18	Argon	A	48	Cadmium	Cd	79	Gold	Au
19	Potassium	K	49	Indium	In	80	Mercury	Hg
20	Calcium	Ca	50	Tin	Sn	81	Thallium	Tl
21	Scandium	Sc	51	Antimony	Sb	82	Lead	Pb
22	Titanium	Ti	52	Tellurium	Te	83	Bismuth	Bi
23	Vanadium	V	53	Iodine	I	84	Polonium	Po
24	Chromium	Cr	54	Xenon	Xe	85	Astatine	At
25	Manganese	Mn	55	Cesium	Cs	86	Radon	Rn
26	Iron	Fe	56	Barium	Ba	87	Francium	Fr
27	Cobalt	Co	57	Lanthanum	La	88	Radium	Ra
28	Nickel	Ni	58	Cerium	Ce	89	Actinium	Ac
29	Copper	Cu	59	Praseodymium	Pr	90	Thorium	Th
30	Zinc	Zn	60	Neodymium	Nd	91	Protactinium	Pa
31	Gallium	Ga	61	Promethium	Pm	92	Uranium	U

THE ARTIFICIAL ELEMENTS

Atomic Number	Name	Symbol	Atomic Number	Name	Symbol	Atomic Number	Name	Symbol
93	Neptunium	Np	97	Berkelium	Bk	101	Mendelevium	Mv
94	Plutonium	Pu	98	Californium	Cf	102	Nobelium	No
95	Americium	Am	99	Einsteinium	E	103	Lawrencium	Lw
96	Curium	Cm	100	Fermium	Fm			

atomic particles

Although the atoms of the different elements have different properties, they all contain the same *subatomic* particles. There are a number of different subatomic particles, but only three of these are of interest in basic electronics: the *proton, the electron,* and the *neutron.* The only way that the atom of one element differs from the atom of another element is in the *number* of subatomic particles that it contains. You will learn more about this later.

The protons and neutrons are contained in the center, or *nucleus,* of the atom, and the electrons *orbit* around the nucleus. The proton is small but very heavy; it is difficult to dislodge from the nucleus. The electron is larger than the proton, but it is about 1840 times as light, and is easy to move.

The electrons and the protons are the particles that have the electrical properties. The electron has a *negative* electrical charge, and the proton has a *positive* electrical charge. These charges are *equal* and *opposite.* The law of electrical charges states that particles with *like* charges *repel* each other, and those with *unlike* charges *attract* each other. This is what keeps the electrons in orbit. The nucleus of the atom contains the positive protons, and so has a positive charge that attracts the negative electrons. The centrifugal force of the orbiting electrons counteracts the attraction of the nucleus to keep the electrons orbiting. Since electrons have like charges, they repel each other, and cause themselves to be spaced equidistant from one another.

Neutrons have no electrical charge; they are *neutral.* They are sometimes thought of as protons and electrons combined, but they are actually different particles. Usually, atoms have the same number of electrons and protons, and so they are electrically neutral. If an atom does have more electrons, it is called a *negative ion.* If it has more protons, it is called a *positive ion.*

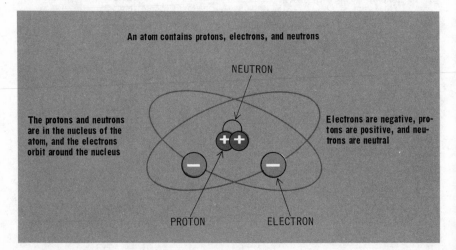

An atom contains protons, electrons, and neutrons

NEUTRON

The protons and neutrons are in the nucleus of the atom, and the electrons orbit around the nucleus

Electrons are negative, protons are positive, and neutrons are neutral

PROTON   ELECTRON

electrical charges

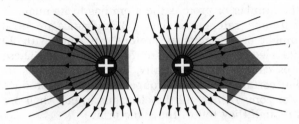

Protons are positive
and repel each other

LIKE CHARGES REPEL

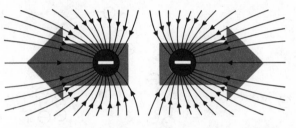

Electrons are negative
and repel each other

LIKE CHARGES REPEL

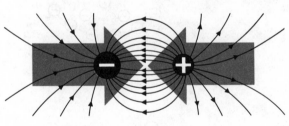

Protons are positive and
electrons are negative, and
they attract each other

UNLIKE CHARGES ATTRACT

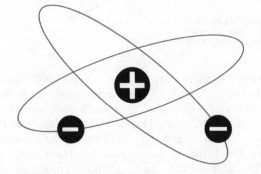

Since the nucleus contains the
positive protons, the nucleus is
positive. The positive nucleus
attracts the negative electrons,
but the centrifugal force of the
orbiting electrons counteracts
the attracting force of the nucleus to keep the electrons in orbit.
The negative electrons repel each
other, and so electrons space
themselves equidistant from one
another around the nucleus

orbital shells

Actually, what differentiates an atom of one element from an atom of another element is the number of protons the atom has in its nucleus. This is what the *atomic number* refers to on page 4-3. And since a neutral atom has the same number of electrons as protons, an atom with 29 protons should have 29 electrons orbiting around its nucleus. These electrons orbit in groups called *shells*. Actually, each electron has its own individual orbit, but certain orbits are grouped together to produce what is called a shell. For convenience, all the electrons in one shell are shown on diagrams as though they follow the same orbit.

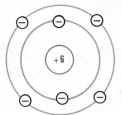

Carbon has two shells

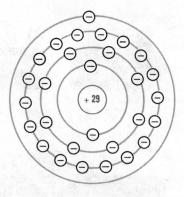

Copper has four shells

Hydrogen has one shell

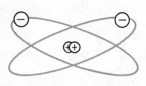

This view shows that the electrons in the same orbit do not follow the same orbital path. They are both equidistant from the nucleus, though, so they are in the same shell

For all of the known elements, there can be up to seven shells in an atom. This is shown on the table for all of the elements on page 4-7. If you study the table briefly, you will notice that each shell can only hold a certain number of electrons in orbit. The first shell, closest to the nucleus, cannot hold more than 2 electrons; the second shell cannot hold more than 8 electrons; the third no more than 18; the fourth, no more than 32; and so on. You can see that up to atomic number 10, the second shell built up to 8 electrons, and since this is the limit, a third shell had to be started for atomic number 11. For atomic numbers 11 through 18, the third shell built up to 8 electrons, and then a fourth shell started; then the third shell continued to build up to its maximum of 18 from atomic numbers 19 through 29.

the elements
and their atomic shells

ELECTRON SHELLS

Atomic No.	Element	1	2	3	4	5
1	Hydrogen, H	1				
2	Helium, He	2				
3	Lithium, Li	2	1			
4	Beryllium, Be	2	2			
5	Boron, B	2	3			
6	Carbon, C	2	4			
7	Nitrogen, N	2	5			
8	Oxygen, O	2	6			
9	Fluorine, F	2	7			
10	Neon, Ne	2	8			
11	Sodium, Na	2	8	1		
12	Magnesium, Mg	2	8	2		
13	Aluminum, Al	2	8	3		
14	Silicon, Si	2	8	4		
15	Phosphorus, P	2	8	5		
16	Sulfur, S	2	8	6		
17	Chlorine, Cl	2	8	7		
18	Argon, A	2	8	8		
19	Potassium, K	2	8	8	1	
20	Calcium, Ca	2	8	8	2	
21	Scandium, Sc	2	8	9	2	
22	Titanium, Ti	2	8	10	2	
23	Vanadium, V	2	8	11	2	
24	Chromium, Cr	2	8	13	1	
25	Manganese, Mn	2	8	13	2	
26	Iron, Fe	2	8	14	2	
27	Cobalt, Co	2	8	15	2	
28	Nickel, Ni	2	8	16	2	
29	Copper, Cu	2	8	18	1	
30	Zinc, Zn	2	8	18	2	
31	Gallium, Ga	2	8	18	3	
32	Germanium, Ge	2	8	18	4	
33	Arsenic, As	2	8	18	5	
34	Selenium, Se	2	8	18	6	
35	Bromine, Br	2	8	18	7	
36	Krypton, Kr	2	8	18	8	
37	Rubidium, Rb	2	8	18	8	1
38	Strontium, Sr	2	8	18	8	2
39	Yttrium, Y	2	8	18	9	2
40	Zirconium, Zr	2	8	18	10	2
41	Niobium, Nb	2	8	18	12	1
42	Molybdenum, Mo	2	8	18	13	1
43	Technetium, Te	2	8	18	14	1
44	Ruthenium, Ru	2	8	18	15	1
45	Rhodium, Rh	2	8	18	16	1
46	Palladium, Pd	2	8	18	18	0
47	Silver, Ag	2	8	18	18	1
48	Cadmium, Cd	2	8	18	18	2
49	Indium, In	2	8	18	18	3
50	Tin, Sn	2	8	18	18	4
51	Antimony, Sb	2	8	18	18	5
52	Tellurium, Te	2	8	18	18	6

Atomic No.	Element	1	2	3	4	5	6	7
53	Iodine, I	2	8	18	18	7		
54	Xenon, Xe	2	8	18	18	8		
55	Cesium, Cs	2	8	18	18	8	1	
56	Barium, Ba	2	8	18	18	8	2	
57	Lanthanum, La	2	8	18	18	9	2	
58	Cerium, Ce	2	8	18	19	9	2	
59	Praseodymium, Pr	2	8	19	20	9	2	
60	Neodymium, Nd	2	8	19	21	9	2	
61	Promethium, Pm	2	8	18	22	9	2	
62	Samarium, Sm	2	8	18	23	9	2	
63	Europium, Eu	2	8	18	24	9	2	
64	Gadolinium, Gd	2	8	18	25	9	2	
65	Terbium, Tb	2	8	18	26	9	2	
66	Dysprosium, Dy	2	8	18	27	9	2	
67	Holmium, Ho	2	8	18	28	9	2	
68	Erbium, Er	2	8	18	29	9	2	
69	Thulium, Tm	2	8	18	30	9	2	
70	Ytterbium, Yb	2	8	18	31	9	2	
71	Lutetium, Lu	2	8	18	32	9	2	
72	Hafnium, Hf	2	8	18	32	10	2	
73	Tantalum, Ta	2	8	18	32	11	2	
74	Tungsten, W	2	8	18	32	12	2	
75	Rhenium, Re	2	8	18	32	13	2	
76	Osmium, Os	2	8	18	32	14	2	
77	Iridium, Ir	2	8	18	32	15	2	
78	Platinum, Pt	2	8	18	32	16	2	
79	Gold, Au	2	8	18	32	18	1	
80	Mercury, Hg	2	8	18	32	18	2	
81	Thallium, Tl	2	8	18	32	18	3	
82	Lead, Pb	2	8	18	32	18	4	
83	Bismuth, Bi	2	8	18	32	18	5	
84	Polonium, Po	2	8	18	32	18	6	
85	Astatine, At	2	8	18	32	18	7	
86	Radon, Rn	2	8	18	32	18	8	
87	Francium, Fr	2	8	18	32	18	8	1
88	Radium, Ra	2	8	18	32	18	8	2
89	Actinium, Ac	2	8	18	32	18	9	2
90	Thorium, Th	2	8	18	32	19	9	2
91	Protactinium, Pa	2	8	18	32	20	9	2
92	Uranium, U	2	8	18	32	21	9	2
93	Neptunium, Np	2	8	18	32	22	9	2
94	Plutonium, Pu	2	8	18	32	23	9	2
95	Americium, Am	2	8	18	32	24	9	2
96	Curium, Cm	2	8	18	32	25	9	2
97	Berkelium, Bk	2	8	18	32	26	9	2
98	Californium, Cf	2	8	18	32	27	9	2
99	Einsteinium, E	2	8	18	32	28	9	2
100	Fermium, Fm	2	8	18	32	29	9	2
101	Mendelevium, Mv	2	8	18	32	30	9	2
102	Nobelium, No	2	8	18	32	31	9	2
103	Lawrencium, Lw	2	8	18	32	32	9	2

the valence shell

The outermost shell of an atom is called the *valence shell*. The word valence is a Greek word meaning hook; it came into use when an old chemical theory considered that atoms had hooks that held them to other atoms. Since we now know that it is the electrons in the outermost shell that enable atoms to join, the word valence was carried over as the name of the outer shell. Electrons that orbit in the outer shell are also known as *valence electrons*.

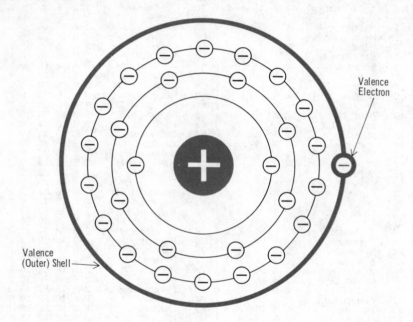

Valence Electron

Valence (Outer) Shell

The outer shell is called the VALENCE SHELL, and the electrons in that shell are called VALENCE ELECTRONS

You may have noticed in the discussion on page 4-6, and in the table on page 4-7, that although the third shell can hold up to 18 electrons, it did not have any more than 8 until a fourth shell started. This is also true of the fourth shell. It will not take on any more than 8 until a fifth shell starts, even though the fourth shell can hold up to 32 electrons. This shows that there is another rule: *The outer shell of any atom cannot hold any more than 8 electrons.* This rule is important because it shows which atoms make up good conductors, insulators, or semiconductors, as you will soon learn.

energy levels

Although every electron has the same negative charge, not all electrons have the same *energy level*. Electrons that orbit close to the nucleus have less energy than those that orbit farther away. The farther the electron orbits from the nucleus, the greater the energy it contains. Actually, the energy contained by the electron determines how far it will orbit. Therefore, if we could add energy to an electron in an inner orbit, we can move it out of that orbit to a higher orbit. And, if enough energy is added to a valence electron, it can be moved out of its orbit; and since there is no higher orbit, the electron will be *freed* from its atom.

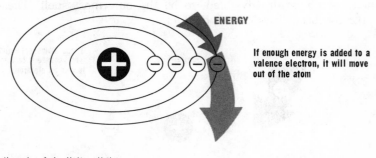

ENERGY

If enough energy is added to a valence electron, it will move out of the atom

For the sake of simplicity, all the inner electrons are not shown

When energy is applied to an atom, by heat or voltage or by other ways, the shell that first receives the energy is the valence shell. Therefore, valence electrons are the ones most easily removed from an atom. This is easy to understand when you consider that valence electrons are also farthest from the attraction of the nucleus, and so are easier to set free.

Energy is applied to the valence shells, and is distributed amongst the valence electrons

ENERGY

stable and unstable atoms

The tendency of an atom to give up its valence electrons depends on *chemical stability*. When an atom is stable, it resists giving up electrons, and when it is unstable, it tends to give up electrons. The level of stability is determined by the number of valence electrons, because the atom strives to have its outer or valence shell completely filled.

If an atom's valence shell is more than half filled, that atom tends to fill its shell. So, since 8 is the most electrons that can be held in the valence shell, elements with 5 or more valence electrons make good *insulators*, since they tend to take on rather than give up electrons. On the other hand, atoms with less than 4 valence electrons tend to give up their electrons to empty the valence shell; this would allow the next shell, which is already filled, to be the outermost shell. These atoms make the best electrical *conductors*.

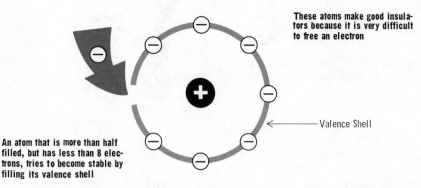

These atoms make good insulators because it is very difficult to free an electron

An atom that is more than half filled, but has less than 8 electrons, tries to become stable by filling its valence shell

Valence Shell

An atom with 8 valence electrons is completely stable, and will resist any sort of activity. These are the *inert gases* (atomic numbers 2, 10, 18, 36, 54, and 86), and are the best insulators. Atoms with only 1 valence electron are the best conductors. As you probably have gathered by now, *semiconductors* have 4 valence electrons, and are neither good conductors nor good insulators.

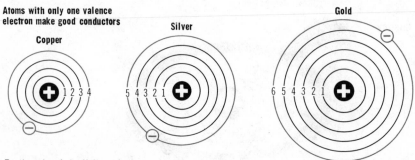

Atoms with only one valence electron make good conductors

Copper

Silver

Gold

For the sake of simplicity, only the valence electrons are shown

energy band diagrams

Since it is *easy* to force a valence electron from an atom of a good conductor, it takes only *little energy* to do this. And, similarly, since it is *difficult* to free an electron from an atom of an insulator, it takes *more energy* to do this. Semiconductors require less energy than insulators, but more than conductors.

Actually, the energy required to release electrons in the three different types of material falls into a certain band called the *conduction band*, and can be shown on *energy band* diagrams to indicate how easy or difficult it is to free an electron to start electrical conduction. The energy band diagrams on this page show only the energy levels from the valence through the conduction bands. Actually, there are other energy levels, one for each shell down to the nucleus of the atom. But we are only interested in the band beginning with the valence shell.

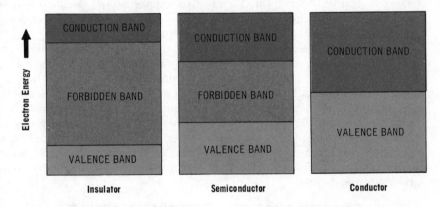

Energy band diagrams show the energy needed to move a valence electron out of the atom to cause conduction

The height of the forbidden band shows the energy needed to free a valence electron

The valence band in each diagram stands for the energy level of the valence electrons; and the conduction band stands for the energy level that must be reached for the valence electrons to be freed from the valence shell. The forbidden band, when it exists, is the energy gap between the other two bands. If only enough energy is added to a valence electron so that its total energy lies in the forbidden band, the valence electron will not be freed; it will stay in the valence shell. You can see, then, that the height of the forbidden band indicates how easy or difficult it is to free a valence electron and start conduction. And, as the diagrams show, insulators have a high forbidden band, semiconductors have a thinner forbidden band, and conductors have no forbidden band. Actually, the valence and conduction bands in good conductors overlap, so that valence electrons in these materials move randomly from one energy level to the next, and continuously move out of the valence shell of one atom into that of another; that is why it is very easy to cause current flow in conductors, as you will learn later.

atomic bonds

Until now, you have studied the characteristics of individual atoms in relation to conductors, semiconductors, and insulators. Actually, we will not use individual atoms in electronics. The atoms must join to form molecules of materials before they can be put to use. And, when these atoms join, their characteristics quite often change because of the chemical nature of the *bond*.

When atoms join to form compounds their characteristics change because the valence shells of the individual atoms *appear* filled. Atoms combine, generally, so that the sum of the valence electrons is 8. In the case of water (H_2O), there are two hydrogen atoms and one oxygen atom in every molecule. Since each hydrogen atom has one valence electron, and the oxygen atom has 6, the molecule has a total of 8. This similar arrangement occurs with most other atomic bonds. For example, copper oxide (Cu_2O) has two copper atoms, each with one valence electron, and one oxygen atom, with six valence electrons; again, there is a total of 8 valence electrons.

Copper oxide clearly illustrates the change brought about in atoms when they form compounds. Pure copper, as you know, is a good conductor because each atom has only one valence electron. But the copper oxide molecule has 8 valence electrons, which makes it stable; as a result, copper oxide is a good insulator. This is true of most compounds. However, keep in mind that the electrical characteristics of many compounds are also affected in other ways, especially by temperature. You will learn more about this later. In any event, you can better understand why molecules tend to become stable if you know more about atomic bonds.

When atoms bond to form molecules, they combine in such a way that the molecule contains 8 valence electrons — a completed outer shell

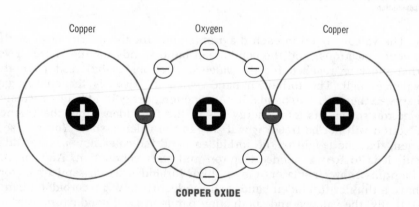

Copper   Oxygen   Copper

COPPER OXIDE

Elements that are normally good conductors, such as copper, can form compounds that are good insulators, such as copper oxide, because the molecule has a completed outer shell

metallic and electrovalent bonds

Atoms are thought to become bonded primarily by *sharing valence electrons*. Electrons can be shared by metallic bonding, electrovalent bonding, and covalent bonding.

Metallic bonding occurs mostly with such good conductors as copper. Each atom has 1 valence electron that follows the conductor energy band diagram shown on page 4-11. There is no forbidden band, and the energy level of the valence electron overlaps into the conduction band. As a result, the valence electron randomly leaves its orbit, but encounters another orbit almost immediately, freeing the valence electron of that atom to repeat the process. This valence electron travel occurs continuously in a random manner so that any one valence electron is always in some orbit, but is not associated with any one particular atom. Therefore, all of the atoms share all of their valence electrons and are bonded.

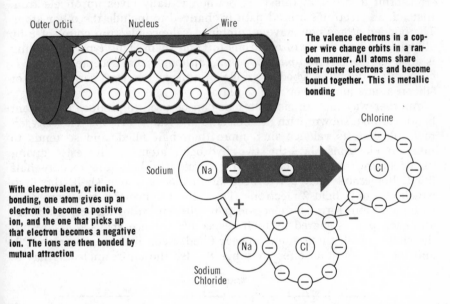

Outer Orbit   Nucleus   Wire

The valence electrons in a copper wire change orbits in a random manner. All atoms share their outer electrons and become bound together. This is metallic bonding

Chlorine

Sodium

With electrovalent, or ionic, bonding, one atom gives up an electron to become a positive ion, and the one that picks up that electron becomes a negative ion. The ions are then bonded by mutual attraction

Sodium Chloride

Electrovalent bonding takes place when atoms of different elements give up or gain valence electrons to or from each other. When this happens, the atoms then have more or less electrons than protons, and so take on an electrical charge; they become *ions*. Since one atom gives up an electron to the other atom, the one that gives up the electron becomes a positive ion and the one that takes it on becomes a negative ion; and since opposite charges attract, the mutual attraction of the ions forms an atomic bond. Since ionic *attraction* is involved, this is also known as *ionic bonding*. Notice in the illustration for sodium chloride (common salt), that the ions combine to form a molecule with 8 valence electrons.

covalent bonds

You may have noticed that atoms that take part in metallic or electrovalent bonding must have certain valence characteristics. In metallic bonding, the atoms must be good conductors with only one valence electron. And in electrovalent bonding, one atom must be unstable so that it gives up an electron to another atom that actively tries to take on an electron. You might wonder, then, what happens when different atoms that resist either giving up or taking on electrons are combined. They must *share* electrons to be bonded. These atoms share electrons in interesting ways.

When two such atoms meet, *each* atom allows one of its valence electrons to be shared by the other. For example, if we have two atoms each having 4 valence electrons, each will allow one to be shared; so they each keep 3 in their own personal orbit, and 2 move alternately from orbit to orbit. In this way, neither actually gives up on electron. Instead, an electron's orbital path is changed to include the other atom. The bonded atoms now have a combined valence electron count of 8 by allowing a shared pair of electrons to bond them. This type of bonding is also called *electron-pair bonding*, although the accepted name is *covalent bonding*. A good example of this is the way germanium or silicon atoms join, as you will see later.

Another way that an electron pair can be used to produce a covalent bond can be shown with a molecule of water (H_2O). The oxygen molecule has its valence shell more than half filled, and so tends to take on electrons; but the two hydrogen atoms each resist giving up or taking electrons because their valence shells are exactly half filled. Remember that a hydrogen atom has only one shell, the first, which can only hold 2 electrons. Thus, the valence electron from each hydrogen atom forms an electron pair with one from the oxygen atom, and each pair is shared by their respective valence shells. As a result, the shells, of all three atoms appear filled. Each hydrogen atom has 2, and the oxygen atom effectively has 8; also the entire molecule has 8.

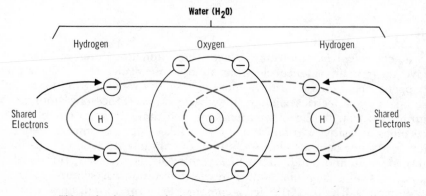

With covalent bonding, a pair of electrons is shared to complete the valence shells of the individual atoms

summary

☐ Atoms of the various elements differ from each other only in the number of subatomic particles each contains. ☐ Protons and neutrons are in the nucleus of the atom, and the electrons revolve in orbits around the nucleus. ☐ The electrons can orbit in up to seven shells with each shell containing a specific number of electrons. ☐ The outermost shell is the valence shell and can contain up to 8 valence electrons.

☐ An atom strives to fill its outer shell with 8 valence electrons. ☐ Atoms with 5 or more valence electrons tend to take on electrons, and thus make good insulators. ☐ Atoms with less than 4 valence electrons tend to give up electrons, and thus make good conductors. ☐ Semiconductors have half-filled outer shells, and are neither good insulators nor good conductors. ☐ Insulators and semiconductors have a forbidden band that represents the amount of energy needed to move a valence electron out of the atom to cause conduction.

☐ Atoms bond together to fill their outer shells by sharing their valence electrons. ☐ Electrons are shared by metallic bonding, electrovalent bonding, or covalent bonding. ☐ Metallic bonding is the random travel of valence electrons from one atom to another to maintain each outer shell filled. ☐ Electrovalent, or ionic, bonding is the giving up and taking on of valence electrons by atoms of different elements to form positive and negative ions. The positive and negative ions are bonded by the attraction of the unlike electrical charges. ☐ Covalent bonding is the sharing of a pair of electrons between atoms to complete the valence shells of the individual atoms.

review questions

1. What particles are found in the nucleus of an atom? In the orbits?
2. What is a *shell*? How many electrons can each shell hold?
3. What is the maximum number of valence electrons?
4. How many valence electrons are in an insulator? In a conductor? In a semiconductor?
5. What is the *forbidden band*?
6. Why do atoms bond together? How is bonding accomplished?
7. What is *metallic bonding*? Give an example.
8. How does electrovalent bonding occur?
9. What is another name for electrovalent bonding?
10. Explain covalent bonding and give an example?

semiconductor atomic structure

The bond that you will have to be familiar with in your study of transistors and other semiconductor devices is the covalent, or electron-pair, bond. Germanium and silicon are joined by covalent bonds, and these are the materials that are used most in semiconductor electronics.

Because of the nature of covalent bonding, the atoms of a semiconductor distribute themselves in a definite geometric pattern. The position of each atom in relation to its bonded atom becomes important if electrons are to pair off. The structure of the atomic pattern that is produced is known as the *crystal lattice*. Crystalline materials are so called because the basic atomic pattern repeats throughout the molecular structure of the material. Other types of materials contain relatively random atomic patterns.

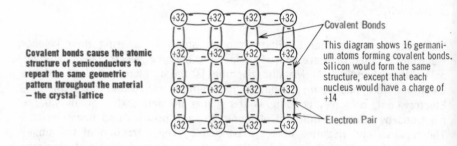

Covalent bonds cause the atomic structure of semiconductors to repeat the same geometric pattern throughout the material — the crystal lattice

Covalent Bonds

This diagram shows 16 germanium atoms forming covalent bonds. Silicon would form the same structure, except that each nucleus would have a charge of +14

Electron Pair

Germanium and silicon each has 4 valence electrons, and the crystalline arrangement allows each valence electron to pair off with an electron of an adjacent atom. Therefore, each atom produces a covalent bond with four adjacent atoms. And each adjacent atom does the same with four others, and so on. This is true of all of the atoms, except, of course, those at the surface of the material, which may not have adjacent atoms. This is why, by the way, the surface of some crystalline materials often does not have the same electrical characteristics as the interior of the material.

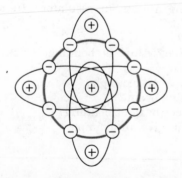

Germanium and silicon atoms form an electron-pair bond with four adjacent atoms. Each adjacent atom then repeats this with four other atoms to produce a crystal lattice

free electrons and holes

A pure semiconductor material allows each of its atoms to "see" 8 valence electrons. Thus, each atom tends to be stable and the entire material acts as an insulator. There are no "free" electrons, which is the term applied to those valence electrons that have an energy level in or near the conduction band so that they can be set free.

In practical use, this is not completely true because, even at room temperature, enough heat energy is available to allow some semiconductor valence electrons to raise their energy level to leave their valence shells. Such electrons are freed and can wander randomly from the valence shell of one atom to another. Now, since the electron-pair bonds between the individual atoms made use of *all* the valence electrons of the atoms, the existence of any *free* electron causes an electron-pair bond to be broken. In such an atom, then, there is a space that should have an electron that does not. This space is called a *hole*. There was a valence electron there, but it was set free by *thermal agitation*.

From a practical viewpoint, therefore, a pure semiconductor, or any compound, for that matter, does have some free electrons that can take part in current flow. And, in addition, semiconductors have holes in the covalent bonds that will readily accept electrons. There is another point to consider. Since the holes will readily accept electrons, and the energy level of various valence electrons is being raised by thermal agitation, many electrons will have their energy level increased to the point where, although they might not be free to wander randomly, they can jump from one shell to fill a hole in the next. When this happens, the hole, effectively, jumps to the covalent bond where that electron came from. That hole, in turn, might be filled by another valence electron, and so the hole "appears" to move again. As a result, a pure semiconductor in practical use has some free electrons and holes moving about in a random way.

The energy of even room temperature is sufficent to free some valence electrons. The free electron produces a gap in the covalent bond called a hole

The hole could be filled by a valence electron from an adjacent atom, producing a hole in that bond. Holes and free electrons, which are generated by thermal agitation, apparently move about at random.

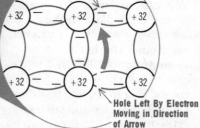

First Hole Now Being Filled By Electron From Lower Bond

Hole Left By Electron Moving in Direction of Arrow

current flow
in a pure semiconductor

Even though a pure semiconductor tends to produce stable atoms, it still *conducts* current with some free electrons the same way a good conductor does. However, a pure semiconductor only has a few free electrons, so only a *slight current* flows. The semiconductor, then, has a *high resistance*. Keep in mind, though, that since free electrons are released by thermal agitation, more current will flow at higher temperatures.

Semiconductor current does differ from that in a normal conductor because of holes in the covalent bonds. In a good conductor all of the valence electrons wander as free electrons to make up current flow; but in a semiconductor, only those freed from the electron-pair bonds can take part in electron current. The holes, though, allow the other valence electrons to move about because the holes continually try to be filled. Those valence electrons do not have to reach the energy level of the conduction band. Their levels need only be in the forbidden or even in the valence band because they only move to an adjacent atom, and the attraction of the hole provides the additional force for them to move. The gap in the covalent bond acts just like a *positive* charge, and so the hole is considered as such.

If a voltage were applied across the semiconductor, the resulting attraction would draw the valence electrons toward the positive potential. This, in turn, would make the holes appear to drift toward the negative potential. The free electrons, of course, would go toward the positive voltage, as in any conductor.

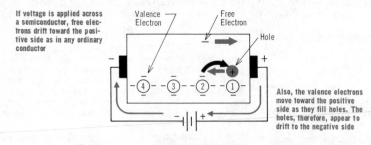

If voltage is applied across a semiconductor, free electrons drift toward the positive side as in any ordinary conductor

Also, the valence electrons move toward the positive side as they fill holes. The holes, therefore, appear to drift to the negative side

You can see then that there are actually two types of current flow. One type takes place in the conduction band with free electrons, and the other takes place in the valence band with valence electrons or holes. Even though the holes are only an "apparent" movement, they are the ones that are usually used to describe current flow in the valence band because they go in the opposite direction to free electron flow. The two currents, therefore, can be differentiated easily. So, a semiconductor has a negative free electron current and a positive hole current. This is shown progressively on the following page.

semiconductor current

This shows four atoms. When voltage is first applied to the semiconductor, there are four atoms, and a hole in the bond of atom 1. There is one free electron.

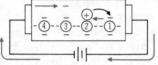

The positive voltage of the battery attracts the free electron to its side, starting electron current. The positive voltage also attracts a valence electron from atom 2, causing it to fill the hole in atom 1. The hole now exists in atom 2.

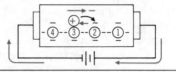

The free electron continues to move toward the positive side. Now a valence electron is attracted from atom 3 to fill the hole in atom 2. The hole is now in atom 3.

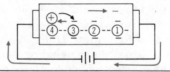

The free electron reaches the positive side. And, a valence electron leaves atom 4 to fill the hole in atom 3. The hole moves to atom 4 at the negative terminal.

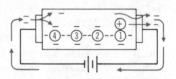

The free electron is attracted from the semiconductor to take part in the wire current flow. At the same time, a free electron from the battery enters the semiconductor at the negative side to replace the one that left, so that the free electron current can continue to flow. In addition, the hole in atom 4 attracts a free electron from the wire and is filled. Now, this free electron went from a high energy level, the conduction band, to a lower level, the valence band. To do this it gave up energy. The energy is transferred to the other valence electrons, and is picked up by the valence electron in atom 1, since it is closest to the positive attraction of the battery. The valence electron in atom 1 then is raised to the conduction band. It is freed and leaves the semiconductor to take part in the electron current flow in the wire. Now, a hole is back in atom 1 to replace the one that was lost in atom 4.

Electron current flow continues because a free electron enters the semiconductor on the negative side for each one that leaves on the positive side. Also, for each hole that is lost, or filled, at the negative side, a new one is created at the positive side. The holes do not leave or enter the semiconductor; they cannot because there are no covalent bonds or holes in the wire. Instead, the hole current is maintained by electrons entering or leaving the semiconductor.

The current flow in the wire is in the same direction for the free electron flow and hole flow. Therefore, both of these currents in the semiconductor are added in the wire.

free electrons, valence electrons, and holes

Current flow in a semiconductor takes part at two different energy levels: one current is in the conduction band with free electrons; and the other is in the valence band with valence electrons, or holes. In an ordinary conductor, current flow takes place only in the conduction band with free electrons.

Remember, the only difference between a free electron and a valence electron is the energy levels they contain. Both are found in the valence shell. Only the free electron is not part of a covalent bond and is so easily released that it drifts randomly. The free electron does *not* wander free of any atom, but it is usually shown that way for convenience.

The valence electron is part of an electron-pair bond and is released with difficulty, and usually only when it is in the vicinity of a hole. Hole current, of course, is only the apparent movement of the holes due to the valence electron current. However, hole current is universally accepted as the current that occurs in the valence band, because it can be confusing to discuss two different electron currents going in the same direction. Hole current goes in the opposite direction, and so is easier to differentiate from free electron current. As a result, the two currents usually discussed are electron current and hole current. But remember, electron current in a semiconductor always refers to free electrons, and hole current always refers to valence electrons.

You might think that there is no reason to differentiate the two currents because in the examples you studied, both electron current and hole current were equal. You recall that the holes and free electrons were both produced by thermal agitation; and a hole was created for each electron that was freed. However, this is only true for a pure semiconductor. You will learn next that semiconductors can be manufactured to have more free electrons than holes, and vice versa. Also, when you think about it, you can see that if a low voltage is applied across the semiconductor, it could move the free electrons, which have a high energy level, but not as many valence electrons, which are at a lower energy level. So, the ratio of the two currents that flow depends on the voltage applied. Current flow in a semiconductor, then, tends to be *nonlinear* at the lower voltages, but could become linear at the higher voltages. Current flow in a conductor is linear. Keep in mind that because of this, it is difficult to use Ohm's Law with semiconductors.

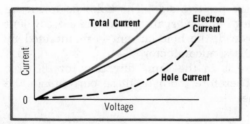

Since hole current depends on low-energy valence electrons, very little might flow at low voltages. When the voltage is sufficiently high, hole current could flow linearly. Free electron current does tend to flow linearly, but the total current shows that the semiconductor is a nonlinear device

current carriers and doping

You have learned that semiconductors have two types of current flow: electron current and hole current. Electron current flow is not actually the "flow" of an electron through a material, but it is the electrical impulse that one electron imparts to another when it starts to move. The electrons do not travel straight through the material to carry the current. Each electron may only move slightly in the direction of the current, but its transfer of energy to other electrons is what comprises the flow. This is easier to visualize with the valence electrons or holes in the illustrations on page 4-19. It took the movement of four *different* valence electrons to get one to leave the material; the holes, too, moved in the same manner. Four different holes had to be created or lost to cause the apparent motion of one hole. Holes and electrons, then, are not the current in themselves. But they are the *carriers* of the current, and this is how they are referred to. Free electrons are *negative current carriers,* and holes are *positive current carriers.*

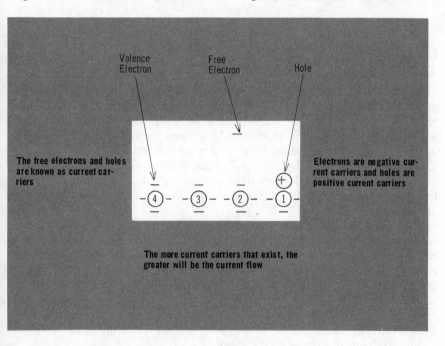

Valence Electron   Free Electron   Hole

The free electrons and holes are known as current carriers

Electrons are negative current carriers and holes are positive current carriers

The more current carriers that exist, the greater will be the current flow

Although the carriers are not the currents in themselves, they do determine how much current will flow. The number of carriers that moves determines how much current energy will be transferred through the semiconductor. A pure semiconductor has only a few current carriers, particularly at the lower temperatures, so very little current can flow. However, semiconductor materials can be made to have more carriers and to provide more current flow. This is done by a process called *doping.*

Atoms that have 5 valence electrons are
PENTAVALENT atoms

Atoms that have 3 valence electrons are
TRIVALENT atoms

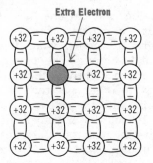

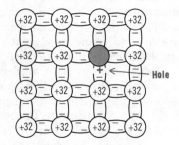

If the impurity atom has 5 valence
electrons, one will not be able to take
part in an electron-pair bond. That
electron will become a free electron

If the impurity atom only has 3 valence
electrons, one covalent bond will have
a hole in it, which can act as a current carrier

doping

You have learned that free electrons and holes are produced in a
pure semiconductor because of thermal agitation, and that since the
electrons that were freed created the holes in the bonds, they were
equal in number. This is true only in a *pure* semiconductor. However,
it is very difficult to manufacture a pure semiconductor. There are
usually *impurities* in the material. This merely means that there are
atoms of other materials mixed with those of the semiconductor. The
impurity atoms also form covalent bonds with the semiconductor
atoms.

The existence of these impurities in the semiconductor can considerably change the characteristics of the material, depending on how
many impurity atoms are present. For example, if the impurity atoms
have 5 valence electrons, only 4 are needed to take part in the covalent
bonds. Therefore, there is an extra electron that is loosely held in the
valence shell. Since the atoms "see" 8 valence electrons without the
extra one, they try to eliminate the extra electron to become stable.
This electron, then, tends to become a free electron that wanders
randomly from one atom to the next.

If, on the other hand, the impurity atoms only have 3 valence electrons, they would allow gaps, or holes, to exist in their covalent bonds.
In any event, you can see that certain types of impurity atoms in the
semiconductor increase the number of current carriers.

When the semiconductor material is being manufactured, the addition of impurities can be *controlled* to give the semiconductor any
desired electrical characteristic. The addition of impurities is known
as *doping*.

penta- and trivalent impurities

Semiconductor materials can be given electrical characteristics to make them more useful by doping them with impurity atoms that either cause an excess of free electrons or holes. The impurity atoms that are added have either 3 or 5 valence electrons. The impurity atom that has only 3 valence electrons is called a *trivalent* impurity. Some typical trivalent impurities are indium, gallium, and boron. The impurity atom that has 5 valence electrons is called a *penta*valent impurity. Some examples of these are arsenic, phosphorus, and antimony.

When a trivalent atom forms a bond with the semiconductor atoms, it only has 3 valence electrons that can pair off with 4 from the adjacent semiconductor atoms. There is, therefore, a gap left in one covalent bond of the trivalent atom. This hole in the bond acts as a positive charge that tends to accept electrons to fill the gap. As a result, these impurities are called *acceptor impurities*. They have atoms with holes that accept electrons.

The pentavalent impurity atom has an electron left over after the covalent bonds are made. It is called a *donor* atom, since it donates a free electron to the semiconductor.

To summarize, trivalent, or acceptor, impurities provide excess holes, or positive current carriers; and pentavalent impurities provide excess free electrons, or negative current carriers.

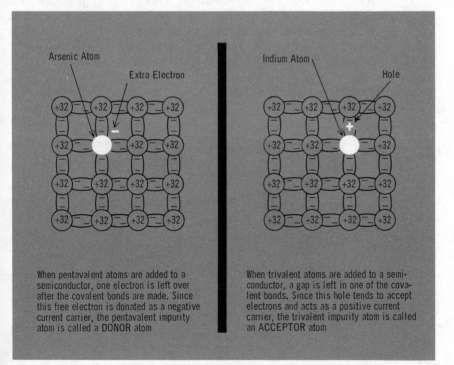

When pentavalent atoms are added to a semiconductor, one electron is left over after the covalent bonds are made. Since this free electron is donated as a negative current carrier, the pentavalent impurity atom is called a DONOR atom

When trivalent atoms are added to a semiconductor, a gap is left in one of the covalent bonds. Since this hole tends to accept electrons and acts as a positive current carrier, the trivalent impurity atom is called an ACCEPTOR atom

p- and n-type semiconductors

When donor atoms are added to a semiconductor, the extra free electrons give the semiconductor a greater number of free electrons than it would normally have. And, unlike the electrons that are freed because of thermal agitation, donor electrons do not produce holes. As a result, the current carriers in a semiconductor doped with penta-valent impurities are primarily negative. Such a semiconductor, as a result, is called an *n-type* semiconductor.

Since n-type semiconductors have extra free electrons, and pure semiconductors do not, the energy band diagram for a doped semiconductor is slightly different from that of a pure semiconductor. In effect, another energy level exists: a level for the donor electron, which is closer to the conductor band. The forbidden band for the donor electron is much narrower than the forbidden band for the valence electron; so, you can see that it is much easier to cause electron flow in an n-type semiconductor.

When acceptor atoms are added to a semiconductor material, more holes are produced than there would have been from thermal agitation alone. And, unlike the holes that are produced from thermal agitation, electrons did not have to be freed to cause them. As a result, the current carriers in a semiconductor doped with trivalent impurities are primarily positive. Such a semiconductor is called a *p-type* semiconductor.

The p-type semiconductor also has an energy band diagram that differs from that of the pure semiconductor. Since there is an extra number of holes, which tend to attract electrons, they aid in starting current flow. As a result, the acceptor energy level is also somewhat higher than that of the valence band. However, it is not as high as the donor level. P-type semiconductors will conduct current easier than pure semiconductors, but not quite as easy as n-type semiconductors.

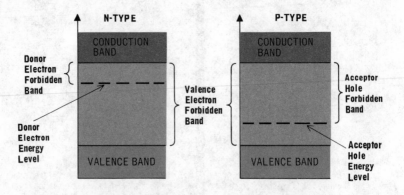

Excess free electrons in n-type semiconductors produce a donor energy level close to the conduction band. Excess holes in p-type semiconductors introduce an acceptor energy level higher than the valence level, but not as high as the donor level. N-type semiconductors, then, conduct current easier than p-type semiconductors

majority and minority carriers

Although an n-type semiconductor conducts more easily than a p-type, this does not mean that one will conduct more than the other for a given voltage. This is because the current flow in each depends on the number of extra carriers that exist, or how much they were doped. If the number of holes in the p-type semiconductor is equal to the number of free electrons in the n-type, more current will flow in the n-type for a given voltage because the donor (free) electrons have a higher energy level than the acceptor holes. But, if the p-type were doped so that it had many more holes, it could conduct more current than the n-type. In effect, the donor and acceptor energy level determines how easy it is to move one electron or hole carrier, but the *number* of carriers moved determines how much current will flow.

The carriers we have been studying are the *main* carriers, or *majority* carriers as they are called, because doping produces an excess of them: free electrons in the n-type, and holes in the p-type. However, there is another carrier: thermal agitation frees some valence electrons, producing an equal number of holes. The freed valence electrons in the n-type merely join the extra free electrons put there by doping to become majority carriers. The holes, though, which effectively flow in the opposite direction, become *minority carriers*. When a voltage is applied to an n-type semiconductor, a relatively heavy free electron majority current flows in one direction, while a smaller hole minority current flows in the opposite direction.

In a p-type semiconductor, the holes produced by thermal agitation merely join the excess holes produced by doping to become majority carriers. The freed electrons, though, because of thermal agitation are much fewer in number, and become minority carriers. So, when a voltage is applied to a p-type semiconductor, a relatively heavy hole majority current flows in one direction while a much smaller free electron minority current flows in the other direction. With both p- and n-types, what is a majority carrier in one is a minority carrier in the other.

Another way to look at the carriers is that the unbonded, or free, electrons traveling from valence shell to valence shell form one current carrier; and bonded, or valence, electrons traveling from hole to hole form the other current carrier.

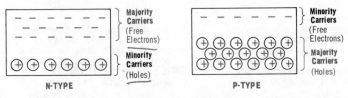

Both p- and n-type semiconductors have two kinds of carriers: majority and minority carriers. The majority and minority carriers flow in opposite directions for any given voltage polarity. In any one type of semiconductor, majority current is much greater than minority current

p and n electrical charges

The basic atom, you recall, normally has the same number of electrons and protons, so that it is neutral. However, atoms go through somewhat of a change when they are part of the crystal lattice of a semiconductor. For example, in the n-type semiconductor, the pentavalent impurity atom uses 4 of its valence electrons to form covalent bonds with its neighboring atoms, and then frees its fifth valence electron. The atom, then, having lost one negative electrical charge, becomes a *positive ion.* And this is true for all other atoms that give up electrons. However, for each positive ion that exists, there is a negative free electron in the semiconductor. So, the overall semiconductor is neutral.

In a p-type semiconductor, the trivalent impurity atom lacks one valence electron, and so causes a hole when the covalent bonds are formed. Normally, because of thermal agitation, these holes are generally filled by valence electrons from the semiconductor atoms, causing the holes to appear in those atoms. During normal atom activity, valence electrons continue to jump their bonds to fill adjacent holes, so that the holes tend to move in a random manner. Since there are more semiconductor atoms than impurity atoms, you will find at any one instant that the hole will exist in the bonds of the semiconductor atoms; and the holes in the impurity atoms will be filled. Since the impurity atoms had to take on extra electrons to completely fill their bonds, they become *negative* ions. However, for each negative ion that exists, there is a positive hole. Another way to look at this is that any semiconductor atom that has a hole had to give up a valence electron, and so these atoms become *positive ions.* In any case, the p-type semiconductor has an equal number of positive and negative charges, and so the overall semiconductor is neutral.

P-TYPE

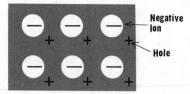

N-TYPE

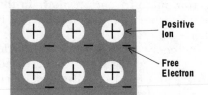

In p-type semiconductors, the semiconductor atoms give up valence electrons to fill the holes in the impurity atom bonds. The impurity atoms, then, become negative ions; but for each of these there is a positive hole in the material. The overall material is neutral

In n-type semiconductors, the impurity atoms give up their excess valence electron. The impurity atoms, then, become positive ions; but for each of these, there is a free negative electron. The overall material is neutral

the thermistor and varistor

By themselves, p- and n-type semiconductors find limited use. Because they have nonlinear electrical characteristics and are affected by temperature, they can be applied in *voltage regulating* circuits.

A doped semiconductor, you recall, has a majority current and a minority current, and the minority current might only become significant at the higher voltages. Therefore, the overall current of a properly doped semiconductor will increase even more as the voltage applied to it is increased than would the current in an ordinary resistor that follows Ohm's Law. As a result, such a semiconductor is said to have a resistance that goes down, or is *inversely proportional*, with *voltage*. One such device is called a *varistor*, and the circuit for using it to regulate voltage is shown.

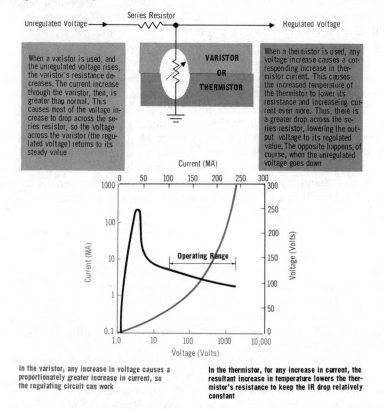

Series Resistor

Unregulated Voltage →   Regulated Voltage

When a varistor is used, and the unregulated voltage rises, the varistor's resistance decreases. The current increase through the varistor, then, is greater than normal. This causes most of the voltage increase to drop across the series resistor, so the voltage across the varistor (the regulated voltage) returns to its steady value

VARISTOR
OR
THERMISTOR

When a thermistor is used, any voltage increase causes a corresponding increase in thermistor current. This causes the increased temperature of the thermistor to lower its resistance and increasing current even more. Thus, there is a greater drop across the series resistor, lowering the output voltage to its regulated value. The opposite happens, of course, when the unregulated voltage goes down

In the varistor, any increase in voltage causes a proportionately greater increase in current, so the regulating circuit can work

In the thermistor, for any increase in current, the resultant increase in temperature lowers the thermistor's resistance to keep the IR drop relatively constant

Remember also that minority carriers are produced because of thermal agitation. A semiconductor can be made so that minority carriers will be more easily produced as the temperature of the semiconductor goes up. Such a device, then, is said to have a resistance that goes down, or is *inversely proportional*, with *temperature*. One such device is called a *thermistor*, and can also be used to regulate voltage as shown.

summary

□ Breaking a covalent bond produces a free electron, which moves about the lattice in a random manner. □ The free electron, in leaving a covalent bond, produces a gap in that bond called a hole. □ A valence electron in the lattice moves to fill a hole, forming a new hole in the lattice at a different covalent bond.

□ Two currents flow in a pure semiconductor: a free electron current in the conduction band, and a valence electron current in the valence band. □ The free electron current consists of valence electrons freed from their covalent bond, and flows towards a positive applied potential. □ The valence electron current consists of valence electrons having insufficient energy to break free of the valence band. This current produces the hole current that flows in the opposite direction to the free electron current. □ The free electrons and the holes are not the current in themselves, but act only as carriers of the current. □ Free electrons act as negative current carriers and holes act as positive current carriers.

□ Impurities are added to pure semiconductors, in a process called doping, to increase the number of current carriers. □ Trivalent, or acceptor, impurities have only 3 valence electrons and form holes in the bonds, which accept electrons from the semiconductor material, making it positive or p-type. □ Pentavalent, or donor, impurities have 5 valence electrons, and produce excess electrons that make the semiconductor material a negative or n-type. □ P-type and n-type refer to the majority current carriers produced by doping; the overall semiconductor remains electrically neutral. □ Minority current carriers, produced by thermal energy, are opposite to the majority carriers.

review questions

1. What is a *crystal lattice*? Draw a crystal lattice.
2. How is a free electron formed in a lattice?
3. What is a *hole*? How is it formed?
4. Describe the two currents that flow in a semiconductor. How are they formed?
5. Free electrons are _____ current carriers and holes are _____ current carriers.
6. Why are impurities added to pure semiconductors?
7. Define *p-type* and *n-type semiconductors*.
8. Why is an n-type semiconductor material electrically neutral although it possesses an excess of free electrons.
9. How are minority carriers formed?
10. What is a *varistor*? A *thermistor*?

the p-n diode

When p- and n-type semiconductors are combined as a p-n unit, a number of new characteristics are produced, which make the newly formed semiconductor useful. In particular, because each half of a p-n unit has opposite majority and minority carriers, the resistance of the unit to current going in one direction is much higher than the resistance to current going in the other direction. Then, such a unit acts the same as an electron-tube diode, and can rectify a-c currents. It is therefore called a *p-n* or *semiconductor diode*.

When p and n sections are combined, the p sections are not merely pressed against the n sections. Semiconductors are generally "grown" during manufacture by dipping and withdrawing a *seed* from a crucible of molten semiconductor material, usually germanium or silicon, and then having the molten material cool and solidify on the seed. As the seed is continually withdrawn, more and more material solidifies and accumulates, and so the crystal "grows."

A p-n diode is made with one section that has an excess of hole carriers, and another section that has an excess of free electron carriers

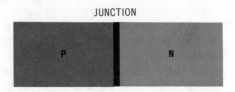

JUNCTION

Because of these opposite carriers, the p-n diode conducts more in one direction than in the other

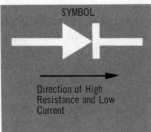

SYMBOL

The arrowhead represents the p section, and indicates the direction of the hole flow, or the high-resistance direction

Direction of High Resistance and Low Current

The low-resistance or high-current direction of free electron flow is opposite the arrow

The molten semiconductor material is first given the proper impurities to produce, for example, a p-type, and then when enough is grown, other impurities are added to make the next growth the n-type. So, the p-n diode is actually one unit, with a section called the *junction* separating the opposite characteristics. This is known as the *grown junction* method of manufacturing a p-n diode. Other methods are the alloy junction, diffusion process, drift technique, meltback methods, mesa, etc.

the depletion region

P- and n-type semiconductors have two types of electrical charges: the ionic charge the atom takes on when it gives up or receives an electron; and the second charge contained by the current carriers. The current carriers are called *mobile charges*. You know that the two charges are equal and opposite, so that the semiconductor is neutral. However, you recall that the covalent bonds produced a repeating crystal lattice structure, consisting of an atom joined to four others. At the surface of the material, however, this was not the case, since there are not any atoms to complete the structure.

As a result, the opposite charges in a semiconductor do not completely cancel, and the mobile charges at the edges and at the junction are easily affected by external charges. In a circuit, there is usually a *surface* current that is relatively independent of the internal current; in some critical applications, it must be considered. Also, because the mobile charges are easily removed with an applied potential, a *surface barrier* may be produced around the semiconductor to inhibit current flow in and out of the device. This characteristic is the one used by a device known as the *surface barrier transistor*, described later.

A similar effect becomes evident in a p-n diode, after the diode is made, because the mobile charges around the junction in each section are attracted by the mobile charges across the junction. As shown, the free electrons in the n section and the holes in the p section around the junction drift toward the junction because of the attraction of the charges to one another. This causes stronger local charges on each side of the junction. Since the free electrons in the n section have a higher energy than the holes, the free electrons are more mobile. They are attracted by the accumulated holes, and drift across the junction to fill the holes. Sometimes a valence electron in the n section will jump its bond to fill a hole in the p section, and this will cause that hole to move across into the n section. But this is minority carrier action, and occurs in only small numbers, and so for the most part can be ignored.

In any event, since the free electrons crossed the junction to fill holes, these majority carriers on either side of the junction were "lost." After the p-n diode is manufactured, then, the majority carriers in the immediate vicinity of the junction are depleted. This region of the diode is therefore called the *depletion region*.

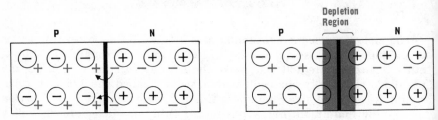

Immediately after the p-n diode is made, a depletion region is produced in the area around the junction

the potential barrier

Before the depletion region was formed, the opposite charges in each section of the p-n diode were equal, so that both sections were electrically neutral. But, after the depletion region was formed, the n section gave up free electrons, or negative charges, and the p section lost holes, or positive charges, as they were filled. As a result, the positive ionic charges in the n section outnumber the negative free electrons, and the n section takes a positive charge.

In the p section, the opposite is true; the p section takes on a negative charge. As more and more free electrons cross the junction to fill holes, these charges become greater and greater. This continues until the overall negative charge of the p section becomes sufficient to repel the free electrons in the n section, keeping them from crossing the junction. At the same time, the overall positive charge built up in the n section attracts the free electrons on their side of the junction. This electrical charge buildup stops the *electron-hole combinations* at the junction, and limits the size of the depletion region.

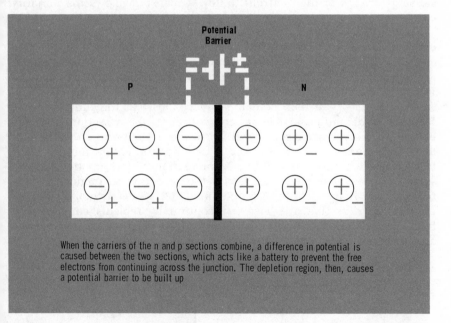

When the carriers of the n and p sections combine, a difference in potential is caused between the two sections, which acts like a battery to prevent the free electrons from continuing across the junction. The depletion region, then, causes a potential barrier to be built up

Because of the depletion region, the p and n sections of the diode now have equal and opposite charges. A voltage, a difference in potential, exists between the two sections. Since this difference in potential inhibits further electron-hole combinations at the junction, it is called a *potential barrier*. The difference in potential is the same as that between the terminals of a battery, and so the potential barrier is often shown as a small battery in the depletion region around the junction.

forward current flow

The natural tendency of the majority carriers, free electrons in the n section and holes in the p section, was to combine at the junction. This is how the depletion region and potential barriers were formed. Actually, the combination of electrons and holes at the junction allows electrons to move in the *same* direction in both the p and the n sections. In the n section, free electrons move toward the junction; in the p section, for the holes to move toward the junction, valence electrons move away from the junction. Therefore, electron flow in both sections is in the same direction. This, of course, would be the basis of current flow.

With the p-n diode alone, though, the action stops because there is no external circuit and because of the potential barrier that builds up. So, for current to flow, a battery can be connected to the diode to overcome the potential barrier. And the polarity of the battery should be such that the majority carriers in both sections are driven toward the junction. When the battery is connected in this way, it provides *forward bias*, causing *forward* or high *current* to flow, because it allows the majority carriers to provide the current flow.

Forward bias is obtained with the negative terminal of the battery connected to the n section, because the negative potential repels free electrons in the n section toward the junction. The positive terminal at the p section attracts valence electrons in the p section away from the junction, allowing the holes to move toward the junction. The free electrons and holes will then combine and be "lost" at the junction. But, for each combination, a free electron will enter the n section from the battery, and a valence electron will leave the p section to go to the battery. Therefore, current flows. And a free electron enters the n section to replace each one that is lost in combination at the junction. At the same time, a valence electron leaves the p section to produce a hole for each one that is lost in combination. Thus, while current flows, the majority carriers that are "lost" are continually replenished. The new free electrons and holes then drift toward the junction to continue the action. This is shown step-by-step on the following page.

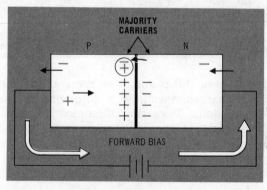

Forward or high current is produced in a p-n diode when forward bias is applied, which repels the majority carriers toward the junction to combine. This allows electrons to move in the same direction in both sections to produce current flow

forward current flow (cont.)

With forward bias applied to the p-n diode, the battery potential overcomes the potential barrier built up by the depletion region, and moves the majority carriers toward the junction.

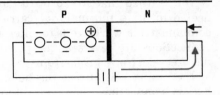

The hole on the p side of the junction attracts the free electron on the n side into it, and when they combine, both carriers are lost. At the same time, a free electron from the battery enters the n section to replace the one that recombined at the junction.

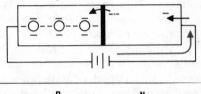

A free electron has an energy level close to or in the conduction band. When that free electron fills a hole at the junction, it becomes a valence electron. Its energy level, therefore, drops to the valence band. The energy it releases is transferred from atom to atom to the side connected to the positive battery. This raises the energy level of the valence electron to the conduction band, allow-

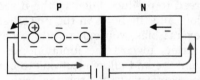

ing the battery to attract it from the p section as a free electron. This produces a hole to replace the one that was lost at the junction.

The positive attraction of the battery aids a valence electron from an adjacent atom in the p section to jump its bond and fill the new hole. The hole then moves to the adjacent atom toward the junction. The free electron that entered the n section is also repelled by the battery toward the junction.

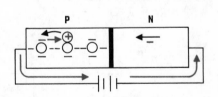

The hole and free electron continue to drift toward the junction until the original condition is recreated. Then, the free electron fills the hole, and the entire process is repeated.

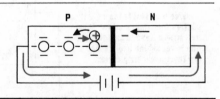

As shown by the step-by-step diagrams above, *forward current* flows as *free electrons* from the negative terminal of the battery, as *free electrons* through the n section, as *valence electrons* through the p section, and as *free electrons* to the positive terminal of the battery. It is usual practice, however, to refer to *hole flow* rather than *valence electron flow* in the p section.

reverse current flow

You learned that for forward current flow, the battery must be connected to drive the majority carriers toward the junction, where they combine to allow electrons to enter and leave the p-n diode. If the battery connections are reversed, the positive potential at the n side will draw the free electrons *away* from the junction. And the negative potential at the p side will attract the holes *away* from the junction. With this battery connection, then, the majority carriers *cannot* combine at the junction, and majority current cannot flow. For this reason, when a voltage is applied in this way, it is called *reverse bias*.

Reverse bias can cause a *reverse current* to flow, however, because *minority carriers* are present in the semiconductor sections. Remember, that although the p section was doped to have excess holes, some electrons were freed because of thermal agitation. Also, although the n section was doped to have excess free electrons, some electrons were freed to produce holes in the n section. The free electrons in the p section, and the holes in the n section are the minority carriers. Now, with reverse bias, you can see that the battery potentials repel the minority carriers toward the junction. As a result, these minority carriers can combine and allow electrons to enter and leave the p-n diode in exactly the same way that the majority carriers did with forward bias. However, since there are much fewer minority carriers than there are majority carriers, this minority current, or reverse current as it is usually called, is much less with the same voltage than majority, or forward, current would be.

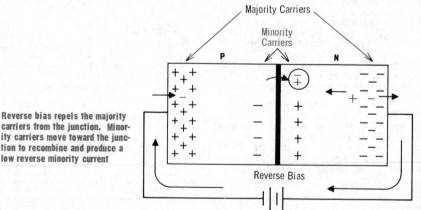

Reverse bias repels the majority carriers from the junction. Minority carriers move toward the junction to recombine and produce a low reverse minority current

The step-by-step description on the following page, describing minority or reverse current flow, will show how it is the same as majority or forward current. The interesting thing about the bias connections is that what is forward bias for the majority carriers is reverse bias for the minority carriers, and vice versa. This results because the majority and minority carriers in each section are opposites.

reverse current flow (cont.)

With reverse bias applied to the p-n diode, the battery potentials cause the majority carriers to drift away from the junction, so that they cannot take part in current flow. The minority carriers, however, are moved toward the junction.

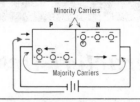

The hole on the n side of the junction attracts the free electron from the p side into it, and when they combine, both carriers are lost. At the same time, a free electron from the battery enters the p section to replace the one that recombined at the junction.

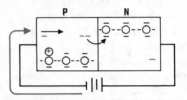

Since the free electron that crossed the junction had an energy level close to the conduction band, it had to release energy when it filled the hole and became a valence electron. The energy was transferred from atom to atom to the side connected to the positive battery terminal. This raised the energy level of a valence electron to the conduction band, allowing the battery to

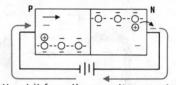

attract it from the n section as a free electron. This produces a hole to replace the one that was lost at the junction.

The positive attraction of the battery aids a valence electron from an adjacent atom in the n section to jump its bond and fill the new hole. The hole, then, moves to the adjacent atom toward the junction. The free electron that entered the p section is also repelled by the battery toward the junction.

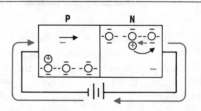

The hole and the free electron continue to drift toward the junction until the original condition is recreated. Then, the free electron fills the hole, and the entire process is repeated.

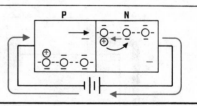

As shown by the step-by-step diagrams above, *reverse current* flows as *free electrons* from the negative battery terminal, as *free electrons* through the p section, as *valence electrons* through the n section, and as *free electrons* to the positive terminal of the battery. It is usual practice, however, to refer to *minority hole flow* in the n section rather than *valence electron flow*.

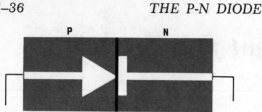

The arrow represents
the p section

characteristics

The arrow in the semiconductor diode symbol represents the p section of the diode. The arrow points in the direction that the holes in the p section *should* flow for easy current. Therefore, since reverse bias attracts those holes in the opposite direction, the arrow will point in the direction of electron current, which in this case is minority current. The arrow, then, points in the direction of high resistance, or low (reverse) current.

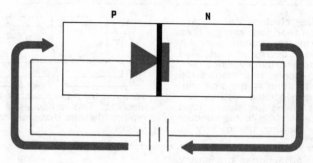

With forward bias, the holes in the p section move in the direction of the arrow toward the junction, and the electrons in the n section also move toward the junction. This allows majority current flow, so that forward (high) current and low resistance are opposite to the arrow.

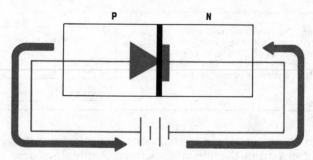

You can see, then, that to get forward current to flow, the negative side of the battery must be connected to the n side of the p-n diode; and vice versa.

the operating curve

Since the p-n diode's resistance changes according to the direction of current flow, it is a *nonlinear* device. Basically, its nonlinearity is dependent on the *polarity* of the applied voltage. For current in the forward direction, it has a resistance of only a few hundred ohms. In the reverse direction, its resistance is often close to 100,000 ohms.

The operating curve of the p-n diode shows how diode current changes with applied bias voltage, in both the forward and reverse directions. As shown, when reverse bias is applied, a slight reverse current flows, but this current increases only negligibly as the bias voltage is increased.

In the forward direction, though, considerably more current flows and the current for the most part, increases linearly as the bias voltage is increased. In the forward direction, then, the p-n diode can be considered a linear device over a large portion of its operating curve. The small part of the curve that is just above zero bias is nonlinear, as you can see. As explained earlier this results because both majority *and* minority current actually comprise the overall current. Since the minority carriers are low-energy carriers, majority current starts first, and then as the voltage is raised, minority current joins in, causing a nonlinear rise in current. But as the voltage is increased further, minority current becomes saturated since there are only few minority carriers. The curve then follows the majority current increase which is linear.

Because of the nonlinear *knee* of the curve, if a very small signal voltage is applied to the diode so that it only operates around the knee, the signal will be distorted. The signals must be large enough so that they operate mostly over the linear part of the curve.

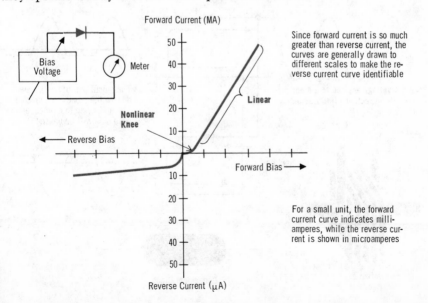

Since forward current is so much greater than reverse current, the curves are generally drawn to different scales to make the reverse current curve identifiable

For a small unit, the forward current curve indicates milliamperes, while the reverse current is shown in microamperes

the p-n diode rectifier

Since the p-n diode conducts current more readily in one direction than in the other, it can be used to convert an alternating current to a *unidirectional current*. When an a-c voltage is applied to a diode circuit, the diode will conduct relatively heavily when the polarity of the voltage produces a forward bias, but it will allow only a negligible current when the a-c polarity reverses to produce reverse bias. As a result, current flows essentially for only one-half cycle to produce a fluctuating dc at the output. This is similar to the way an electron-tube diode works. The electron tube, though, does not conduct at all in the reverse direction, whereas the p-n diode does, if only slightly. As a result, a very small portion of the blocked half of the a-c cycle *does* get through.

The half of the a-c sine wave that causes forward bias depends on the way the diode is connected. By reversing the diode connections, either the positive or the negative half cycle can be passed. Selenium, copper oxide, silicon, and germanium rectifier diodes work in this way. Quite often, rectifier diodes that are used in electronic power supplies have a plus (+) sign marked on one side of the rectifier. The plus sign merely indicates that the fluctuating d-c voltage at that side will be positive when the a-c voltage is applied to the other side. Most small signal diode rectifiers do not have this marking. Instead, they might contain the diode symbol to show the high-resistance direction. With a p-n diode, the *n* section is often called the *cathode,* and the *p* section is commonly called the *anode* for ease of comparison to the operation of tube diodes.

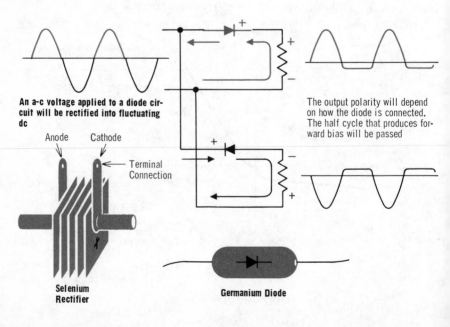

An a-c voltage applied to a diode circuit will be rectified into fluctuating dc

Anode   Cathode

Terminal Connection

Selenium Rectifier

The output polarity will depend on how the diode is connected. The half cycle that produces forward bias will be passed

Germanium Diode

summary

☐ A p-n diode combines a p section containing an excess of hole majority carriers with an n section containing an excess of free electron majority carriers. ☐ Attraction of opposite majority carriers results in electron-hole combinations in the vicinity of the junction. ☐ Electron-hole combinations cause a lack of majority carriers, or a depletion area, at the junction. The loss of majority carriers from each diode section creates local charges on each side of the junction. ☐ A voltage difference, or potential barrier, is produced between the two sections, which repels majority carriers from the junction and inhibits current flow through the junction.

☐ Forward bias repels the majority carriers in both sections of the p-n diode toward the junction, opposing the potential barrier to allow majority carrier current flow. ☐ Reverse bias repels the majority carriers away from the junction to oppose majority current flow. But reverse bias also repels minority carriers toward the junction to allow minority current flow.

☐ The arrow in a p-n diode represents the p section, and corresponds to the anode in an electron tube. ☐ The bar in a p-n diode represents the n-section, and corresponds to the cathode in an electron tube. ☐ The arrow in a p-n diode points in the direction of reverse (minority) current flow. ☐ Forward (majority) current flow is in the direction opposite to the arrow. ☐ P-n diodes convert alternating current to unidirectional current by passing only the half cycle that produces forward bias.

review questions

1. What is a *junction*? How is it formed in a p-n diode?
2. What causes the potential barrier in a p-n diode?
3. The potential barrier increases with _____ bias and decreases with _____ bias.
4. Describe forward current flow in a p-n diode.
5. Describe reverse current flow in a p-n diode.
6. Forward bias utilizes _____ carriers to carry the current flow, and reverse bias utilizes _____ carriers.
7. What symbol represents the p section of a diode?
8. The arrow in a semiconductor diode symbol indicates the direction of what current flow?
9. Why is a diode nonlinear at low current levels?
10. When a p-n diode rectifies an a-c current, why does some current flow in both half cycles?

avalanche breakdown

Remember, minority current also forms a small part of the forward current that flows through a diode; but, when the diode is operated past the knee of the curve, the minority current *saturates* because there are only a few minority carriers compared to the number of majority carriers. Minority carriers in the n section are holes that result from valence electrons being freed. In the p section, these freed valence electrons are the minority carriers. Now, during normal operation, the number of minority carriers is stable. But, if you recall, the valence electrons can be set free if enough energy is applied. This can happen if too high a forward bias is applied to a p-n diode. The high attraction force of the excessive voltage will cause many valence electrons to jump their bonds.

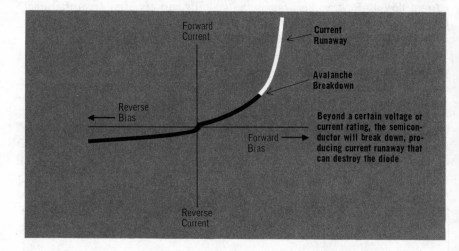

As a matter of fact, if the applied voltage is sufficient, the valence electrons leave their bonds with such speed that they collide with neighboring atoms, causing other valence electrons to be freed, and then these freed electrons can continue the action. The action is regenerative, and an *avalanche* of new carriers is produced. In this way, the number of minority carriers can be increased to where they actually exceed the majority carriers. The forward current then can suddenly rise, and if the diode is not designed to take the current surge, the diode can be destroyed. The point at which this occurs is called the *avalanche break-down* voltage, or *runaway* voltage. Normal rectifier and signal diodes are rated with applied voltage limits to prevent this from happening.

Minority current runaway can also occur if the temperature of the p-n diode becomes too high because of *thermal agitation*. This produces *thermal runaway*. Thermal runaway will also take place if too much forward current flows through the diode, since excessive current will heat up the diode. Therefore, diodes also have a current limit rating.

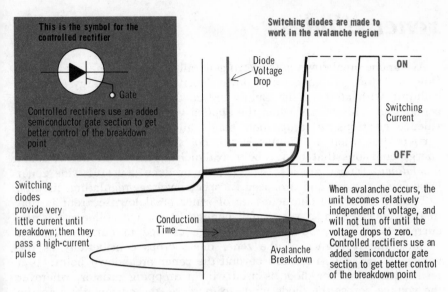

This is the symbol for the controlled rectifier

Gate

Controlled rectifiers use an added semiconductor gate section to get better control of the breakdown point

Switching diodes are made to work in the avalanche region

Diode Voltage Drop

ON

Switching Current

OFF

Switching diodes provide very little current until breakdown; then they pass a high-current pulse

Conduction Time

Avalanche Breakdown

When avalanche occurs, the unit becomes relatively independent of voltage, and will not turn off until the voltage drops to zero. Controlled rectifiers use an added semiconductor gate section to get better control of the breakdown point

switching diodes and controlled rectifiers

Normally, rectifier and signal diodes are destroyed when avalanche breakdown or thermal runaway occurs. Some diodes, however, are manufactured with large semiconductor segments to survive the sudden current surge. This almost instantaneous current change is desirable in circuits that need to be switched on and off electronically, rather than by switches or relays. *Electronic switches* are much faster and longer lasting than mechanical or electromechanical switches.

Diodes designed to work in the *avalanche region* are called *switching diodes*. Such diodes are made with very few majority carriers, and so allow very little forward current until avalanche breakdown occurs. Then, they allow a very high current to pass, energizing a circuit. These diodes are not usually designed to rectify or pass a given waveform. They merely act as high-current switches.

At the avalanche breakdown point, the resistance of the diode drops sharply, so that the voltage dropped by the diode in a circuit also drops to a low value. However, once avalanche current starts, the resistance of the diode remains low, and becomes relatively independent of the voltage across the p-n unit. The switching diode then works similarly to the gas tube diode you learned about in Volume 3. The diode voltage must drop to just about zero before it will stop conducting.

Special controlled rectifier diodes have an additional semiconductor element, called a *gate,* added to give better control of the avalanche breakdown point. This unit works like a thyratron tube, and is described later.

zener diodes

Avalanche breakdown is the term generally used for runaway current. However, since avalanche breakdown depends on high-energy electrons colliding with atoms, it is usually preceded by another breakdown in conduction. This occurs when the applied voltage is sufficient to cause valence electrons to jump their bonds and increase the number of carriers, but when the voltage is still not sufficient to allow the high-energy collisions that bring about avalanche. This is known as *zener breakdown*. Diodes are also designed to produce a useful wide zener breakdown region, and are used in special voltage-regulating circuits.

The one desirable characteristic of zener breakdown current is that in the zener region, a very small change in voltage still controls the current flow, but produces a very large change in current. This is because the resistance of the zener diode drops considerably as the voltage across it is increased beyond the zener breakdown point. As a result, when a zener diode is used with a dropping resistor, wherever the voltage across the diode tends to increase, the current through the diode rises out of proportion and causes a sufficient increase in voltage drop across the dropping resistor to lower the output voltage back to normal. Similarly, when the voltage across the diode tends to decrease, the current through the diode goes down out of proportion so that the dropping resistor drops much less voltage to raise the output voltage to normal. The zener diode is always used in the *reverse* direction.

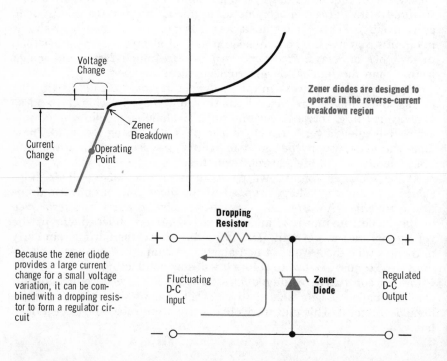

Voltage Change

Current Change

Zener Breakdown

Operating Point

Zener diodes are designed to operate in the reverse-current breakdown region

Dropping Resistor

Because the zener diode provides a large current change for a small voltage variation, it can be combined with a dropping resistor to form a regulator circuit

Fluctuating D-C Input

Zener Diode

Regulated D-C Output

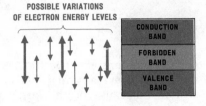

POSSIBLE VARIATIONS
OF ELECTRON ENERGY LEVELS

CONDUCTION
BAND

FORBIDDEN
BAND

VALENCE
BAND

Some electrons can gain enough
energy to go from the valence energy
level to the conduction level; and in
doing so can go from the p to the n
side. This is the tunneling effect

the tunnel effect

Zener and avalanche breakdown depend on valence electrons receiving sufficient energy to break from their covalent bonds and increase
the number of available current carriers, particularly minority carriers.
For zener or avalanche operation, this is easily accomplished with a
high applied voltage. However, some covalent electrons go from the
valence energy band to the conduction band with little or no applied
voltage.

Seemingly, an electron whose energy level is in the valence band
cannot travel out of a covalent bond until its energy level is raised to
the conduction band. However, although energy level diagrams are
shown with clearly defined lines separating the valence, forbidden, and
conduction bands, the energy levels of individual electrons cannot be
that clearly defined.

Actually, a valence electron can have an energy level anywhere within
each band. In addition, since there is electron activity within the semiconductor, because valence or free electrons drift, filling or leaving
holes, the energy level of individual electrons can continually shift
from one band to the next. The reason for this energy level shift is that
when a free electron fills a hole to become a valence electron, it releases
energy to get from the conduction to the valence band. Generally, this
energy is passed to another valence electron that can leave its bond as
its energy level goes from the valence to conduction band.

Many valence electrons have energy levels in the forbidden band.
Thus, they are not free electrons, but rather valence electrons that can
travel freely from hole to hole. Ordinarily, not many drift at random
this way, but when they do, they usually release energy to another
valence electron to put its energy level in the forbidden band so that
it can jump into another hole. However, when a p-n semiconductor is
heavily doped, and has many majority carriers and ions, the hole and
valence electron random drift is heavy. As a result, it is not uncommon
for a large number of electrons to fill holes and release energy to only
a few other valence electrons. These few valence electrons, then, have
their energy levels raised considerably so that they can go into the
conduction band, and even cross from the p to the n section as minority
carriers to fill a hole, even with little or no applied voltage. This action,
which seems to allow a valence electron to go from the valence band
to conduction band and cross a potential barrier without enough
applied external energy is called the *tunnel effect* because it seems as
though the valence electron "tunnels" through the forbidden band.

tunnel diodes

A diode that makes use of the tunneling effect is the *tunnel diode*. It is very heavily doped so that there are many majority carriers and ions in the semiconductor sections. Because of the large number of carriers, most are not used during the initial recombination that produces the depletion region. As a result, the depletion region is very narrow, producing a thin junction that is easily crossed by electrons.

Because of the large number of carriers, there is much drift activity in the p and n sections, causing many valence electrons to have their energy levels raised closer to the conduction region. Therefore, it takes only a small applied forward voltage to cause conduction. As forward bias is *first increased,* diode current rises rapidly; after many carriers start participating in current flow, the random activity of the free electrons filling holes is reduced considerably, so there is much less tendency for valence electrons to be raised in energy to the conduction band. Therefore, the tunnel effect is reduced, and majority carriers make up most of the current flow.

The sharp reduction of the available minority carriers reduces the overall current flow, so that current flow starts to *decrease* as diode applied voltage is increased. As the voltage is further increased, the tunneling effect plays less and less of a part until a *valley* is reached when the p-n unit starts to act as a normal semiconductor diode; the current then rises with voltage. The area after the *tunneling current* reaches its peak is called the negative resistance region because current goes down as voltage is raised. Because of the tunneling effect, the tunnel diode has a quick response, and can be used as a good electronic switch between the peak and valley of current. Also, the negative resistance region allows the diode to be used as an oscillator.

By its nature, the tunnel diode has a rather high reverse current, but operation under this condition is not generally used.

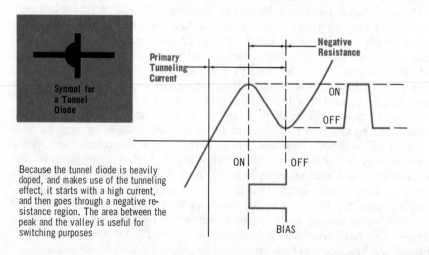

Symbol for a Tunnel Diode

Primary Tunneling Current

Negative Resistance

ON

OFF

ON   OFF

BIAS

Because the tunnel diode is heavily doped, and makes use of the tunneling effect, it starts with a high current, and then goes through a negative resistance region. The area between the peak and the valley is useful for switching purposes

summary

☐ A small minority current flows in p-n diodes under both forward and reverse bias. ☐ The source of minority current is freed valence electrons. ☐ An excessive number of freed valence electrons results in a breakdown. This occurs when the number of available current carriers, particularly minority carriers, increases beyond the current-handling capacity of the diode.

☐ Avalanche beakdown is the runaway increase in minority current carriers during forward current flow. ☐ Avalanche breakdown occurs when many valence electrons are freed with sufficient force to dislodge other valence electrons. Avalanche breakdown is used in switching diodes and special controlled rectifiers. ☐ Zener breakdown is the runaway increase in minority carriers during reverse current flow. It is also caused by the release of high-energy valence electrons. ☐ Zener breakdown is used in voltage-regulating diodes.

☐ The tunnel effect is the movement of valence electrons from the valence energy band to the conduction band with little or no applied energy. ☐ Valence electrons seem to tunnel through the forbidden energy band. ☐ The tunnel effect provides a negative resistance region in the tunnel diode where increasing voltage results in decreasing current. ☐ Tunnel diodes are used in switching and oscillator circuits.

review questions

1. What is the source of minority carriers in p-n diodes?
2. What is *breakdown*? Why does it occur?
3. Define *avalanche breakdown*. What is its cause?
4. Define *zener breakdown*. How does it differ from avalanche breakdown?
5. Excessive forward bias causes _____ breakdown, and excessive reverse bias causes _____ breakdown?
6. How does a zener diode work in a voltage-regulating circuit?
7. What is the *tunnel effect*? How is tunneling caused by an excess of majority carriers?
8. If no voltage is applied to a tunnel diode, what raises the energy levels of valence electrons?
9. What is *negative resistance*?
10. How does negative resistance allow a tunnel diode to work as an oscillator?

the transistor

Until now, we have been mainly concerned with semiconductor materials and semiconductor diodes. These materials and devices have unique properties that make them useful in many applications. However, they do have limitations that prevent them from being used in many other applications.

The biggest limitation of the semiconductor diode is that most cannot amplify a signal in a practical manner. A solid semiconductor is applied mostly in a way that makes use of its nonlinear resistance characteristics, and a p-n diode is used for rectification as well. When amplification is needed, another type of semiconductor device is used: the *transistor.*

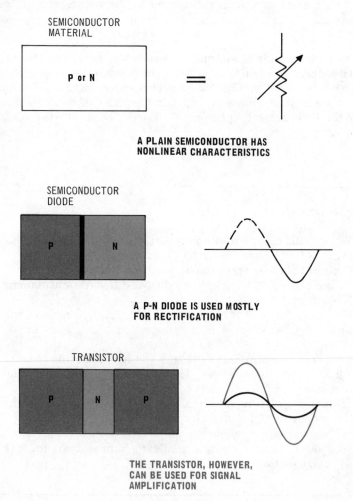

SEMICONDUCTOR
MATERIAL

P or N

**A PLAIN SEMICONDUCTOR HAS
NONLINEAR CHARACTERISTICS**

SEMICONDUCTOR
DIODE

P   N

**A P-N DIODE IS USED MOSTLY
FOR RECTIFICATION**

TRANSISTOR

P   N   P

**THE TRANSISTOR, HOWEVER,
CAN BE USED FOR SIGNAL
AMPLIFICATION**

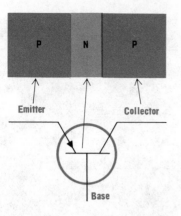

The emitter, whose arrowhead points in the direction of hole flow, indicates whether the transistor is an n-p-n or p-n-p type

the basic transistor

The basic transistor is produced when another semiconductor element is added to the simple p-n diode. The transistor, then, is a *three-element semiconductor*. The three elements are combined so that the two outer elements are doped with the same type of majority carriers, while the element that separates them has the opposite majority carrier. A transistor, then, can be an n-p-n or a p-n-p type.

The three elements of the transistor are the *emitter*, the *base*, and the *collector*. The *emitter* supplies the majority carriers for transistor current flow, and the *collector* collects the current for circuit operation. The *base* provides the junctions for proper interaction between the emitter and collector.

The emitter is shown schematically by an arrow that points in the direction of *hole* flow. Since the emitter is said to inject majority carriers into the base, a *p*-type emitter is shown with the arrow pointing *to* the base; an *n*-type emitter has the arrow pointing *away* from the base to show that electrons are being injected.

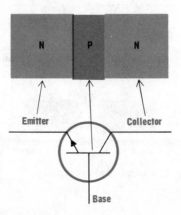

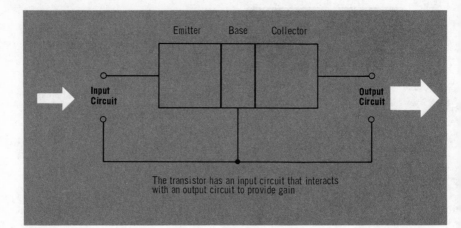

The transistor has an input circuit that interacts
with an output circuit to provide gain

input
and output circuit interaction

Basically, the transistor amplifies in a manner similar to that of an
electron tube. It is set up with two circuits: an *input circuit*, and an
output circuit. The two circuits are arranged so that they interact. The
current that flows in the input circuit controls, to a large extent, the
current that flows in the output circuit. Therefore, when a signal is
applied to the input circuit, it produces a corresponding input current
flow. This, in turn, determines the current that flows in the output
circuit. Because of this, if the input circuit is made a low-voltage circuit,
and the output circuit is made a high-voltage circuit, then small signal
voltage inputs can produce higher signal voltage outputs.

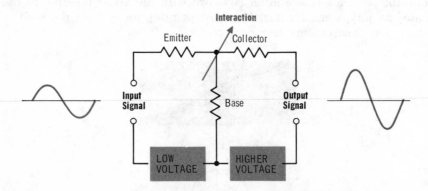

This equivalent circuit shows how the input interacts with the output. The input
signal applied to the low-voltage input circuit controls the resistance of the
higher-voltage output circuit to produce an amplified signal

transistor biasing

One reason that the input and output circuits of a transistor interact is because the base of the transistor is common to both circuits. Another factor that controls interaction is the types of bias used in both circuits.

The input circuit is provided by the emitter and base segments, and the output circuit is provided by the base and collector segments. Since the input circuit current must be determined by the input signal voltage, the emitter and base must be biased in the *forward* direction so that emitter-base current will follow the signal voltage. However, since the output circuit current must be controlled by interaction with the input circuit, the output circuit current should be relatively independent of circuit voltages. This is accomplished by biasing the base-collector circuit in the *reverse* direction. Because reverse bias produces very little current flow, the output current is hardly affected by it.

The input, or emitter-base circuit, is forward biased; and the output, or collector-base circuit, is reverse biased

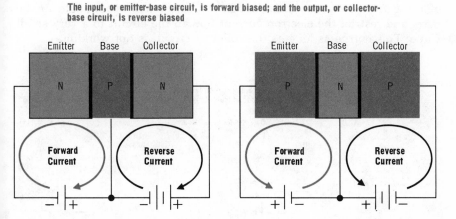

The forward emitter-base bias is generally lower than the reverse collector-base bias, and both currents are almost equal. Also, since both currents flow through the base in opposite directions, they almost cancel and there is very little resultant base current

Ordinarily, the collector current should be very low compared to the emitter current, but it is made high in two ways. The first is by use of a relatively high collector voltage. The second, and most important, way is that, as shown on the diagram, the bias polarities of both circuits are such that they aid emitter current to flow through the collector as well. As a result, collector current is usually almost equal to emitter current. This is how the output current is controlled by the input current.

You might have noticed that the emitter and collector electron currents appear to be going in the same direction. They do in the circuit, but they go in opposite directions through the junctions. Notice that in the n-p-n type, the emitter-base electron current crosses the junction from n to p, but the collector-base electron current crosses from p to n.

n-p-n input circuit operation

Let's see how the n-p-n transistor works with only the emitter-base input circuit connected. You should recall that in p-n diodes *forward* current across a junction is carried out by *majority* carriers, recombining at the junction to allow electrons to flow in and out of the semiconductor. In an n-p-n transistor, the same is true for the input circuit, since the emitter-base junction is forward biased. The bias polarity repels the free electrons in the n-type emitter toward the junction, where they cross to fill holes in the p-type base. However, the transistor differs from the diode in that the two segments on opposite sides of the junction are not equally doped nor are they the same size.

The base is thinner and is doped much less than the emitter. There-fore, it has much less majority carriers than the emitter. As a result, there are more free electron majority carriers that go from the emitter to the base than there are hole majority carriers in the base. So, most of those free electrons cannot recombine; they just accumulate in the base, and restrict the electron current flow in the circuit to a very small value. This is true as long as the collector circuit is not working.

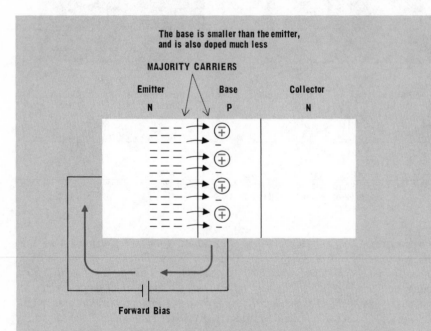

The base is smaller than the emitter, and is also doped much less

MAJORITY CARRIERS

Emitter   Base   Collector

N   P   N

Forward Bias

As a result, when the emitter is forward biased, and free electrons cross the junction into the base, there are not enough holes in the base with which to combine. Thus, current flow is small even though majority carriers are driven toward the junction

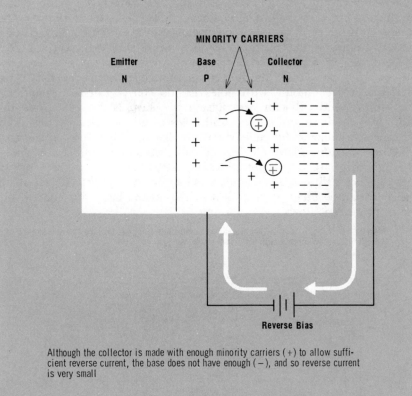

When the collector-base is reverse biased, the minority carriers are driven toward the junction

MINORITY CARRIERS

Emitter   Base   Collector

N   P   N

Reverse Bias

Although the collector is made with enough minority carriers (+) to allow sufficient reverse current, the base does not have enough (−), and so reverse current is very small

n-p-n output circuit operation

As before, let us examine this operation with only the collector-base circuit connected. As with the p-n diode, *reverse* current in a transistor is carried out with *minority* carriers. In the n-type collector, minority carriers are holes; in the p-type base, minority carriers are free electrons. Therefore, the reverse current will depend on the number of free electrons that cross from the base to recombine with holes in the collector.

The collector is made so that it contains a sufficient number of minority carriers to provide a usable reverse current. But, as with emitter-base current, the base also has only a few minority carriers. Therefore, there is very little recombining of minority carriers at the collector-base junction, and so very little reverse current flows. This is true only as long as the emitter circuit is inoperative.

n-p-n input-output interaction

When both the emitter and collector are connected, the operation of the n-p-n transistor changes considerably. Remember that emitter-base forward current was kept low because the base did not have enough majority carriers (holes) to recombine with the free electrons from the emitter. In addition, collector-base reverse current was kept low because the base also did not have enough minority carriers (free electrons) to recombine with holes in the collector. Now, when both the emitter and collector are biased, the surplus free electrons that cross into the base and cannot find holes to fill, accumulate there, and become available to fill holes in the collector. Therefore, since more majority carriers (free electrons) can leave the emitter to *diffuse* through the base and enter holes in the collector, a higher forward emitter current flows. Also, since more minority carriers (holes) in the collector can be filled by free electrons from the base, a higher reverse collector current flows.

When both emitter and collector are biased, the surplus free electrons from the emitter can pass through the base to combine with holes in the collector

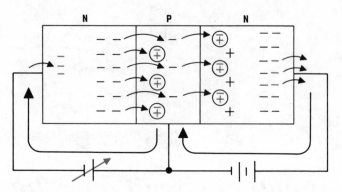

The amount of collector current that flows depends on the number of free electrons supplied by the emitter. If the emitter bias voltage is raised or lowered, emitter current will change, causing collector current to change, too

Since the collector-base is reverse biased, the amount of collector current that flows depends only slightly on the collector voltage. It is determined more by the number of surplus free electrons that the emitter supplies to the base. The emitter-base, on the other hand, is forward biased, and so its current flow will go up or down as emitter bias is raised or lowered. Accordingly, this will also allow the emitter to supply more or less free electrons to the base to cause the collector current to rise and fall. In this way, any change in emitter current will cause a corresponding change in collector current.

It is interesting to note that although the free electrons are majority carriers in the emitter (n), they become minority carriers in the base (p).

n-p-n gain

To make the n-p-n current characteristics useful, it is connected in a way that allows a signal input voltage to be applied to the emitter, and a signal output voltage to be taken from the collector. The input signal voltage, then, will either aid or oppose the forward bias of the emitter circuit. When it aids the bias, emitter current goes up, and vice versa. And, when the signal voltage causes emitter current to change, the collector current changes, too. If a load resistor is put in the collector circuit, any change in collector current will produce a changing voltage drop across the load resistor.

Since the emitter circuit is forward biased, it is a low-resistance circuit. The collector circuit, though is reverse biased, and so is a high-resistance circuit. The load resistor, then, can be made a high value. As a result, the voltage changes across the load resistor will be greater than the input signal voltage variations. You can see this more easily when you realize that the collector current is about equal to the emitter current. This is because the base has so few carriers that only about 2 to 5 percent of the emitter current flows down the base; about 95 to 98 percent of the emitter carriers form the collector current. So, the same current passing through two different resistances will naturally cause a higher voltage drop across the larger resistance.

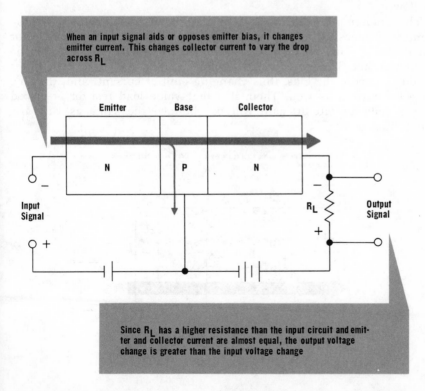

When an input signal aids or opposes emitter bias, it changes emitter current. This changes collector current to vary the drop across R_L

Emitter   Base   Collector

N   P   N

Input Signal

R_L Output Signal

Since R_L has a higher resistance than the input circuit and emitter and collector current are almost equal, the output voltage change is greater than the input voltage change

p-n-p operation

The p-n-p transistor operates similarly to the n-p-n type, except that the majority and minority carriers in the p-n-p transistors are opposite. The emitter-base segments are forward biased and the collector-base segments are reverse biased. The forward bias on the emitter attracts valence electrons away from the junction, causing holes, the majority carriers, to drift toward the junction. The free electron majority carriers in the base then cross the junction to fill holes and allow circuit electron flow to enter the base and leave the emitter. However, the base is made thin and is only slightly doped, so that it does not ordinarily have enough majority carriers to fill holes in the emitter; so emitter current tends to be low. The excess holes in the emitter accumulate at the junction.

Since the collector is reverse biased, the voltage polarity drives the free electrons, which are minority carriers, toward the junction. These free electrons cross the junction to fill minority carrier holes in the base, thus allowing free electron circuit current to flow. However, the base also has very few holes, so that most of the free electrons from the collector tend to accumulate there and restrict current flow. But, these free electrons now become majority carriers in the base, and are attracted across the junction to fill the accumulated holes in the emitter. Because of this, both a high emitter and collector current are allowed to flow.

The amount of collector current that flows is determined by the number of holes in the emitter that accept electrons from the collector via the base. This, in turn, is determined by the forward bias in the emitter circuit. Therefore, a signal voltage can be applied to the emitter to aid or oppose the bias, thus changing emitter current, and, thereby, collector current as well. Then, if a high-value load resistor is placed in the collector circuit, gain will be obtained the same as with the n-p-n transistor.

The p-n-p transistor works the same as the n-p-n transistor, except that opposite carriers are used

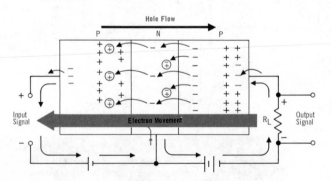

In the p-n-p transistor, collector current changes with emitter current to give gain. Holes, which are the majority carriers, move in the opposite direction to that of the electrons

transistor
element characteristics

Although the transistor theory presented showed that the current flow through the transistor is similar in many respects to p-n diodes, the transistor has certain basic differences that allow it to work as an amplifier.

First, all three segments of the transistor are doped differently, and second, they are "grown" in different sizes. Since the emitter is forward biased, and provides majority current flow, it is heavily doped to produce a large number of majority carriers. The collector, being reverse biased, provides minority current flow, and so is lightly doped to keep majority carriers low. This is important, since the attractive influence of majority carriers would tend to inhibit the production of minority carriers by thermal agitation. Therefore, the collector can produce a larger number of minority carriers in this way.

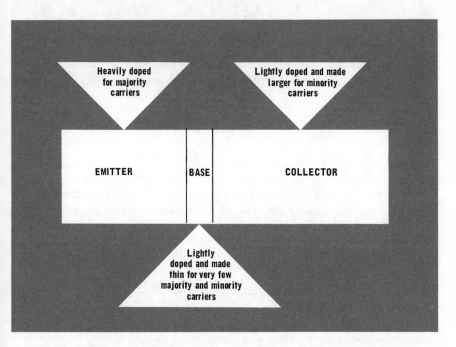

In addition, the collector is made larger than the emitter, so that a sufficient number of minority carriers will be produced with a proper reverse bias so that collector current can be nearly as great as emitter current. The base is very lightly doped to produce very few majority carriers, and is made thin to keep the minority carriers low as well. The thinness of the base is also needed to allow the current carriers to diffuse easily between the emitter and collector.

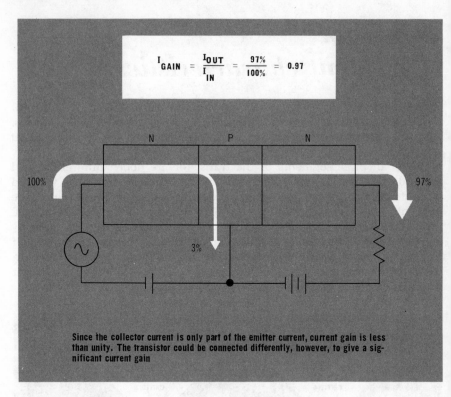

Since the collector current is only part of the emitter current, current gain is less than unity. The transistor could be connected differently, however, to give a significant current gain

current gain characteristics

If you recall, the collector current in a transistor is supplied by the carriers provided by the emitter. Actually, the emitter current follows two paths: one is through the collector, and the other is through the base. Only about 2 to 5 percent of the emitter current goes through the base, while the other 95 to 98 percent becomes the collector current. Since the emitter current is the input current, and the collector current is the output current, the current gain can be computed by:

$$\text{Current gain} = \frac{\text{output current}}{\text{input current}}$$

Therefore, since the collector current in this type of circuit is about 97 percent of the emitter current, the current gain is

$$\text{Current gain} = \frac{97\%}{100\%} = 0.97$$

You can see then that for the type of circuit shown, the current gain is slightly less than unity (a slight loss). However, you will learn that the transistor can be connected in other ways to give an actual current gain.

resistance, voltage, and power gains

Resistance gain is computed similarly to current gain. It is the ratio of the output resistance to the input resistance:

$$\text{Resistance gain} = \frac{\text{output resistance}}{\text{input resistance}}$$

Since the reverse biased base-collector junction provides a high output resistance, and the forward biased base-emitter junction provides a low input resistance, this type of circuit gives a high resistance gain. For example, suppose a transistor is biased in such a way that the emitter-to-base resistance is 150 ohms, and the collector-to-base resistance is 15,000 ohms. The resistance gain would be:

$$\text{Resistance gain} = \frac{\text{output resistance}}{\text{input resistance}} = \frac{15,000}{150} = 100$$

The signal voltage gain could be found by dividing the output voltage change for a given input voltage change, if you wanted to take measurements. However, since you know the current gain and the resistance gain, you can find the voltage gain by Ohm's Law:

$$\text{Voltage gain} = I_{GAIN} \times R_{GAIN} = 0.97 \times 100 = 97$$

This means that the output voltage change will be 97 times greater than the input voltage change.

Power gain can be found in a similar way:

$$\text{Power gain} = E_{GAIN} \times I_{GAIN} = 97 \times 0.97 = 94.09$$

or $\quad$ $$\text{Power gain} = I_{GAIN}^{2} \times R_{GAIN} = 0.97 \times 0.97 \times 100 = 94.09$$

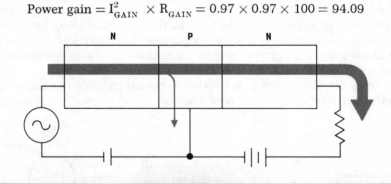

Gain	Equation
Current Gain	$I_{GAIN} = I_{OUT} \div I_{IN} = E_{GAIN} \div R_{GAIN}$
Resistance Gain	$R_{GAIN} = R_{OUT} \div R_{IN} = E_{GAIN} \div I_{GAIN}$
Voltage Gain	$E_{GAIN} = E_{OUT} \div E_{IN} = I_{GAIN} \times R_{GAIN}$
Power Gain	$P_{GAIN} = P_{OUT} \div P_{IN} = E_{GAIN} \times I_{GAIN}$
	$= I_{GAIN}^{2} \times R_{GAIN} = E_{GAIN}^{2} \div I_{GAIN}$

comparison of tubes and transistors

You can see that although electron tubes and transistors are completely different types of devices, which operate in different ways, they are somewhat related. It might be useful, then, to compare them to get a better idea of how each can be used to do similar jobs.

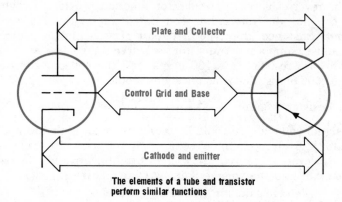

Plate and Collector

Control Grid and Base

Cathode and emitter

**The elements of a tube and transistor
perform similar functions**

In a tube, the plate *collects* the current, as does the collector in the transistor; so, these two elements can be considered to serve similar functions. In the tube, the current carriers are sent to the plate by the *emission* of the cathode, which is similar to how the emitter supplies carriers to the collector in a transistor. In a tube, the current carriers pass through the control grid; and in the transistor, they pass through the base. In the tube, a bias voltage between the control grid and cathode controls the plate current; and in the transistor, a bias voltage between the base and emitter controls the collector current.

From the above, you can see that it is also possible to compare basic transistor circuits to basic tube circuits.

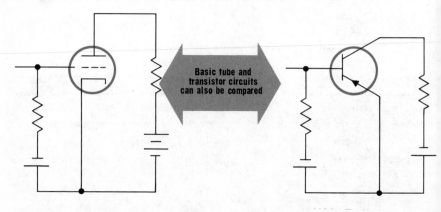

Basic tube and
transistor circuits
can also be compared

summary

☐ Transistors are three-element semiconductors that can amplify a signal.
☐ Transistors have an emitter, a base, and a collector. ☐ The emitter
supplies the majority carriers for current flow. ☐ The collector collects the
emitter's majority carriers for circuit operation. ☐ The base controls the
current flow between the emitter and the collector. ☐ The emitter is represented
by an arrow that points in the direction of hole flow. ☐ The arrow points
towards the base for a p-type emitter and away from the base for an n-type
emitter.

☐ The base in a transistor is common to both the emitter and collector
circuits. ☐ Since the emitter-base circuit is forward biased, majority carriers
cross the junction from the emitter into the base. The base provides few
majority carriers to combine with the incoming emitter majority carriers. ☐
The collector-base circuit is reverse biased, and minority carriers in the
collector are attracted to the base junction. The base provides few minority
carriers to combine with the collector minority carriers. ☐ The excess majority
carriers from the emitter pass through the base and are attracted to the
collector where they combine with the minority carriers. ☐ The entire emitter
current (less the 2 to 5% that flows down the base) reaches the collector.

☐ Current gain of a transistor $= I_{OUT} \div I_{IN} = E_{GAIN} \div R_{GAIN}$. Current gain in
a circuit with a common base is less than 1 due to the input current that flows
in the base. ☐ Resistance gain $= R_{OUT} \div R_{IN} = E_{GAIN} \div I_{GAIN}$. The reverse-
biased collector-base output circuit provides a high resistance compared with
the forward-biased emitter-base input circuit; typically, it is 100 times greater.
☐ Voltage gain $= E_{OUT} \div E_{IN} = I_{GAIN} \times R_{GAIN}$. The resistance of the output
circuit provides voltage gain although the current gain is less than 1. ☐ Power
gain $= P_{OUT} \div P_{IN} = E_{GAIN} \times I_{GAIN}$. In a circuit with a common base,
power gain is slightly less than voltage gain due to lack of current gain.

---

review questions

1. Describe the function of each element in a transistor.
2. Draw the symbol for a p-n-p transistor.
3. Draw the symbol for an n-p-n transistor.
4. Why is the emitter-base circuit forward biased?
5. Why is the collector reverse biased?
6. How is voltage gain provided in a transistor?
7. Write the equations for current gain.
8. Write the resistance and power gain equations.
9. Explain why the current gain in a transistor with a common-base circuit is always less than 1.
10. How much emitter current flows down the base?

the common-base circuit

As shown, the common-base circuit is the type you have been studying all along. It is so called because the base is common to both the input and output. Since the base in a transistor has a similar function to the control grid in a tube, the common-base circuit is similar to the common-, or grounded-, grid amplifier.

In the common-base amplifier, the input signal is applied to the emitter, and the output signal appears across R_L at the collector. When the input signal aids the emitter-base bias, the emitter current, I_E, goes up. This causes the collector current, I_C, to go up also, producing a larger voltage drop across the load resistor. Since the change in collector current is almost equal to the change in emitter current, and the output resistance is much greater than the input resistance, the voltage change across the load resistor is greater than the input signal swing. Thus, the signal is amplified.

By the same token, since the change in input current is about the same as the change in output current, but the output voltage swing is greater, the output power is greater than the input power. This is explained more fully later.

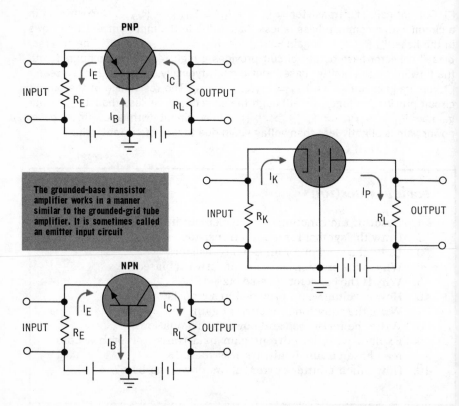

The grounded-base transistor amplifier works in a manner similar to the grounded-grid tube amplifier. It is sometimes called an emitter input circuit

The same phase input signal affects the n-p-n and
p-n-p circuits differently

NPN

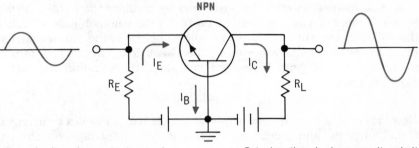

N-p-n circuits and p-n-p circuits are affected differently by the same phase input signal because they have opposite-polarity emitter bias

But, since they also have opposite-polarity collector bias, the output phases of both are the same. There is no phase reversal in a common-base circuit

PNP

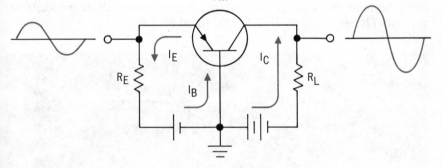

input and output phases

From Volume 3, you should recall that the grounded-grid tube amplifier did *not* reverse the phase of the input signal. Neither does the common-base amplifier. In the n-p-n circuit, when the input signal goes positive, it *subtracts* from the emitter bias, reducing the overall bias. This reduces the emitter current and the collector current as well. With less collector current, the drop across the load resistor is less. Therefore, the voltage at the collector, which is the output voltage, goes more positive. The output voltage, then, goes in the same direction as the input voltage, and has the same phase.

With the p-n-p circuit, when the input signal goes positive, it *aids* the emitter bias, and causes more emitter and collector current to flow. The increased collector current causes a greater drop across the load resistor. As a result, the collector voltage becomes less negative, or swings in the positive direction, following the phase of the input signal.

Even though the same signal affects the n-p-n and p-n-p currents differently, the output phases are the same because of the opposite bias polarities.

current gain

As you learned, current gain is found by dividing the output current by the input current. The output current in a common-base circuit is the collector current (I_C), and the input current is the emitter current (I_E). In the common-base circuit, the Greek letter *alpha* (α) is used to signify current gain. Using symbols, then, the equation for current gain becomes:

$$\alpha = I_C/I_E$$

Now, suppose a typical common-base circuit had an emitter current of 6 milliamperes, and a collector current of 5.83 milliamperes. The current gain would be

$$\alpha = I_C/I_E = 5.83/6 = 0.97$$

As you know, the current gain in this type of circuit has to be less than unity because the emitter current is always greater than the collector current. Therefore, α is always less than 1.

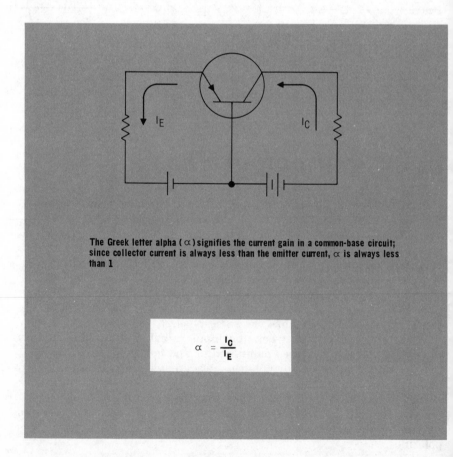

The Greek letter alpha (α) signifies the current gain in a common-base circuit; since collector current is always less than the emitter current, α is always less than 1

resistance, voltage, and power gains

For the common-base circuit, even though it does not have a true current gain, it can give voltage and power gains because of its resistance gain. The resistance gain is brought about because the collector circuit is reverse biased, and the input circuit is forward biased; thus, the output circuit has a much higher resistance than the input circuit.

Actually, it is the output load resistor (R_L) that determines the output resistance, since it produces the varying output voltage as the collector current changes. If this load resistor could be made equal to the collector-base junction resistance, the maximum gain could be realized. But this resistance could be up in the megohm range, and such a higher value would require a very large bias battery to get the proper bias current to flow. So, the load resistance is usually much less. A typical circuit could have an input resistance of 300 ohms, and an output resistance of 15,000 ohms. The resistance gain of such a circuit is:

$$R_{GAIN} = R_{OUT}/R_{IN} = 15,000/300 = 50$$

By Ohm's Law, then, if this circuit had a current gain of 0.97, the voltage and power gains are

$$E_{GAIN} = \alpha \times R_{GAIN} = 0.97 \times 50 = 48.5$$
$$P_{GAIN} = E_{GAIN} \times \alpha = 48.5 \times 0.97 = 47.04$$

Of course, both voltage and power gains could also be found by:

$$E_{GAIN} = E_{OUT}/E_{IN} \qquad P_{GAIN} = P_{OUT}/P_{IN}$$

Gain	Equation
Current Gain	$\alpha = \dfrac{I_C}{I_E}$
Resistance Gain	$R_{GAIN} = \dfrac{R_{OUT}}{R_{IN}}$
Voltage Gain	$E_{GAIN} = \alpha \times R_{GAIN}$
	$E_{GAIN} = \dfrac{E_{OUT}}{E_{IN}}$
Power Gain	$P_{GAIN} = E_{GAIN} \times \alpha$
	$P_{GAIN} = \alpha^2 \times R_{GAIN}$
	$P_{GAIN} = \dfrac{E_{GAIN}^2}{R_{GAIN}}$
	$P_{GAIN} = \dfrac{P_{OUT}}{P_{IN}}$

the common-emitter circuit

In the *common-emitter* circuit, the emitter is common to both the input and output. Since the function of the emitter is similar to that of a cathode, the common-emitter transistor amplifier is similar to the common-, or grounded-, cathode tube amplifier. And like its tube counterpart, the grounded-emitter amplifier is the type of circuit used most often. It is sometimes called a *base input* circuit.

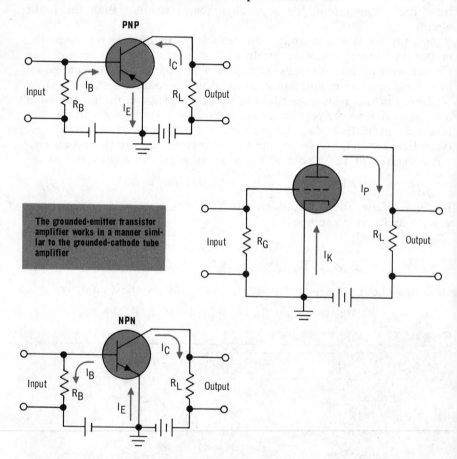

The grounded-emitter transistor amplifier works in a manner similar to the grounded-cathode tube amplifier

The input signal in this type of circuit is applied to the base, and the output signal appears across R_L at the collector. The input signal either aids or opposes the base-emitter bias battery. When it aids the bias battery, the base current, I_B, goes up, because the emitter current, I_E, is increased due to the higher forward bias. Therefore, the collector current, I_C, goes up, too, to increase the drop across the load resistor. The opposite happens when the input signal goes down. The output voltage swing is greater than the input signal to give voltage gain.

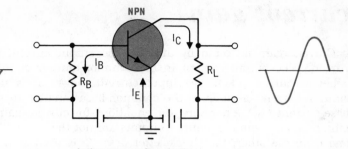

In the common-emitter circuit, there is a 180-degree phase reversal of the signal voltage

input and output phases

From the previous description, you may have the idea that the grounded-emitter amplifier works just like the grounded-base amplifier. There is one big difference, however. In Volume 3, you learned that the phase of a signal is *reversed* in a grounded-cathode tube; this also happens in a grounded-emitter transistor. The reason for this is that in the grounded-emitter circuit, the input signal is applied from base to emitter, whereas in the grounded-base circuit, the signal is applied from emitter to base. As a result, the same phase input signal affects the base-emitter bias in both circuits in opposite ways.

For example, in the n-p-n common-emitter circuit, when the input signal goes positive, it *adds* to the base-emitter bias, increasing emitter and base currents. It also increases the collector current to cause a greater drop across the load resistor. As a result, the voltage at the collector becomes less positive, or swings in a negative direction. The output voltage, then swings *opposite* to the input voltage.

With the p-n-p circuit, a positive input voltage *opposes* base-emitter bias, lowering the base, emitter, and collector currents. This reduces the drop across the load resistor, so that the collector voltage becomes more negative, which again is opposite to the input signal phase.

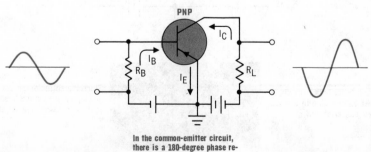

In the common-emitter circuit, there is a 180-degree phase reversal of the signal voltage

current gain

Current gain is found by dividing the output current by the input current. The output current in the common-emitter circuit is still the collector current (I_C). The input current, however, is no longer the emitter current, as it is in the common-base circuit; instead, it is the base current (I_B). Therefore, the equations for current gain in the common-base and common-emitter circuits are not the same. To distinguish one from the other, the Greek letter *beta*, β, is used as the symbol for current gain in a common-emitter circuit. Therefore, the equation for current gain becomes:

$$\beta = I_C/I_B$$

Remember, the current gain in the common-base circuit was less than unity because the input current (I_E) was greater than the output current (I_C). However, since the input current in the common-emitter circuit is the base current (I_B), the output current is much greater than the input current; and so the circuit has a high current gain. For example, suppose the circuit shown has a collector current of 5.83 milliamperes, and an emitter current of 6 milliamperes; find the current gain. As you can see, first you have to find the base current. Since the emitter current is the sum of the base and collector currents, the base current can be found by:

$$I_E = I_C + I_B \quad \text{and} \quad I_B = I_E - I_C = 6 - 5.83 = 0.17 \text{ ma}$$

Now you can find current gain by:

$$\beta = I_C/I_B = 5.83/0.17 = 34.29$$

The high current gain of a common-emitter circuit is the property that makes this circuit much more useful than the common-base circuit.

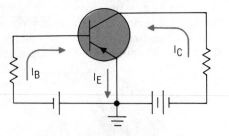

The Greek letter beta (β) signifies the current gain in a grounded-emitter circuit

$$\beta = \frac{I_C}{I_B}$$

Since the collector current is always greater than the base current, β is always greater than 1

resistance, voltage, and power gains

Since the grounded-emitter amplifier has high current gain, it is capable of giving much higher voltage and power gains than the grounded-base circuits. This is particularly true since the resistance gain of the grounded-emitter circuit is just as high as in the grounded-base circuit; remember, the input and output junctions, and, therefore, resistances are the same in both circuits.

Suppose a circuit had an input resistance of 500 ohms, an output resistance of 5000 ohms, and a β of 35. The resistance gain, then, is

$$R_{GAIN} = 5000/500$$
$$= 10$$

Using Ohm's Law, then, since β is 35, the voltage gain is

$$E_{GAIN} = R_{GAIN} \times \beta$$
$$= 10 \times 35$$
$$= 350$$

The power gain is

$$P_{GAIN} = E_{GAIN} \times \beta$$
$$= 350 \times 35$$
$$= 12{,}250$$

As with the grounded-base circuit, both voltage and power gains could also be found by:

$$E_{GAIN} = E_{OUT}/E_{IN}$$

and

$$P_{GAIN} = P_{OUT}/P_{IN}$$

Gain	Equation
Current Gain	$\beta = I_C/I_B$
Resistance Gain	$R_{GAIN} = R_{OUT} \div R_{IN}$
Voltage Gain	$E_{GAIN} = \beta \times R_{GAIN}$
	$E_{GAIN} = E_{OUT} \div E_{IN}$
Power Gain	$P_{GAIN} = E_{GAIN} \times \beta$
	$P_{GAIN} = \beta^2 \times R_{GAIN}$
	$P_{GAIN} = E_{GAIN}^2 \div R_{GAIN}$
	$P_{GAIN} = P_{OUT} \div P_{IN}$

the common-collector circuit

In the *common-collector* circuit, the collector is common to both the input and output. Since the function of the collector is similar to that of a tube's plate, the common-collector transistor circuit is similar to the common-, or grounded-, plate amplifier. And, like its tube counterpart, if the collector is not actually at d-c ground, it must be kept at a-c ground with a bypass capacitor. In the tube circuit, since the output voltage is taken off the cathode, the circuit is often called a *cathode follower*. For the same reason, the transistor circuit is also called an *emitter follower*.

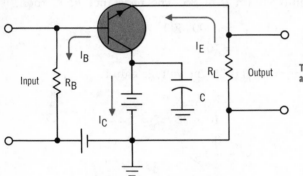

This is one way of representing an emitter follower

The input signal to this circuit is applied to the base, and the output signal is taken off across R_L, in the emitter. As in the other circuits, the input signals either aid or oppose the input bias voltage, but unlike the other circuits there is no gain, as you will learn. Essentially, the collector circuit performs no active function, and the input signal merely causes the emitter current to rise and fall.

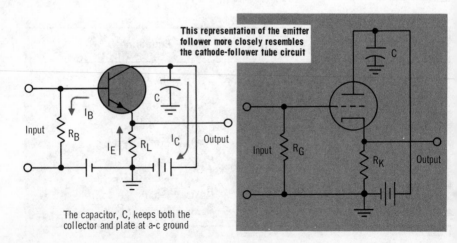

This representation of the emitter follower more closely resembles the cathode-follower tube circuit

The capacitor, C, keeps both the collector and plate at a-c ground

input and output phases

You can see now that the emitter follower operates on the same principle as the other circuits. The input signal either aids or opposes the base-emitter bias voltage to increase or decrease the emitter current. However, the effect that this has on the collector current is not significant. Essentially, the collector is connected in the circuit to allow emitter current flow. Remember, as you learned earlier, that without the collector to pick up current carriers, the carriers from the emitter would accumulate in the base to restrict emitter-current flow. So the collector is merely used to complete the d-c current path and is kept at a-c zero so that it does not carry signal current.

The circuit configuration of the emitter follower on this page shows how simply the circuit works. In the n-p-n transistor, when the input signal swings positive, it *aids* the bias to increase emitter current. The increased emitter current raises the voltage drop across the load resistor, R_L, to make the output voltage more positive; so the input and output signals are *in phase*.

With the p-n-p transistor, a positive input signal *opposes* the bias to reduce emitter current. This lowers the voltage drop across R_L. But, because of the direction of current flow, the emitter becomes less negative, or swings in a positive direction; the input and output signals, then, are in phase.

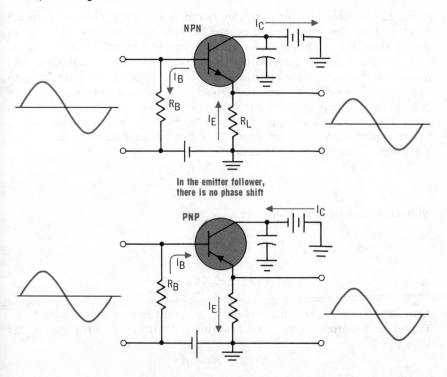

In the emitter follower,
there is no phase shift

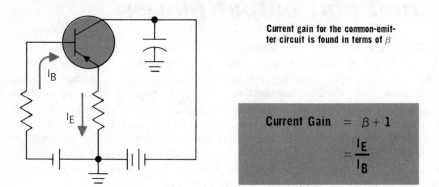

Current gain for the common-emitter circuit is found in terms of β

Current Gain $= \beta + 1$

$= \dfrac{I_E}{I_B}$

current gain

Current gain in the emitter follower is found by dividing the output current by the input current, just as with the other circuits. However, the input current here is the base current (I_B), and the output current is the emitter current (I_E), so the equation is

$$\text{Current gain} = I_E/I_B \qquad (1)$$

Since the emitter current in the common-collector circuit is much greater than the base current, the current gain is very high, even higher than for a comparable common-emitter circuit. Although alpha (α) denotes current gain in the common-base circuit, and beta (β) for the common-emitter circuit, there is no symbol for current gain in the common-collector circuit. Instead, it is given in terms of β, since β is the characteristic most often supplied by transistor manufacturers. Since β is found with I_C and I_B, these terms must be substituted for I_E in the common-collector equation. This can be done since $I_E = I_C + I_B$. Therefore, equation (1) becomes:

$$\text{Current gain} = \frac{I_C + I_B}{I_B}$$

which can also be shown as:

$$\text{Current gain} = \frac{I_C}{I_B} + \frac{I_B}{I_B}$$

or $\qquad\qquad \text{Current gain} = \dfrac{I_C}{I_B} + 1$

Also, if you check the equation for β, you will find that it equals I_C/I_B. Therefore, by substituting β, we find that the current gain for the emitter follower is

$$\text{Current gain} = \beta + 1$$

resistance, voltage, and power gains

You might think that since the emitter follower has a higher current gain than even the common-emitter circuit that it would also have higher voltage and power gains. It does not because the circuit has a resistance gain *much lower* than unity. You can see this when you realize that the input circuit is the base-collector, which is reverse biased, and the output is the emitter-collector, which is forward biased. Therefore, using the resistance gain equation, you can see that the gain is very low:

$$R_{GAIN} = R_{OUT}/R_{IN} = R_{LOW}/R_{HIGH} = \text{much less than 1}$$

Actually, a typical input resistance for this circuit is about 300K, and a typical output resistance is about 300 ohms. So, you can see that the resistance gain is very low. It is so low, in fact, that even though the circuit has a high current gain, the voltage gain that results from multiplying the current and resistance gains amounts to a loss. For example, using the resistance figures given above with a current gain of 800, the voltage gain would be

$$E_{GAIN} = R_{GAIN} \times (\beta + 1) = 0.001 \times 800 = 0.8$$

Power gain, though, can be greater than 1 because it is found by squaring the current gain:

$$P_{GAIN} = (\beta + 1)^2 \times R_{GAIN}$$

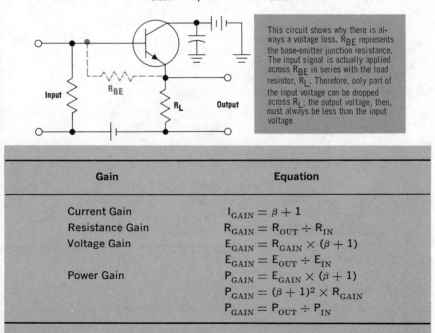

This circuit shows why there is always a voltage loss. R_{BE} represents the base-emitter junction resistance. The input signal is actually applied across R_{BE} in series with the load resistor, R_L. Therefore, only part of the input voltage can be dropped across R_L; the output voltage, then, must always be less than the input voltage

Gain	Equation
Current Gain	$I_{GAIN} = \beta + 1$
Resistance Gain	$R_{GAIN} = R_{OUT} \div R_{IN}$
Voltage Gain	$E_{GAIN} = R_{GAIN} \times (\beta + 1)$
	$E_{GAIN} = E_{OUT} \div E_{IN}$
Power Gain	$P_{GAIN} = E_{GAIN} \times (\beta + 1)$
	$P_{GAIN} = (\beta + 1)^2 \times R_{GAIN}$
	$P_{GAIN} = P_{OUT} \div P_{IN}$

alpha and beta

Transistors are manufactured for certain values of α and β. But, as mentioned earlier, the common-emitter circuit is the one that is used most often. As a result, transistor manufacturers usually only give the β characteristic for the transistor. However, the common-base circuit is still used, and so it is important also to know α. So, if only β is known, there should be some way of finding α without making too many measurements. The same is true if you only know α, and β is needed. Fortunately, there is a definite relationship between the two, so that each can be expressed in terms of the others. These equations are

$$\beta = \frac{\alpha}{1 - \alpha}$$

and
$$\alpha = \frac{\beta}{1 + \beta}$$

These equations were derived by substituting expressions in the basic equation for α and β to find each in terms of the other. So, if you know one, you can find the other.

Solving for β in terms of α

1. Since $\alpha = I_C/I_E$, solving for I_C, we have: $I_C = \alpha I_E$.
2. Therefore, since $\beta = I_C/I_B$, then by substituting for I_C, $\beta = \alpha I_E/I_B$.
3. Also, $I_B = I_E - I_C$. And solving for I_C, we have: $I_C = I_E - I_B$.
4. Therefore, substituting for I_C found in step 1, $I_E - I_B = \alpha I_E$.
5. Then by transposing all the terms with I_E to the left, $I_E - \alpha I_E = I_B$, which is simplified to $I_E(1 - \alpha) = I_B$.
6. Now the β found in step 2 can become $\beta = \dfrac{\alpha I_E}{I_E(1 - \alpha)}$
7. Factoring the I_E, the equation is simplified to:

$$\beta = \frac{\alpha}{1 - \alpha}$$

Solving for α in terms of β

1. Since $\beta = \alpha/(1 - \alpha)$, then by transposing, $\alpha = \beta - \beta\alpha$.
2. Transposing further, $\alpha + \beta\alpha = \beta$.
3. Simplifying, $\alpha(1 + \beta) = \beta$.
4. Solving for α, we have

$$\alpha = \frac{\beta}{1 + \beta}$$

summary

☐ No phase reversal occurs between the input and output signals in the common-base circuit. ☐ Alpha (α) signifies current gain in the common-base circuit and equals I_C/I_E. ☐ Alpha (α) is always less than 1 since the collector current is always less than the emitter current because of current flow in the base. ☐ The common-base circuit provides voltage and power gains due to the resistance gain of the reverse-biased output circuit compared with the forward-biased input circuit.

☐ Phase reversal occurs between the input and output signals in the common-emitter circuit. ☐ Beta (β) signifies current gain in the common-emitter circuit, and equals I_C/I_B. ☐ Beta (β) is always much greater than 1 since the collector current is always greater than the base current. ☐ The common-emitter circuit provides the highest voltage and power gains due to the high current gain and resistance gain.

☐ The output of the common-collector circuit is taken from the emitter; this circuit is also called an emitter follower. ☐ No phase reversal occurs between the input and output signals in the common-collector circuit. ☐ Current gain in the common-collector circuit is given in terms of β and equals $\beta + 1 = (I_C + I_B)/I_B$. ☐ The common-collector circuit provides the highest current gain since the base current is only a small part of the emitter current. ☐ The common-collector circuit provides no voltage gain and low power gain due to low resistance gain. ☐ α and β are related and can be expressed in terms of one another: $\alpha = \beta/(1 + \beta)$ and $\beta = \alpha/(1 - \alpha)$.

---

review questions

1. Why is the common-base circuit also called an emitter input circuit?
2. What does α signify?
3. How is α calculated?
4. How does the common-base circuit provide voltage and power gains if there is no current gain?
5. Why is there phase reversal in the common-emitter circuit, but not in the common-base circuit?
6. What does β signify? How is it calculated?
7. Why is the common-collector circuit also called an emitter follower?
8. The current gain for a common-collector circuit can be expressed in terms of β. Why is this possible?
9. Explain why the voltage gain of a common-collector circuit must always be less than 1.
10. Express α and β in terms of each other.

transistor characteristics

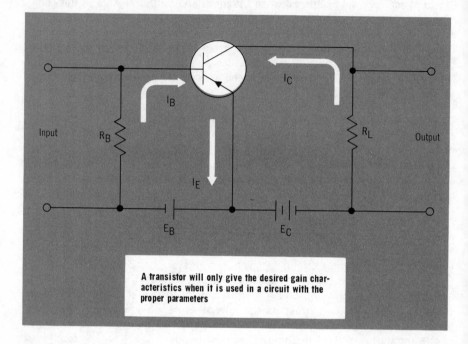

A transistor will only give the desired gain characteristics when it is used in a circuit with the proper parameters

As you learned, transistors are manufactured to have specific characteristics that will give them certain values of alpha and beta. However, these current gain values will not be produced if the transistor is connected in a circuit that does not have the proper *parameters*. In other words, the circuit must provide certain specified values of bias voltages and bias currents, as well as certain load resistances, to bring about the characteristics that the transistor was designed to have. As with electron tubes, there are many different types of transistors, each providing certain desired characteristics when they are used in the proper circuits. Basically, the circuit must be designed to certain values of:

1. Emitter-base bias voltage.

2. Collector-base bias voltage.

3. Emitter bias current.

4. Base current.

5. Collector bias current.

6. Input resistance.

7. Output load resistance.

operating curves

As with electron tubes, transistors are manufactured to have certain characteristics under various operating conditions. The transistor does not have to be used only for one set of circuit parameters, but can be operated with different combinations of bias voltages and currents to give the desired performance. The various possible combinations of parameters are indicated by a family of *operating curves,* which is provided by the manufacturer for each transistor type. Such a set of characteristic curves is shown.

Each characteristic curve represents a specific value of base current that can be used, and with the curve chosen, you can find an operating point that will give the needed collector current that will flow for a certain collector voltage. You probably recall that collector current is actually determined by emitter current and voltage. However, the base current is also determined by emitter current, and so can be used to indicate it. It is a standard established by transistor manufacturers to plot the curves around base current, since the base input, or common-emitter circuit is used the most. Remember, though, that a measurement of base current is essentially also an indication of how much emitter current is flowing.

For any value of base current, you can choose the desired combination of collector voltage and current from this family of operating curves

Operating point A shows that if the circuit causes a 60-μA base current, with a bias voltage of 7 volts from the collector to the emitter, the circuit will provide about 2.5 milliamperes of collector current

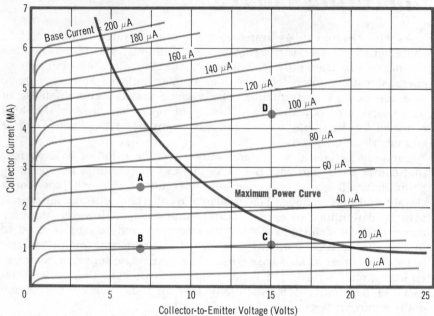

All operating points must be kept to the LEFT of the maximum power dissipation curve, or the transistor will burn out

maximum power dissipation

If we take the circuit used for the example on page 4-75, and change the resistance of the base-emitter circuit so that 20 microamperes of base current flow instead of 60, then the *operating point* will move to point B. Then, for a collector voltage of 7 volts, only slightly under 1 milliampere of collector current will flow. Now, if you keep the base current at 20 microamperes, but change the collector voltage to 15 volts, the collector current will go up to point C, slightly over 1 milliampere. This shows that the collector voltage affects collector current only slightly.

Now, with 15 volts applied to the collector, if you change the base circuit to provide 100 microamperes (point D), collector current will go up to about 4.33 milliamperes. This shows that a *change* in base current of 80 *micro*amperes produces a *change* in collector current of about 3.25 *milli*amperes (3250 microamperes), which is a current gain of:

$$\beta = 3250/80 \cong 40$$

Every transistor can only handle up to a certain power level, which is given as a maximum wattage rating, determined by the collector voltage and current ($P = EI$). Therefore, certain operating points can burn out the transistor. When a maximum power dissipation curve is given as shown on this page, any operating point to the *right* of the curve, such as point D, will exceed the safe wattage rating of the transistor.

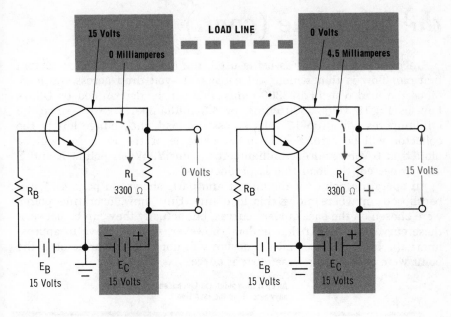

the load line

The manner by which you determine an operating point depends on the parameters with which you start. You can arbitrarily pick your own parameters, but, in many cases, you may have a particular power source or a particular transistor available that you must use. Sometimes, you must use a specific load, while other times you will have some leeway in selecting the load. In some cases, you may be limited to a certain level input signal, and at other times, you might have some control over the input signal. Many times, you can use the "typical values" supplied by the manufacturers, and other times these might not suit your application. All of these conditions affect the way you design a circuit.

For our example, assume that you must use a 3300-ohm load, that you only have two 15-volt batteries, and that the transistor has the proper β characteristic to give enough gain.

The first thing you must do is to draw a *load line,* which will show, with the voltages you have, all of the possible operating points you can use. In effect, the load line is drawn between the point of *maximum* collector *voltage* with *minimum* collector *current,* and *minimum* collector *voltage* with *maximum* collector *current.* Since you have a 15-volt battery for collector bias, you can get a maximum of 15 volts on the collector if 0 volts is dropped across the load, R_L. And this can only happen if there is zero collector current. One end of the load line then is at the point that shows 15 volts and 0 milliamperes. This is shown as point X on the curve (see page 4-78). The next extreme of the load line is found by determining the maximum current that can flow in the collector circuit.

the load line (cont.)

Since a 15-volt battery is being used, the maximum collector current that can flow is that which will cause a 15-volt drop across the load. Since the load resistor is 3300 ohms, this can be determined by Ohm's Law as $I = 15$ volts/3300 ohms, or 4.5 milliamperes. Now, since 4.5 milliamperes will drop 15 volts across the load, the voltage left at the collector will be zero. So, the other extreme of the load line will be plotted at 0 volts and 4.5 milliamperes, point Y. When points X and Y are connected, the load line is produced.

An operating point for the circuit and parts shown on page 4-77 can be chosen anywhere along this load line. Until now, operating points were chosen on the base current curves, but actually they can be between these curves as well. If that is done, however, you will have to approximate the base current, and the design will not be as accurate as if the point were chosen on a base current curve.

An operating point can be chosen anywhere along the load line

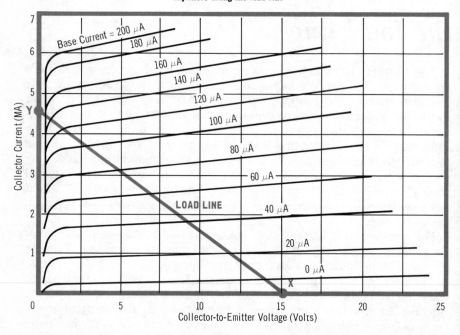

Although this load line was drawn based on a battery and load resistor on hand, you could first draw a load line, and then determine what bias battery and load resistor you would need. But, if you do it this way, you might come up with required battery and resistor values that are not readily available. It is best to start with standard parts, and compute the load line. If the parts you choose produce an undesirable load line, change the parts to shift the line to the desired position.

You must choose an operating point that will fit
the output signal voltage of the circuit

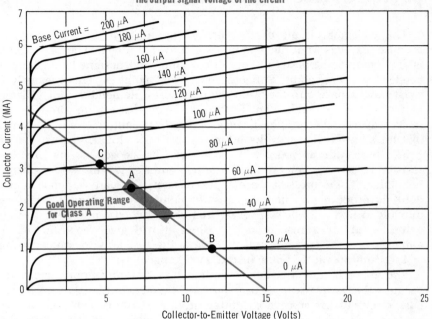

Collector Current (MA)

Collector-to-Emitter Voltage (Volts)

choosing an operating point

Some operating points might be better than others, depending on the circuit's purpose. For example, suppose the circuit is to be a class A amplifier, and the output signal voltage must swing 10 volts peak to peak. You would have to select the operating range shown to allow the collector voltage to vary between about 1 and 14 volts; this would permit a 5-volt swing on each side of the operating point, or 10 volts peak to peak, for any operating point in that range. The swing should never reach the actual extremes of the load line, or distortion will occur as the collector current reaches cutoff or saturation.

If you use point B as the operating point, which is at a collector voltage of about 12 volts, one half of a 10-volt peak-to-peak signal will only be able to go about 3 volts in one direction before it is clipped. Ordinarily, this would be considered distortion; but in some circuits, such as limiters or clippers, this is desirable, so you would want to use point B. (These circuits are covered in later volumes.) Of course, if you were just handling 10-volt pulses that go in only one direction, both points B and C would be good, depending on the pulse polarity. For convenience, let's choose the operating point at point A for 60 microamperes of base current. The center of the good operating range would be best, but then we would have to approximate the base current, which may not necessarily change linearly between curves.

setting the bias currents

The collector circuit of the circuit we are designing is complete because that was what the load line was drawn to match. The base circuit is not complete, however. This circuit must be designed to give the needed operating point. Suppose you choose point A. This means you must have a base current of 60 microamperes. Remember, only 15-volt batteries are available. Thus, for a 15-volt battery to produce 60 microamperes, the total resistance of the base-emitter circuit is found by Ohm's Law as R = 15 volts/60 microamperes = 250,000 ohms.

The base-emitter, you recall, is forward biased so that its junction resistance is very low (a few hundred ohms); it can be considered negligible. Therefore, the base input resistor, R_B, can be made about 250K to produce 60 microamperes for point A operation. It might be difficult to find a 250K resistor, so you should choose one close to that value. A 0.27-Meg resistor is fine since it will give about 55 micro-amperes of base current, and will allow the resistor's tolerance rating to keep the operating point in the good range.

The above is how a circuit is designed as a common-emitter circuit, because the battery affects base current directly. But, with a common-base circuit, it must be done differently: the battery controls emitter current. However, this is also done simply, when you remember that emitter current is the total of base and collector currents. The collector current at point A is about 2.5 milliamperes, so $I_E = I_C + I_B = 2.5$ millia-amperes + 60 microamperes = 2.56 milliamperes. With Ohm's Law, the total emitter resistance should be: 15 volts/2.56 milliamperes, or 5869 ohms. With this low value of resistance, however, the resistance of the base-emitter junction is no longer insignificant. If the junction resistance is, say, 400 ohms, then the emitter resistor must be about 5400 ohms to give the proper emitter and base currents. (A 5600-ohm resistor is the practical equivalent of the 5400 ohms needed.)

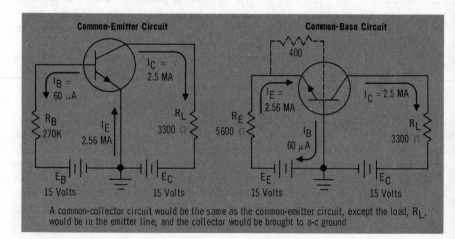

A common-collector circuit would be the same as the common-emitter circuit, except the load, R_L, would be in the emitter line, and the collector would be brought to a-c ground

changing values

For the example of designing the transistor circuit, the parts were, at first, arbitrarily chosen. Once the circuit is designed, the collector circuit cannot be changed without changing the load line. The base-emitter circuit, though, could be changed because it is just a specific bias current with which you are interested. For example, if you now wanted to use a 7.5-volt battery, the base resistor, R_B, could be changed to 133K to get a base current of 60 microamperes; and with a 3-volt battery, R_B would be 56K; and so on.

ALL THREE CIRCUITS WILL OPERATE ON POINT A OF THE LOAD LINE

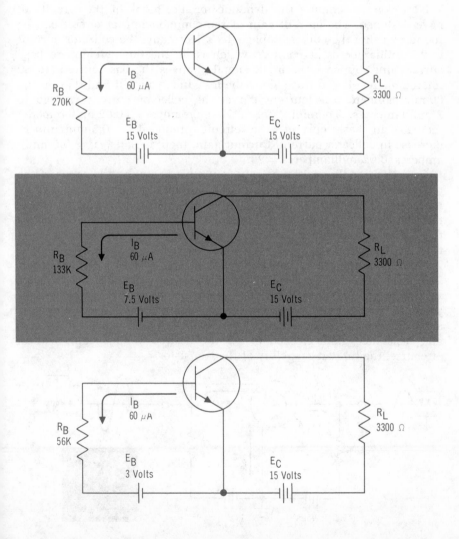

dynamic gain

Earlier, you learned that current gain is found by comparing output current to input current, and you used the actual d-c levels of current to find α and β. However, since you only used d-c, or static, levels of current, only the *static gains* were determined. With signal amplification, it is the *change* in output compared to the *change* in input that determines *dynamic gain*. A change in value is shown by the Greek letter delta (Δ), so a change in current is represented by ΔI, and a change in voltage is shown as ΔE. Actually, these represent the a-c signal current and voltage, which can be represented by another standard method: i and e. Lower case letters are used to represent ac, and capital letters for dc.

Now, let us compute the dynamic, or a-c, gains of the circuit we have designed. The current gain of the common-emitter circuit can be found by using the curves on page 4-79. Normally, the collector current is 2.5 milliamperes at point A, which is on the 60-microampere base current line. Suppose the input signal changes the base current to 80 microamperes. If you trace along the load line, you will find that on the 80-microampere base current curve, the collector current will go to 3 milliamperes. Therefore, for a 20-microampere (0.02-milliampere) increase in base current, the circuit produced a 0.5-milliampere increase in collector current. Current gain, then, is $\beta = i_C/i_B = 0.5$ milliamperes/0.02 milliamperes $= 25$.

To determine the resistance gain, you must know the resistance of the base-emitter junction, since this is the input resistance faced by the input signal. Earlier, we assumed this to be 400 ohms. As you were taught, the output resistance is the load, because that is what develops the output signal. Since the load is 3300 ohms, the resistance gain is $r_{GAIN} = 3300/400 \cong 8$.

Now the voltage gain can be found as $e_{GAIN} = \beta \times r_{GAIN} = 25 \times 8 = 200$. This means that a 20-millivolt input signal will cause the collector voltage to change 4 volts. If you wanted to increase the gain, another load line would have to be established with a larger collector voltage and load resistance. In this way, you could establish whatever current and resistance gains needed to get the desired voltage gain, within, of course, the limited capability of the transistor.

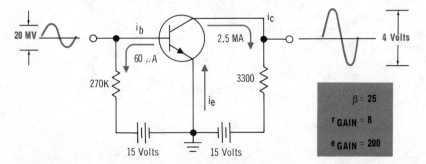

summary

□ A transistor gives the desired gain only when it is used in a circuit with the proper parameters. □ Circuit parameters are indicated by a family of characteristic curves. □ Collector current, I_C, plotted against collector-to-emitter voltage, V_{CE}, for various base currents, I_B, is the most common family of characteristic curves. □ The maximum power dissipation curve indicates the safe current-handling capacity of the transistor under various operating conditions.

□ Load lines show all possible operating points for a chosen collector voltage. □ The load line is drawn between the point of maximum collector voltage with minimum collector current, and minimum collector voltage with maximum collector current. □ The operating point is selected so that the input signal does not reach the extremes of the load line where the collector current is not linear. □ The load line sets the design of the collector-base circuit. □ The base current at the operating point sets the design of the base-emitter circuit in common-emitter circuits. □ The emitter current at the operating point sets the design of the base-emitter circuit in common-base circuits. □ The design of common-collector circuits is the same as that for common-emitter circuits except the load is in the emitter circuit and the collector is at a-c ground.

□ Static gain is determined by d-c or static levels, and is represented by capital letters. □ Dynamic gain is determined by changes in the output for changes in the input. □ Dynamic gain uses a-c levels, and is represented by small letters. □ Varying the load line and the bias values changes the dynamic current and resistance gains. □ Dynamic voltage gain and circuit amplification are established by the dynamic current and resistance gains.

review questions

1. List the seven principal transistor design parameters.
2. What are *characteristic curves*?
3. Why are characteristic curves usually plotted around the base current?
4. Define the *maximum power dissipation curve*.
5. What does the load line show?
6. From what two points is the load line drawn?
7. What is the *operating point*? How is it selected?
8. Why is the maximum power dissipation curve needed?
9. How does *dynamic gain* differ from *static gain*?
10. How is a set transistor voltage gain obtained?

THESE CIRCUITS ARE EQUIVALENT

(A)

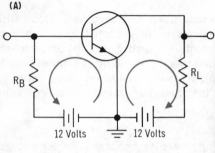

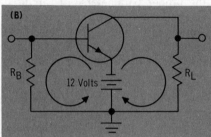

(C)

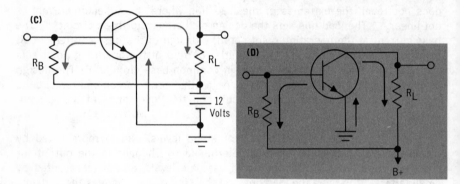

using one bias battery

Until now, the input and output circuits of the transistor used their own battery to produce the bias currents. The value of the collector battery is important in establishing a load line, but, as you learned, the actual voltage of the base-emitter battery is not that important. The circuit on page 4-82 shows that the emitter has the same polarity with respect to the base as it does to the collector. This permits the use of only one battery to establish the same circuit parameters as with two batteries. The circuit operation is essentially the same, except one bias battery supplies two paths, and the values of the resistances determine the parameters. The size of the battery establishes the maximum collector voltage for the load line, and the value of R_B sets the base current. As the diagrams show, this can be done in two ways. Circuit C is the one most often used. Circuit D shows how circuit C is usually drawn with a regular supply voltage on overall schematic diagrams, where a common remote power supply is used to feed a number of different circuits.

fixed bias

In all of the circuits you have been studying thus far, the bias currents for the input and output circuits were derived directly from the battery; the input circuit was in series with a resistor to limit the input bias current to the desired level. This type of bias is known as *fixed bias*, since a fixed d-c voltage source and resistance path are used.

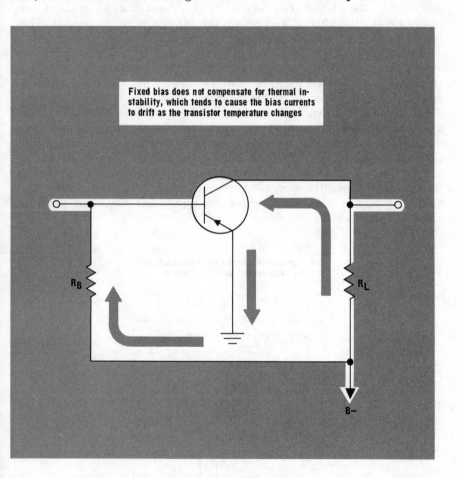

Fixed bias does not compensate for thermal instability, which tends to cause the bias currents to drift as the transistor temperature changes

Fixed bias has some drawbacks because it does not compensate for variations in the static bias currents that may occur due to changing circuit characteristics. For example, as the temperature of the transistor changes, its junction resistances will also change, varying the bias currents. Any change in bias current will shift the operating point of the circuit, which, in turn, can adversely affect the gain of the transistor. This is known as *thermal instability,* and fixed bias is greatly affected by it.

self bias

The ability of a circuit to compensate for temperature changes is known as *thermal stability*. The transistor is naturally affected by temperature, and so to provide for thermal stability, any unwanted change in bias current that takes place should be used to *counteract* the change. Since any change in bias current will show up in the output circuit, the change can be *fed back degeneratively* to the input to counteract the change and return the bias currents to normal. This is also known as *negative feedback*.

One way to do this is with *self bias*. This is so called because the actual bias current in the input circuit is determined primarily by the voltage at the collector. This is done by connecting the input current-limiting resistor directly to the collector rather than to the battery. Then, the voltage available for bias to the input is what is left over after the drop occurs across the output load. So, if temperature causes the transistor bias current to rise, the increased collector current will cause a bigger drop across the output load, and the voltage at the collector will go down. This will reduce the input bias current, causing the collector current to decrease to normal. Of course, the opposite will happen if the transistor temperature goes down. Self bias, then, provides some thermal stability.

Self bias is obtained when the input bias is gotten from the collector instead of the battery

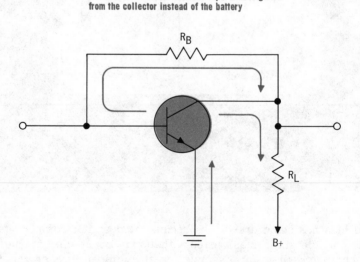

Changes in collector voltage, therefore, will be fed back to the input to stabilize the transistor against temperature variations

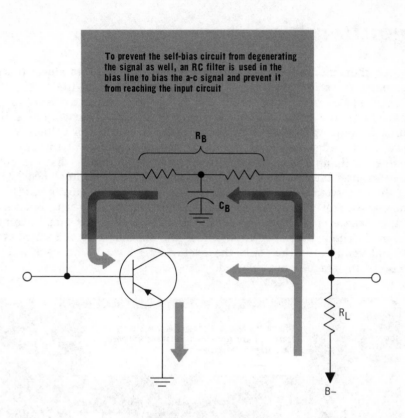

To prevent the self-bias circuit from degenerating the signal as well, an RC filter is used in the bias line to bias the a-c signal and prevent it from reaching the input circuit

degenerative feedback

Self bias is better than fixed bias because it uses negative feedback to bias itself and thus compensate for thermal changes. However, self bias, as shown on the previous page, also has a disadvantage. Since it uses degenerative feedback, the amplified *signal* at the collector is also fed back to reduce the input signal. This essentially reduces the gain of the stage. The self-bias circuit, then, should be arranged to feed back back only the d-c changes at the collector, and not the a-c changes. This is simply accomplished by using an RC filter in place of the bias current-limiting resistor. The capacitor in the filter will bypass any a-c signal to ground so that it will not degenerate the input signal. The gain of the stage will not be affected by the feedback.

The d-c feedback, still exists though, since the d-c current through R_B is still controlled by the static, or average, level of collector voltage. A centertapped resistor, or two resistors, must be used to isolate the capacitor from the input and output circuits. Otherwise, the capacitor would bypass the input or output circuits. As shown, the capacitor only bypasses the feedback line.

emitter bias

Another method of obtaining a bias voltage to produce thermal stability is *emitter bias*. Since the emitter current is the total of the base and collector currents, any drift in the average d-c level of bias current in the common-emitter circuit will also occur in the emitter line. By putting a resistor in series with the emitter, a voltage will be produced at the emitter that opposes the bias voltage at the base. The values of R_B and R_E in such a circuit must be chosen so that the proper base-emitter bias current will flow under ordinary circumstances. Then, if the transistor temperature changes to increase bias currents, the drop across R_E will go up to raise the emitter voltage. This will oppose the input bias to reduce the base, and thus, the collector bias current to normal. The capacitor is used across the emitter resistor to bypass the signal voltages so that only the average d-c level is fed back and the gain of the stage is not reduced.

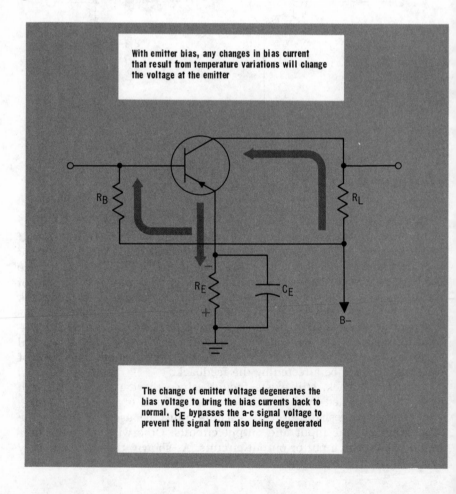

With emitter bias, any changes in bias current that result from temperature variations will change the voltage at the emitter

The change of emitter voltage degenerates the bias voltage to bring the bias currents back to normal. C_E bypasses the a-c signal voltage to prevent the signal from also being degenerated

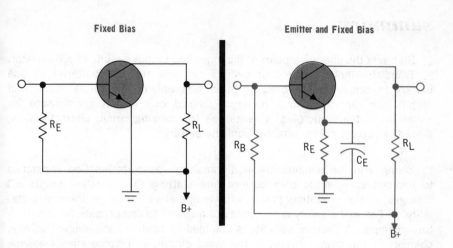

Fixed Bias — Emitter and Fixed Bias

combination bias

Actually, as noted on the previous page, emitter bias was not used by itself; it was combined with fixed bias. The fixed bias was used to set the base-emitter current, and the emitter bias merely modifies that current for stability. In this way, fixed bias can be used to get some degree of thermal stability. In the same way, emitter bias can be combined with self bias to improve the thermal stability of the circuit even further.

Emitter bias cannot be used alone because it really does not provide an input current path; it only produces a degenerative voltage. Self bias and fixed bias could be combined, but nothing would be gained by this because, for self bias to be effective, it would have to be the major path for the bias current, and the fixed bias resistor would only serve as an unnecessary voltage divider.

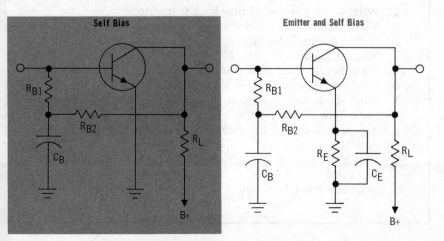

Self Bias — Emitter and Self Bias

summary

☐ Bias sets the operating point of the input and output circuits of a transistor. ☐ Transistor input and output circuits can use separate batteries or one battery to supply proper bias. ☐ Fixed bias obtains the proper input and output bias directly from a battery. ☐ Fixed bias cannot compensate for variations in the static bias currents due to changing circuit characteristics, since the current comes directly from the battery.

☐ Changes in the temperature of a transistor cause its junction resistance to change, varying the bias current and shifting the operating points. ☐ Changes in the operating points with temperature result in thermal instability. ☐ Thermal stability is the ability of a circuit to compensate for temperature changes. ☐ Thermal stability is obtained by feeding back, degeneratively, changes in the output circuit to the input circuit. ☐ Degenerative feedback is also known as negative feedback. ☐ Self bias obtains the proper input bias with negative feedback from the collector circuit. Self bias feeds back unwanted changes in the collector voltage to the base to bring the input current back to normal.

☐ Thermal stability can also be obtained with emitter bias. ☐ Emitter bias feeds back undesirable changes in the emitter voltage, due to changes in the input current, to the base to bring the input current back to normal. ☐ Emitter bias must always be combined with another form of bias to provide an input current path. ☐ Emitter bias is combined with fixed bias to provide thermal stability, or it can be combined with self bias to improve thermal stability.

review questions

1. What is the purpose of bias for a transistor?
2. What is *fixed bias*? What is its main disadvantage?
3. Define *thermal stability*.
4. What is *negative feedback*?
5. What is *self bias*? How is it obtained in a transistor circuit?
6. Explain how emitter bias is produced.
7. Since both self bias and emitter bias use negative feedback, how do they differ?
8. Are both a-c and d-c negative feedback supplied by self bias and emitter bias?
9. Why must emitter bias always be combined with some other form of bias?
10. Why are fixed bias and self bias usually not combined?

stabilization

The bias circuits that provide thermal stability compensate for the effect of temperature by responding to changes in current *after* they occur. They do so because the changes must occur first, to some degree, before they can be fed back for compensation. Also, because of this, complete compensation is impossible because, if the static bias currents were actually returned to their proper levels, the feedback would be lost. Actually, then, the bias circuits only oppose the changes due to thermal instability in an attempt to keep the variations that occur within tolerable limits.

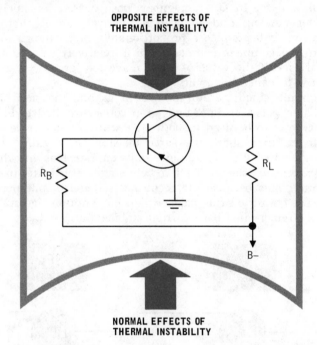

OPPOSITE EFFECTS OF
THERMAL INSTABILITY

NORMAL EFFECTS OF
THERMAL INSTABILITY

A good stabilizing circuit will produce effects that are opposite to those of ordinary temperature changes, and so will cancel thermal instability before it occurs

Therefore, stabilizing circuits, to be more effective, should not rely on feedback that results from thermal instability; they should prevent the bias currents from changing in the first place. One way to do this is to produce an effect on the transistor that is opposite to the normal effect of thermal instability. The following are ways this can be accomplished:

1. Use one transistor to stabilize another.
2. Use a thermistor to control bias current.
3. Use a diode to control emitter-base current.
4. Use a diode to control collector-base current.
5. Use combinations of stabilizing circuits.

common circuit stabilization

One way to accomplish better stabilization is to have the individual transistor stages share a *common circuit*, as shown. These circuits use common bias paths for both stages. In the circuit, the B-minus supply and resistor R_E provide bias currents for the emitter of Q_1 and the base of Q_2. If the temperature goes up to increase the emitter current of Q_1, the drop across R_E will also go up, and thereby leave less voltage to be applied to the base of Q_2. The base bias current in Q_2, then, will go down. The effect of temperature on Q_1, as a result, was produced in an opposite way in Q_2, so that any gain changes that take place in Q_1 will be compensated for in Q_2. Remember, base current is much smaller than emitter current, and so even a relatively small change in Q_1 emitter current will produce a proportionately high change in Q_2 base current, so that complete compensation is relatively easy to attain. As a matter of fact, if the value of R_E is made too large, Q_2 can be *overcompensated* to cause instability.

In the circuit, since the emitter bias of Q_1 and the base bias of Q_2 have the same polarity, n-p-n and p-n-p transistors had to be used. If the same type is to be used in both stages, a circuit can be employed where both emitters share the same resistor. Stabilization is not as good, though, since this is actually only emitter bias in which both current changes vary the feedback to both stages. It is better than single-circuit emitter bias because the feedback is doubled, but not as good as that in the circuit on this page, which has emitter bias stabilization for Q_1, and compensated base current stabilization for Q_2.

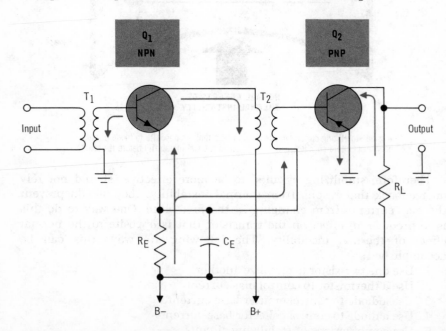

thermistor stabilization

It is possible to use one transistor to stabilize another because they are both similarly affected by temperature. Also, any other part could be used to stabilize a transistor if that part too were affected by temperature similar to a transistor. One such device is the *thermistor,* which, as you learned earlier, also has its resistance reduced as temperature rises. One use of the thermistor is shown in A. The thermistor forms a voltage divider with R_1 to provide fixed bias for the base. Then, as temperature goes up, tending to increase base bias current, the resistance of the thermistor goes down. Thus, it drops less voltage for the base, so that the base bias current tends to go down. When the circuit is properly designed, the thermistor tends to reduce the base current by the same amount that the transistor temperature tends to raise it; so, base bias current stays constant.

In B, the thermistor is used as part of a voltage divider with an emitter bias resistor. The base is supplied with fixed bias, and the emitter bias provides the usual stabilization. But the action of the thermistor increases the emitter stabilization for complete compensation. When the temperature goes up, tending to increase base current, the resistance of the thermistor goes down, causing the emitter to go more negative. This reduces the base-emitter bias sufficiently, so that the base current is lowered by the same amount it tended to increase.

In both circuits, since the thermistor and the transistor are affected by temperature at the same time, compensation takes place before the bias currents can change.

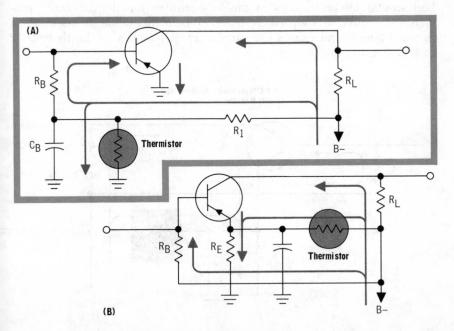

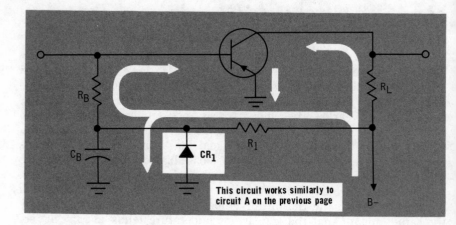

This circuit works similarly to circuit A on the previous page

diode stabilization

In the previous circuit, the best results will be obtained when the *negative temperature coefficient* of the thermistor most nearly matches that of the transistor. However, it is very difficult to have a thermistor act exactly like a transistor over a range of temperature variations since both devices are not near enough alike physically. The emitter-base circuit of the transistor that is being compensated is actually a p-n junction, and the thermistor is just a slab of semiconductor material. So, if a p-n diode were used in place of the thermistor, and the diode had similar characteristics to the base-emitter junction, it could provide more precise thermal stability. When the diode is used, it is forward biased and causes the same current changes as the thermistor to stabilize the circuit.

This circuit works similarly to circuit B on the previous page

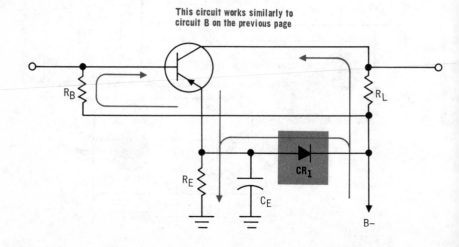

collector-base current stability

The previous diode stabilizing circuit only compensated for changes in base-emitter bias current, and thereby prevented the collector current from varying with such changes. However, the collector current itself can change with temperature, although the base-emitter current is stabilized. This is because the previous diode stabilizing circuit is a forward biased circuit, and so only compensated for changes in forward, or majority, current. But, as you learned in semiconductor theory, when temperature goes up, it also increases *minority carriers*. The minority carriers are increased in both the base and collector, but since the actual collector current is determined by the number of minority carriers in the base, those are the ones for which compensation is needed.

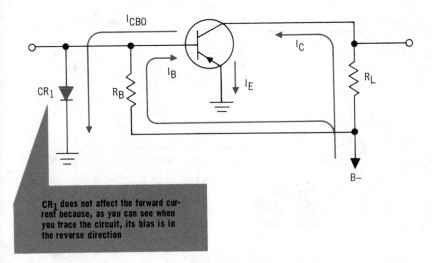

CR$_1$ does not affect the forward current because, as you can see when you trace the circuit, its bias is in the reverse direction

Actually, there are two currents flowing in the base: collector-base current in one direction, and emitter-base current in the other direction. The difference between the two, which is known as the base current, I$_B$, is a very small current that flows in the same direction as emitter-base current, since that is the larger of the two. In any event, if the base-collector current, which is known as I$_{CBO}$, changes with temperature, it will cause I$_B$ to change also, but in the opposite direction because I$_B$ is a *difference* current. To compensate for this, a reverse biased diode is connected in the base circuit to match the temperature characteristics of the reverse biased base-collector junction. When temperature goes up, and the number of minority carriers are increased in the base, the resistance of the diode goes down to drain off the excess minority carrier current (I$_{CBO}$), so that the difference, or base current (I$_B$), remains the same.

combined diode stabilization

You can see that for complete thermal stability, both I_B and I_{CBO} must be compensated for when diodes are used. This is done by using two diodes in the base bias circuit. One diode is forward biased to control base-emitter current, and the other diode is reverse biased to control base-collector current. The resistances of both diodes go down with temperature. But, since diode CR_1 is forward biased, it has a much lower resistance than diode CR_2; so, CR_1 has much more effect in the voltage divider line. Diode CR_1 lowers the voltage when the temperature goes up to keep the base-emitter current from rising with the temperature. Since diode CR_1 is forward biased, it conducts forward, or majority carrier, current.

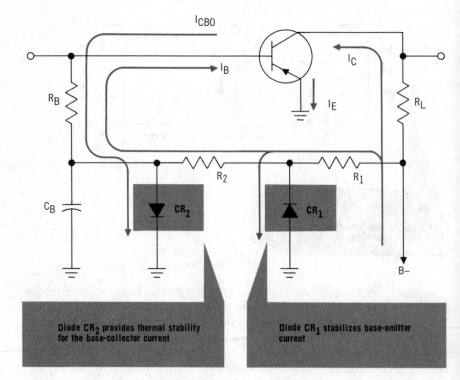

Diode CR_2 provides thermal stability for the base-collector current

Diode CR_1 stabilizes base-emitter current

Diode CR_2 is reverse biased, has a high resistance, and conducts reverse, or minority carrier, current; so it does not affect the majority carriers of the base-emitter circuit. It does, though, pass the base-collector minority current, and drains off the extra minority carriers produced in the base when temperature rises; thus it keeps I_{CBO} constant. Both diodes are needed for the circuit to have full thermal stability.

summary

☐ Simple bias stabilization circuits provide thermal stability by responding to changes in output current after they occur. ☐ Bias stabilization circuits can use semiconductors to prevent the current from changing in the first place. ☐ Semiconductors cancel the effect of thermal instability by producing an effect opposite to that of thermal instability. ☐ One transistor can stabilize another through a common bias circuit. ☐ The bias is generated by the compensating transistor and is applied to the compensated transistor to provide either emitter bias or base current stabilization. ☐ Base current stabilization provides complete compensation; emitter bias stabilization only provides increased bias feedback.

☐ Thermistor semiconductor devices can also stabilize a transistor since both are similarly affected by temperature variations. ☐ The thermistor replaces a resistor to supply fixed bias to the base that decreases with increasing temperatures or to supply reverse emitter bias that increases with increasing temperatures.

☐ P-n diodes can stabilize a transistor since they possess a p-n junction that is similarly affected by temperature variations. ☐ A forward-biased diode replaces a thermistor to provide fixed or emitter bias that varies with changes in temperature. ☐ Full thermal stability of a transistor is achieved by compensating both the emitter-base and the collector-base junctions. ☐ The collector-base junction is compensated for increases in minority carriers due to temperature variations. ☐ A reverse-biased diode is connected to the base circuit to drain off any excess collector minority carriers caused by increasing temperatures.

review questions

1. What is the main disadvantage of simple bias stabilization circuits?
2. How do semiconductors provide bias stabilization?
3. List 5 types of semiconductor stabilization circuits.
4. What is *common circuit stabilization?*
5. Why is base current stabilization superior to emitter bias stabilization?
6. How is a transistor overcompensated?
7. What is *thermistor stabilization?*
8. How does a diode compensate an emitter-base junction?
9. How does a diode compensate for thermal instability of minority carriers?
10. Why are two diodes always needed for full thermal stabilization?

circuit configurations

The basic transistor circuits you have studied thus far were built up slowly and methodically, so that by now you should be able to recognize the types of circuits and the kinds of bias used. However, when you use many commercial schematic diagrams, the circuits may not be as easy to recognize because they can be drawn in so many different configurations.

It would be good practice to redraw some commercial circuits to make them look like the basic circuits you have studied. This will help you to recognize various circuit configurations, and even help you to understand more about circuit theory.

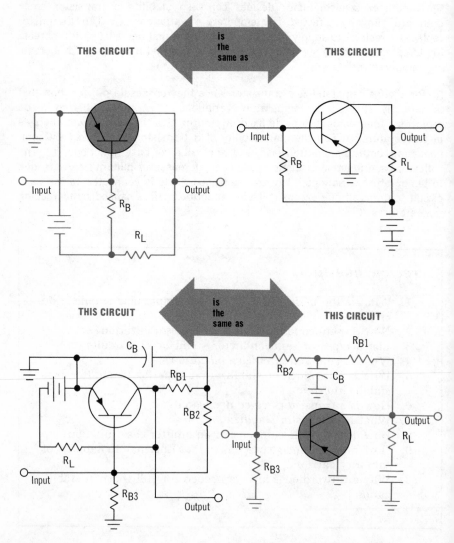

circuit configurations (cont.)

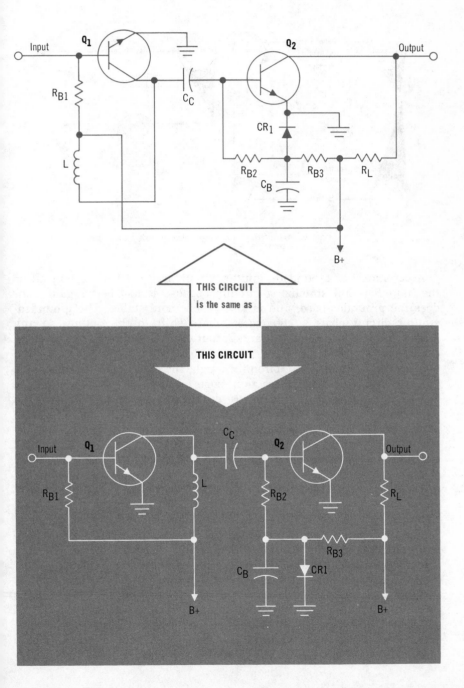

oscillation

Since the input and output signals of a grounded base circuit are in phase, that circuit is not as stable for amplifying, but is much more useful for oscillating

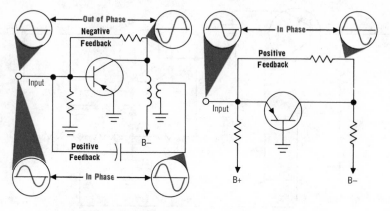

In the circuits, positive feedback means regenerative feedback, and negative feedback means degenerative feedback

A common-, or grounded-, emitter circuit was used to explain all of the amplifier and stabilizing circuits because it has better gain than does the grounded-base, and is also much more stable. The grounded-emitter circuit gives a 180-degree phase shift to the output, so any interaction between the input and output circuits will only cause degeneration.

With the grounded-base circuit, though, the input and output signals are in phase, so if any interaction exists, *regeneration* will take place. For example, if in a grounded-base circuit, the input signal raises the emitter current, this will increase the collector current. Then because of the bias polarity, collector voltage will go in a positive direction. If part of this positive swinging output voltage is fed back to the emitter circuit, it will raise the emitter current again, which in turn wll increase the collector current, and so on. The output then is said to reinforce or regenerate the input, and the current will run away with itself and cause the circuit to generate its own signals. This is known as *oscillation,* and is more completely taught in a later volume.

The tendency to oscillate prevents us from using the feedback stabilizing circuits with the grounded-base circuit that we can use with the grounded-emitter circuits. However, this is not a completely undesirable characteristic. This is why the grounded-base circuit is most popular with *oscillator* circuits. The grounded-emitter circuit can be made to oscillate, but the output signal, which is 180-degrees out of phase with the input signal, must first be inverted. This could be done with a transformer or another transistor; but with a common-base circuit, it can be done simply by adding a self-bias circuit.

classes of operation

You learned in Volume 3 that electron tubes have certain classes of operation that can be used to obtain certain characteristics. Transistors can be operated in the same ways to get the same results. The emitter voltage – collector current curve of a transistor shows how the transistor can be operated class A for linearity, class B for rectification, and class C for efficiency. The circuits that employ these specific applications are covered in later volumes. The classes of operation for a transistor do differ somewhat from those of a tube, though, for two reasons. One is the reverse-current characteristic, and the other is its forward-current saturation operation.

Class C operation cannot be too far from the cutoff point because then the size of the input signal that would be required to drive the circuit into conduction would also drive the emitter circuit into the zener breakdown region. The bias point and the amplitude of the input signal are therefore limited by the reverse-current characteristics of the input circuit.

Transistors have more useful saturation characteristics than tubes because they are less prone to damage from saturation current, and the impedance of the output circuit can drop to about a few hundred ohms through collector current saturation. This makes the transistor useful in pulse switching circuits.

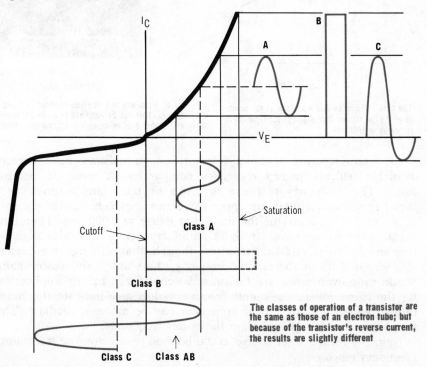

The classes of operation of a transistor are the same as those of an electron tube; but because of the transistor's reverse current, the results are slightly different

frequency response

One of the early major disadvantages of the transistor was its poor frequency response. The frequencies of the signal that the transistor can handle are determined by the transit time of the current carriers from the emitter through the collector. This is analogous to the transit time of the electrons from the cathode to the plate in the electron tube. The faster the current carriers move through the transistor, the higher the frequency they can handle. Since the velocity, or *mobility,* of the carriers depends, to a large extent, on the attractive forces of the bias voltages, better frequency responses can be obtained with higher voltages. In addition, since free electrons are easier to free and move than holes, n-p-n transistors have better frequency responses than comparable p-n-p transistors.

Another characteristic of the transistor that affects frequency response is the capacitance across each of the junctions, which tends to bypass higher frequency signals to ground. These *junction capacitances* are kept low to improve frequency response by making the base as thin as possible.

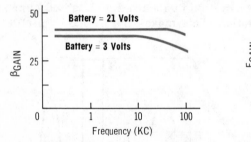

The cutoff frequency of a transistor is the point at which the current gain drops to 0.707 (3 db) of its value at 1000 cps

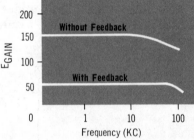

Cutoff frequency can be given in terms of alpha or beta. This can be improved in a circuit, though, with higher bias voltages and degenerative feedback

As manufacturing techniques improved, transistors have become available with frequency responses comparable to those of electron tubes. The frequency response is given by the manufacturers as a *cutoff frequency.* This is the upper frequency at which the current gain drops to 0.707 (3 db) of the gain that exists at 1000 cps. Therefore, a transistor would have an *alpha* cutoff frequency, and a *beta* cutoff frequency. You should keep in mind, though, that although the current gain drops 3 db at the cutoff frequency, the voltage and power gains would drop even more, so this must be considered in any application. By the same token, the cutoff frequency does *not* indicate the maximum frequency at which the transistor can be made to oscillate. This frequency is much greater than the cutoff frequency.

Negative feedback, of course, could be used to improve the transistor's frequency response.

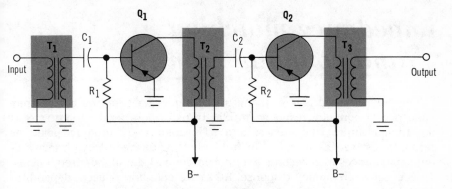

impedance matching and coupling

A transistor circuit has a low input impedance, up to around 1000 ohms, and a relatively high output impedance, about 20,000 ohms. These impedances must be considered when transistor circuits are used in *cascade,* since to get the maximum transfer of signal strengths, the output impedance of one stage should match the input impedance of the next. This *impedance match* is not always easy since the impedances are not close together. If the stages are connected directly, the input impedance of the second stage will shunt and lower the output impedance of the first stage and reduce its gain.

Probably the easiest way to match impedances is by use of transformers, with the primary winding acting as the high-output impedance of the first stage, and the secondary winding matching the low-input impedance of the first stage. Although this would require a step-down voltage action, it provides a step-up *current gain;* and since the transistor is current-sensitive, the overall gain is improved with *transformer coupling.*

You will probably notice that many transistor circuits use tapped transformers for loads. This is done so that the transformers can be designed for good coupling and gain purposes, and the taps can be provided for the best impedance matching.

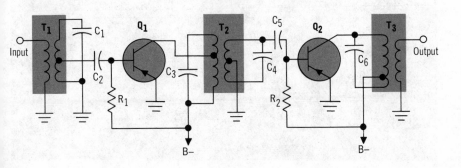

impedance matching and coupling (cont.)

The only disadvantage of using transformers for coupling is that they have poor frequency response. Audio transformers tend to saturate at the higher audio frequencies, and r-f transformers tend to peak, or resonate, as well as increase in inductance with frequency. Interwinding capacitances also become a shunt problem at the higher frequencies. To get a good frequency response, RC or LC coupling is used, depending on the frequencies involved.

RC COUPLING

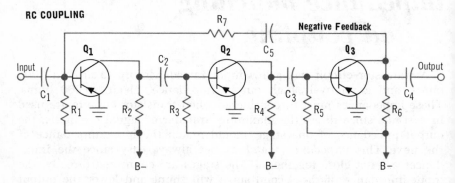

When *RC* or *LC* coupling is used, impedance matching must be compromised for frequency response. As a result, the gains of the stages are somewhat reduced. Because of this, the stages must be designed for greater gain in the first place to compensate for the loss, or an extra stage must be added to give the extra gain. With LC coupling, though, tapped coils can be used to obtain the proper impedances through *autotransformer* action. The coupling networks can be designed for better impedance matching also if negative feedback is used to broaden the frequency response. But this, too, lowers the gain, and might require an additional stage.

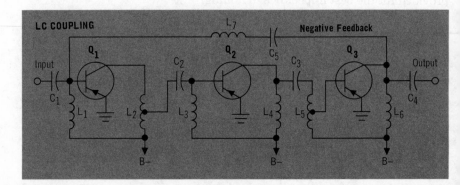

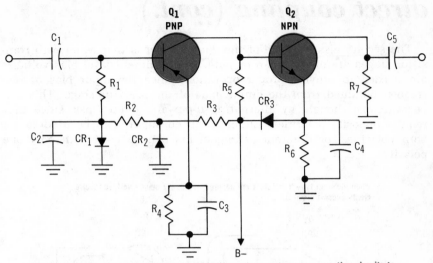

D-c amplifiers have considerable thermal instability and so must use compensating circuits to minimize gain drift

direct coupling

Direct coupling is often used for a good frequency response since it eliminates the inductive or capacitive reactances in the signal path, and so allows very little impedance change with frequency. Direct coupling has disadvantages, though. One is that the base circuits also amplify direct-current signals, and since the bias currents are dc, any changes in d-c bias current will be amplified. Thus, the d-c amplifier is very *temperature sensitive* and needs *stabilizing circuits* to minimize *gain drift*.

Two same-type transistors directly coupled need stepped-up bias voltages to get proper bias currents

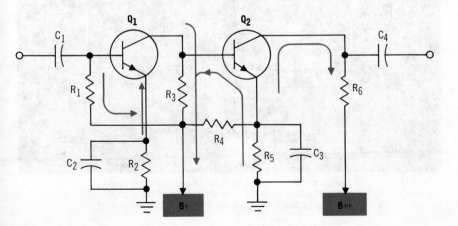

direct coupling (cont.)

The second disadvantage of the *d-c amplifier* is that when both transistor stages are of the n-p-n or p-n-p type, different level bias voltages are needed to provide proper operation, since the input bias of one stage is obtained from the output bias of the previous stage. This can be overcome though, by alternating n-p-n and p-n-p types, since they require opposite polarities. Either a tapped supply can be used to get both polarities, or different arrangements can be used with only one polarity.

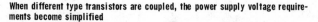
When different type transistors are coupled, the power supply voltage requirements become simplified

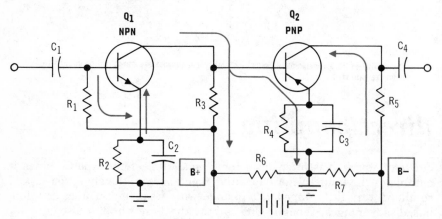

This circuit works the same as the above circuit. The collector of Q_2 is still negative with respect to the base and emitter

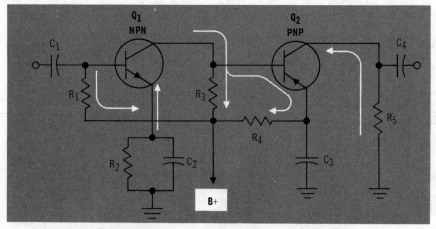

The resistance values are very important in the base and emitter circuit to provide the proper base-emitter forward bias. Part of the collector current of Q_1 actually flows through the emitter of Q_2

photodiodes and phototransistors

Semiconductors work the way they do because current carriers are produced when energy is applied to release electrons from their bonds. This energy is, in effect, producing current carriers. You know that energy can be applied in the form of heat or voltage. Any other form of energy can also be used to produce the same effect, such as *light* or *photon energy*. The *photodiodes* and *phototransistors* operate on this principle.

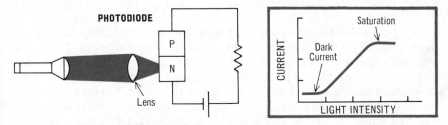

A simple photodiode is connected in a circuit with forward bias with a certain current flow. Then when light strikes one of its elements, the photon energy is given off to the atoms to release more current carriers. This reduces the resistance of the diode, and current flow goes up. When a transistor is made this way, and light energy is applied to the emitter or base, the current changes that result from the light can be amplified in much the same way as in a regular transistor circuit.

With photodiodes and phototransistors, the current that flows when no light is applied is called *dark current;* current will then increase when light is applied, and increase further when the intensity of the light goes up. When the point is reached where a further increase in light intensity does not increase the current further, the device is *saturated.* A lens is used with these devices to focus the light rays on a small area to increase sensitivity.

A special balanced input phototransistor is made with its emitter and collector having the same size and doping, so that it acts like two p-n diodes back to back. There is no amplification. It only *compares* light intensities.

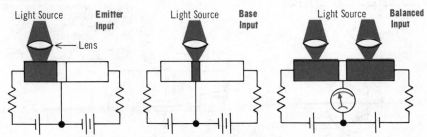

The phototransistor amplifies the effect of the light. The balanced-input phototransistor is specially constructed to compare the intensities of the two light sources

types of transistors

The transistor theory that you learned was based on the junction transistor because that is the most common type. There are other types, though, which will be described next. Some do not function internally in the exact same way as the junction transistor. They can all be considered, however, to have emitters, bases, and collectors, and their *interactions* are essentially similar. Therefore, the overall theory you have learned applies to all of them.

The *point-contact transistor* was the first type made. In this type, a large base material is used, and two "cat's whisker" wires are connected to the base close together. Then, emitter and collector areas are formed around the wire contacts, so that virtual junctions also exist. The point-contact transistor works similarly to the junction transistor, except that the point-contact transistor gives much greater current gain; even with a common-base circuit, you can get alpha to exceed 1. This is probably because extra carriers are formed in the large base for any additional carriers supplied by the emitter. The point-contact transistor is available only for experimental use because it is difficult to manufacture, cannot carry large currents, and is unstable.

The *tetrode transistor* is the same as the junction transistor, except that it provides an extra lead for applying a potential *across the base*. This potential sets up an electrostatic field that attracts and repels the normal current carriers, so that they are concentrated in a smaller area. This has the effect of increasing response time, lowering base resistance, and decreasing junction capacitance, all of which increase frequency response. Since the tetrode potential affects base resistance, it can be varied to control gain, or it can be used as a modulating signal input for heterodyning.

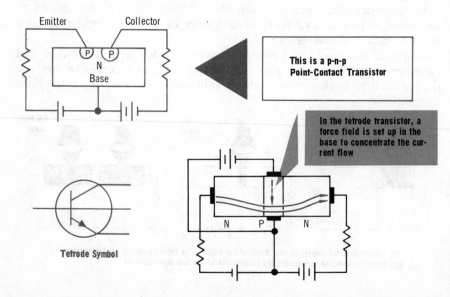

Emitter   Collector

N
Base

This is a p-n-p
Point-Contact Transistor

In the tetrode transistor, a force field is set up in the base to concentrate the current flow

N   P   N

Tetrode Symbol

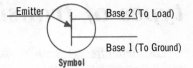

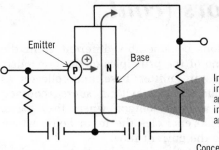

In the unijunction transistor, a forward-biased emitter injects carriers into the base to change its resistance and control base current flow. In this case, holes are injected in the base to allow the recombinations which are necessary for electron current to flow

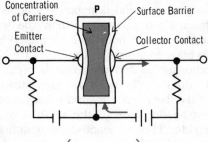

In the surface barrier transistor, there are no junctions. The emitter potential controls the width of the surface barrier to determine the collector current flow

types of transistors (cont.)

The *unijunction transistor* is more of a *controlled-diode* type of device, although it can amplify. It contains a base slab, and an emitter at its center. There is no collector, and so there is only one junction. A voltage is applied *across* the base, so that at the center, where the emitter is, this voltage is divided in half. The voltage applied to the emitter, then, will determine whether that junction is forward or reverse biased. If a 12-volt battery is applied across the base, and 6 volts is applied to the emitter, then no bias voltage will appear across the junction since the base is also 6 volts at that point. The current flow through the base will be low and only depend on the base battery. But, if the emitter voltage is made +7.5 volts, the junction will be forward biased with 1.5 volts; the emitter will then inject majority carriers into the base to reduce its resistance and increase its conduction. This device is usually used in this way with the emitter input used to gate or trigger conduction through the base. When the opposite ends of the base are connected, the unijunction transistor acts like a simple p-n diode.

The *surface barrier transistor* also uses a large base material, but no real emitter and collector junctions. Instead only contacts are used across a wafer thin section of the base. Its operation depends on a depletion region that develops around the surface of the semiconductor material, as was explained on page 4-30. The current carriers in the base accumulate in a region beneath the surface. A near empty region around the surface acts as a barrier to collector current flow. The varying potential at the emitter has the effect of widening or narrowing the barrier area, through electrostatic attraction and repulsion, to change the resistance to current flow in the collector circuit.

types of transistors (cont.)

The *field-effect transistor* functions considerably different from the ordinary transistor, and utilizes some of the principles of the previously described transistors. It does not use an emitter, base, and collector as such, but instead has a semiconductor block with a *source* contact, where majority carriers enter, and a *drain* contact, where they leave. In addition, a semiconductor material encircles the main body, which is called the *gate* because it controls the current flow.

The gate material is oppositely doped from the main body to form a continuous p-n junction. When the gate is not biased, current flows through the main body as determined by the battery voltage. When the gate is biased with respect to the main body, the current flow is restricted in proportion to this bias. This is because an electrostatic field is set up within the main body by the gate because of the difference of potentials that exist between the main body and gate. This force field is very narrow on one side of the main body, but becomes thick toward the other side. This is because, although the potential across the gate is constant, the voltage *gradient* through the main body increases with respect to the gate toward the drain potential. The gate is reverse biased with respect to the main body, and so injects *minority carriers* into it along its surface in proportion to the rising voltage gradient.

In the example shown, since a p-type gate is used with an n-type main body, free electrons are injected. Some of these free electrons take part in electron flow to the drain, but most accumulate in the force field to build up a space charge that inhibits free electron flow through the n-type main body. If a signal is injected to lower or raise the gate bias, fewer or more minority carriers will be injected into the main body to change the space charge, and hence the size of the force field. The current through the main body then will vary in accordance with the input signal. These transistors are referred to as *FET's*.

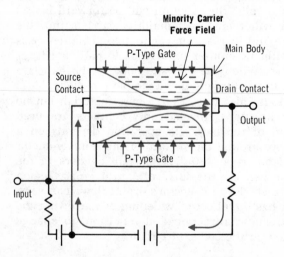

Although this representation of the field-effect transistor shows two leads to the gate, only one is needed since the gate forms a continuous ring around the main semiconductor body

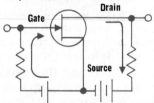

So, the schematic diagram can be similar to that of a junction transistor, except, of course, the gate is reverse-biased and the symbol is different

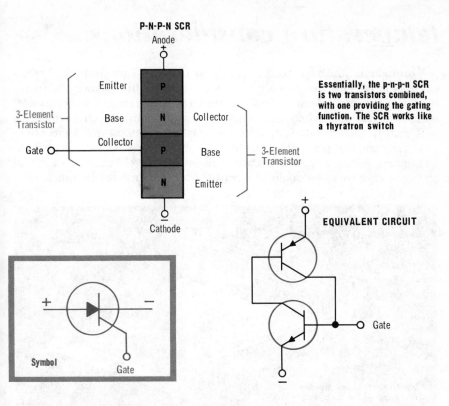

P-N-P-N SCR

Anode

Emitter | P
Base | N | Collector
Collector | P | Base
| N | Emitter

3-Element Transistor

Gate

Cathode

3-Element Transistor

Essentially, the p-n-p-n SCR is two transistors combined, with one providing the gating function. The SCR works like a thyratron switch

EQUIVALENT CIRCUIT

Gate

Symbol

Gate

SCR transistors

Earlier, in the section covering diodes, you were introduced to the fact that special controlled rectifiers are also being used. These are often referred to as *SCR's*, an abbreviation for *silicon controlled rectifiers*. Most of these units use four elements (pnpn) that act similar to two transistors in series. When one of the transistor base elements has no voltage applied, that transistor section is cut off. And when that section does not conduct, the other will not because the two sections are in series. But when a forward-bias *gating pulse* is applied to the base of the first transistor, it is taken out of cutoff, and the entire p-n-p-n unit conducts heavily. After heavy conduction starts, *avalanche breakdown* occurs, and the gating pulse no longer has effect. Either *cathode* or *anode* bias must be changed to shut the unit off. In this way, the p-n-p-n SCR's act like *thyratron* tubes.

The *thyristor* is a special three-element SCR that also provides high breakdown currents when a heavy gating pulse is applied to the base. This transistor uses an extra collector section that is heavily doped to provide breakdown current. When small bias voltages are used, the thyristor will work like a regular transistor; but with high voltage, it works like a thyratron tube.

temperature considerations

Throughout you have been taught that the transistor and other semi-conductor devices are *temperature sensitive*. Within certain temperature ranges, the effect of heat on the current carriers is *reversible*, which means that when the transistor cools again, its characteristics will return to normal. But, above a certain temperature, *irreversible changes* can take place that would make the transistor useless because its characteristics would not return to normal. To avoid these irreversible changes, care must be taken to limit how hot a transistor becomes.

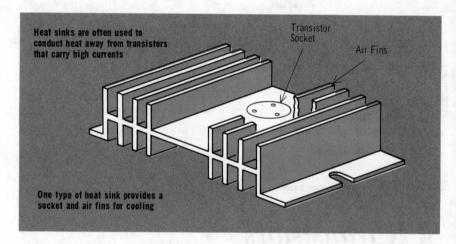

Heat sinks are often used to conduct heat away from transistors that carry high currents

Transistor Socket

Air Fins

One type of heat sink provides a socket and air fins for cooling

A special cooler-running soldering iron must be used to solder and unsolder transistor leads; and a metal tool, such as a long-nose pliers, must be held on the lead being soldered to conduct the heat away. Transistors should not be mounted near heat-producing parts, and where heat presents a problem, a *heat sink* should be used. Heat sinks are metal parts that a transistor can be mounted on or within, so that the heat will be conducted by the sink. Generally, heat sinks are *lamp black* so that they will radiate their heat to the air.

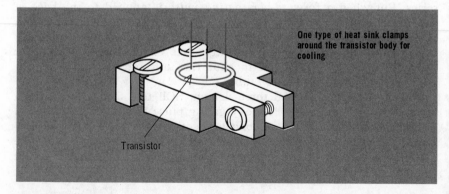

One type of heat sink clamps around the transistor body for cooling

Transistor

summary

☐ Transistor circuits oscillate by feeding back a portion of the output in phase with the input. ☐ Common-base transistor circuits oscillate readily, since the input and output signals are ordinarily in phase. ☐ For common-emitter transistor circuits to oscillate, they must be fed with a phase-reversed signal from a transistor, since there is a 180-degree phase shift between the input and output circuits. ☐ The classes of operation, A, B, and C, differ from transistors to tubes due to differences in operating characteristics. ☐ Transistor cutoff frequencies are comparable to tubes, and are given in terms of α cutoff for common-base circuits, and β cutoff for common-emitter and common-collector circuits.

☐ Maximum transfer of a signal requires matching the high output impedance of one stage to the low impedance of the next stage. ☐ Transformer coupling provides impedance matching, but has poor frequency response. ☐ RC and LC coupling improves the frequency response, but results in a loss of gain. ☐ Direct coupling provides excellent frequency response, but is extremely sensitive to bias and temperature changes.

☐ Photodiodes and phototransistors convert light variations to resistance changes. ☐ Point-contact transistors work similarly to junction transistors. ☐ Tetrode transistors work similarly to junction transistors but provide improved frequency response due to a concentration of current flow in the base caused by an applied electrostatic field. ☐ The unijunction transistor is a single-junction controlled diode that uses resistance changes in its base section. ☐ The surface barrier transistor amplifies a signal by changing the width of a surface barrier to control the collector current. ☐ The field-effect transistor uses an electrostatic field and injected minority carriers to control the output current flow. ☐ The silicon controlled rectifier is a four-element p-n-p-n device that acts like a thyratron tube.

review questions

1. Why do common-base circuits readily oscillate?
2. What is the difference between α and β cutoff frequencies?
3. Why is impedance matching important?
4. Why is direct coupling of transistor stages used?
5. What is the *tetrode transistor*?
6. How does a unijunction transistor work?
7. How does the surface barrier transistor work?
8. How does a field effect transistor operate?
9. How is avalanche breakdown used in an SCR?
10. Draw the symbols for the transistors of Questions 5 through 9.

electronics
five

power supplies

The electron tubes and transistors used in electronic equipment require definite operating voltages for proper operation. A power supply is normally used to furnish these voltages at the necessary current ratings. Except for the filament voltage of tubes, operating voltages must be nearly *pure dc*. Some equipment contains batteries to supply these d-c voltages. In most equipment, though, some form of *electronic power supply* is used. These power supplies convert a-c input power, usually from a commercial source, into one or more d-c voltages. In equipment that uses electron tubes, the power supply also furnishes the low-voltage, relatively high-current a-c power required by the tube filaments.

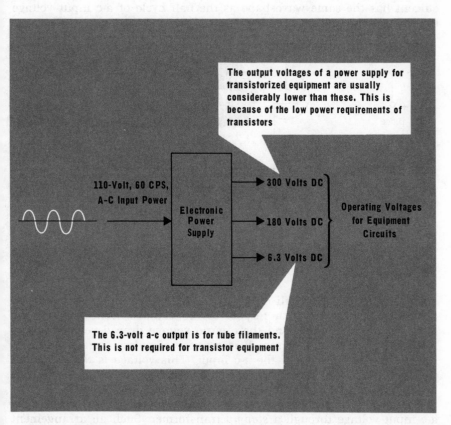

The output voltages of a power supply for transistorized equipment are usually considerably lower than these. This is because of the low power requirements of transistors

110-Volt, 60 CPS, A-C Input Power

Electronic Power Supply

300 Volts DC
180 Volts DC
6.3 Volts DC

Operating Voltages for Equipment Circuits

The 6.3-volt a-c output is for tube filaments. This is not required for transistor equipment

To accomplish its function, a power supply: (1) *rectifies* the sinusoidal a-c power input; and (2) smooths, or *filters*, the resulting fluctuating dc. In addition, many power supplies contain a transformer to step up the a-c input voltage before rectification and filtering take place, and also contain regulator circuits to keep the d-c voltages from fluctuating.

the basic half-wave rectifier

Rectification, you recall, is the removal of *one-half* of a sinusoidal or other symmetrical wave. One of the most widely used devices for accomplishing rectification is the electron-tube or semiconductor diode. This is because of the diode's *unidirectional* conduction characteristics. The diode only conducts in one direction. When a sinusoidal voltage is applied between the plate and cathode, this condition exists only during alternate half cycles.

A basic diode rectifier circuit is shown. In the electron tube, the positive half cycles of the a-c input voltage cause the plate of the diode to be positive with respect to the cathode. As a result, the tube conducts and current flows through resistor R. The voltage drop produced by this current has the same waveshape as the half cycle of a-c input voltage that causes the diode to conduct.

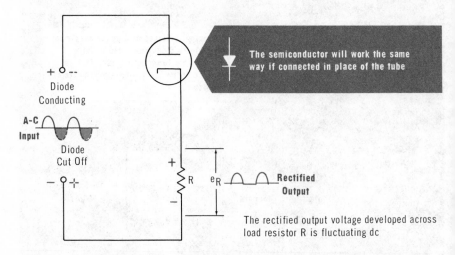

The semiconductor will work the same way if connected in place of the tube

The rectified output voltage developed across load resistor R is fluctuating dc

During the negative half cycles of the a-c input voltage, the plate of the diode is negative with respect to the cathode. Consequently, the diode does not conduct, and there is no voltage drop developed across resistor R. The voltage across R is a series of pulses corresponding to the positive half cycles of the a-c input. This voltage is the output of the rectifier. Such a rectifier is called a *half-wave rectifier*, since it delivers an output during only half of the input voltage cycle.

The output voltage from a rectifier can be increased by applying the a-c input voltage through a *step-up* transformer. Such an arrangement is shown in A on the next page. Although the available a-c source voltage is 115 volts, a transformer with a step-up turns ratio increases the voltage to 450 volts. In this case, this is done before the voltage is applied between the plate and cathode of the diode. Such a transformer is called a power transformer, since it normally handles a considerable amount of electrical power.

other half-wave rectifiers

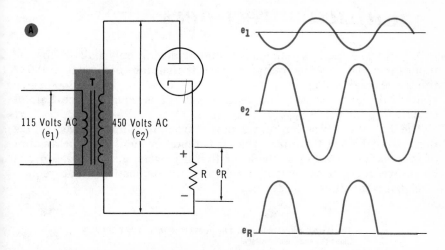

A half-wave rectifier circuit using a semiconductor rectifier is shown in B. This circuit is the same as the tube circuit shown in A, except that the tube diode has been replaced by a semiconductor diode. The semiconductor diode has a low forward resistance, and, therefore, conducts heavily when the applied voltage has the polarity shown. When the voltage polarity reverses, the diode conducts very little. This reverse current is so small that for practical purposes it can be neglected.

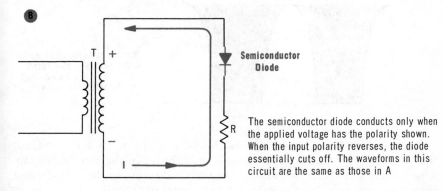

The semiconductor diode conducts only when the applied voltage has the polarity shown. When the input polarity reverses, the diode essentially cuts off. The waveforms in this circuit are the same as those in A

In other words, the diode will conduct electron current in the *forward* direction, which is opposite to the direction in which the arrow portion of the diode symbol points. The diode will not conduct in the direction of the arrow, which is called the *reverse* direction. The arrow portion of the diode symbol thus corresponds to the plate of the vacuum-tube diode, and is sometimes called the *anode*. The arrow is said to point in the direction of *high* resistance.

characteristics of half-wave rectifiers

A half-wave rectifier delivers an output during only half of the a-c input cycle. The average output voltage is therefore not equal to 0.637 times the peak voltage (e_{PEAK}), as is the case for a full 360-degree sinusoidal wave. Instead, the average voltage is equal to one-half of 0.637 e_{PEAK}, or 0.318 e_{PEAK}.

The half-wave rectifier draws power from the input power source during only half of the input cycle. It is therefore limited in the amount of *current* it can supply to the loads that it powers. For this reason, the half-wave rectifier is usually used only in applications that require a relatively small current drain.

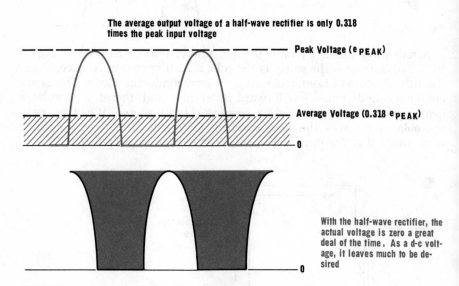

The average output voltage of a half-wave rectifier is only 0.318 times the peak input voltage

Peak Voltage (e_{PEAK})

Average Voltage (0.318 e_{PEAK})

0

With the half-wave rectifier, the actual voltage is zero a great deal of the time. As a d-c voltage, it leaves much to be desired

0

Another disadvantage of the half-wave rectifier is that the current flow in the power transformer secondary is always in the same direction. This causes a considerable amount of *core saturation* in the transformer iron core and reduces the efficiency of the transformer.

Probably the biggest disadvantage of the half-wave rectifier is that its output is far from a *perfect* d-c voltage. This is because the individual output pulses are relatively widely spaced with periods of no output voltage between them. Where a steady d-c output is required, therefore, the half-wave rectifier is unsuitable.

Of course, the polarity of the output voltage can be changed by reversing the diode connection, so that the other half of the sine wave will be rectified.

the full-wave rectifier

The disadvantages of the half-wave rectifier can be overcome by using what is called a *full-wave rectifier*. In this type of rectifier, *two* diodes are connected so that each conducts during alternate half cycles of the a-c input. The two diodes have a *common load* and the current flow through this load is always in the same direction.

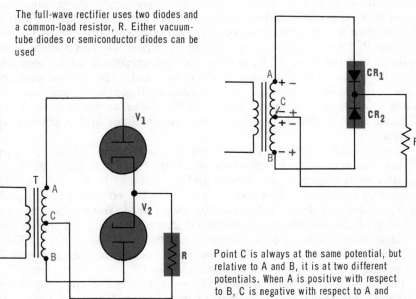

The full-wave rectifier uses two diodes and a common-load resistor, R. Either vacuum-tube diodes or semiconductor diodes can be used

Point C is always at the same potential, but relative to A and B, it is at two different potentials. When A is positive with respect to B, C is negative with respect to A and positive with respect to B. The opposite is true when A is negative with respect to B

A basic full-wave rectifier circuit is shown. The circuit uses two diodes, with the anodes of the diodes connected to opposite ends of the transformer secondary. The common-cathode resistor, R, is connected between the two cathodes and a centertap on the secondary winding of the transformer. When an a-c input is applied to the transformer primary, it appears as a stepped-up voltage across the entire transformer secondary (points A and B). Since point C is the *electrical center* of the secondary, half of the induced voltage exists between points A and C, and half between B and C. These two voltages, however, are always 180 degrees out of phase, since they are measured with respect to the common reference point, C. The voltage between A and C is applied between the plate and cathode of diode V_1, and the voltage between B and C is applied to V_2.

Special full-wave rectifier tubes are made that have two diodes in one envelope. They can have either common or separate cathodes. Full-wave semiconductor diodes are also made as integral units.

operation of
the full-wave rectifier

The two 180-degree, out-of-phase voltages developed across the center-tapped transformer secondary cause the two diodes of the full-wave rectifier to conduct on alternate half cycles of the a-c input. This is shown on the following page. During each negative half cycle of the a-c input, as shown in A, the end of the secondary winding connected to diode V_1 is positive and the end connected to V_2 is negative. Point C is therefore negative with respect to point A and positive with respect to point B. This means that the plate of V_1 is positive with respect to its cathode and the plate of V_2 is negative with respect to its cathode. As a result, diode V_1 conducts and diode V_2 is cut off. The current path for V_1 is from point C, through load resistor R, through V_1, and back to point A of the transformer. The voltage developed across resistor R has a waveshape similar to the half cycle of a-c input and a polarity as shown.

During each positive half cycle of the input, the voltage polarity across the transformer secondary *reverses*. Now, the plate of V_2 is positive with respect to its cathode and the plate of V_1 is negative with respect to its cathode. V_2 conducts and V_1 is cut off. The current path as V_2 conducts is shown in B on the following page. You can see that the polarity of the output pulse developed across the load resistor is the same as that produced by a negative half cycle of the a-c input. Each half cycle of the a-c input therefore produces output pulses across R all having the *same polarity*. This is shown in C.

The full-wave rectifier thus produces a rectified output for every half cycle of the a-c input, instead of only for alternate half cycles, as done by the half-wave rectifier. The average value of the output voltage is the same as that of a sine-wave voltage, or 0.637 times the peak voltage, and the rms value is 0.707 peak.

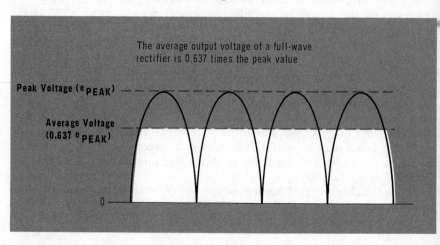

The average output voltage of a full-wave rectifier is 0.637 times the peak value

Peak Voltage (e_{PEAK})

Average Voltage
(0.637 e_{PEAK})

0

operation of the full-wave rectifier (cont.)

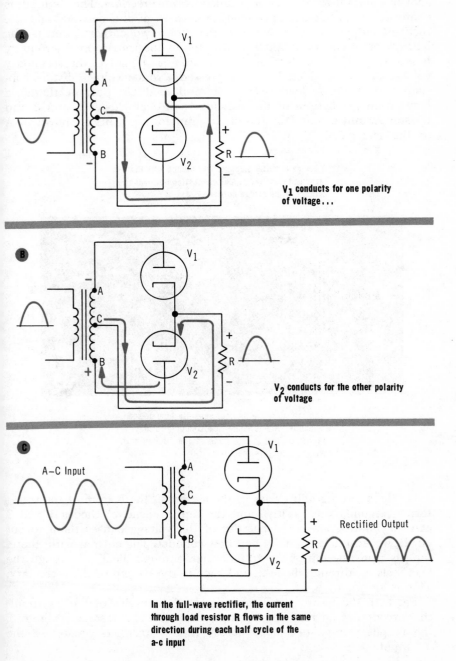

V₁ conducts for one polarity of voltage...

V₂ conducts for the other polarity of voltage

A–C Input

Rectified Output

In the full-wave rectifier, the current through load resistor R flows in the same direction during each half cycle of the a-c input

the bridge rectifier

A special type of full-wave rectifier in which *four* diodes are used is shown. This full-wave rectifier is called a *bridge rectifier*. The a-c input is connected to two diagonally-opposite corners of the network and the rectified output is taken between the other two corners. During the half cycles of the a-c input when the top of the transformer secondary is positive and the bottom of the secondary is negative, the secondary voltage can be considered to be impressed across a voltage divider consisting of diode 1, load resistor R, and diode 3. Current therefore flows from the bottom of the secondary, through diodes 1 and 3 and resistor R, and back to the top of the transformer. This is shown in A on the next page.

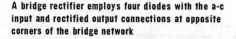

A bridge rectifier employs four diodes with the a-c input and rectified output connections at opposite corners of the bridge network

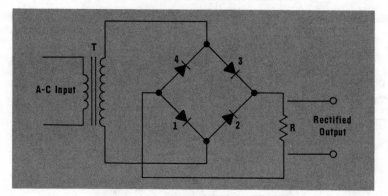

The rectifiers can be four separate tube or semiconductor diodes; some semiconductor bridge rectifiers, though, are made as one integral unit, with four rectifier sections

On the alternate half cycles of the a-c input, the bottom of the transformer secondary is positive and the top is negative. Diodes 1 and 3 cannot conduct, since the polarity of the voltage causes them to cut off. However, diodes 2 and 4 can now conduct. The current path, therefore, is from the top of the transformer, through diode 4, through the load resistor, through diode 2, and back to the bottom of the secondary. This is shown in B.

For both the positive and the negative half cycles of the a-c input, the direction of current flow through resistor R is the same. Therefore, the output voltage developed across R is a rectified version of the a-c input.

the bridge rectifier (cont.)

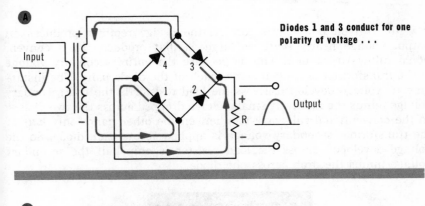

A

Input

Diodes 1 and 3 conduct for one
polarity of voltage . . .

Output

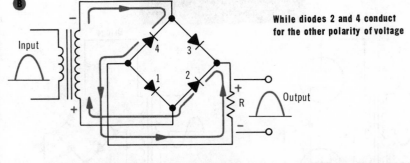

B

Input

While diodes 2 and 4 conduct
for the other polarity of voltage

Output

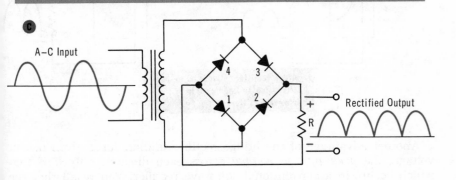

C

A–C Input

Rectified Output

In the bridge rectifier, two of the four diodes conduct during the positive
half cycles of the a-c input and the other two conduct during the negative
half cycles. During both half cycles, the current flow through load resistor
R is in the same direction

characteristics of the bridge rectifier

With a given power transformer, the bridge rectifier produces an output voltage nearly *twice* as large as that produced by a conventional full-wave rectifier. This is because the *entire* secondary voltage of the transformer is applied across each of the diode pairs. The instantaneous voltage developed across the load resistor is the full secondary voltage minus the relatively small voltage dropped across the two diodes. In the conventional full-wave rectifier, on the other hand, only *half* of the transformer secondary voltage is applied across each diode. So the voltage developed across the load resistor is only half the secondary voltage minus the drop across one diode.

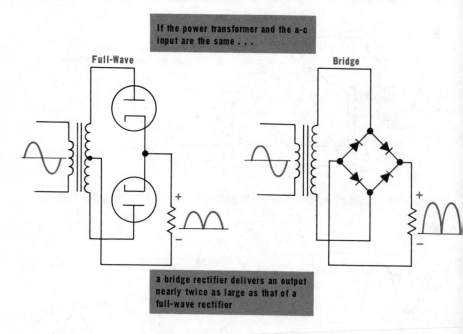

If the power transformer and the a-c input are the same . . .

Full-Wave

Bridge

a bridge rectifier delivers an output nearly twice as large as that of a full-wave rectifier

Another advantage of the bridge rectifier is that, for a given output voltage, the *peak inverse voltage* across each diode is only *half* that which occurs in a conventional full-wave rectifier. You recall that the peak inverse voltage is the maximum voltage across a diode when its plate is negative with respect to its cathode. If this voltage exceeds the diode's rated value, breakdown occurs within the diode.

A disadvantage of the bridge rectifier is that a single-filament transformer cannot supply filament voltage for all four tubes when electron-tube diodes are used. Because of this necessity for multiple-filament transformers, tubes are not used frequently in bridge rectifier circuits.

output polarities

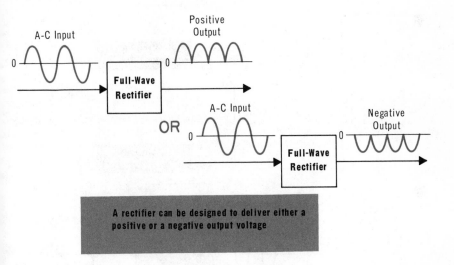

A-C Input

Positive Output

Full-Wave Rectifier

OR

A-C Input

Full-Wave Rectifier

Negative Output

A rectifier can be designed to deliver either a positive or a negative output voltage

The output of a rectifier is developed across a resistive load, represented in the previous examples by load resistor R. The amplitude of the output voltage depends on the current flowing through the load resistance. The polarity, since it is a rectified voltage, is always the same. However, although the polarity is always the same, it can be either a positive or a negative voltage, depending on the desired output characteristics.

It should be understood here that this choice of output polarity is with respect to *ground*. The basic characteristics of a rectifier are such that it has a *negative side*, which in a full-wave rectifier is the transformer secondary centertap, and a *positive side*, which is the cathode side of the load resistance. This is shown in A on the following page. Either one of these sides can be connected to ground to provide a common reference potential.

If the *negative side* of the rectifier is grounded, the rectifier output is a *positive voltage*. This is shown in B on the following page. The voltage at the top of the load resistance increases and decreases, but is always at or above ground potential. If the cathode, or *positive*, side of the load is grounded, the output voltage is *negative*, as shown in C. This is because the positive side of the load remains at constant ground potential, so the varying voltage produced across the load is reflected as a changing potential at the negative side of the load. This changing negative potential with respect to ground is a negative voltage.

As shown in D, if the load resistance is split and the center point grounded, both a positive and a negative output can be obtained. Of course, the polarities can also be changed by reversing all of the diode connections.

output polarities (cont.)

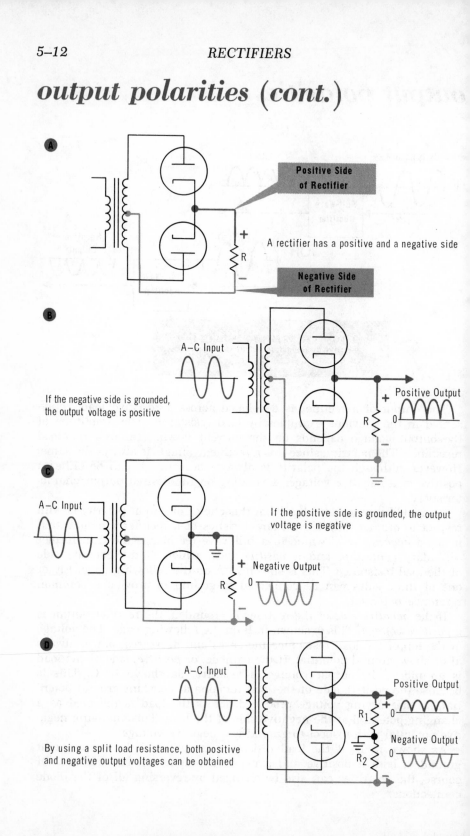

A

Positive Side of Rectifier

A rectifier has a positive and a negative side

Negative Side of Rectifier

B

A–C Input

If the negative side is grounded, the output voltage is positive

Positive Output

C

A–C Input

If the positive side is grounded, the output voltage is negative

Negative Output

D

A–C Input

Positive Output

Negative Output

By using a split load resistance, both positive and negative output voltages can be obtained

summary

☐ An electronic power supply converts a-c input power into one or more d-c voltages. It does this by first rectifying the sinusoidal ac, and then smoothing, or filtering, the resulting fluctuating dc. ☐ A half-wave rectifier delivers an output during only half of the input voltage cycle. ☐ A simple half-wave rectifier consists of a tube or semiconductor diode and a load resistor. The diode conducts only when its plate, or anode, is positive with respect to its cathode. ☐ Half-wave rectifiers are limited in the amount of output current that they can deliver. In addition, their output voltage fluctuates widely, requiring a considerable degree of filtering if a smooth dc is required.

☐ The full-wave rectifier delivers an output during both halves of the input voltage cycle. ☐ A basic full-wave rectifier consists of two diodes having a common load. The diodes conduct during alternate half cycles of the input and both produce current through the load in the same direction. ☐ Since a full-wave rectifier produces an output pulse for every half cycle of the input, its output generally requires much less filtering than a half-wave rectifier.

☐ A bridge rectifier is a special type of full-wave rectifier. It consists of four diodes and a common load. ☐ The output voltage produced by a bridge rectifier is nearly twice as large as that produced by a comparable conventional full-wave rectifier. ☐ The peak inverse voltage across each diode of a bridge rectifier is only half that which occurs across each diode of a conventional full-wave rectifier. ☐ In a rectifier circuit, the input a-c voltage is often increased by being applied through a step-up power transformer. ☐ The output of a rectifier circuit can be either a positive or a negative voltage, depending on which side of the rectifier is grounded.

review questions

1. Describe the operation of a vacuum-tube half-wave rectifier.
2. Draw a diagram of a full-wave semiconductor rectifier.
3. How would you change to output polarity?
4. What is meant by the peak inverse voltage of a rectifier?
5. Draw a diagram of a bridge rectifier.
6. Why are transformers used in power supplies?
7. What is the rms value of a full-wave rectified waveform?
8. What is the rms value of a half-wave rectified waveform?
9. State one advantage that a half-wave rectifier has over the bridge rectifier.
10. If the peak voltage across a transformer secondary is 100 volts, what is the peak value of a half-wave rectified voltage? Full-wave? Bridge?

filter circuits

You have seen on the previous pages how various types of rectifiers convert an a-c input into a fluctuating d-c output. The fluctuation of the d-c output above and below its average value is called *ripple*. In a *half-wave* rectifier, the frequency of the ripple is the *same* as the frequency of the a-c input, because it produces one pulse per cycle. In a *full-wave* rectifier, the ripple frequency is *twice* that of the a-c input, because two pulses per cycle are produced. Thus, if the input is from a 60-cps source, a half-wave rectifier has a ripple frequency of 60 cps, and a full-wave rectifier has a ripple frequency of 120 cps.

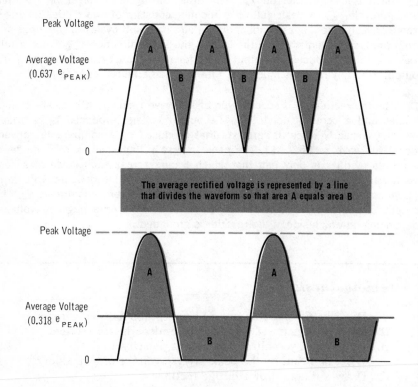

The average rectified voltage is represented by a line that divides the waveform so that area A equals area B

Most electronic equipment requires smooth d-c operating voltages. The output of a rectifier cannot be applied directly to such equipment because of the ripple. Consequently, the ripple must be eliminated. Circuits for accomplishing this are called *filter circuits*.

Essentially, a filter circuit compresses the peaks of the individual, fluctuating d-c pulses and fills in the valleys between pulses. The net result is an essentially smooth d-c voltage. The more elaborate the filter circuit, the more closely the output resembles the perfect dc of a battery.

the capacitance filter

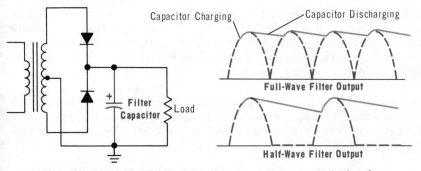

The discharge of the filter capacitor is greater between output pulses from
a half-wave rectifier than it is from a full-wave rectifier. This means that
the half-wave rectifier has poorer filtering regulation, since the filtered
output voltage decreases between rectified pulses

The ripple output of a rectifier represents energy being supplied to
the load in pulses. The ripple fluctuations can be reduced considerably
if some of the output is *stored* while the rectifier is delivering a pulse
and then *released* to the load between output pulses. This is the basic
operating principle of the simple capacitance filter.

As shown, such a filter consists of a capacitor connected across the
rectifier output. The capacitor charges rapidly, usually within a few
cycles, to the *peak* rectifier voltage. When the rectifier output drops to
zero between output pulses, the capacitor voltage supplies the load.
The capacitor voltage also begins to fall off, since the capacitor starts
to discharge through the load.

However, the rate of discharge is long compared to the time between
rectifier output pulses. So, instead of falling off to zero between output
pulses, the voltage applied to the load is maintained, although at a
gradually diminishing level. Before the capacitor voltage drops too low,
another output pulse is delivered by the rectifier. This recharges the
capacitor to the peak voltage, so the capacitor is again ready to supply
the load voltage when the rectifier output drops.

The rate at which the capacitor discharges, and, therefore, the average
level at which the output voltage is maintained, depends on the RC
time constant of the capacitor and the load resistance. For low values
of load resistance, the discharge is fairly rapid, so the output voltage
falls rather quickly between rectifier pulses. Such a condition, known
as poor *regulation,* is highly undesirable. For this reason, the simple
capacitor filter is not used with rectifiers that must supply a large load
current, or, in other words, rectifiers that have low load resistances.

Mostly, *electrolytic* capacitors are used in filter circuits. These are
special capacitors that are polarized. Usually, the positive side of the
capacitor is marked so that it can be connected properly. If it is hooked
up backwards, it will be destroyed, and might burst.

the inductance filter

An *inductor* is another device that can alternately store and release electrical energy. It does this by extracting energy from a flowing current and storing it in a magnetic field when the current is increasing. Then it releases the energy to keep the current flowing when the current begins to decrease. This ability of an inductor to store and release energy can be used to help prevent the abrupt changes in the output of a rectifier. To do this, the inductor is inserted in the rectifier circuit in *series* with the load, as shown. The inductor tends to prevent the output current from building up or dying down. Its effect on the output waveform is as shown.

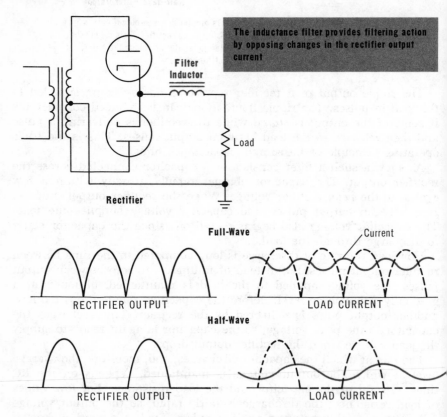

The inductance filter provides filtering action by opposing changes in the rectifier output current

The inductance filter prevents the current, and, therefore, the output voltage, from ever reaching the peak value that would be obtained if the inductor were not in the circuit. Therefore, a rectifier that has an inductance filter will not produce as high an output voltage as one that has a capacitance filter. However, a larger load current can be drawn from the inductance filter without seriously changing the output voltage.

the capacitor-input filter

Neither the simple capacitance or inductance filter is capable of removing ripple voltage to a high degree. Consequently, when effective filtering is required, capacitance and inductance filtering are used together. One such *LC* filter is shown below. This is called the capacitor-input filter, because a capacitor (C_1) is the *first* filtering element directly after the rectifier.

The capacitor-input filter is probably the most widely used type of filter in applications involving low-current devices, such as radio receivers. It is also called the "pi" filter because of its schematic resemblance to the Greek letter π

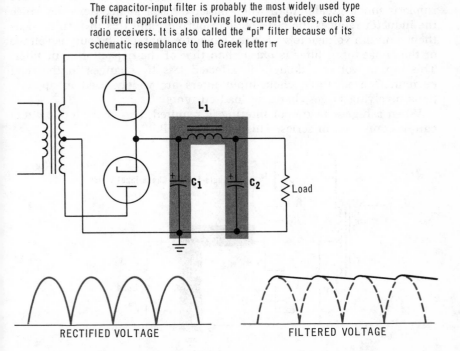

RECTIFIED VOLTAGE   FILTERED VOLTAGE

In the capacitor-input filter, capacitor C_1 performs the same function as the simple capacitor filter previously described. It charges on the peaks of the rectified output pulses and then discharges, supplying energy to the load, when the rectifier output falls. Capacitor C_2 provides similar filtering action, although to a lesser degree. Inductor L_1 adds to the overall filtering action by opposing changes in both the output current filtered by C_2 and the current drawn by the load. The actions of L_1 and of C_2 are closely interrelated, and their values are chosen in conjunction with one another.

The output of a well-designed capacitor-input filter contains only a small amount of ripple, which for most practical applications can be ignored. However, the voltage regulation of such a filter is relatively poor. This is because of the decrease in the voltage across C_1 as it discharges between rectified pulses, as well as the d-c voltage drop produced by the load current flowing through L_1.

the choke-input filter

When an inductor is used as the primary filtering element in an LC filter, the network is called a choke-input filter. The term *choke* is used because of the inductor's ability to stop, or choke, the passage of ripple voltage to the load.

A simple choke-input filter is shown in A. The inductor opposes current changes, while the capacitor charges and discharges in standard filter-capacitor fashion. The combined effect of the two in reducing ripple is much greater than when either is used alone. However, since the inductor reduces the peak rectifier current, and this in turn reduces the maximum voltage to which the capacitor charges, the output voltage of the choke-input filter is *lower* than that of the capacitor-input filter. This output voltage, though, is affected less by changes in the load current. Consequently, choke-input filters are widely used in applications involving large, changing load currents.

When a higher degree of filtering is required, two choke-input filters can be connected in series. This is shown in B.

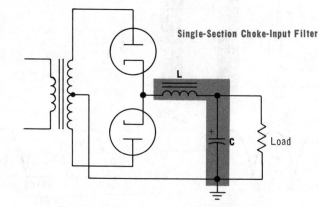

Single-Section Choke-Input Filter

The output voltage from a choke-input is approximately the average value of the a-c voltage applied to the rectifier

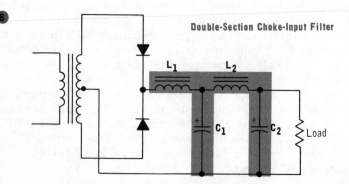

Double-Section Choke-Input Filter

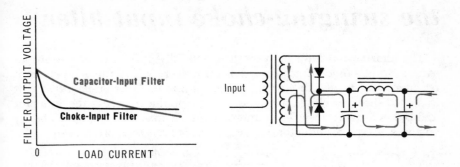

The output voltage from a choke-input filter is considerably more constant over a range of load current than is the output from a capacitor-input filter, because the charge on the capacitor is reduced as the load draws current

capacitor vs. choke-input filter

In a choke-input filter, current is supplied to the load through rectifier conduction directly. But with a capacitor-input filter, the current is supplied to the load primarily by the capacitor. The rectifier conducts to charge the capacitor. If the load did not draw current, and there was no bleeder resistor, the rectifier would not conduct because the voltage on the capacitor would put the cathode of the rectifier at the same potential as the anode. However, the load does draw current, which the capacitor discharges to supply, and the rectifier conducts to recharge the capacitor. Normally, the rectifier conducts only brief bursts of current to cause a pip-type waveform.

With very little current being drawn, the capacitor-input filter delivers an output voltage almost equal to the peak value of the a-c input to the rectifier. If the load draws an increasing amount of current, however, the output voltage falls because the rectifier cannot conduct long enough to recharge the input capacitor. To provide a sufficient charge on the capacitor would require a very large peak-rectifier current, which might damage the rectifier diodes. Consequently, capacitor-input filters are only used where *small* or *constant* load currents are involved.

With *no load* current being drawn, the output of the choke-input filter is also nearly equal to the peak value of the rectifier's a-c input because the capacitor has time to charge to peak. But, when a small amount of load current flows, the output voltage drops sharply to the average value of the a-c input because of the inductive action of the choke. As the load current is increased further, though, there is very little change in the output voltage. Thus, the choke-input filter is highly suitable for *heavy* or *variable* load current applications. Usually, a bleeder resistance is made a part of the choke-input filter. Thus, some load current always flows, preventing the large output voltage change that would otherwise occur between no-load and small-load conditions.

the swinging-choke input filter

The choke-input filter delivers an essentially constant voltage output over a wide range of load current. However, when the load current becomes *very heavy,* the output voltage starts to fall significantly. This is due to the d-c voltage drop the current produces across the inductor and power transformer. To counteract this decrease in voltage at heavy currents, a type of inductor called a *swinging choke* is often used.

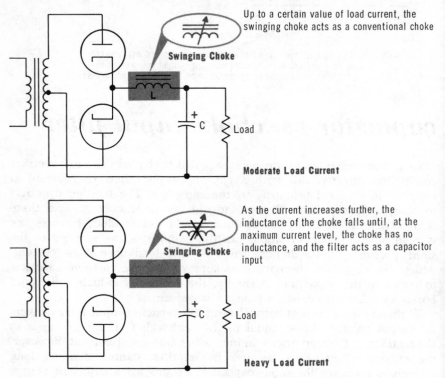

Up to a certain value of load current, the swinging choke acts as a conventional choke

Swinging Choke

Moderate Load Current

As the current increases further, the inductance of the choke falls until, at the maximum current level, the choke has no inductance, and the filter acts as a capacitor input

Swinging Choke

Heavy Load Current

Such an inductor does not have a constant inductance value. Instead, the inductance is relatively constant until a certain current flow is reached. Then, the inductance *decreases* as the current increases. This characteristic is due to the type of iron core used in the swinging choke. The choke actually starts saturating at a certain current level, and saturates more and more as the current goes up, so that the effective inductance continues to go down accordingly.

The swinging-choke input filter acts as a conventional choke-input filter below the point where saturation starts. Above the saturation point, the current increases, the inductance of the choke falls proportionately, and the filter becomes more and more like a capacitor-input filter. So, the capacitor can charge to a higher voltage, thus compensating for the decrease in output voltage that would otherwise occur because of the d-c losses in the choke and transformer.

the RC filter

In applications where less filtering can be tolerated, an RC filter is sometimes used. As shown, such a filter is similar to the capacitor-input filter, except that a *resistor* is used in place of the inductor. Although the resistor aids in the filtering by increasing the discharge time of capacitor C_1 and the charge time of capacitor C_2, it has a considerably higher *d-c resistance* than an inductor. Because of this, the RC filter is not suitable when large load currents must be supplied. Such large currents would produce an excessive voltage drop across the resistor, which would cause the output voltage to drop significantly.

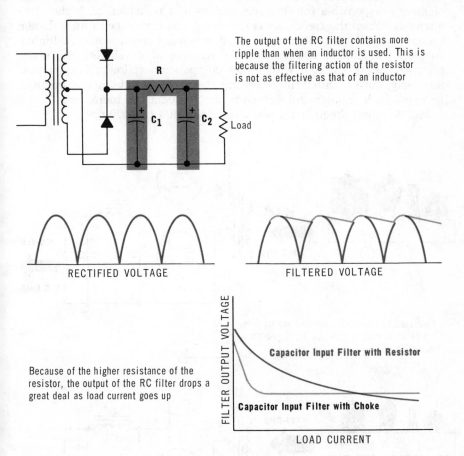

The output of the RC filter contains more ripple than when an inductor is used. This is because the filtering action of the resistor is not as effective as that of an inductor

RECTIFIED VOLTAGE   FILTERED VOLTAGE

Because of the higher resistance of the resistor, the output of the RC filter drops a great deal as load current goes up

FILTER OUTPUT VOLTAGE

Capacitor Input Filter with Resistor

Capacitor Input Filter with Choke

LOAD CURRENT

Although they are not used extensively in power supplies, RC filters are commonly employed as *decoupling networks* in amplifiers. The values of the RC components are different when they are used for decoupling purposes, because of the much higher frequencies to be filtered. However, the basic filtering principles are the same.

the effect of frequency on rectifiers and filters

Most electronic power supplies are designed to operate from a-c power sources that have a frequency of 60 cps. However, for frequency ranges of the a-c input that are greater than 60 cps, the rectifier and its filter can be made smaller and lighter. This characteristic is quite important in aircraft and other mobile applications, where size and weight are significant considerations.

Basically, the *reactive components* in the power supply are the elements responsible for this size and weight reduction at higher frequencies. When the frequency is increased, the reactance of an inductor increases, while that of a capacitor decreases. Consequently, at higher frequencies, smaller components are capable of developing the same filtering action obtained with larger components at lower frequencies. Similarly, power transformers having the necessary characteristics can be made both smaller and lighter as the frequency is increased.

Mobile power frequencies often run from 400 to 1000 cps.

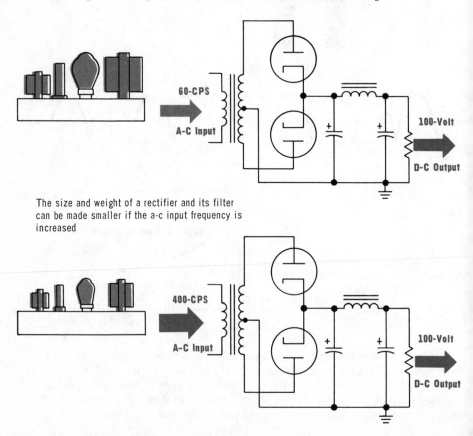

The size and weight of a rectifier and its filter can be made smaller if the a-c input frequency is increased

summary

☐ Fluctuation of the d-c output from a rectifier above and below its average value is called ripple. ☐ The ripple frequency for a half-wave rectifier is the same as the input frequency. ☐ For a full-wave rectifier, the ripple frequency is twice the input frequency. ☐ A simple capacitance filter consists of a capacitor connected across the rectifier output. Such a filter is not used with rectifiers that must supply large load current, since it has poor regulation. ☐ The inductance filter consists of an inductor connected in series with the rectifier load. Although it will not produce as high an output voltage as the capacitance filter, it has better regulation.

☐ The capacitor-input filter is a type of LC filter that can produce relatively large output voltages. Like all LC filters, it reduces ripple to a low value, but it has relatively poor voltage regulation. ☐ Choke-input filters, which are another type of LC filter, have good regulation. However their output voltages are less than those of capacitor input filters. ☐ Two choke-input filters are sometimes connected in series when a higher degree of filtering is required. ☐ The swinging-choke input filter uses a swinging choke, whose inductance decreases at heavy currents. This improves regulation when large load currents are drawn. ☐ The RC filter is similar to the capacitor-input filter, except that a resistor is used in place of the inductor. RC filters are used only for small current loads.

☐ Power supplies operating at higher frequencies require smaller components for filtering action. This is because the reactances of the components vary with frequency. ☐ Mobile power frequencies run from 400 to 1000 cps.

---

review questions

1. Draw a diagram of a capacitor-input filter. Explain its operation.
2. What is *ripple?*
3. Is a ripple voltage a d-c or an a-c voltage? Explain.
4. Why does an RC filter have poor voltage regulation?
5. The input frequency to a bridge rectifier is 500 cps. What is the ripple frequency?
6. Would the ripple frequency change if the bridge rectifier had a swinging-choke-input filter connected to it?
7. Which has a greater ripple frequency: a half-wave rectifier whose input is 500 cps, or a full-wave rectifier whose input is 300 cps?
8. Why are electrolytic capacitors used in filters?
9. Why is electrolytic *polarity* important?
10. Why are high input frequencies used for mobile equipment?

the load resistor

In all the schematic illustrations shown previously, a resistor has been connected across the output of the filter. This resistor has represented the total resistance of the load being supplied by the power supply. In practice, an *actual* resistor is almost always placed across the filter output. Sometimes, the purpose of this resistor is to provide a fixed load for the power supply even when the external circuits being supplied draw no current. Such a resistor, called a *load resistor,* has a resistance value such that it draws about 10 percent of the full-load current. The resistor helps regulate the voltage when little load current is drawn.

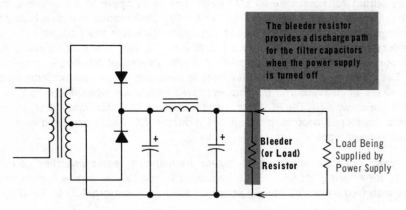

The bleeder resistor provides a discharge path for the filter capacitors when the power supply is turned off

Bleeder (or Load) Resistor

Load Being Supplied by Power Supply

Without the bleeder resistor path, dangerously high voltages could exist at various points in the equipment for some time after it is deenergized. The bleeder resistor sometimes also provides a fixed load for the supply to improve regulation

As mentioned earlier, in a choke-input filter the output voltage drops sharply from no load to a small load. When a load resistor is used, there cannot be a no-load condition, since the resistor is always drawing current. Thus, there will be no initial sharp drop in the curve. During operation, the resistor helps regulation because it is supplying a current that causes an internal voltage drop in the supply. If the output voltage tends to go down for some reason, the current drawn by the resistor also goes down, causing somewhat less of a drop in the supply. This offsets some of the output voltage drop. This is explained more fully later.

If the resistor is used to provide a discharge path for the filter capacitors when the power supply is turned off, it is also called a *bleeder resistor.* When used only for this purpose, the resistor has a very high resistance value so that it will draw very little current.

Very often, the resistor serves as both a bleeder and a fixed load. Its resistance value is then selected accordingly.

the voltage divider

In many equipments, a single power supply provides two or more output voltages. This is done by using series resistors or a tapped resistor in place of a single load resistor. The rectifier current flowing through the series resistors produces a total voltage drop equal to the filter output voltage. But this voltage is *divided* into separate voltage drops across the individual resistors. This is shown in A.

Resistors R_1, R_2, and R_3 form a voltage divider across the filter output. With no external load connected and 300 volts at the output of the filter, 2 milliamperes of current flow through the voltage divider network. This is found simply with an application of Ohm's Law. One hundred volts is therefore dropped across each resistor.

Normally, some point on the voltage divider is grounded, and all voltages are measured with respect to that point. Various output voltages can then be obtained, depending on what point is grounded. This is shown in B and C.

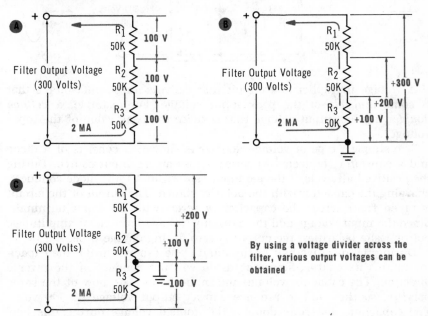

By using a voltage divider across the filter, various output voltages can be obtained

In A, B, and C, it is assumed that *no external load* is connected to the voltage divider. If a load, or loads, is connected, the voltage divisions shown are not correct. This is because the resistance of the load forms a parallel circuit with the portion of the divider it is connected across. This changes the resistance of that portion of the divider, and, therefore, affects the total resistance, the current, and all of the voltages. For this reason, such voltage dividers are designed for the particular load conditions under which they will operate.

voltage multipliers

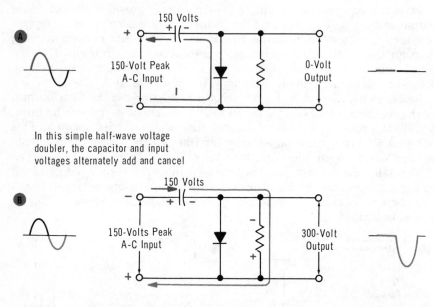

In this simple half-wave voltage
doubler, the capacitor and input
voltages alternately add and cancel

A voltage multiplier is a circuit that delivers an output voltage that is some *multiple* of the peak input voltage. For example, a *voltage doubler* has an output voltage that is *twice* the peak value of the input voltage.

The simplest type of voltage doubler is shown. It consists of a diode and a capacitor connected in series across an a-c input source. During the positive half cycle of the a-c input (shown in A), the diode conducts, charging the capacitor with the polarity shown. The output of the circuit is taken from across the capacitor *in series* with the input terminals. Since the input voltage and the capacitor voltage have equal amplitudes, but opposite polarities, the output is zero during charge time.

During the negative half of the input cycle (shown in B), the capacitor retains its charge, since the diode will not conduct in the reverse direction. The capacitor voltage and input voltage are now of the same polarity, so they add to produce a peak output voltage of 300 volts. The capacitor, therefore, doubles the applied voltage during this half cycle. This is why it is often referred to as the *doubling capacitor*. The output voltage, then, varies between zero on one half cycle, to twice the peak of the a-c input during the other half cycle. Such a circuit is called a *half-wave doubler*.

The simple voltage doubler shown here is not very practical. Not only does the output drop to zero during the positive half cycles of the input, but any current drawn by the load during the negative half cycles discharges the doubling capacitor, thus reducing the output voltage considerably.

a practical half-wave doubler

In order to make the previous circuit more practical, the output must be prevented from dropping to zero when the charge on the doubling capacitor opposes the input voltage, and the load must be kept from draining the doubling capacitor. This is done: (1) by adding another capacitor to store the output charge and supply current to the load, and (2) by adding another diode to isolate the input circuit when the doubling voltage cancels the input voltage. This is shown in the circuit on this page.

Capacitor C_1 and diode CR_1 function the same as the simple doubler circuit just described. Capacitor C_2 was added to charge to the output voltage, and diode CR_2 was added to isolate C_2 when the charge on C_1 cancels the input voltage. During the half cycle when the charge on C_1 *aids* the input voltage, the polarity of CR_2 is such that it is biased in the *forward* direction, and so allows C_2 to charge to the doubled voltage. On the other half cycle, when the charge on C_1 *opposes* the input voltage, diode CR_2 is *reverse biased*, and so offers a high resistance. It effectively opens the circuit to C_2, so that even though the sum of the charge on C_1 in series with the input voltage equals zero, capacitor C_2 still applies the doubled voltage to the load. Although C_2 does discharge somewhat to supply current to the load, its charge is replenished during the next half cycle.

Since C_2 can only charge during alternate half cycles, high current drains will cause C_2 to discharge considerably to lower the output voltage. Thus, this is a half-wave doubler circuit that is fit only for supplying a small output current. This circuit is also known as a *cascade* doubler, as will be explained later.

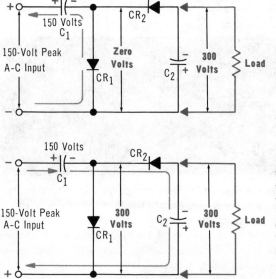

When C_1 is charging and its voltage cancels the input voltage, the sum of zero volts applied to CR_2 reverse biases CR_2, which opens the circuit to C_2. C_2 can then still supply its charge to the load

When the input polarity aids the charge on C_1, the doubled voltage is applied to CR_2. Then, when the charge on C_2 drops as it supplies current to the load, CR_2 conducts to recharge C_2

the full-wave doubler

A full-wave doubler circuit utilizes *both* cycles of the a-c input to replenish the output voltage. Essentially, two capacitors are charged on alternate cycles of the input and arranged so that their voltages *add* in the output. Such a doubler circuit is shown in A.

When point A on the transformer secondary is positive with respect to point B, diode V_1 conducts and charges capacitor C_1 to the peak value of the input, with the polarity shown. When the input reverses polarity and point B on the transformer secondary becomes positive with respect to point A, diode V_2 conducts. This charges capacitor C_2 to the peak value of the input, with the polarity shown.

Capacitors C_1 and C_2 are in *series* across the output. Their polarities are such that their voltages add. Since one capacitor is always being charged in any given half cycle, the voltage does not drop as much as it would for the half-wave doubler when the load draws current. Thus, this type of doubler circuit can be used for average load currents, but is not fit for heavy currents.

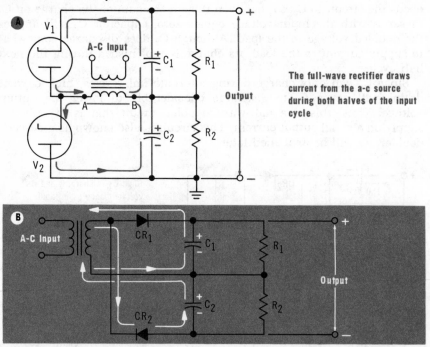

The full-wave rectifier draws current from the a-c source during both halves of the input cycle

The semiconductor version shown in B is the same circuit, arranged differently to show how different schematic representations can be used. Diodes CR_1 and CR_2 conduct on alternate half cycles of the input, charging their respective capacitors, C_1 and C_2. The load is connected so that the two capacitors are in series across it. The output voltage is, therefore, twice the peak value of the input.

the cascade doubler

As you have learned, the basic half-wave doubler circuit is called a *cascade doubler*. The tube version of this circuit is shown connected for a positive output. When point A on the transformer secondary is negative with respect to point B, diode V_1 conducts. The conduction path is through capacitor C_1, which causes C_1 to charge to the peak value of the applied ac. When the polarity of the a-c input reverses, point A on the transformer becomes positive with respect to point B. The input voltage and the voltage across capacitor C_1 are now effectively in series between the plate and cathode of diode V_2. Therefore, V_2 conducts, and, in doing so, charges capacitor C_2 to *twice* the peak value of the a-c input.

The cascade doubler, as well as any other voltage doubler, can be used with or without an input power transformer

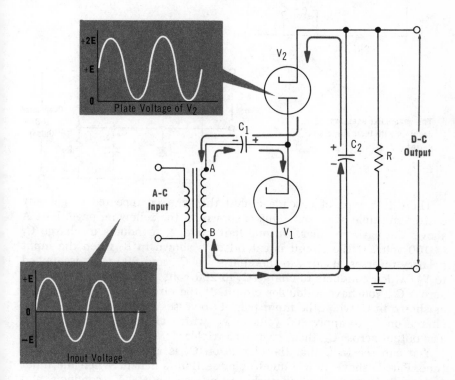

In effect, therefore, capacitor C_1 and diode V_1 cause the plate voltage of diode V_2 to vary between zero and twice the peak value of the input. This voltage is used to recharge capacitor C_2 when diode V_2 conducts. Resistor R serves as a bleeder or load resistor.

triplers, quadruplers, and quintuplers

Actually, voltage multipliers can be combined in various ways so that the output voltage is any multiple of the input. Many different methods can be used to do this. One simple method of making a tripler is shown on this page. A doubler and a simple rectifier are combined so that their outputs add to get three times the input voltage. Two doublers with the right polarities are combined to form a quadrupler.

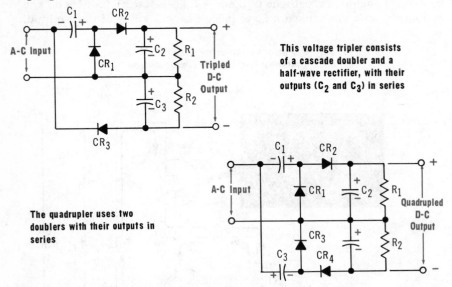

This voltage tripler consists of a cascade doubler and a half-wave rectifier, with their outputs (C_2 and C_3) in series

The quadrupler uses two doublers with their outputs in series

There is a type of cascade circuit that can be repeated to get any desired multiple of output. This is shown on the following page. Part A shows the basic rectifier. On one half cycle, V_1 conducts to charge C_1 to 100 volts. If the circuit is extended as shown in B, when the input polarity reverses, it adds to the charge on C_1, and 200 volts is applied to V_2, which conducts to charge C_2 to 200 volts. If you take the output across C_2, you have a doubler circuit. If the circuit is extended again, as shown in C, when the input polarity reverses again, it adds with the charge on C_2 to apply 300 volts to V_3, which charges C_3 to 300 volts. The output across C_3, then, gives us a tripler.

You can see in C that the charge on C_1 is also replenished at this time. Part D shows how a quadrupler section is added. When the input voltage is in series aiding with the charge on C_3, V_4 conducts and charges C_4 to 400 volts. With the quintupler section (E), when the input and the charge on C_4 add, V_5 conducts to charge C_5 to 500 volts.

This pattern can be repeated for any voltage multiplication desired, but it is generally inefficient after quadrupling. The voltage is not quite doubled each time because of losses.

triplers, quadruplers, and quintuplers (cont.)

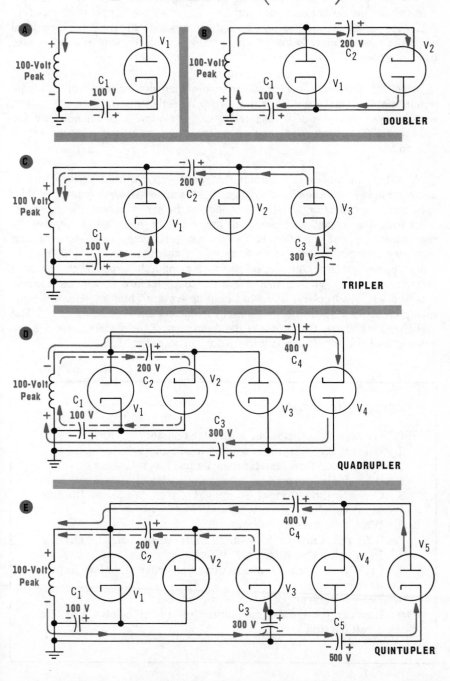

summary

☐ A load or bleeder resistor is usually connected across the output of a filter. ☐ The purpose of a load resistor is to provide a fixed load even when the external circuits do not draw current. This improves the supply regulation. ☐ A bleeder resistor is used to provide a discharge path for the filter capacitors when the power supply is turned off. ☐ Sometimes the load resistor is also used as a bleeder.

☐ A voltage divider is used to obtain more than one voltage from a single power supply. Usually a divider is a group of series resistors or one tapped resistor used in place of a load resistor. ☐ Normally, some point on the voltage divider is grounded, and all voltages are measured with respect to that point.

☐ A voltage multiplier is a circuit that delivers an output voltage that is some multiple of the peak input voltage. ☐ A simple half-wave voltage doubler consists of a capacitor and diode connected in series across the input ac. Such a doubler is not very practical, and must be modified to improve its regulation. ☐ The modified half-wave voltage doubler contains a second capacitor and diode, and is also known as a cascade doubler. ☐ The full-wave doubler utilizes both cycles of the a-c input to produce the doubled output voltage. ☐ Voltage multipliers can be combined in various ways so that triplers, quadruplers, and even quintuplers are obtained. However, any multiplier above a quadrupler is generally inefficient because of losses. ☐ The higher the multiplier, the poorer is the regulation of the system; even a small value of load current will cause a sharp drop in output voltage.

review questions

1. What is the purpose of a bleeder resistor?
2. What is the purpose of a fixed load resistor?
3. Can a fixed load resistor ever be used as a bleeder?
4. What is the purpose of a voltage divider?
5. Can a voltage divider ever yield a voltage greater than the input voltage?
6. What is a *voltage multiplier*?
7. Is there a limit to the voltage increase that can be obtained from voltage multipliers? Why?
8. Draw a diagram of a practical half-wave doubler. Explain its operation.
9. Draw a diagram of a full-wave doubler.
10. How can more than one polarity of voltage be obtained from a voltage divider?

vibrator power supplies

The vibrator power supply is a special kind of supply used to produce a high value of dc from a low-voltage d-c source. Usually, the low-voltage source is a storage battery. Vibrator supplies are used in such mobile equipment as the automobile radio.

The basic principle on which the vibrator supply works is illustrated here. A vibrating armature, or reed, is connected in series with a low-voltage d-c source and the centertap of a transformer primary. The armature is made to vibrate rapidly, alternately making contact with terminals 1 and 2. When the armature contacts terminal 1, current flows through the upper half of the transformer primary. When the armature contacts terminal 2, current flows through the lower half. The alternate currents in the primary halves induce voltages of opposite polarity in the transformer secondary. The secondary voltage is therefore continuous ac, having a modified square-wave waveshape.

Since a step-up transformer is used, the output developed across the secondary is considerably greater than the input voltage. The a-c output voltage is then rectified and filtered to produce the required d-c voltage. The manner in which the armature is made to vibrate is shown on the following pages.

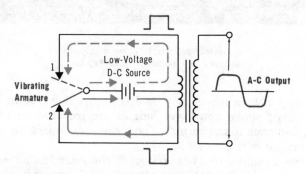

As the armature vibrates, current alternately flows in opposite directions in the upper and lower halves of the transformer primary. This induces a stepped-up a-c voltage in the secondary

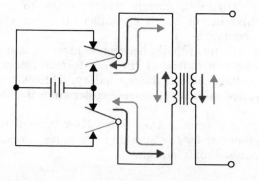

The same thing can be accomplished without a centertapped transformer. Double-pole, double-throw contacts switch the battery connections across the entire primary

the nonsynchronous vibrator power supply

A typical *nonsynchronous* vibrator power supply is shown. This is called a nonsynchronous supply because it requires a *rectifier* to produce the output dc. The vibrating armature is caused to vibrate between contacts 1 and 2 by the action of an electromagnetic relay, K. The armature is pulled against contact 1 by a spring when the vibrator is deenergized.

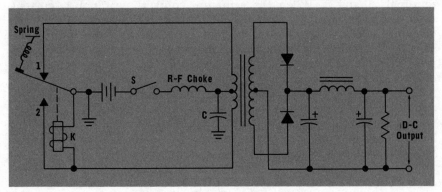

A nonsynchronous vibrator power supply requires
a rectifier in the transformer secondary circuit

When vibrator switch S is closed, current flows from the battery through the r-f choke, the lower half of the transformer primary, and the relay, and back to the battery. The current energizes the relay, which pulls the armature to contact 2.

When the armature touches contact 2, the relay is shorted out of the circuit. As a result, it no longer attracts the armature, which is then returned to contact 1 by the spring. When the armature touches contact 1, current flows from the battery through the upper half of the transformer primary. This current is also of short duration, though, since when the armature leaves contact 2, current again begins to flow through the relay. When this current builds up sufficiently, the relay again pulls the armature to contact 2.

In this way, the armature vibrates rapidly between contacts 1 and 2. The resulting currents in the two halves of the transformer primary produce a stepped-up a-c voltage across the secondary. This voltage is rectified and filtered by a conventional full-wave rectifier and capacitor input filter.

The r-f choke and capacitor C form a *hash filter*. They prevent the electrical noise, or hash, produced by the sparking armature contacts from being passed to the power-supply output.

the synchronous vibrator power supply

A synchronous vibrator supply needs only a filter, since the vibrator and transformer produce a fluctuating d-c voltage

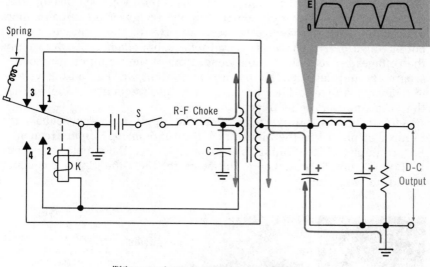

With every change in current direction in the primary, the secondary winding connections are reversed so that dc is applied to the filter

A *synchronous* vibrator power supply is one that does not require a separate rectifier to produce the d-c output. Such a vibrator supply delivers a *fluctuating* d-c output across the secondary of the transformer. All that is required is a filter network to smooth out the fluctuations in the output.

A typical synchronous vibrator supply is shown. You can see that it is similar to the nonsynchronous supply, except that it has two additional vibrator contacts (3 and 4), each connected to the *opposite* side of the transformer secondary. When the armature touches contact 1, it also touches contact 3, when it touches contact 2, it also touches contact 4.

The extra contacts *ground* the end of the transformer secondary to which they are connected when their respective main contacts (1 or 2) are made. This causes all of the current pulses induced in the secondary to flow in the same direction. Thus, instead of an a-c secondary voltage, a fluctuating dc is produced. A conventional filter is then used to smooth the fluctuating dc. Essentially, every time the direction of current changes in the primary winding, which tends to alternate the voltage induced in the secondary winding, the connections to the secondary windings are reversed so that dc is applied to the filter.

multiphase (polyphase) power supplies

All of the electronic power supplies described thus far have operated from single-phase a-c input power. Power supplies that must deliver great amounts of d-c power, such as a kilowatt or more, generally operate from multiphase power sources. From your studies of electricity, you recall that such sources supply a-c power on three or more conductors, with the voltage between any two of the conductors equal but having *different phases*. In a multiphase, or *polyphase*, power supply, the voltages between the various conductors of the a-c input are rectified separately and developed across a *common output*. The output voltage is relatively simple to filter because the ripple frequency is higher than that of a single-phase rectifier.

Actually, for a half-wave rectifier, the ripple frequency equals the number of phases in the input times the fundamental input frequency. For example, if the input is 3-phase, 60-cps, the ripple frequency is 3 × 60, or 180 cps. For a full-wave rectifier, the ripple frequency would be twice this.

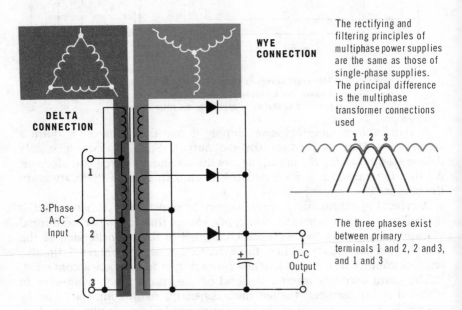

The rectifying and filtering principles of multiphase power supplies are the same as those of single-phase supplies. The principal difference is the multiphase transformer connections used

The three phases exist between primary terminals 1 and 2, 2 and 3, and 1 and 3

A basic 3-phase, half-wave power supply is shown. The primary windings of the power transformer are connected in the *delta* configuration, while the *wye* connection is used for the secondaries. Actually, a study of multiphase power supplies is in large part a study of multiphase transformer connections.

voltage regulation

You have seen how one very important characteristic of any power supply is the degree to which its output voltage remains *constant* despite changes in the amount of current drawn from the supply by the load. This characteristic is called the *regulation* of the supply. A supply whose output voltage changes little over a wide variation in load current is said to have *good* regulation. One whose output voltage falls sharply as the load current increases has *poor* regulation. Certain types of power supplies have inherently good regulation, mainly because of the type of filter used. However, for many applications, even these supplies do not have good enough regulation. Additional circuits must be added so that the output voltage remains constant. These additional circuits are called *voltage regulator* circuits.

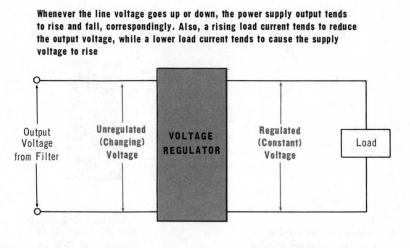

Whenever the line voltage goes up or down, the power supply output tends to rise and fall, correspondingly. Also, a rising load current tends to reduce the output voltage, while a lower load current tends to cause the supply voltage to rise

A voltage regulator is connected in the output of a power supply to maintain the voltage delivered to the load constant

Basically, the output voltage tends to vary because of two things: (1) fluctuating line voltage and (2) fluctuating load current. Every time the line voltage goes up, the output voltage will go up. But when the load current goes up, the output voltage will go down. This is because the output voltage is actually what is left after the internal voltage drops of the supply are taken away from the output. As the load increases, the internal drops increase and less is left for the output.

Generally, supplies are rated with percentages of regulation within certain load and line variations. For example, a 1% rating means that the output voltage will not vary more than 1 percent for load and line changes within specified limits.

principles

Voltage regulation is the last step in a power supply's conversion of a-c input power into an almost perfectly constant d-c output voltage. Increases in output voltage, which would otherwise be caused by a drop in the load current drawn from the supply or a rise in the level of the a-c input to the supply, are prevented from occurring by a voltage regulator. Decreases in output voltage, such as those caused by an increase in the load current drawn from the supply or a fall in the a-c input level, are also prevented.

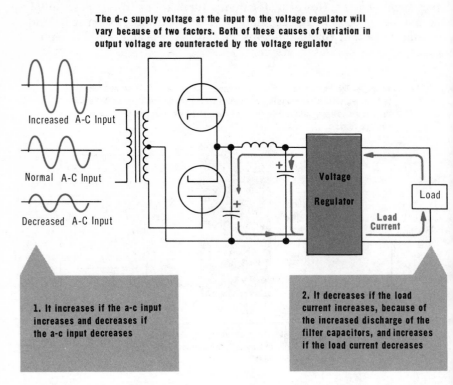

The d-c supply voltage at the input to the voltage regulator will vary because of two factors. Both of these causes of variation in output voltage are counteracted by the voltage regulator

Increased A-C Input

Normal A-C Input

Decreased A-C Input

Voltage Regulator

Load

Load Current

1. It increases if the a-c input increases and decreases if the a-c input decreases

2. It decreases if the load current increases, because of the increased discharge of the filter capacitors, and increases if the load current decreases

The basic voltage regulator circuit works by inserting resistance in the output of the supply, so that the output voltage is somewhat *less* than it would be without the regulator. Then, when the supply voltage varies, the resistance added by the regulator automatically changes to compensate for the voltage changes. In effect, the regulator circuit absorbs the voltage changes, dropping less of the output voltage when the voltage decreases and more when the output voltage increases. The net effect is that, after the voltage regulator, the supply output voltage is constant.

load resistor regulation

As was pointed out previously, when a load resistor is connected across the power-supply filter, it provides a small degree of regulation, especially when the load current is relatively small. Although the load resistor is an inefficient regulator, a description of the way it provides regulation is useful as an introduction to voltage regulators in general.

As shown, the load resistor is in parallel with the load; both are connected directly across the power-supply output. Under normal conditions, current flow through the supply is what is drawn by both resistor R and the load. Therefore, the current drawn by the resistor partly determines the internal supply voltage drops and, hence, the output voltage. So, when either the load current increases or the a-c input voltage decreases, the supply output voltage and, therefore, the voltage across R, tend to decrease—less current flows through R in accordance with Ohm's Law. As a result, the portion of the internal voltage drop in the supply caused by R goes down somewhat to increase the output voltage by the same amount.

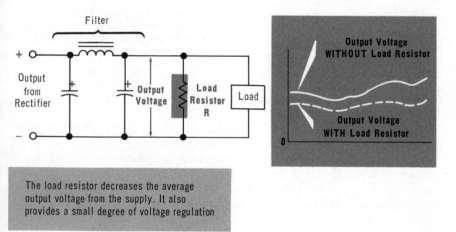

The load resistor decreases the average output voltage from the supply. It also provides a small degree of voltage regulation

The opposite situation occurs if the output voltage tends to increase. The resulting higher voltage causes more current to flow through the load resistor, which increases the internal voltage drops of the supply so that the output voltage goes down.

As was mentioned, the load resistor provides only a small degree of regulation. This is because the fluctuating output voltages only cause small changes in the load resistor currents. These small changes are not great enough to vary the internal voltage drops of the supply to bring the output voltage back to normal.

The load resistor regulator is sufficient with supplies where the line and load do not vary much. This regulator is most efficient when the load resistor draws 10 percent of what the load draws.

the gas-tube regulator

If the load resistor is replaced by a device that would cause large changes in internal voltage drops for small changes in output voltage, much better regulation could be obtained. Such a device could not follow Ohm's Law, since as the voltage across it went up or down, its resistance would have to go down or up to cause a higher than usual current change. Such a device is called *nonlinear*.

One such type of voltage regulator uses gas-filled, glow-discharge tubes, whose resistance is determined by the degree of ionization of the gas in the tube, which in turn depends on the current. The higher the current through the tube, the greater is the ionization, and the lower is the resistance. Theoretically, the resistance drops in proportion with any current increase so that the IR drop across the tube is constant. But in actual use, the series resistor is needed to bring this about.

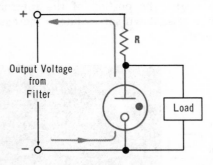

Changes in supply voltage appear across dropping resistor R. The voltage across the glow tube, and, therefore, the load voltage, remain constant

Both the load current and the glow-tube current flow through dropping resistor R. Part of the output voltage of the supply is dropped across resistor R, and the remaining voltage, which is the regulated output, is dropped across the gas tube. When the voltage across the tube tends to go up, more current flows through the tube. Gas ionization, then, increases, and the resistance of the tube goes down. As a result of this decrease in resistance, then, an even greater current flows through the tube. This would tend to increase ionization again, and reduce resistance to increase current again, but a stabilizing point is reached where the initial increase in voltage across the tube results in a much higher increase in current than could be obtained with a resistor. As a result, the voltage dropped across resistor R goes up sufficiently to lower the voltage across the tube to normal. Of course, the opposite occurs when the voltage across the tube tends to go down.

The value of dropping resistor R is very important, since it must match the current changes to pick up all of the voltage fluctuations. Also, the tube cannot give perfect regulation, for if the voltage returned to its exact value, the ionization within the tube would do so, also, and the action would repeat itself, causing the output voltage to fluctuate up and down. So, the regulated output voltage is only returned *close* to its regulated value for stabilization purposes.

series gas-tube regulators

Gas tubes are rated according to the constant voltage that they are designed to drop, as well as the maximum current that they can carry. For example, the VR 75-30 maintains a relatively constant 75-volt output and can carry up to 30 milliamperes. Various type tubes are available for different voltages. Sometimes, a larger supply output voltage must be regulated than is possible with the characteristics of a *single* tube. Two or more tubes can then be connected in *series*, and the regulated output taken from across the combination. Such an arrangement is shown in A. The operation of the circuit is essentially the same as that of a single-tube regulator.

A series arrangement of glow tubes can also be used to provide more than one regulated output voltage. In this case, different loads are connected across the various tubes in the series arrangement. Such a circuit is shown in B.

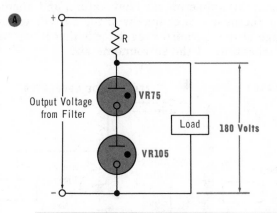

Gas-type regulator tubes can be connected in series, as well as singly

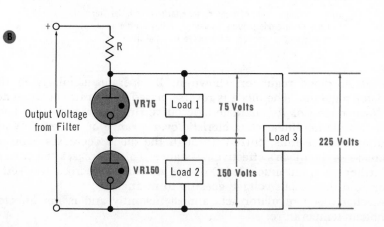

semiconductor regulators

Various semiconductor devices have certain nonlinear characteristics which, like the gas tube, make them suitable for voltage regulation purposes. Regulator circuits using two of these devices, the *thermistor* and the *zener diode*, are shown.

The thermistor, shown in A, has an extreme *negative temperature coefficient*. When current through it increases, the temperature is raised, and the resistance of the thermistor decreases. The thermistor is connected in series with a dropping resistor across the filter output. When the supply voltage rises, the voltage across the thermistor goes up, and so does the current through it. The higher current causes an increase in temperature that causes the resistance of the thermistor to decrease. This increases the current through the thermistor still further, so more voltage is dropped across the dropping resistor, and the output voltage reduces back to normal.

The thermistor regulator is only effective against *slow* changes in the supply voltage because it takes time for the temperature, and, therefore, the resistance, of the thermistor to change with the current variations. Another disadvantage of the thermistor regulator is that it can be affected by changes in temperature of the surrounding air.

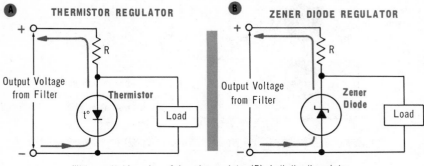

With a suitable value of dropping resistor (R), both the thermistor and the zener diode provide a constant voltage to the load despite changes in the output voltage from the filter

The zener diode regulator, shown in B, operates similarly to the thermistor regulator. The diode is reverse biased to operate on the zener breakdown region of its characteristic curve. In this region, the diode exhibits a wide nonlinear characteristic over a range of currents. When the output voltage falls, current through the diode decreases, causing an increase in the diode's effective resistance. This decreases the current still further, so that much less voltage is dropped across the series resistor, and the output voltage goes up to normal.

The zener diode regulator acts almost instantly and is not affected by ambient temperature.

summary

☐ The vibrator power supply produces a high value of dc from a low-voltage d-c source. The heart of a vibrator supply is a vibrating reed that chops the d-c input voltage. ☐ A nonsynchronous vibrator supply changes the d-c input voltage to ac, which is then stepped up by a step-up transformer and applied to a rectifier and filter. ☐ A synchronous vibrator power supply does not require a separate rectifier. It produces a stepped-up fluctuating d-c output that is then smoothed by a filter.

☐ In a multiphase or polyphase supply, the variously phased voltages are rectified separately and developed across a common output. ☐ The ripple frequency of a multiphase supply is proportional to the number of phases of the input. The higher the ripple frequency, the easier it is to filter.

☐ The load regulation of a power supply is the degree to which its output voltage remains constant despite changes in the amount of current drawn by the load. Voltage regulating circuits are used to keep the supply output voltage constant despite changes in load current. ☐ Load resistor regulation is most efficient when the load resistor draws only up to 10 percent of what the load draws. ☐ The gas tube regulator acts as a nonlinear device that tends to maintain a constant voltage across itself in spite of current changes through it. In this way it keeps the voltage applied to the load relatively constant. ☐ Specific voltage regulator tubes have a rated voltage that they are designed to drop, as well as a maximum current that they can safely carry. ☐ Gas regulator tubes can be arranged in series to provide for regulation of a greater voltage than is possible with a single tube. ☐ Certain semiconductor devices also have nonlinear characteristics that make them suitable as voltage regulators. Two such devices are the thermistor and the zener diode.

review questions

1. Draw a diagram of a nonsynchronous vibrator supply.
2. Explain the operation of a synchronous vibrator.
3. Does a synchronous vibrator require a transformer to operate?
4. What is meant by *regulation of a power supply*?
5. How does the thermistor voltage regulator work?
6. Draw a gas tube regulator.
7. Why is the series resistor needed?
8. How does a zener diode provide voltage regulation?
9. Why is a multiphase power supply used?
10. Draw a diagram showing how three loads can be regulated with only two glow tubes.

vacuum-tube voltage regulators

By using a vacuum tube as the voltage-regulating element, a much higher degree of regulation is possible than with the circuits previously described. This is because of the *amplifying* characteristic of a vacuum tube. Even very small voltage changes can be eliminated, since they are amplified sufficiently to cause the regulator circuit to operate better.

A simple vacuum-tube regulator circuit is shown in A. Triode V_1 acts as a variable resistance in series with the load. Battery B provides a bias for V_1 such that the tube has the proper plate resistance to drop the right amount of voltage to get the required output voltage. It is important to realize that the bias battery (B) voltage is *independent* of the supply output voltage. It remains constant regardless of how the supply voltage varies and serves as a *reference voltage*.

Vacuum-tube regulator circuits provide a very high degree of regulation. The tube acts like a variable resistor with gain to vary its voltage drop and keep the load voltage constant

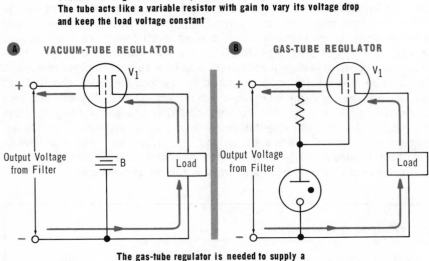

The gas-tube regulator is needed to supply a stabilized reference source for the bias

If the supply voltage increases, the cathode voltage of V_1, which is also the load voltage, tends to become more positive. This causes the negative bias on V_1 to increase also, since the grid battery voltage does not change. Consequently, the effective plate resistance of V_1 increases, as does the *IR* drop across V_1. Because of the tube's gain, the plate resistance increases by an amount sufficient to counteract the supply output voltage increase, so that the load voltage is returned to an essentially constant output. Because of the voltages involved, it usually is inconvenient to use batteries for the grid voltage. A gas tube with the proper voltage characteristic is used for this purpose. Its operation is the same as the gas-regulator tubes previously discussed.

the amplified voltage regulator

Because of the high amplification of the voltage fluctuations, this circuit is capable of compensating for even extremely small changes in output voltage

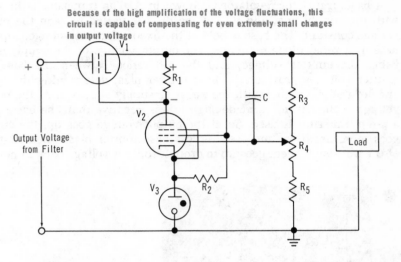

In the simple tube regulator, the change in plate resistance for a given change in bias is still not enough to give perfect regulation. However, it can be improved by first amplifying the voltage change.

In the circuit, triode V_1 and resistors R_3, R_4, and R_5 make up a voltage divider across the filter output. The resistor portion of the divider is in parallel with the load, so the load voltage appears across it. Pentode V_2 senses changes in the supply voltage, amplifies them, and varies the bias of V_1 to compensate for the changes. The cathode of V_2 is kept at a constant reference potential by gas regulator tube V_3. The control grid voltage of V_2 is tapped off of resistor R_4 and is *less positive* than the cathode voltage. It is initially adjusted to establish proper operation under normal load conditions. It accomplishes this by setting the bias of V_2 so that its plate current will drop enough voltage across R_1 to bias triode V_1 properly.

Because of the high gain of this regulator circuit, the divider resistor values are chosen to tap down the output voltage enough so that after the change is amplified, it will exactly cancel the output change.

Capacitor C increases the *response time* of the regulator in compensating for extremely *rapid changes* in supply voltage. The a-c component of these spurious voltage variations is coupled directly to the control grid of V_2 by the capacitor, which has a very low reactance at the high frequencies represented by sudden transient voltage changes. Capacitor C also eliminates any *ripple voltage* that still exists after filtering. It does this by applying the ripple voltage variations directly to the grid of V_2. The regulator thus compensates for these variations even more than it does for any other voltage changes, since these changes are not tapped down first.

transistor voltage regulators

A basic transistor regulator is shown in A. The transistor is in series with the supply line, and its voltage drop is varied to keep the output voltage constant. The base is held at the fixed reference voltage, supplied here by a zener diode regulator. The output voltage of the supply establishes the emitter voltage, and the difference between the base and emitter voltages provides the base-emitter bias, determining the resistance of the transistor. With the negative supply shown in A, the output voltage at the emitter is made slightly less negative than the base, since a p-n-p transistor is used. So, if the output voltage goes up, the emitter goes more negative, and there is less base-emitter bias. The resistance of the transistor, then, goes up to drop the output voltage back to normal.

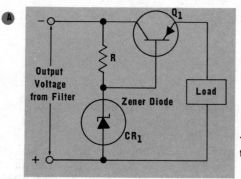

Transistor regulators perform the same function as their electron-tube counterparts

A transistor-amplifier regulator, comparable in operation to the tube-amplifier regulator of the previous page, is shown in B. Q_2 amplifies the tapped-down portion of the output voltage variations and varies the drop across R_1 to change the base voltage of Q_1. This varies the base-emitter bias on Q_1, so that the resistance, and, hence, the voltage drop across Q_1, will change to keep the output voltage constant.

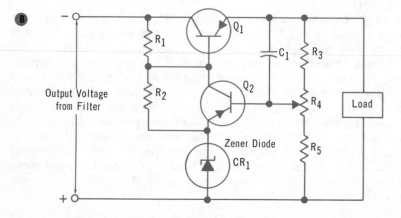

line regulators

Regulation can also be accomplished by increasing or decreasing the level of the *a-c input* to the supply to compensate for changes in supply output voltage. This is called a-c *line regulation*. It is accomplished by using a *saturable reactor* in series with the primary winding of the power transformer. If the impedance of the reactor is changed, the reactor will drop more or less voltage, and will allow less or more voltage to be applied to the power transformer. The impedance of the saturable reactor is changed by a d-c current from an amplifier that controls the degree to which the reactor is saturated. In the line regulator shown in A, a reduced output voltage will lower the bias to the amplifier, which then provides more saturating current for the saturable reactor. The more the reactor is saturated, the less inductance it has, the less a-c voltage it drops, the more ac is applied to the transformer, and the higher is the power-supply output voltage.

Often, a line regulator is used to compensate only for changes in the a-c input level. This is done, as in B, by using a second secondary winding on the power transformer to apply a portion of the a-c voltage to a separate rectifier, which feeds a d-c output to the control amplifier.

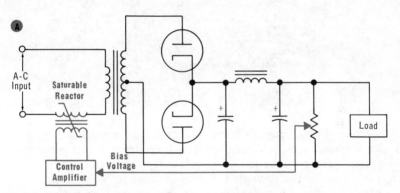

In this circuit, the a-c input voltage is varied to compensate for changes in the d-c output voltage. If the output voltage goes up, the bias to the amplifier will go up to reduce the saturating current. The impedance of the saturable reactor will go up to reduce the primary voltage, and, hence, the supply output voltage

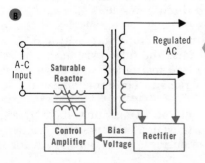

This line regulator maintains a constant a-c output from the power transformer regardless of variations in the a-c input

current regulation

Sometimes a power supply must deliver a *constant current* regardless of changes in supply voltage or load. This can be done utilizing the circuit shown.

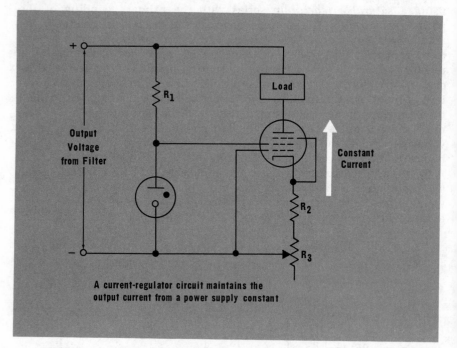

A current-regulator circuit maintains the output current from a power supply constant

A pentode is connected in series with the load across the supply output. So, the supply output current must flow through the pentode. Two factors cause the pentode to pass a relatively constant current: (1) the plate resistance of the pentode is set by its bias to be high compared to the resistance of the load, so that any changes in load resistance have less effect on the load current drawn; (2) the manner in which the pentode's bias is developed, an explanation of which follows.

The control grid is connected directly to the negative side of the supply and the cathode is connected through resistors R_2 and R_3 to the same point. The load current passes through these resistors. If the load resistance drops to draw more current, the drops across R_2 and R_3 will go up to increase the tube bias and raise the tube resistance. The tube resistance will go up as much as the load resistance went down, so that the total resistance across the supply remains constant to keep the load current constant.

The screen grid in this circuit is held at a constant voltage by a gas regulator tube. This is necessary to prevent fluctuations in the screen voltage, which would affect the plate current. Resistor R_3 is set for the desired load current level.

the complete power supply

You have now seen the various circuits that make up an electronic power supply. The different types and combinations of these circuits that are used in a particular power supply depend on the requirements of the supply. A power supply can be as simple as that below, consisting merely of a half-wave rectifier and a capacitor filter, or it can be as complete as that shown on the following page.

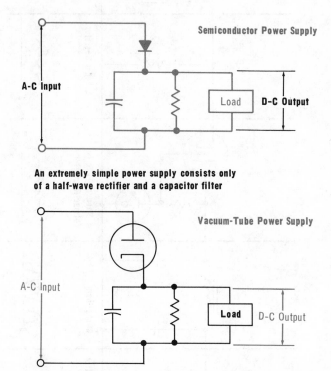

An extremely simple power supply consists only of a half-wave rectifier and a capacitor filter

In the supply shown on the next page, a power transformer first steps up the a-c input voltage to a considerably higher value. The transformer secondary is centertapped, and the voltages across the two halves are applied to the diodes of a full-wave rectifier. The diodes conduct on alternate half cycles of the a-c voltage and deliver a fluctuating d-c output to a capacitor-input pi filter.

In the filter, the fluctuating dc is smoothed by the charging and discharging of the capacitors and the choke's opposition to current changes. The rectified and filtered voltage is then held relatively constant by a vacuum-tube voltage regulator. The load, therefore, receives a constant voltage. A bleeder resistor is used across the output of the supply to provide a discharge path for the filter capacitors when the supply is turned off.

the complete
full-wave rectifier

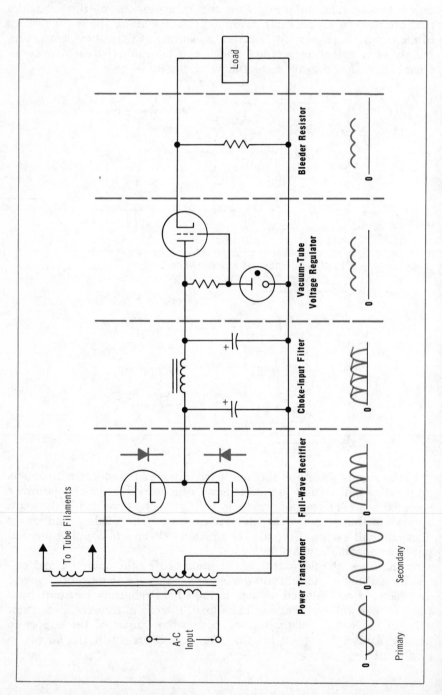

power supply characteristics

You have now learned about the various types of circuits that make up a power supply, the functions of these circuits, and the way in which they operate. All of the individual circuits of any given power supply function together to give that supply its overall operating characteristics. These characteristics then define the capability of the supply. From a functional standpoint, a power supply can be fully described on the basis of the characteristics given below.

POWER SUPPLY CHARACTERISTICS

Characteristic	Description
Input	The a-c input power that must be applied to the supply for it to deliver its rated output. It includes the required amplitude, frequency, and phase. For example, a typical power supply might require an input of 110 volts, 60 cps, single phase.
Output	The rated voltage output of the supply, together with the maximum current that can be drawn without affecting the voltage. If a supply produces more than one output voltage, its rated output consists of each of these voltages and their associated maximum currents. For example, the output of a typical supply might be +250 volts dc at 50 milliamperes and −80 volts dc at 100 milliamperes.
Percent Regulation	The percentage decrease in the supply's output voltage from no-load to full-load conditions. The higher the percentage of regulation, the more the output voltage falls as the load is increased. Thus, if a supply had zero percent regulation, its output voltage would remain absolutely constant from no load to full load.
Percent Ripple	The amount of ripple voltage that is not removed by the filter, and which therefore appears at the output of the supply. The lower the percentage of the ripple, the more nearly the output voltage approaches pure dc.

summary

☐ Vacuum tubes or transistors, because of their ability to amplify, can provide a very high degree of regulation. ☐ In an amplified voltage regulator, changes in the supply output voltage are amplified before being applied to the regulating portion of the voltage regulator circuit. This makes the circuit capable of compensating for even extremely small changes in output voltage. ☐ The operating point of a tube or transistor regulator is set by a reference voltage that is independent of the supply output voltage. Gas regulator tubes or zener diodes are used to establish the reference voltage.

☐ Regulation of a supply output voltage can also be accomplished by increasing or decreasing the level of a-c input to the supply. This is called a-c line regulation. ☐ In a-c line regulation, a saturable reactor is used to change the impedance of the power transformer primary winding in accordance with changes in the supply output voltage. ☐ A line regulator can also be used to compensate for changes in the a-c input level to the supply.

☐ Current regulation is used when a power supply must deliver a constant output current regardless of changes in line or load voltage. ☐ A pentode, connected in series with the load, is one method used for current regulation. The high plate resistance of the pentode causes it to act as a constant-current source. ☐ The choice of a power supply for a particular application is determined by the requirements of the situation. Some important characteristics of a supply are input, output, percent regulation, and percent ripple.

review questions

1. Why is an amplified voltage regulator an improvement over a simple regulator?
2. What is meant by the *response time* of a voltage regulator?
3. Why are pentodes used for current regulation?
4. Are pentodes ever used for voltage regulation?
5. What is a *saturable reactor*?
6. Name three important characteristics of a power supply.
7. What device is used in an a-c line regulator?
8. What is the difference between an a-c line regulator and a regular voltage regulator?
9. Draw a schematic diagram of a simple transistor voltage regulator. Describe its operation.
10. What is meant by the *percent ripple* of a power supply?

amplifier circuits

In practically every piece of electronic equipment there are at least one or two, and, often, many circuits whose only function is to *increase* the *level* of the signal. These *amplifier circuits* may use electron tubes or transistors, since both are essentially amplifying devices. Besides the tube or transistor, an amplifier circuit includes all of the circuit components that provide *bias*, as well as any components used to *compensate* for undesired *distortion* of the signal that occurs during amplification.

Sometimes, an amplifier is designed *purposefully* to distort the signal to obtain some desired waveform characteristic. When this is the case, components that contribute to the desired distortion are also part of the amplifier circuit. Very often, a signal is so small that one amplifier circuit cannot amplify it to the desired level. In these cases, two or more amplifier circuits are connected in *sequence*, with the amplified output of the first being used as the input to the second for further amplification, and so on.

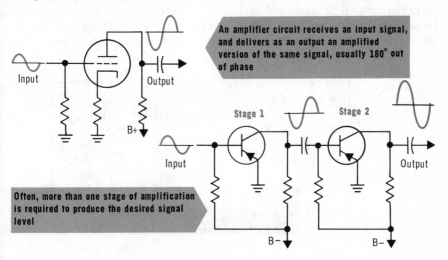

An amplifier circuit receives an input signal, and delivers as an output an amplified version of the same signal, usually 180° out of phase

Input   Output

B+

Stage 1   Stage 2

Input   Output

Often, more than one stage of amplification is required to produce the desired signal level

B–   B–

You recall from your previous studies that *coupling circuits* must then be used between the individual amplifier circuits. When more than one amplifier circuit is used, it is convenient to refer to each as a *stage*, and then consider the signal as having undergone one, two, three, etc., stages of amplification.

Amplifier circuits can be classified in a wide variety of ways. They can be classified according to their *use*, the type of *bias* used, the *frequency* or *bandwidth* of the signals they are to amplify, the type of *coupling*, if more than one stage is used, and their circuit *configuration*. The various types of amplifiers within each of these classifications have already been covered for the most part in previous volumes; they will therefore be summarized on the following pages.

amplifiers
according to use

When amplifiers are classified according to their use, they fall into two broad groups: *voltage amplifiers* and *power amplifiers*. Voltage amplifiers, as their name implies, increase the voltage level of an applied signal. Since the output voltage of an amplifier is determined by the voltage drop across the output load, the *impedance* of the load is made as *large* as is practical in most voltage amplifiers.

Power amplifiers are designed to deliver a large amount of current to the output load. To accomplish this, the load impedance is usually *low enough* to allow a high current output, but at the same time it is not so low that it produces excessive distortion of the signal. Power amplifiers are also called *current amplifiers*.

Some other classifications of amplifiers according to use are the *buffer* amplifier, which is used to isolate other stages, the *square-wave* amplifier, which is designed to handle a specific waveshape, and the *frequency-doubler* amplifier, which increases the signal frequency. There are many other such amplifiers, which you will learn about later.

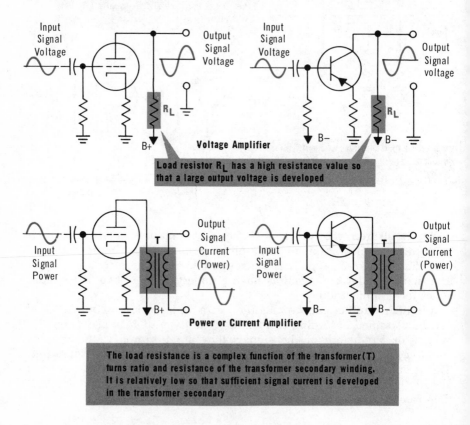

Voltage Amplifier

Load resistor R_L has a high resistance value so that a large output voltage is developed

Power or Current Amplifier

The load resistance is a complex function of the transformer (T) turns ratio and resistance of the transformer secondary winding. It is relatively low so that sufficient signal current is developed in the transformer secondary

amplifiers according to bias

Amplifiers are also classified according to their biasing conditions, or, in other words, according to the portion of the input signal voltage cycle during which output current flows. There are four classes of amplifiers according to bias: class A, class B, class AB, and class C.

Class A amplifiers are biased in the center of their operating curves so that output current flows during the *entire* cycle of the input voltage. This results in *minimum distortion* of the output signal, and, as a result, class A amplifiers are widely used in audio systems, where low distortion is important.

Class B amplifiers are biased at cutoff so that output current flows for approximately *one-half* of the input-signal voltage cycle. When no input signal is present, no output current flows. In effect, a class B amplifier cuts off one half of the a-c input-signal waveform.

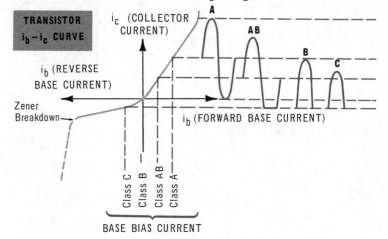

Transistor classes of operation differ somewhat from tubes because there is a reverse current beyond cutoff. Also, class C cannot be far beyond cutoff because the signal swing might drive the transistor into the zener breakdown region

Class AB amplifiers are biased so that output current flows for *appreciably more* than one half of the input cycle, but for less than the entire cycle. Essentially, class AB amplifiers are a compromise between the low distortion of class A amplifiers and the high efficiency of class B amplifiers.

Class C amplifiers are biased beyond cutoff so that output current only flows during the *positive-going peak* of the input cycle. Such amplifiers have high power outputs. They also have a high degree of distortion, which prevents their being used for audio applications.

The curves shown on the next page represent the various classes of bias for electron-tube circuits. Similar curves are developed for transistor circuits.

amplifiers according to bias (cont.)

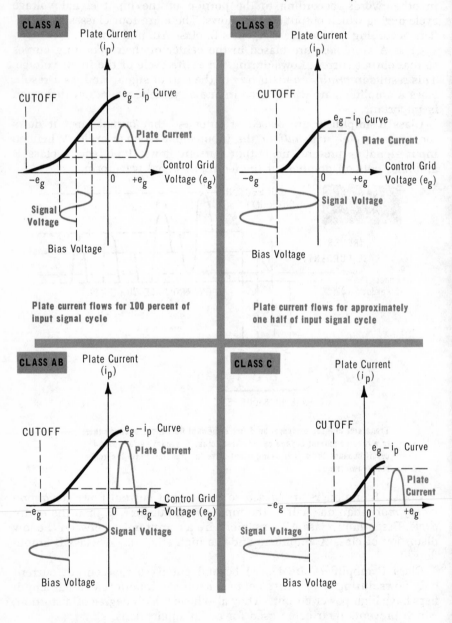

CLASS A

Plate Current (i_p)

CUTOFF

$e_g - i_p$ Curve

Plate Current

Control Grid Voltage (e_g)

$-e_g$ 0 $+e_g$

Signal Voltage

Bias Voltage

Plate current flows for 100 percent of input signal cycle

CLASS B

Plate Current (i_p)

CUTOFF

$e_g - i_p$ Curve

Plate Current

Control Grid Voltage (e_g)

$-e_g$ 0 $+e_g$

Signal Voltage

Bias Voltage

Plate current flows for approximately one half of input signal cycle

CLASS AB

Plate Current (i_p)

CUTOFF

$e_g - i_p$ Curve

Plate Current

Control Grid Voltage (e_g)

$-e_g$ 0 $+e_g$

Signal Voltage

Bias Voltage

Plate current flows for more than half but less than 100 percent of signal cycle

CLASS C

Plate Current (i_p)

CUTOFF

$e_g - i_p$ Curve

Plate Current

$-e_g$ 0 $+e_g$

Signal Voltage

Bias Voltage

Plate current flows only for small portion of input signal cycle

amplifiers according to coupling

In applications where *more* than a single amplifier stage is used, the amplifiers are often classified according to the way in which they are coupled. The basic coupling methods are: *resistance-capacitance* (RC) coupling, *impedance* coupling, *transformer* coupling, and *direct* coupling. These are illustrated on the following page.

When amplifiers are RC coupled, the output load is a resistance, usually of relatively high value. RC-coupled amplifiers have good frequency-response characteristics over a relatively wide frequency range. Above and below this range, the gain falls off. The decrease in gain at the lower frequencies is caused by the increased reactance of the coupling capacitor. At the higher frequencies, the decrease in gain is caused by the decreased reactance of the interelectrode capacitances of the stages, as well as the stray capacitance of the wiring between stages. The decrease in these capacitances causes more of the signal voltage to be shunted, or bypassed, to ground.

In impedance coupling, a *coil* is used as the output load instead of a resistance. The frequency response of an impedance-coupled amplifier is not uniform, or flat, like that of an RC-coupled amplifier, because the impedance of the load coil varies with frequency, causing the amplifier voltage gain to increase with frequency up to the point where it is limited by the circuit shunting capacitances.

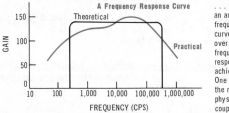

... is a graph of the gain of an amplifier plotted against frequency. A perfect response curve would be absolutely flat over the entire range of frequencies amplified. Such a response is impossible to achieve in actual circuits. One of the reasons for this is the reactive components, both physical and stray, in the coupling circuits

In transformer coupling, the output of one circuit is coupled to the input of the next circuit by means of a transformer. This can also provide additional amplification if the transformer has a step-up turns ratio. Transformer coupling, though, is expensive and bulky. It very often has poorer frequency response at the higher and lower audio frequencies than does an RC-coupled amplifier.

In direct coupling, the output of one stage is applied directly to the input of the next stage. A rather elaborate voltage distribution arrangement is required to provide the proper d-c operating voltages to amplifiers coupled in this way. When direct coupling uses *no reactive components*, it is especially suitable for amplifying low frequencies, as well as d-c signals. The absence of reactive components results in direct coupling having a frequency response that is uniform over a very wide range. However, d-c amplifiers are affected by voltage *drift*.

This has only been a brief summary. Detailed information on coupling was given in Volumes 3 and 4.

amplifiers
according to coupling (cont.)

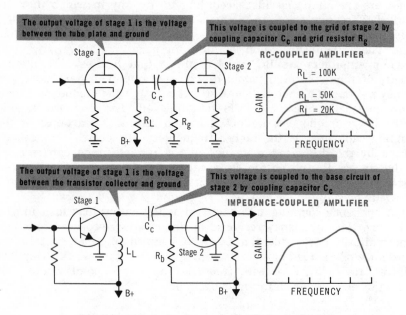

The output voltage of stage 1 is the voltage between the tube plate and ground

This voltage is coupled to the grid of stage 2 by coupling capacitor C_c and grid resistor R_g

Stage 1

Stage 2

RC-COUPLED AMPLIFIER

$R_L = 100K$

$R_L = 50K$

$R_L = 20K$

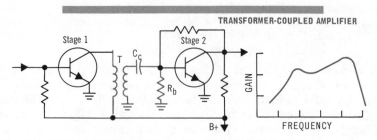

The output voltage of stage 1 is the voltage between the transistor collector and ground

This voltage is coupled to the base circuit of stage 2 by coupling capacitor C_c

Stage 1

IMPEDANCE-COUPLED AMPLIFIER

The response curve of an impedance-coupled amplifier is not as flat as that of an RC-coupled amplifier because the reactance of L_L and, therefore, the signal voltage, increases with frequency

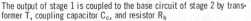

TRANSFORMER-COUPLED AMPLIFIER

Stage 1

Stage 2

The output of stage 1 is coupled to the base circuit of stage 2 by transformer T, coupling capacitor C_c, and resistor R_b

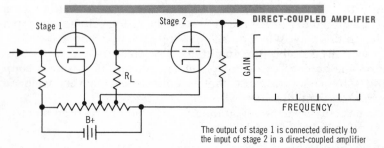

Stage 1

Stage 2

DIRECT-COUPLED AMPLIFIER

The output of stage 1 is connected directly to the input of stage 2 in a direct-coupled amplifier

amplifiers according to circuit configuration

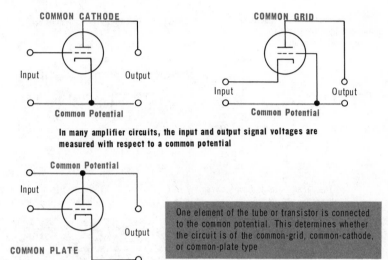

COMMON CATHODE

Input Output

Common Potential

COMMON GRID

Input Output

Common Potential

In many amplifier circuits, the input and output signal voltages are measured with respect to a common potential

Common Potential

Input

Output

COMMON PLATE

One element of the tube or transistor is connected to the common potential. This determines whether the circuit is of the common-grid, common-cathode, or common-plate type

The common potential is usually the zero reference for voltage measurements, and is designated as ground

Another way of classifying amplifiers is to specify the principal elements returned to *ground.* Thus, in amplifier circuits using electron tubes, there are grounded-cathode amplifiers, grounded-grid amplifiers, and grounded-plate amplifiers. Similarly, in transistor amplifier circuits, there are grounded-base amplifiers, grounded-emitter amplifiers, and grounded-collector amplifiers.

You should understand that an element does not have to be connected *directly* to ground to be considered grounded. It may be connected to ground through a component, such as a resistor or capacitor. The important point is that the potential of the element is at *a-c ground,* which is the *zero-potential reference point* for measuring all *signal* voltages, both input and output.

Another way of looking at this is to consider an amplifier as a *four-terminal circuit.* The input signal is applied to two of the terminals and the output is taken from the other two. However, one input terminal and one output terminal are usually *common* and are connected to the same tube or transistor element. You then have a common cathode, common emitter, and so forth, circuit. The common reference point is usually designated as ground.

The different amplifiers typed according to circuit configuration are shown on the following page.

amplifiers according to circuit configuration (cont.)

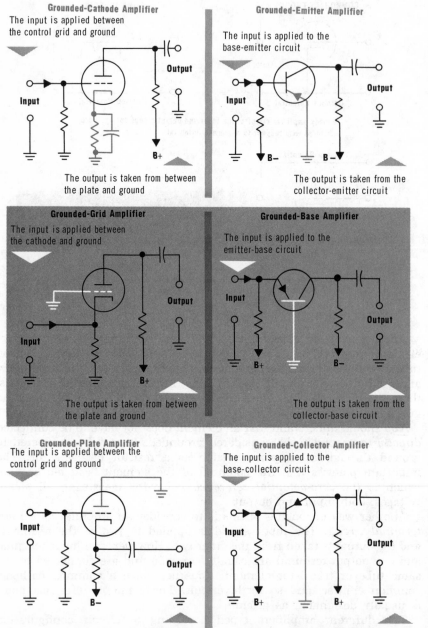

Grounded-Cathode Amplifier
The input is applied between the control grid and ground

Output

Input

B+

The output is taken from between the plate and ground

Grounded-Emitter Amplifier
The input is applied to the base-emitter circuit

Output

Input

B−   B−

The output is taken from the collector-emitter circuit

Grounded-Grid Amplifier
The input is applied between the cathode and ground

Output

Input

B+

The output is taken from between the plate and ground

Grounded-Base Amplifier
The input is applied to the emitter-base circuit

Input

Output

B+   B−

The output is taken from the collector-base circuit

Grounded-Plate Amplifier
The input is applied between the control grid and ground

Input

B−

Output

The output is taken from between the cathode and ground

Grounded-Collector Amplifier
The input is applied to the base-collector circuit

Input

Output

B+   B+

The output is taken from the emitter-collector circuit

amplifiers according to bandwidth

Sometimes, amplifiers are classified according to bandwidth. On this basis of classification, there are two principal types of amplifiers: those that are *tuned* and amplify a *restricted range* of frequencies; and those that are *untuned* and amplify a *wide range* of frequencies.

A tuned amplifier usually has a tuned (*resonant*) circuit in its input or output, or both, that passes only a relatively narrow band of frequencies. The center of this frequency band is the resonant frequency of the tuned circuit. The width of the band depends on the Q of the tuned circuit. In some tuned amplifiers, the band of frequencies that is amplified is *permanently fixed* by the values of the tuned-circuit components. In other tuned amplifiers, the frequency band that is amplified can be *varied* by changing the value of one of the components of the tuned circuit.

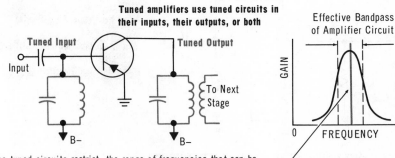

Tuned amplifiers use tuned circuits in their inputs, their outputs, or both

Tuned Input   Tuned Output

Input   To Next Stage

B–   B–

The tuned circuits restrict the range of frequencies that can be amplified by the amplifier to a relatively narrow band centered around the resonant frequency of the tuned circuit

Effective Bandpass of Amplifier Circuit

GAIN

0   FREQUENCY

Resonant Frequency of Tuned Circuit

Untuned amplifiers are not tuned to any specific band of frequencies. The range of frequencies that they can amplify, though, is still limited to some extent by the circuit components and stray capacitances. Compared to tuned amplifiers, however, they can amplify an extremely wide range of frequencies.

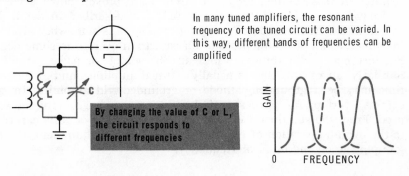

In many tuned amplifiers, the resonant frequency of the tuned circuit can be varied. In this way, different bands of frequencies can be amplified

By changing the value of C or L, the circuit responds to different frequencies

GAIN

0   FREQUENCY

amplifiers according to frequency

The most common amplifier classification is according to *frequency*. This is especially useful in the description and analysis of circuits and equipments used for the radio transmission of electronic signals. According to frequency, amplifiers are classified as: *direct-current* (d-c) amplifiers, *audio-frequency* (a-f) amplifiers, *intermediate-frequency* (i-f) amplifiers, *radio-frequency* (r-f) amplifiers, and *video-frequency* amplifiers.

As their name implies, d-c amplifiers amplify d-c signals. Audio amplifiers operate in the audio-frequency range, or from about 20 to 20,000 cps. Video amplifiers are capable of amplifying signals from the lower audio frequencies to as high as 4 or 5 megacycles. You can see that video amplifiers are characterized by *very wide bandwidths*.

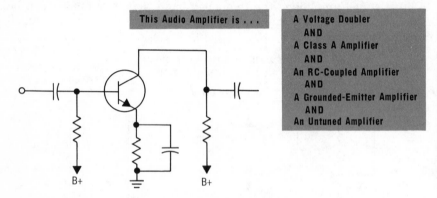

This Audio Amplifier is . . .
A Voltage Doubler
AND
A Class A Amplifier
AND
An RC-Coupled Amplifier
AND
A Grounded-Emitter Amplifier
AND
An Untuned Amplifier

Practically every amplifier circuit fits into all of the different classifications previously described

I-f and r-f amplifiers are not defined in terms of a specific frequency range. Instead, they are defined by the *nature* of the frequencies they amplify. Generally, they are *tuned* amplifiers, and therefore amplify a relatively small band of frequencies. I-f amplifiers operate at the intermediate frequency of a particular piece of equipment, and r-f amplifiers are tuned to the frequencies of various r-f carrier waves.

Later in this volume, amplifier circuits are broken down according to frequency (audio, video, r-f, and i-f), and described in detail. You will find that this method of grouping amplifiers is somewhat arbitrary, inasmuch as all of the methods of classification overlap to some degree. For instance, audio amplifiers may also be voltage or power amplifiers. Similarly, an r-f amplifier is usually a tuned amplifier, and at the same time may be a grounded-cathode or grounded-grid amplifier. In spite of this overlap, for purposes of description, some grouping must be used. From the standpoint of learning how amplifier circuits contribute to the overall operation of many types of electronic equipment, the best grouping is on the basis of frequency.

amplifier distortion

With the exception of certain waveshaping and special-purpose amplifiers, the output of an ideal amplifier is *identical* to the input except for an increase in amplitude, and, more often than not, a 180-degree phase reversal. In practical amplifiers, however, these ideal conditions are not met. Special distortion of the output signal always occurs.

Amplifier circuits are designed so that the degree of distortion is kept to a level that can be tolerated. Sometimes this can be accomplished by using one particular type of amplifier circuit rather than another. In other cases, though, it requires the use of additional components or circuits to compensate for distortion.

There are three main types of amplifier distortion: *frequency distortion, phase distortion,* and *amplitude distortion.* Frequency distortion occurs when some frequency components of a signal are amplified more than others. This type of distortion results because various circuit components, such as coupling capacitors, respond differently to different frequencies.

Phase distortion occurs because most coupling circuits *shift* the phase of a sine wave by an amount that depends on its frequency. Thus, each sine-wave component of a complex waveform is shifted in phase by a different amount. This causes distortion of the overall waveform. Phase distortion is not important in the processing of signals that represent voice or music, since the human ear cannot detect phase shifts of the individual components of a complex wave. In applications such as radar or television, though, phase distortion is of considerable importance.

Amplitude distortion occurs when equal changes in the amplitude of the amplifier input signal do not produce proportionate changes in the output. An extreme example of this is an input signal that drives an amplifier into *saturation.* As maximum output current flows at saturation, when the input increases further, the output amplitude does not change.

Input Voltage   Output Voltage   **Input Voltage**   Output Voltage

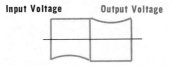

Frequency distortion occurs when some frequency components of a signal are amplified more than others

Phase distortion occurs when the various frequency components of a signal are shifted in phase by different amounts

Input Voltage   Output Voltage

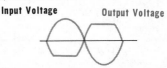

Amplitude distortion occurs when equal changes in the input signal do not produce proportionate changes in the output

For convenience of presentation, little difference in overall amplitude is shown. In actual amplifiers, the output voltages are many times greater than the inputs. The effects of the various types of distortion on the output waveforms, though, are as shown

summary

☐ An amplifier circuit includes all of the circuit components that provide bias, as well as any used in compensating networks. ☐ According to use, the two main amplifier classifications are voltage amplifiers and power amplifiers. Voltage amplifiers increase the voltage level of a signal, while power amplifiers deliver large currents to their output load.

☐ According to bias, amplifiers are classified as class A, class B, class AB, and class C. ☐ According to the coupling method used, amplifiers are classified as resistance capacitance (RC) coupled, impedance coupled, transformer coupled, and direct coupled. ☐ According to circuit configuration, amplifiers are classified on the basis of the principal elements returned to a-c ground. For example, grounded-grid amplifier. ☐ According to bandwidth, there are two principal types of amplifiers: those that are tuned and amplify a restricted range of frequencies; and those that are untuned and amplify a wide range of frequencies. ☐ According to frequency, amplifiers are classified as direct-current (d-c) amplifiers, audio-frequency (a-f) amplifiers, intermediate-frequency (i-f) amplifiers, radio-frequency (r-f) amplifiers, and video-frequency amplifiers.

☐ The output of an ideal amplifier is identical to the input except for an increase in amplitude, and often there is a 180-degree phase-reversal. In practical amplifiers, though, some distortion always occurs. ☐ There are three main types of amplifier distortion: frequency distortion, phase distortion, and amplitude distortion. ☐ An extreme example of amplitude distortion is an input signal that drives an amplifier into saturation. ☐ Frequency distortion occurs when some frequency components of the signal are amplified more than others. ☐ Phase distortion occurs because coupling circuits often shift some frequency components of the signal more than others.

review questions

1. What is the difference between a voltage amplifier and a power amplifier?
2. Name four types of amplifiers classified by frequency.
3. How does saturation cause distortion?
4. What is the difference between a class AB and a class B amplifier?
5. Name the four basic coupling methods.
6. How do tuned and untuned amplifiers differ?
7. What are *compensating networks*?
8. What causes frequency and phase distortion in an amplifier?
9. Is distortion in an amplifier always undesirable?
10. Which is more efficient: a class A or a class C amplifier?

audio amplifier circuits

Audio amplifier circuits of some type are used in every piece of electronic equipment whose function is to transmit, receive, or otherwise process sound signals. Audio amplifiers are used in radio and television receivers, transmitter modulators, tape recorders, phonographs, and public address systems. In radio and television receivers, the audio amplifier circuits receive the audio signal after it has been removed from the AM or FM carrier by detection. They amplify this weak signal to the level required to drive the receiver loudspeaker. In tape recorders and phonographs, the audio amplifier circuits receive their input signal from *pickup devices*, which develop audio signal voltages that correspond to the audio intelligence contained on the tapes or records. The circuits amplify these audio signals to the point where they can suitably drive the equipment loudspeaker.

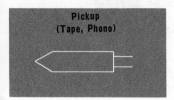

Microphone

These are the schematic diagram symbols for the input and output devices commonly used with audio amplifiers

In other applications, such as transmitter modulators, the input to the audio amplifier circuits is often supplied by a microphone. The modulator circuits amplify the low-level output of the microphone so that when it modulates the r-f carrier, the desired percentage, or level, of modulation will be realized. The audio circuits of a public address system amplify the microphone output so that it can be sent over the system interconnecting wires and provide satisfactory driving power for the system loudspeakers.

Although all audio amplifiers distort the amplified signal to some extent, the degree of distortion that can be tolerated varies widely depending on the application. In the high-fidelity reproduction of music, for example, very little distortion is permissible. But in public address systems, where intelligibility rather than fidelity is important, a considerable amount of distortion can be tolerated.

the basic two-stage audio amplifier

Both a tube and a transistor version of a basic two-stage audio amplifier are shown on the following page. A functional diagram of the tube amplifier is shown below. As you can see from the functional diagram, the basic tube amplifier circuit consists of two stages: an audio *voltage* amplifier and an audio *power* amplifier. Both stages are biased for *class A* operation to minimize distortion of the amplified signal.

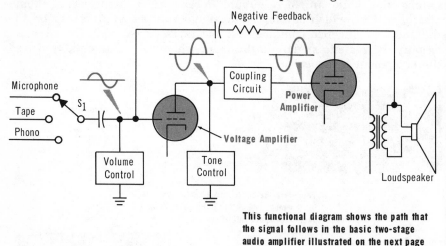

This functional diagram shows the path that the signal follows in the basic two-stage audio amplifier illustrated on the next page

The voltage amplifier stage receives an audio input signal from a microphone, a magnetic tape unit, or a phono pickup cartridge, depending on the position of switch S_1. The purpose of the voltage amplifier is to increase the *voltage level* of the input signal to the point where it is sufficient to drive the power amplifier stage. This voltage increase is necessary, since the power amplifier requires a relatively large input voltage in order to develop a large current or power output. The amplified signal voltage at the output of the voltage amplifier is coupled to the power amplifier, which produces the audio power required to drive the loudspeaker. *Transformer coupling* is used between the output of the power amplifier and the loudspeaker to obtain the proper impedance match, and, therefore, maximum transfer of power.

Additional features of the two-stage audio amplifier include a *tone control* circuit, *volume control*, and the use of *negative feedback* in the power amplifier stage. The two-stage amplifier shown here and on the next page illustrates many of the characteristics and elements of audio amplifier circuits in general. The various portions of the basic amplifier, together with their function and operation, are described in detail on the following pages. In addition, for each portion of the circuit, other methods of accomplishing the same function will be covered.

the basic two-stage audio amplifier (cont.)

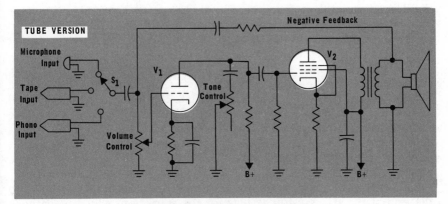

An important difference between two-stage tube and transistor amplifiers is the type of coupling used between stages

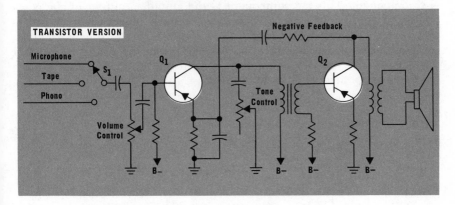

An important difference between the tube and transistor versions of this two-stage audio amplifier is the coupling used between the stages. Although RC coupling is satisfactory for the tube version, it is impractical when transistors are used because of the large difference in input and output impedance that is characteristic of transistor amplifiers. If RC coupling was used, the decrease in overall amplification caused by the impedance mismatch would make it necessary to use more than two amplifier stages to produce a gain equivalent to that of the two-stage tube amplifier. By using transformer coupling, though, the impedances can be matched to produce maximum amplifier gain.

Sometimes, the first transistor stage is called a driver, or a driver stage. The driver is biased to produce maximum *power gain*, while the power amplifier is biased to produce maximum *power output*.

the a-f voltage amplifier

Triodes are used for a-f voltage amplifiers in applications requiring relatively *low voltage gain.* When *high gain* is required, *pentodes,* with their large values of mu, are usually used. A typical pentode a-f voltage amplifier is shown in A. The pentode stage is similar to the triode shown on the previous page, with the exception of its screen and suppressor grid circuits.

The stage is biased for class A operation, which means that plate current flows for the *complete* cycle of the input signal and the grid is *never* driven positive by the input signal. The input voltage is applied across capacitor C_1 and volume control R_g, which together form a voltage divider. At audio frequencies, the reactance of C_1 is low, so that most of the signal voltage appears across R_g. Resistor R_g is variable and is adjusted to tap off a signal level for the desired loudness level at the amplifier loudspeaker.

The voltage between the movable arm of R_g and ground is applied to the grid of the stage. *Cathode bias* for the stage is provided by cathode resistor R_k and capacitor C_k. The variations in plate current produced by the input signal cause the voltage drop across load resistor R_L to have an a-c component. This a-c component is the amplified output of the stage and is coupled to the a-f power amplifier through capacitor C_2. C_2 passes the a-c component and blocks the dc. Resistor R_s is the screen dropping resistor and provides the proper screen grid operating voltage. Capacitor C_s bypasses the variations in screen current to ground, preventing them from causing variations in screen voltage.

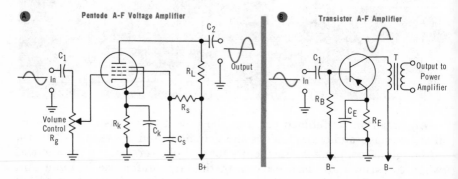

In the driver amplifier of the transistorized two-stage amplifier shown in B, the input signal is coupled through capacitor C_1 to the base-emitter circuit of the grounded-emitter amplifier. The amplified output signal is developed across the primary of transformer T in the collector circuit. The turns ratio of T is such that it matches the output impedance of the driver to the input impedance of the power amplifier. Resistor R_E and capacitor C_E in the emitter circuit of the stage maintain bias stability by providing negative d-c feedback to the base.

the a-f power amplifier

In the tube version of our two-stage audio amplifier, the power amplifier is a high-mu pentode biased for class A operation. This a *single-ended* power amplifier, since a *single tube* is used. You will learn later about other types of power amplifiers, such as *push-pull* amplifiers.

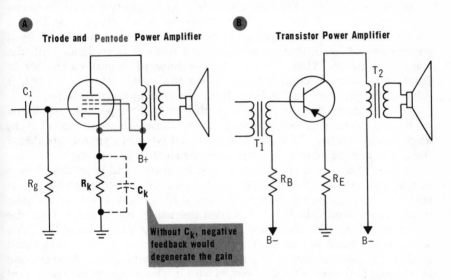

A Triode and Pentode Power Amplifier

B Transistor Power Amplifier

Without C_k, negative feedback would degenerate the gain

A single-ended pentode power amplifier is shown in A. If you ignore the elements shown in color, you can see how *triodes* can also be used for a-f power amplifiers. However, because of their low gain, triodes require larger input signal voltages. The input signal is coupled to the control grid by C_1 and R_g. Bias for the stage is provided by cathode resistor R_k and bypass capacitor C_k. Since *maximum power* is to be developed in the plate circuit, the plate load, which is the impedance offered to the signal current by the transformer primary, is relatively low. Transformer coupling of the output signal to the loudspeaker is necessary to match the amplifier output impedance to the very low impedance of the loudspeaker. A *step-down* transformer is used, so a relatively low-voltage, high-current signal is applied to the loudspeaker.

The a-f power transistor differs from the a-f driver mainly in size. The power transistor is larger, since it must handle considerably more power. In the basic amplifier, shown in B, the power-stage input is applied to the base-emitter circuit by transformer T_1. The amplified output is coupled to the loudspeaker by impedance-matching transformer T_2. Both a-c and d-c negative feedback are provided by unbypassed emitter resistor R_E. The d-c feedback provides bias stability; the a-c feedback reduces distortion. This is covered in more detail later in this volume.

the speaker

The output of our basic audio amplifier drives a loudspeaker, which we will refer to from now on as a *speaker*. The function of the speaker is to convert the *current variations* delivered to it by the power amplifier into *sound waves*.

As you know, sound waves are made up of alternate compressions and rarefactions of the air, which cause the sensation of sound when they enter the ear. In a speaker, the sound waves are produced by a paper *cone*, or horn, that moves back and forth in accordance with the signal variations. When the cone moves forward, it pushes the air in front of it, causing compressions; when the cone moves backward, it releases the pressure on the air in front of it, causing rarefactions.

Most speakers used today are of the *dynamic* type and are based on the interaction of two magnetic fields whose directions are at right angles to each other. There are two principal types of dynamic speakers: the *permanent-magnet* (PM) type and the *electrodynamic* type.

In the PM dynamic speaker, a strong magnetic field is produced by a *permanent magnet*. The flux lines of this field are concentrated in a soft iron core shaped as shown. Mounted in the gap between the pole pieces of the iron core is a coil, called the *voice coil*, which carries the audio signal current from the output of the a-f power amplifier. The voice coil is mounted in such a way that it is free to move back and forth for a small distance in a longitudinal direction. The speaker cone is attached to the voice coil and moves with it. The magnetic field produced by the signal current in the voice coil is at right angles to the field of the permanent magnet. The two fields attract or repel each other, depending on the amplitude and polarity of the signal current. This attraction or repulsion causes an inward or outward movement of the voice coil and the cone, and thus produces sound waves that correspond to the variations in signal current.

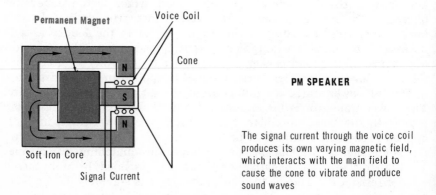

Permanent Magnet   Voice Coil

Cone

Soft Iron Core

Signal Current

PM SPEAKER

The signal current through the voice coil produces its own varying magnetic field, which interacts with the main field to cause the cone to vibrate and produce sound waves

the speaker (cont.)

The voice coil consists of only a few turns of low-resistance wire and has a relatively *low impedance* throughout the audio frequency range. At the lower audio frequencies, the impedance is generally somewhere between 2 and 8 ohms. It is because of this low impedance of the voice coil that an impedance-matching transformer must be used between the output of the power amplifier and the speaker.

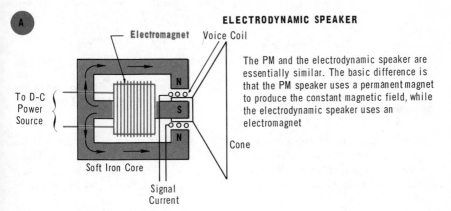

A

ELECTRODYNAMIC SPEAKER

Electromagnet   Voice Coil

The PM and the electrodynamic speaker are essentially similar. The basic difference is that the PM speaker uses a permanent magnet to produce the constant magnetic field, while the electrodynamic speaker uses an electromagnet

To D-C Power Source

N
S
N

Cone

Soft Iron Core

Signal Current

The electrodynamic speaker is similar to the PM speaker. The basic difference is that an *electromagnet* is used to generate the constant magnetic field instead of a permanent magnet. This, of course, requires that a d-c power source supply energizing current to the electromagnet. An electrodynamic speaker is shown in A. It is not used as often as a PM speaker because it is more expensive.

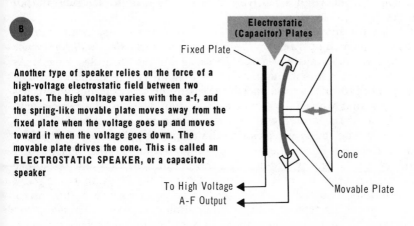

B

Electrostatic (Capacitor) Plates

Fixed Plate

Another type of speaker relies on the force of a high-voltage electrostatic field between two plates. The high voltage varies with the a-f, and the spring-like movable plate moves away from the fixed plate when the voltage goes up and moves toward it when the voltage goes down. The movable plate drives the cone. This is called an **ELECTROSTATIC SPEAKER**, or a capacitor speaker

Cone

To High Voltage
A-F Output

Movable Plate

the microphone

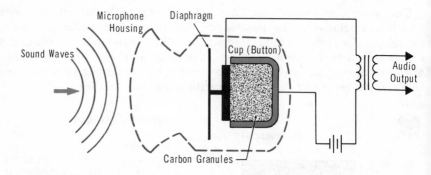

The carbon granules of a carbon microphone make up a resistance whose value is varied by the pressure of the sound waves

The principal disadvantage of the carbon microphone is that it requires an external voltage source

One of the inputs to our basic audio amplifier is from a microphone, which converts sound waves into corresponding electrical signals. There are many types of microphones in use today. The type chosen for any particular application depends on mechanical characteristics, such as size, weight, and ruggedness, as well as electrical characteristics, such as frequency response, impedance, and sensitivity.

A microphone's frequency response is the range of audio frequencies over which the microphone can respond uniformly. The impedance of a microphone is important with respect to the input impedance of the circuit that the microphone is driving. To deliver maximum output to its load, these impedances must be of the same order. Otherwise, impedance-matching devices, such as transformers, are required. The sensitivity of a microphone is a measure of how much electrical power the microphone delivers to a load having a matched impedance for a given input sound level. High sensitivity thus means a high electrical output for a given sound level.

Probably the most common type of microphone in use is the *carbon microphone,* which operates on the principle that the *electrical resistance* of carbon granules varies as the *pressure* on the granules varies. As shown, a carbon microphone consists of a small cup of carbon granules and a diaphragm that exerts varying pressure on the granules when it is struck by sound waves. To produce an output voltage, the cup is connected in a *series circuit* with a battery and the primary of a transformer. When no sound waves strike the diaphragm, a steady d-c current flows in the circuit, so there is no audio output in the transformer secondary. But sound waves striking the diaphragm vary the resistance of the carbon granules and a varying d-c current flows in the circuit. The *variations,* coupled to the transformer secondary, are the microphone output. This type of carbon microphone is called a *single-button* microphone, since it contains a single cup, or button, of carbon granules.

other types of microphones

Other frequently used types of microphones are the *dynamic micro-phone* and the *crystal microphone*. As shown in A, the dynamic micro-phone is similar to the PM speaker, except that it converts sound energy into electrical energy. The diaphragm of the microphone, which corre-sponds to the cone of the PM speaker, moves, or vibrates, when struck by sound waves. The voice coil is attached to the diaphragm and moves with it. Since the voice coil is positioned in the magnetic field of a permanent magnet, it cuts flux lines when it moves. As a result, a voltage is induced in the voice coil corresponding to the sound waves striking the diaphragm.

The crystal microphone, shown in B, operates on the principle that certain crystal materials generate a voltage when *mechanical stress* is applied to them. This is called the *piezoelectric effect*. A basic crystal microphone consists of a crystal, a diaphragm that contacts one side of the crystal, and an electrode plate that contacts the other side of the crystal. Sound waves striking the diaphragm cause the diaphragm to apply a varying stress to the crystal. The crystal, in turn, generates a voltage that has essentially the same waveform as the sound waves.

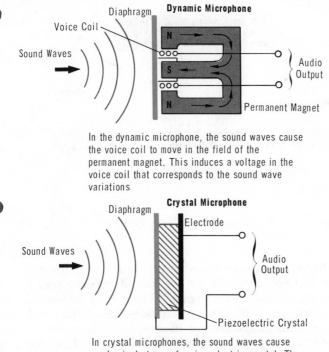

A — Dynamic Microphone

Diaphragm · Voice Coil · Sound Waves · N · S · N · Audio Output · Permanent Magnet

In the dynamic microphone, the sound waves cause the voice coil to move in the field of the permanent magnet. This induces a voltage in the voice coil that corresponds to the sound wave variations

B — Crystal Microphone

Diaphragm · Electrode · Sound Waves · Audio Output · Piezoelectric Crystal

In crystal microphones, the sound waves cause mechanical stress of a piezoelectric crystal. The crystal produces a voltage that corresponds to the sound wave variations

the phono
and magnetic-tape pickups

Our basic two-stage audio amplifier is equipped with both a phono and a magnetic-tape input. Both of these inputs, like the microphone input, consist of signal voltages that vary at an audio rate in accordance with the signal intelligence. The only difference between any of the inputs is the manner in which they are generated before being applied to the audio amplifier.

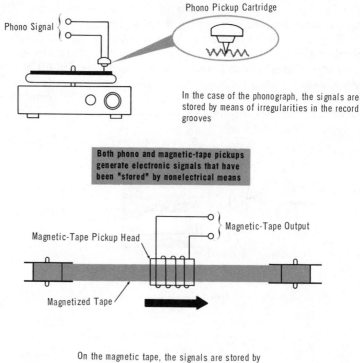

Phono Pickup Cartridge

Phono Signal

In the case of the phonograph, the signals are stored by means of irregularities in the record grooves

Both phono and magnetic-tape pickups generate electronic signals that have been "stored" by nonelectrical means

Magnetic-Tape Output

Magnetic-Tape Pickup Head

Magnetized Tape

On the magnetic tape, the signals are stored by magnetized particles

The phono input is generated by a pickup cartridge that converts the *movements* of the phono needle in the record grooves into a corresponding, varying voltage. This signal voltage may be on the order of millivolts when magnetic pickup cartridges are used, and nearly one volt when crystal cartridges are used.

The magnetic-tape input is generated by a pickup head in a tape recorder. Essentially, a pickup head is a coil that has a voltage *induced* in it when a magnetized tape moves past it. The magnitude and polarity of the induced voltage correspond to the variations in tape magnetization.

volume control

The volume control of both versions of our two-stage amplifier consists of a *variable resistor* that is manually adjusted to provide the desired listening output level from the speaker. The volume control operates by setting the *amplitude* of the signal input to the first stage of the amplifier. The signal current flows through the volume control resistor and develops a voltage across it. The larger the resistance, the greater is the voltage drop, and the larger is the input signal to the stage.

The basic difference between the volume control circuits used in our tube and transistor circuits is the manner in which the signal voltage picked off the volume control resistor is applied to the first amplifier stage. In the tube circuit, the signal voltage can be applied *directly* to the grid. In the transistor circuit, the signal is *capacitively coupled* to the base circuit. If this capacitive coupling were not used, the base-emitter bias of the transistor would change every time the volume control was adjusted. The capacitor prevents this from happening by isolating the volume control resistor from the d-c bias circuit of the transistor.

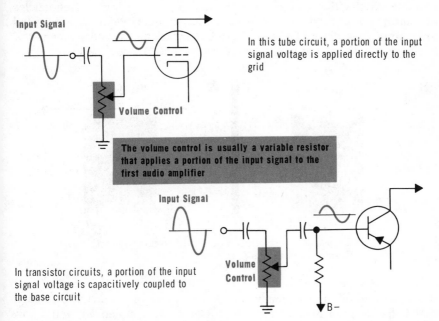

Input Signal

In this tube circuit, a portion of the input signal voltage is applied directly to the grid

Volume Control

The volume control is usually a variable resistor that applies a portion of the input signal to the first audio amplifier

Input Signal

In transistor circuits, a portion of the input signal voltage is capacitively coupled to the base circuit

Volume Control

B–

In tube circuits, the a-f signal taken off the volume control can also be capacitively coupled. There is little difference in most tube circuits whether it is or is not. In tube amplifier stages that use grid-leak or contact bias, capacitive coupling should be used or the tube will be affected by the setting of the volume control in the same fashion that a transistor is.

tone control

Tone controls are essentially *variable filter circuits* that alter the output frequency response of an audio amplifier. A tone control may be included in an audio amplifier to permit the output tonal quality to be adjusted for most pleasant listening, or it may be included out of necessity. An example of this would be in an equipment that uses a small-diameter speaker. Such speakers accent the high frequencies of the audio output and must generally be compensated for by tone controls that attenuate or reduce the high frequencies. Strictly speaking, these circuits are really filter circuits instead of tone controls, since they are not variable. The basic principles on which they operate, however, are the same as those involved in tone controls.

The simplest type of tone control consists of a capacitor and a variable resistor connected between the plate of a tube, or the collector of a transistor, and ground. This is shown in A. Such a tone control is a *treble control,* since it acts on the *high frequencies* of the audio signal. The capacitor presents a relatively low reactance to the higher frequencies and a high reactance to the lower frequencies. The setting of the variable resistor then determines to what degree the higher frequencies are shunted to ground. Very little of the low-frequency energy is shunted to ground, regardless of the setting of the variable resistor, because of the high reactance the capacitor offers to these frequencies.

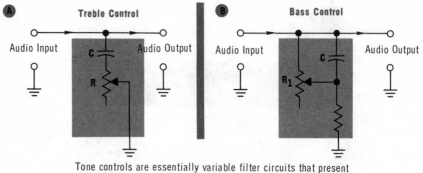

Tone controls are essentially variable filter circuits that present different impedances to different frequencies

A simple *bass control* is shown in B. This type of tone control acts at the *lower end* of the frequency range. The value of capacitor C is such that it has a large reactance at the lower audio frequencies and a low reactance at the higher frequencies. This causes the voltage drop between the top of C and ground to be larger at low frequencies than at high frequencies. Variable resistor R_1 shunts capacitor C, and essentially reduces the boosting effect of C on the low frequencies. The setting of R_1 determines just how much the effect of C is reduced.

More elaborate tone controls combine *both* treble and bass control circuits.

negative current feedback

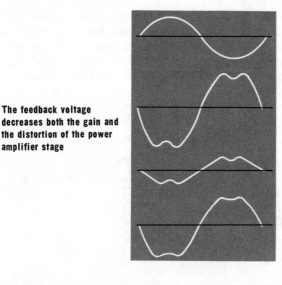

Input Signal

The feedback voltage decreases both the gain and the distortion of the power amplifier stage

Output Signal If Negative Feedback Were Not Used

Feedback Signal When Negative Feedback Is Used

Output Signal When Negative Feedback Is Used

As you learned, negative feedback in an amplifier is a process whereby a portion of the output signal is fed back to the input of the amplifier *180 degrees out of phase* with the input signal. Because of the phase difference, the feedback signal *cancels* part of the input signal, so the gain of the stage is less than it would be if feedback were not used. However, as shown, the feedback not only cancels a portion of the input signal, but it also tends to *cancel distortion* in the output signal caused by nonlinearities in the stage. As a result, negative feedback is often used in audio amplifiers in spite of the decrease in gain that it causes.

Negative feedback in a grounded-emitter amplifier is accomplished by using an unbypassed emitter resistor. The audio signal variations that appear across the emitter resistor produce a feedback voltage that opposes the input signal

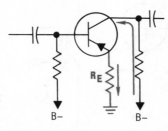

Negative feedback cannot be produced in this way in a grounded-base or grounded-collector amplifier. In these types of amplifiers, an unbypassed resistor in series with the common element would produce a feedback voltage that aided the input signal. The feedback would therefore be positive

In the transistor version of our basic two-stage audio amplifier, negative feedback is used in the power amplifier stage. One kind of feedback is produced by using an *unbypassed emitter resistor*. You recall that the emitter bypass capacitor charges and discharges with the audio variations of the emitter current. This, in effect, bypasses the audio variations around the emitter resistor and maintains a steady current and, therefore, voltage drop, in the emitter circuit.

negative current feedback (cont.)

If the emitter resistor is unbypassed, though, the current in the emitter circuit, as well as the voltage drop across the emitter resistor, *varies* according to the audio signal. These audio variations in the emitter circuit are 180 degrees out of phase with the input signal applied to the base, and oppose or cancel a portion of the input signal. This cancellation, or *degeneration*, as it is called, significantly reduces distortion of the signal introduced within the transistor.

With current feedback, the audio variations in tube current produce a varying voltage drop across the unbypassed cathode resistor. This voltage includes the signal variations plus the nonlinear distortion introduced in the tube. Since the cathode voltage is 180° out of phase with the signal voltage on the grid, the feedback voltage opposes the grid voltage. In this way the feedback voltage decreases both the gain and the distortion of the stage

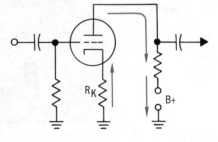

Negative feedback produced by an unbypassed emitter or cathode resistor is called *current feedback,* since it is derived from the signal current variations in the stage. As you will see, negative feedback can also be produced by transferring a portion of the output voltage of a stage directly back to the input. This is called *voltage feedback.*

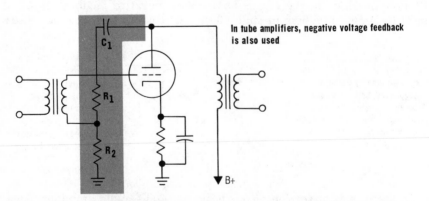

In tube amplifiers, negative voltage feedback is also used

In this circuit, a portion of the output voltage is fed back to the grid circuit by C_1, R_1, and R_2. C_1 passes only the audio signal variations, thereby isolating the grid circuit from the plate B+ supply. R_1 and R_2 form a voltage divider. Their values are chosen so that the desired feedback voltage is developed across R_2, which is in series with the second- ary of the input transformer as far as the input signal is concerned. Because of the 180° phase shift introduced by the tube, the feedback voltage across R_2 is in phase opposition to the input signal voltage developed across the secondary of the input transformer. The feedback voltage is therefore negative

negative
voltage feedback

Negative feedback in an amplifier can be accomplished not only by using the current variations in the stage to transfer part of the output signal back to the input, but also by feeding a portion of the *output voltage* directly back to the input. A frequently used grounded-emitter circuit employing negative voltage feedback is shown.

In this circuit, feedback resistor R_F is connected between the collector and the base input circuit. Since resistor R_F is not bypassed by a capacitor, it provides a-c, or signal, feedback, as well as d-c feedback for bias stability. When a *positive-going* input signal is applied to the base, the output voltage at the collector becomes more *negative* as a result of the 180-degree phase shift introduced by the stage. A portion of this output signal voltage is fed back to the base by the feedback resistor, and therefore *opposes* the input signal, causing degeneration.

Feedback resistor R_F transfers a portion of the output signal voltage back to the amplifier input

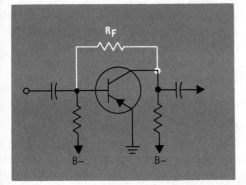

The feedback voltage is out of phase with the input signal because of the 180° phase shift introduced by a grounded-emitter amplifier

The situation is similar when a negative-going input signal is applied to the base. A portion of the positive increase in collector voltage is coupled back to the base by the feedback resistor. Again, you should be aware that this type of voltage feedback would cause regeneration, or positive feedback, in grounded-base or grounded-collector amplifiers, unless some means is taken to shift the phase of the feedback voltage. This could be done, effectively, by using the feedback signal from one stage to degenerate the input of another stage. Quite often, the output of a string of amplifiers is fed back to one of the input stages to obtain good negative feedback.

summary

☐ A basic two-stage audio amplifier consists of an audio voltage amplifier and an audio power amplifier. Both stages are biased for class A operation to minimize distortion. ☐ RC coupling is generally used in tube-type audio amplifiers. In transistor amplifiers, an interstage transformer is generally used. ☐ The first stage of a transistor audio amplifier is called a driver, and is biased to produce maximum power gain. The power amplifier is biased to produce maximum power output. ☐ In tube-type audio amplifiers, triodes are used for the voltage amplifier in applications requiring relatively low voltage gain, while pentodes are generally used when high gain is required. The power amplifier is usually always a pentode.

☐ The speaker converts the current variations produced by the power amplifier into sound waves. ☐ There are two principal types of dynamic speakers: the permanent-magnet (PM) type and the electrodynamic type, which uses an electromagnet. ☐ The microphone converts sound waves into corresponding electrical signals. ☐ The most common type of microphone in use is the carbon microphone. Other frequently used types of microphone are the dynamic microphone and the crystal microphone, which operates on the principle of the piezoelectric effect. ☐ The phono input is generated by a pickup cartridge, which converts movements of the phono needle in the record grooves into a varying voltage. Either a magnetic pickup or crystal pickup can be used. ☐ The magnetic-tape input is generated by a pickup head in a tape recorder.

☐ The volume control on an audio amplifier is used to control the output level from the speaker. It does this by varying the input signal applied to the first stage. ☐ The tone control alters the output frequency response to permit the tonal quality of the audio amplifier to be adjusted. ☐ Negative feedback significantly reduces distortion in an audio amplifier. It does this by canceling distortion introduced by the amplifier.

review questions

1. How does the carbon microphone operate?
2. What is meant by the *sensitivity* of a microphone?
3. On what principle is the crystal microphone based?
4. What is meant by a *pickup cartridge*? Name two types.
5. What is *negative feedback*? Why is it used?
6. What is a *PM speaker*?
7. In a two-stage transistor audio amplifier, what type of coupling is generally used between stages? In a tube amplifier?
8. How does the tone control work?
9. What is an electrostatic speaker?
10. What is a driver?

the push-pull power amplifier

In a conventional tube-type audio power amplifier, the input signal is applied to the control grid of the amplifier stage, and the amplified output is developed across the secondary of a transformer in the plate circuit of the stage. Such a circuit is often called a *single-ended amplifier* to distinguish it from a special type of amplifier called a *push-pull amplifier*. In a push-pull amplifier, the signal to be amplified is applied simultaneously to *two tubes*, and the amplified output signal is developed across a transformer that is connected *between* the plates of the two tubes.

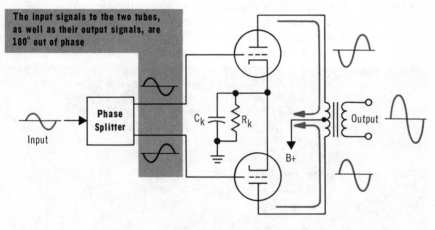

In a push-pull amplifier, the output signals of the two tubes combine across the common plate circuit transformer to produce a common signal that has a large power content and relatively small distortion

The basic principle on which the push-pull amplifier works is that the input signal is converted, before amplification, to *two* separate signals, which are identical except for a *180-degree phase difference*. Each of these signals is applied as the input to one of the tubes of the push-pull amplifier. Therefore, since the inputs to the two tubes are 180 degrees out of phase, so, also, are the outputs of the tubes. The output transformer in the plate circuits of the tubes is connected in such a way, though, that the audio components of the two separate plate currents combine to produce an *overall* audio signal having the *same waveshape* as the original input signal. The magnitude of this combined output signal is larger and contains less distortion than could be obtained with a comparable single-ended amplifier.

Push-pull amplifiers are normally operated class A, AB, or B. In class B operation, current for each tube flows for approximately *one half* of the input signal cycle. Each stage, though, amplifies a different half, so that the entire signal is reproduced in the output.

developing the output signal

The operation of transistor push-pull amplifiers is basically the same as the operation of tube types. In the class A grounded-emitter circuit shown, input signals 180 degrees out of phase are applied to the bases of transistors Q_1 and Q_2, respectively. The output signals from the two transistors are also 180 degrees out of phase and combine across the output transformer to produce an overall signal that is coupled by transformer action to the transformer secondary.

The way in which the outputs of the two transistors produce the overall output signal is shown in A through C. When analyzing these figures, remember that it is the *change* in the collector currents of the two transistors that creates a voltage across the transformer primary. These induced voltages combine to produce the output signal.

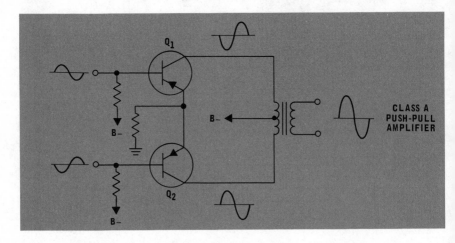

CLASS A
PUSH-PULL
AMPLIFIER

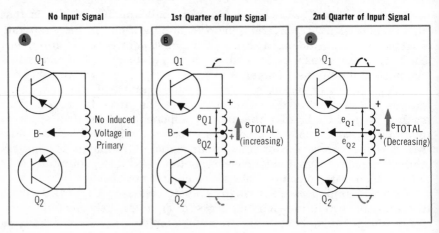

No Input Signal   1st Quarter of Input Signal   2nd Quarter of Input Signal

developing
the output signal (cont.)

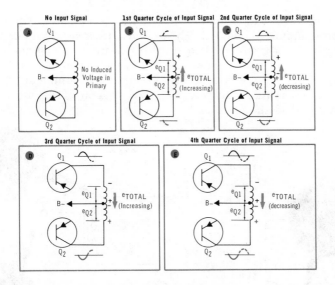

In A, there is *no* input signal, so d-c current flows from the B—
supply through one half of the primary to the collector of Q_1 and
through the other half of the primary to the collector of Q_2. This d-c
current induces no voltage in the transformer primary. Actually, no
magnetic field at all is built up around the primary, since the mag-
netizing forces in the two halves of the primary effectively *cancel* each
other.

During the first quarter cycle of the input signal, as shown in B,
collector current increases in Q_1 and decreases in Q_2. These changes
in current cause induced voltages in the two halves of the primary.
These voltages have polarities as shown. You can see from the polarities
that the induced voltages add to produce one voltage across the primary.
The amplitude of the overall voltage increases at the same rate as the
current varies.

In the second quarter cycle of the input signal, shown in C, collector
current decreases in Q_1 and increases in Q_2. These current changes
induce voltages in the primary that have the same polarity as during
the first quarter cycle, but which are decreasing in amplitude. The
induced voltages have like polarities with respect to the primary winding,
so they add together to produce the overall output voltage.

During the second half cycle of the input signal, as shown in D and
E, the conditions that exist in the transformer primary are opposite
to those existing during the first half cycle. The two induced voltages
again always have like polarities, although the polarity is opposite
to that of the first half cycle.

the cathode-coupled push-pull amplifier

A type of push-pull amplifier that does not require two separate out-of-phase inputs is shown. This circuit uses a grounded-cathode stage that drives a grounded-grid stage by means of a *common-cathode resistor*. The single input signal is applied to the grounded-cathode stage, V_1, by capacitor C_1 and resistor R_1. As in a conventional grounded-cathode amplifier, this causes an *inverted* version of the input signal to be developed at the plate of V_1.

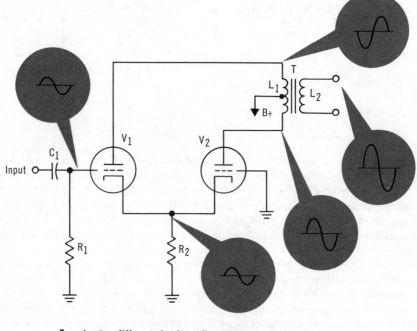

By using two different circuit configurations, one that produces a polarity reversal and another that does not, a push-pull amplifier can be operated without the need for a phase splitter

The variations in tube current through V_1 also produce a varying voltage across common-cathode resistor R_2 that is in phase with the input signal. Since the grid of V_2 is grounded, the voltage variations across R_2 serve as the input signal to V_2. As a result, the output signal at the plate of V_2 is *in phase* with the variations in cathode voltage, which are in phase with the input signal to V_1. Thus, the voltage variations at the plate of V_2 are in phase with the input signal, while those at the plate of V_1 are 180 degrees out of phase with the input signal. These voltage variations combine across transformer primary L_1, as described on the previous page.

the emitter-coupled push-pull amplifier

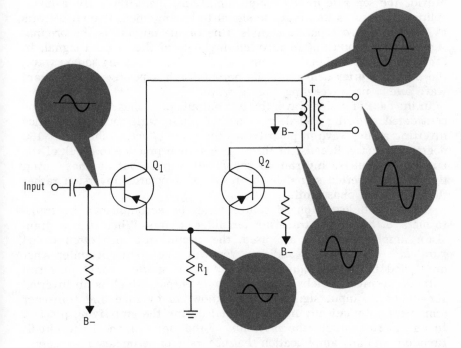

In both versions of this circuit, component values and characteristics must produce equal output voltages for each stage for a given input signal

A basic transistor circuit similar to the tube circuit shown on the preceding page is shown here. A common-emitter and a common-base stage are used, with the signal coupled from Q_1 to Q_2 by resistor R_1, which is in the emitter circuit of both Q_1 and Q_2. The collector signals of the two stages are 180 degrees out of phase, since a signal inversion takes place in a common-emitter stage but not in a common-base stage. The two out-of-phase signals combine across the primary of the output transformer to produce the overall output signal.

In both the tube and transistor versions of this circuit, the characteristics and values of the components must be such that equal output voltages are developed by both stages for a given input signal.

Frequently, a circuit of the type described above, instead of being used as a push-pull amplifier, is used to produce the out-of-phase input signals for a push-pull amplifier. The operation of the circuit is the same, except that the two outputs are usually capacitively coupled to the push-pull stages. Such a circuit is called a cathode-coupled or emitter-coupled phase splitter.

phase splitters

As was pointed out previously, phase splitters are the circuits that provide the separate inputs for push-pull amplifiers. Basically, a phase splitter receives as its input the signal to be amplified. It then delivers as its output *two* separate signals. One of the outputs is the *original* signal and the other is an *inverted* duplicate of the original signal. In other words, if the signal to be amplified is a positive-going square wave, the phase inverter delivers as its outputs both a positive-going square wave and a negative-going square wave.

In the case of a sine wave, the two outputs of a phase splitter can be considered as being 180 degrees out of phase with each other, since inverting a sine wave in polarity has the *same effect* as shifting it 180 degrees in phase. Because of this, it is common practice to speak of the outputs of a phase inverter as being 180 degrees out of phase, even though the inverted signal is the result of a polarity inversion rather than an actual phase shift.

As you will learn, phase splitting can be accomplished by transformers, or by tube or transistor amplifier circuits. When tube or transistor amplifier circuits are used, the circuits are also often called *paraphase amplifiers*. In addition, you will also often encounter what are called *inverter circuits*. Unlike a phase splitter, which has two outputs, an inverter delivers only a *single* output, which is an inverted version of its input signal. As you know, many tube and transistor amplifiers automatically invert a signal during the amplifying process. In an inverter circuit, the *inversion* of the signal is the basic circuit function, and any amplification that occurs is of secondary importance. In a conventional amplifier, the opposite is true.

A Phase Splitter . . .

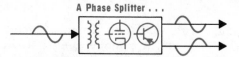

. . . is any transformer, tube, or transistor circuit that receives a single
input and delivers two outputs of opposite instantaneous polarity

A Paraphase Amplifier . . .

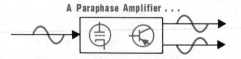

. . . is any tube or transistor amplifier circuit used as a phase splitter

. . . is any circuit whose primary purpose is to deliver a single output
of opposite instantaneous polarity to the input signal

transformer-type phase splitters

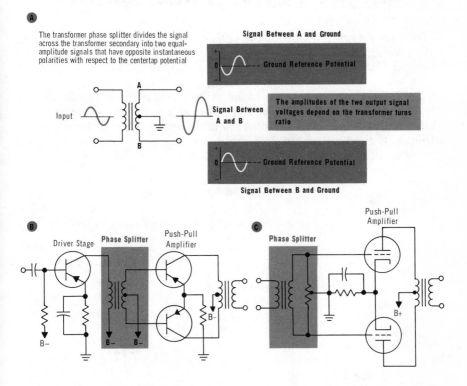

The transformer phase splitter divides the signal across the transformer secondary into two equal-amplitude signals that have opposite instantaneous polarities with respect to the centertap potential

Signal Between A and Ground

Ground Reference Potential

Signal Between A and B

The amplitudes of the two output signal voltages depend on the transformer turns ratio

Ground Reference Potential

Signal Between B and Ground

In a transformer-type phase splitter, a transformer having a *center-tapped secondary* is generally used. As shown in A, *two* separate signal voltages can be obtained from the secondary, since the secondary is centertapped to the zero potential reference point, or ground. One of these signals is taken from between the top of the secondary (point A) and the centertap, and the other is taken from between the bottom of the secondary (point B) and the centertap. Because of normal transformer action, points A and B always have opposite polarities.

The centertap is located at the *electrical center* of the secondary, so both of the output signals always have the same instantaneous amplitudes, as well as *opposite* instantaneous *polarities*. When these two signals are applied to the inputs of a push-pull amplifier (shown in B), they have the required characteristics for push-pull operation.

As shown in C, instead of directly centertapping the transformer secondary, a centertapped resistor connected across the secondary can be used to obtain the two output signals. The resistor then serves as the load for the signal induced in the transformer secondary, and the two opposite voltages across the balanced resistor are used as the outputs.

the single-tube
balanced-type phase splitter

In a single-tube, balanced-type phase splitter, a single stage, often called a single-tube paraphase amplifier, provides two outputs having the required 180-degree phase difference. The basic single-tube phase splitter is shown.

The input signal is coupled to the control grid of the stage by capacitor C_1 and resistor R_1. One of the outputs is taken from between the *cathode* and *ground* and the other is taken from between the *plate* and *ground*. The output taken from the cathode is the voltage developed across cathode resistor R_3 by the tube current.

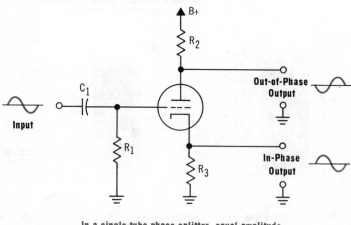

In a single-tube phase splitter, equal-amplitude but out-of-phase outputs are developed at the plate and cathode of the stage

Since cathode current increases when the input signal applied to the grid goes more positive, and decreases when the input signal goes less positive (or negative), the signal voltage developed across the cathode resistor by the cathode current is *in phase* with the input signal. The signal voltage at the plate, though, is 180 degrees *out of phase* with the input signal. The reason for this is that the signal voltage at the plate is equal to the B+ supply voltage minus the voltage drop across plate load resistor R_2 caused by the signal current. Thus, when the input signal goes more positive, plate current increases, the voltage drop across R_2 increases, and the signal voltage at the plate decreases. The converse is true when the input signal goes less positive, or negative.

Cathode resistor R_3 and plate load resistor R_2 have *equal* resistance values. Since cathode and plate current are equal in a triode, this means that both resistors produce equal voltage drops. Thus, the two output signals are of equal amplitude and 180 degrees out of phase.

the single-tube balanced-type phase splitter (cont.)

In the single-tube phase splitter, the two output signals are actually a-c variations of d-c voltage levels. The d-c component is removed by capacitive coupling

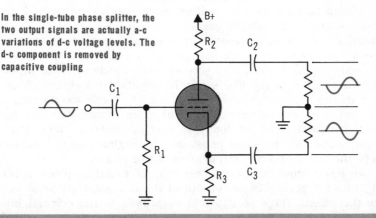

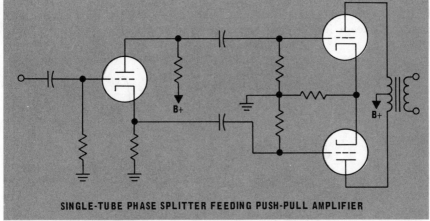

SINGLE-TUBE PHASE SPLITTER FEEDING PUSH-PULL AMPLIFIER

An important point you should understand here is that the output signals are actually the *a-c components* of the voltages appearing at the cathode and plate of the tube. These a-c components, in effect, ride on a d-c voltage level that is different at the plate than it is at the cathode. For example, with no input signal, tube current might produce a d-c voltage of 50 volts at the cathode and 250 volts at the plate. With an input signal applied, the variation in tube current might then produce voltage drops across the cathode and plate load resistors such that the voltage at the cathode varies between 40 and 60 volts, while the voltage at the plate varies between 240 and 260 volts. In both cases, the a-c component, which is the signal voltage, is 20 volts. The a-c signal component of these voltages is coupled to the next stage, which is usually a push-pull amplifier, by capacitors.

two-stage phase splitters

Single-tube phase splitters have the disadvantage of low or, actually, no gain. Each of the output signal voltages is *smaller* than the input voltage. Where amplification as well as phase splitting is desired, two-tube phase splitters are usually used.

Essentially, a two-tube phase splitter consists of *two amplifier stages*. The first stage receives the input signal, amplifies it, and inverts it in conventional amplifier style. The second stage receives as its input a *portion* of the output of the first stage. It amplifies this signal and also inverts it in the conventional way. The output of the second stage is thus an amplified version of the original input signal that has been inverted *twice*. Because of the double inversion, therefore, the output of the second stage has the same phase as the original input. Thus, the outputs of the two stages are 180 degrees out of phase.

The two basic requirements of this type of two-tube phase splitter are: (1) that the portion of the output of the first stage supplied as an input to the second stage be *equal* in *amplitude* to the original input to the first stage, and (2) that both stages amplify their inputs equally. If these two conditions are met, the outputs of the two stages are identical except for the 180-degree phase difference.

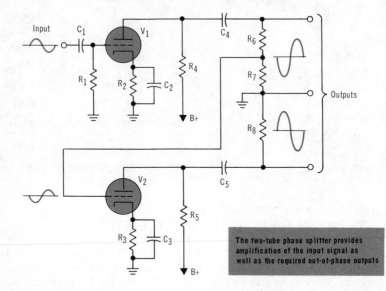

The two-tube phase splitter provides amplification of the input signal as well as the required out-of-phase outputs

In the circuit shown, the input signal is applied to the grid of V_1 by capacitor C_1 and resistor R_1. Stage V_1 is a conventional voltage amplifier, with cathode bias provided by cathode resistor R_2 and bypass capacitor C_2. The output of V_1 is coupled through capacitor C_4 and developed across resistors R_6 and R_7, which form a voltage divider. A small portion of the overall output voltage is tapped from the junction of R_6 and R_7 and applied to the grid of V_2.

two-stage phase splitters (cont.)

The input voltage to V_2 is the portion of the V_1 output signal developed across resistor R_7. The value of R_7 must be such that this small signal voltage is of the same amplitude as the input to tube V_1, which produced it. V_2 is also a conventional voltage amplifier and amplifies and inverts its input signal. The output of V_2 is coupled through capacitor C_5 and developed across resistor R_8.

The two output signals thus appear across resistors R_6 and R_7 and resistor R_8, respectively. The output across R_6 and R_7 has been inverted once, so it is 180 degrees out of phase with the original input signal. However, the output signal across R_8 has been inverted twice, so it has the same phase as the original input signal.

Another type of two-tube phase splitter was mentioned previously in the discussion of the cathode-coupled push-pull amplifier. In this circuit, the signal is eventually inverted by one stage but not by the other. The outputs of the two stages are therefore 180 degrees out of phase.

Q_1 amplifies and inverts the input signal. A portion of the output signal is taken off resistor R_7 and fed to Q_2. Q_2 amplifies and inverts this signal

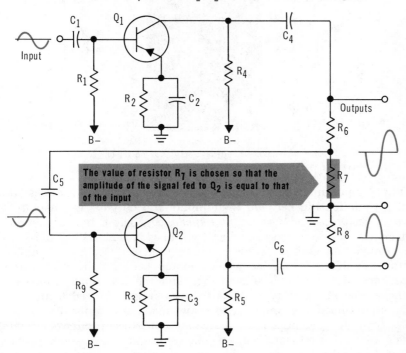

Since Q_2 amplifies and inverts the signal, its output will be equal and opposite to the output of Q_1 if Q_1 and Q_2 have the same gain

follower circuits

The term follower circuit is frequently applied to *grounded-plate amplifiers* as well as *grounded-collector amplifiers*. The term originated from the fact that in a grounded-plate amplifier the input is applied to the control grid and the output is taken from across an unbypassed cathode resistor. When an input signal is applied to such a stage, the signal current that flows in the cathode circuit produces a voltage drop across the unbypassed cathode resistor that is in phase with, or *follows*, the input signal. Thus, since the output signal at the cathode follows the variations in the input signal, such a circuit is called a *cathode follower*. Grounded-collector transistor amplifiers have characteristics similar to those of cathode followers, so they are frequently referred to as *emitter followers*.

The high input impedance and low output impedance of follower circuits make them highly suitable for impedance-matching purposes

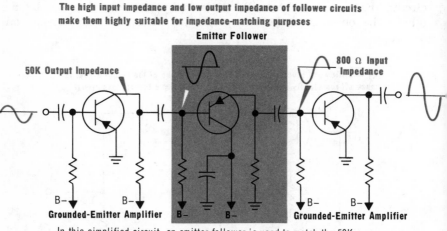

In this simplified circuit, an emitter follower is used to match the 50K output impedance of one grounded-emitter amplifier to the 800-ohm input impedance of another grounded-emitter amplifier

Other important characteristics of follower circuits besides the in-phase relationship between their inputs and outputs are their *high-input impedances* and *low-output impedances*. These impedance relationships make them very suitable for impedance-matching purposes. For example, an emitter follower can be used between two grounded-emitter amplifiers to provide a good match between the high output impedance of the first amplifier stage and the low input impedance of the second stage. Or, a cathode follower might be used to match a high-output-impedance amplifier to a low-impedance transmission line.

To obtain the good impedance-matching properties of follower circuits, voltage gain must be sacrificed. All follower circuits have a voltage gain of *less* than unity. This means that the output voltage is always slightly less than the input voltage. However, relatively large values of current or power gain can be obtained.

operation

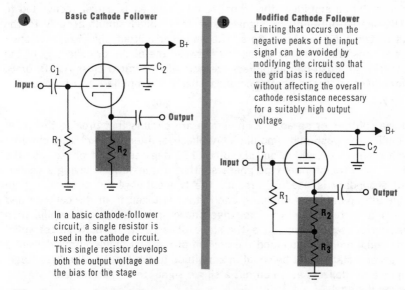

Basic Cathode Follower

In a basic cathode-follower circuit, a single resistor is used in the cathode circuit. This single resistor develops both the output voltage and the bias for the stage

Modified Cathode Follower

Limiting that occurs on the negative peaks of the input signal can be avoided by modifying the circuit so that the grid bias is reduced without affecting the overall cathode resistance necessary for a suitably high output voltage

The basic cathode-follower circuit is shown in A. It essentially is a *class A degenerative amplifier,* with the plate grounded for the a-c signal by capacitor C_2 and the output taken from across unbypassed cathode resistor R_2. Since the stage is biased class A, the no-signal current flowing through R_2 establishes the normal bias for the circuit.

When an input signal is applied to the control grid, it causes the plate current to vary and produces a corresponding a-c voltage drop across cathode resistor R_2. These voltage variations make up the output signal and also vary the bias of the stage in the same direction as the input signal to cause degeneration. The degeneration, though, is responsible for the high-input impedance of the circuit, since within certain limits it prevents a large input signal from causing large changes in plate current.

Very large input signals will cause amplitude distortion of the output signal. This occurs if the input signal goes so far negative that it cuts off the tube, or so far positive that it causes the grid to draw current. If the amplitude distortion, or *limiting,* as it is called, occurs only on the negative peaks of the input signal, the modified cathode-follower circuit shown in B can be used.

In this circuit, the output signal is taken from across both of the resistors that form a voltage divider in the cathode circuit. This provides maximum output voltage. However, the grid resistor is connected to the junction of the two resistors. This reduces the grid bias by an amount equal to the voltage drop across the lower resistor, R_3. Notice that although the cathode follower is referred to as a grounded-plate amplifier, the plate does not actually have to go to d-c ground. The capacitor (C_2), though, keeps it at *a-c* or *signal ground.*

summary

☐ In a push-pull amplifier, the signal to be amplified is usually converted to two 180-degree out-of-phase signals that are applied simultaneously to the inputs of two tubes or transistors. The amplified output signal is developed across a transformer that is connected between the plates or collectors of the two stages. ☐ Push-pull amplifiers are normally operated class A, AB, or B. ☐ Cathode-coupled and emitter-coupled push-pull amplifiers can be operated with only a single input signal.

☐ Phase splitters or paraphase amplifiers are circuits that provide the separate inputs for push-pull amplifiers. A phase splitter delivers two outputs: one the same as the input, and the other 180 degrees out of phase with the input. ☐ In a transformer-type phase splitter, a transformer having a center-tapped secondary is used to produce the two out-of-phase outputs. ☐ In a single-tube paraphase amplifier, one output is taken from the cathode and the other from the plate. ☐ Two-stage phase splitters provide amplification as well as phase splitting. In a two-stage phase splitter, both stages must provide equal amplification, and the portion of the first stage output delivered to the second stage must be equal in amplitude to the input to the first stage. ☐ An inverter delivers as an output a single signal that is an inverted version of the input signal.

☐ Grounded-plate and grounded-collector amplifiers are frequently called follower circuits. ☐ Follower circuits have high input impedances and low output impedances, which make them suitable for impedance-matching purposes.

review questions

1. What is a *single-ended amplifier?*
2. What is the difference between an inverter and a phase splitter?
3. Which of these are follower circuits: a grounded-plate amplifier, a grounded-cathode amplifier, and a grounded-emitter amplifier?
4. What is a *paraphase amplifier?*
5. What is the advantage of two-stage phase splitters?
6. What is a *push-pull amplifier?*
7. Are push-pull amplifiers ever biased class C?
8. Draw a push-pull amplifier and explain its operation.
9. Do all push-pull amplifiers require two out-of-phase input signals?
10. What are the impedance characteristics of follower circuits?

video amplifiers

Any amplifier capable of uniformly amplifying signals that contain an extremely *wide range of frequencies* is considered to be a video amplifier. Generally, the frequency range of video amplifiers is from about 30 cps to several megacycles. Television, radar, and telemetering are some of the applications in which these amplifiers are widely used.

Essentially, most video amplifiers are somewhat similar to class A audio voltage amplifiers. The principal difference is that video amplifiers incorporate special *compensating circuits*. These circuits make possible the required wide frequency response. *Without* the compensating circuits, the gain of a video amplifier would be uniform over only a limited range. Frequencies above and below this limited range would be amplified very little, or not at all.

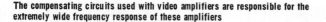

The compensating circuits used with video amplifiers are responsible for the extremely wide frequency response of these amplifiers

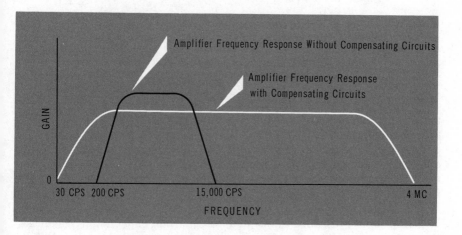

Some overall gain, however, is sacrificed to obtain the wide frequency response

Two types of compensating circuits are used with video amplifiers: those that increase the *low-frequency response* and those that increase the *high-frequency response*. These are discussed separately on the following pages.

As you will see, the wide-band requirements of video amplifiers make the selection of tubes and transistors for these circuits an important consideration. In tube-type video amplifiers, high-gain pentodes having large values of transconductance (g_m) and low values of interelectrode capacitances are generally used. In transistor circuits, good quality r-f transistors with frequency cutoffs of 100 megacycles and higher are usually used.

high-frequency compensation

A simplified video amplifier without compensating circuits is shown. In this circuit, the high-frequency response is limited by the three capacitances indicated in color. Capacitance C_o is the output capacitance of tube V_1, C_i is the input capacitance of tube V_2, and C_d is the *distributed* or stray capacitance of the circuit wiring. These three capacitances, although not physical capacitors, have the same electrical effect as if they were.

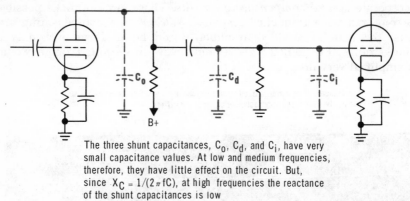

The three shunt capacitances, C_0, C_d, and C_i, have very small capacitance values. At low and medium frequencies, therefore, they have little effect on the circuit. But, since $X_C = 1/(2\pi fC)$, at high frequencies the reactance of the shunt capacitances is low

As all three of the capacitances are directly between the *signal path* and *ground,* they tend to *shunt* a portion of the signal to ground. The three capacitances have very small values, so at low and medium frequencies their reactance is very high and they have little or no shunting effect on the signal. But at higher frequencies, the reactances of the three capacitances get smaller and smaller, so more and more of the signal is shunted to ground.

The input and output capacitances (C_o and C_i) can be minimized by using tubes with low values of interelectrode capacitance. Likewise, the distributed wiring capacitance can be minimized by careful physical layout of the circuit tubes and wires. However, although they can be minimized, the three capacitances can *never* be entirely eliminated. Consequently, if the circuit is to amplify very high frequencies, some method must be used to eliminate the *effects* of these capacitances at the frequencies involved. This is the purpose of the high-frequency compensating circuits.

In transistor video amplifiers, the gain at high frequencies is limited by shunt capacitances similar to those in tube circuits. In addition, however, the high-frequency performance of a transistor depends on its alpha cutoff frequency, which is the frequency at which the current gain of a transistor connected as a grounded-base amplifier drops a definite percentage. The actual cutoff frequency depends not only on the particular transistor used, but on how it is connected (grounded-base, grounded-emitter, etc.).

circuits for high-frequency compensation

Essentially, high-frequency compensation is accomplished by using a *small inductor* to form a *parallel* resonant circuit with the shunt capacitances (*shunt compensation*), or a *series* resonant circuit with the shunt capacitances (*series compensation*).

An example of shunt compensation is shown in A. The total load impedance consists of L_1 and R_1. Capacitance C_T, which is the sum of the shunt capacitances C_o, C_d, and C_i, is effectively in parallel with L_1 and R_1. The value of peaking coil L_1 is chosen so that at the frequency at which the gain of the amplifier begins to fall off, the reactances of L_1 and C_T are equal, and they form a parallel resonant circuit. At this resonant frequency, the total plate load impedance is therefore maximum, and the output voltage is, in effect, boosted, or prevented from falling off.

In series compensation, as shown in B, a coil, L_1, is added in the signal path in series with coupling capacitor C_1. This coil forms a series resonant circuit with shunt capacitances C_d and C_i. The value of L_1 is such that at the frequency at which the amplifier gain begins to fall off, L_1 resonates with the combination of C_d and C_i. As a result, a large voltage drop is produced across C_d and C_i. Thus, the signal voltage is prevented from falling off.

Quite often, *both* series and shunt coils are used. A resistor is used in parallel with the coil to prevent a sharp resonance peak, which would amplify one frequency too much. The resistor lowers the Q of this coil to cause a very broad resonance curve that compensates for a wide band of high frequencies. Also, if the resistor were not used, a strong signal could cause the resonant circuit to produce damped oscillations, which is known as *ringing*. Usually, the coil is wound right around the resistor, and the whole unit is called a *peaking* coil.

 Shunt Compensation

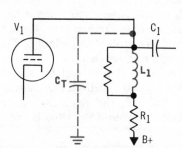

The coil connected in series with the plate load resistor forms a parallel resonant circuit with C_T, which is the total of the circuit shunt capacitances

B Series Compensation

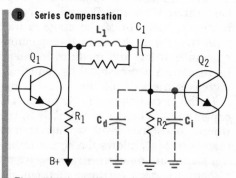

The coil connected in series with the signal path forms a series resonant circuit with the parallel shunt capacitances, C_d and C_i

other high-frequency compensation circuits

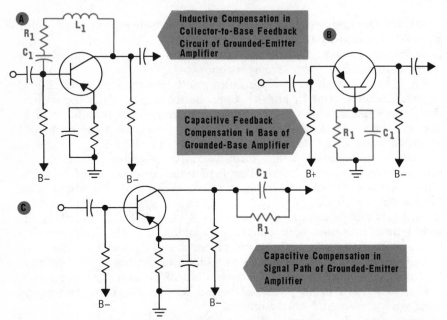

In addition to the basic series and shunt methods of compensation described on the previous page, various other methods of high-frequency compensation are often used in video amplifier circuits. One of these, called *combination* compensation, is merely the use of both series and shunt peaking coils in the same circuit. Other methods frequently used with transistor video amplifiers are illustrated in A through C.

In the circuit shown in A, the increase in the reactance of coil L_1 at high frequencies reduces the negative feedback from collector to base through resistor R_1 and coupling capacitor C_1. With less negative feedback, the gain of the stage is increased at the higher frequencies.

In the circuit shown in B, capacitor C_1 in the base circuit has a high reactance at low and medium frequencies. At high frequencies, though, its reactance decreases, thus reducing the base circuit impedance. This increases the gain of the stage at the high frequencies.

In the circuit shown in C, the parallel combination of resistor R_1 and capacitor C_1 is connected directly in the signal path. At high frequencies, where the signal level would otherwise fall off, the decrease in the reactance of C_1 allows the signal to be shunted around R_4, thus decreasing signal attenuation.

Actually, each of these methods differs from those on the previous page because those increased the high frequencies to the level of the low frequencies, whereas these methods only degenerate the lows to the level of the highs.

low-frequency compensation

The fall off in gain of a video amplifier at the low frequencies is due primarily to the *decrease* in the *reactance* of the circuit *coupling capacitor*. In addition, the low-frequency gain is also influenced by the various *bypass capacitors* used in the circuit.

In the circuit shown below, the output signal from stage V_1 is coupled through coupling capacitor C_1 and developed across grid resistor R_1. Effectively, C_1 and R_1 form a voltage divider, with the voltage appearing across R_1 being the input for stage V_2. At high frequencies the reactance of C_1 is almost zero, so for practical purposes the entire output signal from V_1 is developed across grid resistor R_1 and applied to stage V_2. At low frequencies, however, a substantial portion of the signal is dropped across the increased reactance of C_1, and the input to V_2 is decreased accordingly.

Low-frequency response is affected by the decrease in reactance of capacitors C_1, C_2, and C_3 at the lower frequencies. The values of these capacitors determine the low-frequency falloff

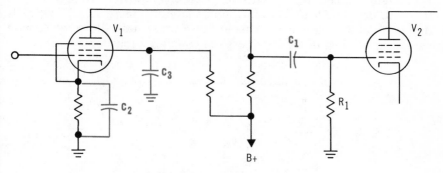

The effect of the increased reactance of C_1 at low frequencies can be avoided somewhat by increasing its capacitance value. However, if C_1 is made too large, it will start developing grid-leak bias for the stage and cause distortion. Since the signal loss across C_1 cannot be avoided, therefore, some method must be used to compensate for it.

Cathode and screen bypass capacitors C_2 and C_3, respectively, affect the low-frequency gain of the amplifier also, as a result of their increased reactance at the lower frequencies. At medium and high frequencies, the reactances of C_2 and C_3 are low enough for the capacitors to shunt the current variations around their respective resistors effectively. But at low frequencies, C_2 and C_3 no longer provide effective shunting action. As a result, the signal current variations flow through the cathode resistor and the screen current variations flow through the screen dropping resistor. Both of these conditions cause *degeneration* and, consequently, reduce the low-frequency gain of the stage.

circuits
for low-frequency compensation

The signal attenuation caused by the increased reactance of a video-amplifier coupling capacitor at low frequencies can be overcome in two basic ways. One method, which is frequently used in transistor circuits, is to eliminate the coupling capacitor and use *direct coupling* between stages. When this is done, d-c bias stability is extremely important, since the separate stages are not independent in regard to dc. Any bias instabilities of the first stage could be amplified by the second stage.

In both tube and transistor circuits, the low-frequency effects of the coupling capacitor are frequently compensated for by *dividing* the load resistance and bypassing *one part* of it with a capacitor. As shown, the plate load consists of resistors R_1 and R_2, with R_2 bypassed by capacitor C_1. At high frequencies, the reactance of C_1 is low, effectively bypassing R_2, so the plate load consists of only R_1. But at low frequencies, the reactance of C_1 is large, so the plate current variations are no longer bypassed around R_2. This has the effect of inserting R_2 in the plate load circuit, since the plate current variations now flow through R_1 and R_2. With the plate load resistance thus increased, more signal voltage is developed at the plate of V_1. This increase compensates for the decrease caused by the loss of signal across the coupling capacitor.

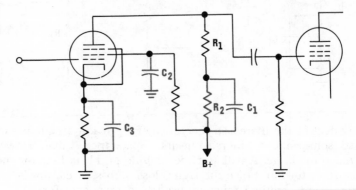

Low-frequency compensation in tube-type video amplifiers is often accomplished by using a partially-bypassed split-load resistance in the plate circuit and large value screen and cathode bypass capacitors

To compensate for the degeneration caused by the decreased reactance of bypass capacitors, video amplifiers use *large-value capacitors* for bypass purposes. These capacitors usually have values many times larger than those used in comparable audio amplifiers. In this way, even at low frequencies the capacitor reactance is low enough to provide the required bypass action and avoid degeneration.

r-f amplifiers

R-f amplifiers could be defined as circuits that amplify voltages and currents having frequencies that lie in the r-f portion of the frequency spectrum. However, this definition is not very satisfactory, since there is no definite agreement as to just what frequencies make up the r-f portion of the frequency spectrum. A better definition of r-f amplifiers is based on their *function,* which is to be able to select and amplify a *narrow band* of high frequencies.

Only a very narrow band of frequencies is amplified by an r-f amplifier at one time. The center frequency of this narrow band, though, can be varied by changing the resonant frequency of the tuned circuits that make up part of the r-f amplifier

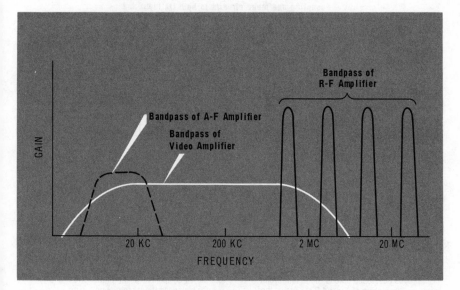

Thus, as shown above, while a-f and video amplifiers amplify only a fixed band of frequencies, the frequencies to be amplified by an r-f amplifier can be varied

Generally, r-f amplifiers are characterized by *tuned,* or resonant, circuits in their inputs and outputs. The resonant frequency of these tuned circuits can usually be changed.

There are various types of r-f amplifiers, which, although basically similar, have definite differences. Because of these differences, each type of r-f amplifier will be covered separately on the following pages. These various types include voltage amplifiers, buffer amplifiers, frequency multipliers, and power amplifiers.

r-f voltage amplifiers

R-f voltage amplifiers, as their name implies, simply amplify the signal voltages applied to their inputs. They are generally operated class A and have plate load impedance values that produce large output voltages. In these respects, they are similar to audio voltage amplifiers. However, audio voltage amplifiers are designed to amplify equally *all* signal voltages having frequencies within the desired frequency response range of the amplifier. R-f voltage amplifiers, on the other hand, are designed to select and amplify only a *narrow band* of frequencies, and to reject, or suppress, all frequencies outside of this band.

One type of basic r-f amplifier uses transformer coupling and tuned circuits in both its input and its output

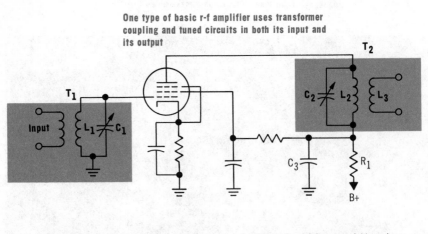

The input signal is transformer coupled to the tuned circuit consisting of transformer secondary L_1 and capacitor C_1. Maximum grid input signal is developed at the tuned frequency; little or no signal at other frequencies. The output signal is developed across the tuned circuit consisting of L_2 and C_2. Again, the maximum signal output is developed at the tuned frequency

Capacitors C_1 and C_2 are variable and are adjusted so that both tuned circuits resonate at the same frequency. Resistor R_1 and capacitor C_3 in the plate circuit of the stage form a decoupling network. R_1 offers a high impedance to the r-f component of the plate current and C_3 bypasses the r-f to ground. This keeps the r-f out of the B+ supply

This frequency *selectivity* is accomplished by tuned circuits that form part of the input or output (or both) of the amplifier. If there is a tuned circuit in the input, it passes those frequencies in the narrow band to which it is tuned to the amplifier input and rejects all other frequencies. If there is a tuned circuit in the output, it generally presents a large output load impedance at its tuned frequency and a low impedance at all other frequencies. Since the amplitude of the output signal depends on the value of output impedance, large outputs are delivered only at the tuned frequency.

r-f voltage amplifiers (cont.)

You can see that if tuned circuits are used in both the input and output of the amplifier, they must both be tuned to the *same frequencies*. When a new band of frequencies is to be amplified, both circuits must be retuned to the new frequencies.

It should be mentioned here that it is common practice to speak of an r-f amplifier or a tuned circuit as being tuned to *one* frequency, such as 1200 kilocycles or 27 megacycles. This single frequency is the *resonant frequency* of the tuned circuit, or circuits, involved. However, no practical tuned circuit can pass a single frequency and suppress all others. Some frequencies on both sides of the resonant frequency are always passed with essentially the same amplitude as the resonant frequency. These frequencies of significant amplitude make up the pass band, or *bandpass,* of the tuned circuit.

Tuned circuits used with transistor r-f amplifiers must not only develop maximum signal at the tuned frequency, they must also match the transistor input and output impedances. The method shown here, in which the tuned circuits are tapped, is often used

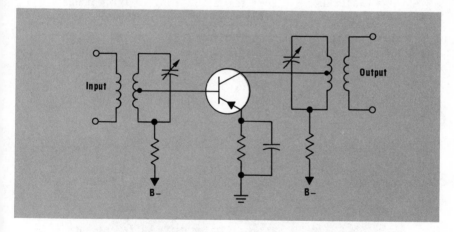

As you probably realize by now, the study of r-f amplifiers is in large part a study of tuned circuits. For this reason, a summary of tuned circuits and their properties is given on the following pages.

Transistor as well as tube circuits are covered on the following pages. Strictly speaking, the transistor circuits are not voltage amplifiers, since, as you know, all transistors are current-sensitive devices. Instead, the transistor amplifiers covered under r-f voltage amplifiers really come under the category of *small-signal* amplifiers, as opposed to power-amplifier transistor circuits. However, to avoid the necessity of continually switching terminology, both small-signal, transistor r-f amplifiers and tube-type, r-f voltage amplifiers will be covered under the heading of r-f voltage amplifiers.

the tuned circuit

A tuned circuit, as you know, is merely another name for a resonant circuit. From your studies of basic electricity, you recall that there are two types of resonant circuits: *series* resonant circuits and *parallel* resonant circuits. Both types consist of an inductance (L) and a capacitance (C) with the two elements connected in series in a series resonant circuit and in parallel in a parallel resonant circuit.

An important point for you to understand here is that the series or parallel arrangement of the inductance and capacitance in resonant circuits is with respect to the *applied voltage*. If the input voltage is applied across both the L and C components in parallel, it is a parallel resonant circuit. If the voltage is applied in series with L and C, it is a series resonant circuit. Thus, as shown, if the L component of a resonant circuit is the secondary of a transformer, the circuit is a series resonant circuit. This is because the transformer secondary voltage is induced *within* the secondary winding, which is the input to the resonant circuit. It acts as if it were an a-c generator in *series* with the secondary winding.

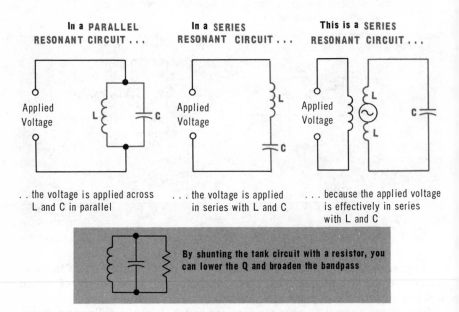

In a PARALLEL
RESONANT CIRCUIT . . .

In a SERIES
RESONANT CIRCUIT . . .

This is a SERIES
RESONANT CIRCUIT . . .

. . . the voltage is applied across
L and C in parallel

. . . the voltage is applied
in series with L and C

. . . because the applied voltage
is effectively in series
with L and C

By shunting the tank circuit with a resistor, you
can lower the Q and broaden the bandpass

In both series and parallel tuned circuits, resonance occurs when the *reactances* of the inductive and capacitive elements are *equal*. For any combination of inductance and capacitance, this occurs at only a *single* frequency, f_R, which can be calculated from the equation:

$$f_R = \frac{1}{2\pi\sqrt{LC}}$$

the tuned circuit (cont.)

Some Characteristics of Tuned Circuits

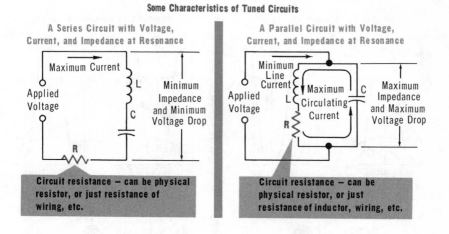

A Series Circuit with Voltage, Current, and Impedance at Resonance

Maximum Current

Applied Voltage

L

C

Minimum Impedance and Minimum Voltage Drop

R

Circuit resistance – can be physical resistor, or just resistance of wiring, etc.

A Parallel Circuit with Voltage, Current, and Impedance at Resonance

Minimum Line Current

Applied Voltage

L

Maximum Circulating Current

R

C

Maximum Impedance and Maximum Voltage Drop

Circuit resistance – can be physical resistor, or just resistance of inductor, wiring, etc.

At the resonant frequency, a *series* resonant circuit has *minimum impedance* and *maximum current;* a *parallel* resonant circuit at the resonant frequency exhibits *maximum impedance* and *minimum line current.* This minimum line current is the current entering and leaving the parallel resonant circuit.

Within the tank circuit, as it is called, large values of *circulating current* flow as a result of the alternate storage and release of electrical energy by the magnetic field of the inductance and electrostatic field of the capacitance. At frequencies above and below resonance, the impedance of a series resonant circuit increases, while its current decreases. Similarly, above resonance, the impedance of a parallel resonant circuit decreases and line current increases. The degree with which these conditions change at frequencies above and below resonance is a measure of the circuit's ability to *discriminate* between frequencies.

This ability to discriminate between frequencies is called the Q of the circuit, and can be calculated from the equation:

$$Q = X_L/R \quad \text{or} \quad X_C/R$$

where X_L and X_C are the respective, and equal, reactances at the resonant frequency, and R is the resistance of the circuit. You can see from this that the larger the value of the circuit resistance, the lower the Q of the resonant circuit, and, therefore, the less able it is to discriminate between various frequencies.

Some of the more important characteristics of tuned circuits are illustrated on the following page. In some circuits, where we want to widen the bandpass, or make the tank less selective, say to make sure that all signal side bands are passed, we lower the Q of the tank by shunting it with a resistor of the proper value.

characteristics
of the tuned circuit

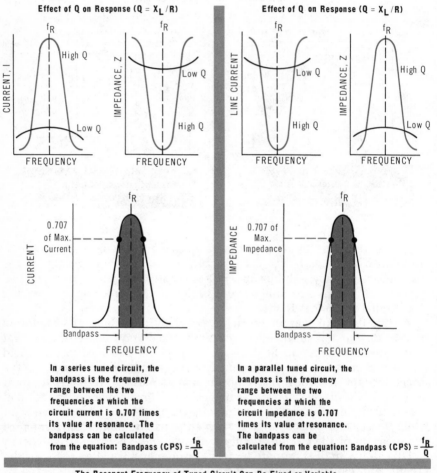

Effect of Q on Response (Q = X_L/R)

Effect of Q on Response (Q = X_L/R)

In a series tuned circuit, the bandpass is the frequency range between the two frequencies at which the circuit current is 0.707 times its value at resonance. The bandpass can be calculated from the equation: Bandpass (CPS) = $\dfrac{f_R}{Q}$

In a parallel tuned circuit, the bandpass is the frequency range between the two frequencies at which the circuit impedance is 0.707 times its value at resonance. The bandpass can be calculated from the equation: Bandpass (CPS) = $\dfrac{f_R}{Q}$

The Resonant Frequency of Tuned Circuit Can Be Fixed or Variable

Fixed Tuned Circuits

Variable Tuned Circuits

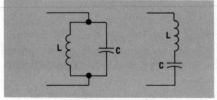

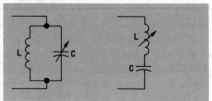

If the values of L and C are fixed, the circuit has one resonant frequency, which cannot be changed

If either L or C, or both, are variable, the resonant frequency of the circuit can be changed

r-f amplifier tuned circuits

A simplified, tube-type r-f amplifier stage is shown in A. The input signal to this circuit comes from an *untuned* antenna circuit consisting of a receiving antenna and antenna coil L_1. The antenna coil forms the primary of a transformer (T_1), whose secondary is the inductive element of a *series* resonant circuit made up of L_2 and C_1.

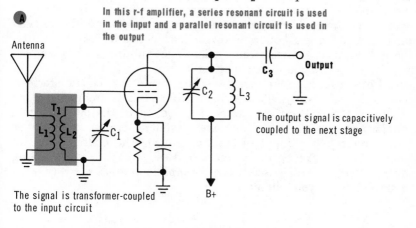

A

In this r-f amplifier, a series resonant circuit is used in the input and a parallel resonant circuit is used in the output

Antenna

C_3 Output

C_2 L_3

The output signal is capacitively coupled to the next stage

The signal is transformer-coupled to the input circuit   B+

The output signal can also be transformer-coupled to the next circuit using . . .

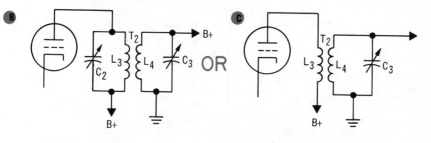

B   **C**

T_2 B+ T_2

L_3 L_4 C_3 OR L_3 L_4 C_3

C_2

B+   B+

a parallel resonant circuit to transformer-couple the signal to series resonant circuit. This is frequently done in i-f amplifiers

only a coil as the plate load impedance and a series resonant circuit as the input to the next stage

Although signal currents of many frequencies flow through the antenna coil, only at the resonant frequency of L_2 and C_1 is an appreciable signal coupled to the tuned circuit. This is because at all but the resonant frequency the tuned circuit offers a high impedance. At the resonant frequency, though, a *large signal current* flows in the tuned circuit, creating a substantial voltage drop across capacitor C_1. This voltage drop follows the signal variations and serves as the grid input to the stage. Capacitor C_1 is variable and permits the resonant frequency of the tuned circuit and, therefore, the frequency of the selected signal to be changed.

r-f amplifier
tuned circuits (cont.)

The output load impedance of the stage is provided by the *parallel* resonant circuit consisting of coil L_3 and capacitor C_2. At the resonant frequency, this tuned circuit offers a high impedance to the a-c component of the plate current, so maximum output voltage is developed. To signal currents that are not of the resonant frequency, the parallel combination of C_2 and L_3 offers a low impedance, so little or no output voltage is developed at these frequencies. The output signal is coupled to the next stage by coupling capacitor C_3.

Instead of capacitive coupling, the output could also be transformer-coupled to the next stage. Two ways in which this is frequently done are shown in B and C on the preceding page. In B, the output signal is transformer-coupled by the parallel resonant circuit to a series resonant circuit in the input of the next stage. The coils of the two resonant circuits make up the primary and secondary of the coupling transformer. This is called *double-tuned coupling* and is used very often for i-f amplifiers, as you will learn later.

Quite often, at the higher frequencies, a capacitor is not needed to resonate with the coil; there is enough capacitance between the windings of the coil to produce a tuned circuit

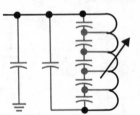

The coil is tuned with a slug to resonate with the interwinding capacitance

In C, the parallel resonant circuit is eliminated and only a coil is used as the plate load. This coil serves as the primary of the transformer for coupling the signal to a tuned circuit in the input of the next stage. This is called *single-tuned coupling*. The particular type of coupling used with r-f amplifiers depends on the desired characteristics, such as gain, bandwidth, and selectivity. You will learn more about this later.

As shown above there is usually enough capacitance between the windings of a coil at the higher frequencies so that a capacitor is not needed to form a tuned circuit. The coil then resonates with its own interwinding capacitance. The coil is tuned with a powdered iron or brass slug that is moved in and out of it.

tuned circuits for transistor r-f amplifiers

The tuned circuits used in the inputs and outputs of transistor r-f amplifiers perform the same function that they do in tube circuits. In other words, they make possible the selection of the desired signal frequencies and the rejection of all other frequencies. However, in transistor circuits the necessity of *matching* the input and output impedances of the transistors to the impedances of the tuned circuits creates problems in the design of the tuned circuits. This is especially true of the tuned circuits used as inputs to grounded-emitter and grounded-base amplifiers, which have *very low input impedances.* If such tuned circuits were of the same design as those of comparable tube circuits, they would require impractical and inefficient component values.

To overcome this problem, the tuned circuits used with transistor r-f amplifiers are designed for efficient tuning, and are then *tapped,* so that, in effect, the transistor "sees" the required lower value of impedance. A typical circuit of this kind is shown in A. By tapping the coil at the proper point, the required low impedance is matched to the transistor input. Other ways in which a tuned circuit can be tapped to provide lower impedance values are shown in B through D.

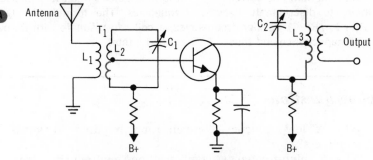

By tapping the tuned circuits, the transistor uses only the impedances of the lower portions of the tuned circuit coils. The impedances of these portions of the coils match the transistor input and output impedance

These are some other methods used to tap the tuned circuits to accomplish the same impedance matching results

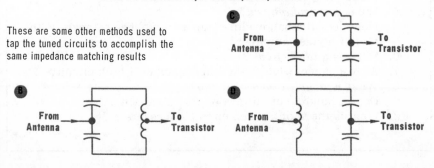

summary

☐ High-frequency compensation is required in video amplifiers because of the shunting effect caused by the input and output capacitances of the circuits and the distributed or stray capacitance of the circuit wiring. ☐ High-frequency compensation circuits prevent the output of the amplifier from falling off at high frequencies. ☐ Low-frequency compensation is required in video amplifiers because of the increase in circuit reactances, especially that of the coupling capacitor. The low-frequency compensation circuits prevent the output of the amplifier from falling off at low frequencies. ☐ In the transistor video amplifiers, low-frequency compensation is often accomplished by eliminating the coupling capacitor and using direct coupling between stages. ☐ Large-value bypass capacitors are used in video amplifiers for low-frequency compensation.

☐ R-f amplifiers are able to select and amplify a narrow band of high frequencies. ☐ Frequency selectivity of r-f amplifiers is accomplished by tuned, or resonant, circuits that form part of the input or output circuit of the amplifier.

☐ In both series and parallel tuned circuits, resonance occurs when the reactances of the inductive and capacitive elements are equal. ☐ At resonance, a series resonant circuit has minimum impedance and maximum current. ☐ A parallel resonant circuit at the resonant frequency exhibits maximum impedance and minimum line current. ☐ The Q of a tuned circuit is a measure of its ability to discriminate between frequencies. The formula for Q is $Q = X_L/R$ or X_C/R. ☐ At high frequencies, a coil can resonate with its own interwinding capacitance and thus act as a tuned circuit.

review questions

1. Why is low-frequency compensation required in video amplifiers?
2. Why is high-frequency compensation required in video amplifiers?
3. What are some of the methods used for low-frequency compensation?
4. What is a *peaking coil*?
5. How does the bandwidth of an r-f amplifier compare with that of a video amplifier?
6. What is a *tank circuit*?
7. At resonance, what is the impedance of a tank circuit?
8. What is *double-tuned coupling*?
9. Does a tank circuit always require a capacitor?
10. What is the Q of a tuned circuit a measure of?

bandwidth and selectivity

The bandwidth of an r-f amplifier is the range between the two frequencies at which the amplified output voltage falls to a value 0.707 times its value at the frequency to which the amplifier is tuned. Thus, if the output voltage of an amplifier tuned to 500 kilocycles is 100 volts at 500 kilocycles, and the output falls to 70.7 volts at 495 kilocycles as well as 70.7 volts at 505 kilocycles, the bandwidth of the amplifier is 505 − 495 kilocycles, or 10 kilocycles.

You will recognize that the definition of amplifier bandwidth is essentially the same as that of the bandwidth of a simple tuned circuit, which was discussed previously. This is natural, of course, since tuned circuits provide an amplifier with its frequency-discriminating ability, and, hence, its bandwidth.

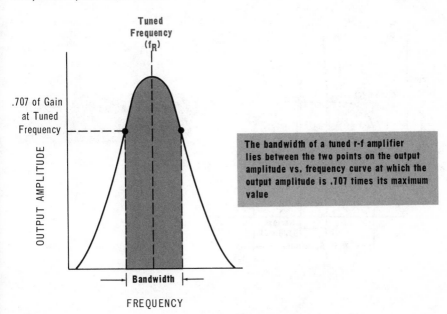

The bandwidth of a tuned r-f amplifier lies between the two points on the output amplitude vs. frequency curve at which the output amplitude is .707 times its maximum value

The bandwidth of an r-f amplifier determines how well it can select and amplify a desired signal and reject all other signals, even those very close in frequency to the desired one. An amplifier with a *narrow bandwidth* has *good selectivity*. This means that it can select the desired signal from other signals close to it in frequency. These adjacent channel signals are greatly attenuated (not amplified) so that they do not exist in the amplifier output. An amplifier with a *wide bandwidth* has *poor selectivity*. Although it amplifies the desired signal, it also amplifies with appreciable amplitude some of the adjacent channel signals. The adjacent channel signals therefore appear in the amplifier output along with the desired signal, resulting in distortion of the desired signal.

bandwidth and selectivity (cont.)

It may seem that it is desirable for an r-f amplifier to have as narrow a bandwidth as possible, since selectivity is directly related to bandwidth. This is not necessarily always the case, however. If the amplifier is to receive *modulated signals,* its bandwidth must be wide enough so that it will equally amplify all of the frequencies contained in the modulation. In the case of a conventional broadcast AM signal, this means that the r-f amplifier must have a bandwidth of at least 10 kilocycles, since the side bands of such signals cover a 10 kilocycle range. A bandwidth of less than 10 kilocycles would result in severe amplitude distortion of the amplified signal.

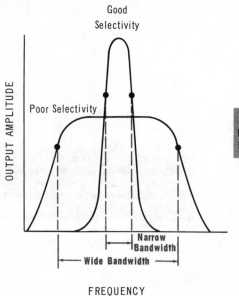

An r-f amplifier with a narrow bandwidth has good selectivity. One with a wide bandwidth has poor selectivity

For amplifiers that have single-tuned circuits, the bandwidth is equal to:

$$\text{Bandwidth} = f_R/Q$$

where f_R is the frequency to which the amplifier is tuned and Q is the Q of the tuned circuits used. You will recognize this as the equation for the bandwidth of a simple resonant circuit. If double-tuned circuits are used, this equation no longer holds, since the degree of magnetic coupling between the two tuned circuits then plays an important role in determining bandwidth. As was pointed out previously, double-tuned circuits are used more with i-f amplifiers than with r-f amplifiers. The effect of the degree of coupling on the amplifier bandwidths will therefore be covered later in this volume in the discussion of i-f amplifiers.

triodes vs. pentodes

Any *noise* introduced by the r-f stage is amplified together with the signal and tends to reduce the *signal-to-noise ratio* of the amplified output.

In tube circuits, the type of tube used has a significant effect on the noise generated by a stage. Triodes, because they have fewer grids, are inherently less noisy than are pentodes. From a noise standpoint, therefore, they are frequently desirable for r-f amplifiers. However, pentodes provide greater gain than do triodes, so from a gain standpoint, pentodes are often preferred.

In addition to affecting the noise introduced by the amplifier, the choice of a triode or a pentode also affects the circuit configuration of the amplifier. When *pentodes* are used, the circuit is usually a *grounded-cathode amplifier*, since this type of circuit provides the largest voltage gain. Triode r-f amplifiers, on the other hand, are not generally used in the grounded-cathode configuration, particularly when tuned circuits are used in both the input and output. The reason for this is that such circuits tend to oscillate like tuned-plate, tuned-grid oscillators as a result of positive feedback through the plate-to-grid interelectrode capacitance of the tube. If triodes are used in this way, *neutralization* must be employed to eliminate the feedback. This is covered on the following page. Oscillation is covered in Volume 6.

More commonly, triodes are used as *grounded-grid r-f amplifiers*. In this way, positive feedback and oscillation are not a problem, since the input signal is introduced into the cathode circuit. However, grounded-grid amplifiers, because of their low input impedance, do not have as large a voltage gain as grounded-cathode amplifiers. Because of this, it is sometimes necessary to use additional stages of r-f amplification.

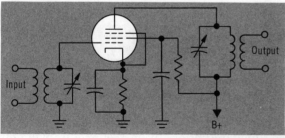

Pentodes are generally used as grounded-cathode r-f amplifiers. If triodes are used in this way, neutralization is necessary

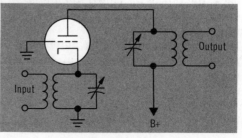

Triodes are commonly used as grounded-grid amplifiers. The relatively low gain of both the triode and the grounded-grid configuration often make additional stages of r-f amplification necessary

neutralization

You learned on the previous page that when a triode is used in a grounded-cathode amplifier having tuned circuits in both the input and output, positive feedback can occur, and the circuit may tend to function as a tuned-plate, tuned-grid oscillator. This effect becomes especially significant at signal frequencies above about 500 kilocycles, since at these high frequencies the reactance of the tube's interelectrode capacitance feedback path is relatively low.

In transistor circuits, a similar situation exists because of the internal feedback caused by the transistor's *collector-to-base capacitance*. Neutralization is essentially a process of *externally* feeding back from output to input a signal that is almost *equal in amplitude* to but *opposite in phase* with the unwanted internal feedback. Strictly speaking, in transistor circuits neutralization does not completely cancel the unwanted feedback signal. Instead, it only cancels enough of the feedback to ensure stable operation.

The triode can be neutralized in the following manner

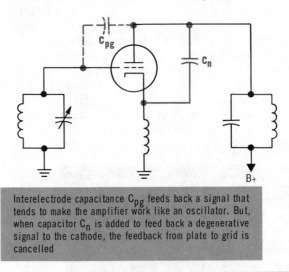

Interelectrode capacitance C_{pg} feeds back a signal that tends to make the amplifier work like an oscillator. But, when capacitor C_n is added to feed back a degenerative signal to the cathode, the feedback from plate to grid is cancelled

When the external feedback completely cancels the internal feedback, the process is called *unilateralization*. In this volume, we will only cover transistor neutralization, since it is used more commonly than unilateralization.

In tube-type r-f voltage amplifiers, neutralization is not always employed, since the problem of unwanted feedback can be avoided by using certain tubes (pentodes) or circuit configurations (grounded-grid). In r-f power amplifiers, though, grounded-cathode triode amplifiers are highly desirable, so neutralization is used extensively. This will be covered later in the discussion of r-f power amplifiers.

neutralization (cont.)

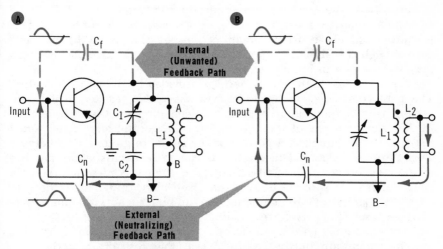

Neutralization prevents oscillation by feeding back to the input a signal
that is 180° out of phase with the unwanted internal feedback signal. The
two signals cancel each other enough to provide stable operation

For transistor r-f voltage amplifiers, neutralization is almost always
used. The unwanted collector-to-base feedback, although not as likely
to cause oscillation as is the case in tube circuits, causes undesirable
distortion of the amplifier waveform. To cancel this feedback, various
types of neutralizing circuits can be used.

In the circuit shown in A, the unwanted collector-to-base feedback
is represented by the capacitor C_f. Coil L_1 and capacitor C_1 make up
the output tuned circuit, and capacitor C_2 causes the signals at the
opposite ends of L_1 (points A and B) to be of opposite polarity with
respect to ground. Thus, since the unwanted feedback signal is coupled
to the base from the top (point A) of L_1, and the neutralizing signal is
coupled from the bottom (point B) through capacitor C_n, the two feedback signals are 180 degrees out of phase. The circuit components are
selected so that the neutralizing signal has sufficient amplitude to
cancel enough of the internal feedback to ensure stable operation.

Another method of neutralization is shown in B. Here the neutralizing
signal is obtained from the secondary, L_2, of the coupling transformer.
Because of the 180-degree phase reversal that takes place in a transformer, the signal at the top of the secondary (L_2) is 180 degrees out
of phase with the signal at the top of the primary (L_1). In this way,
the unwanted feedback signal coupled to the base through C_f is out of
phase with the neutralizing signal coupled through C_n. When this
method is used, care must be taken that the neutralizing signal is
taken from the correct side of the coupling transformer secondary,
or else the two feedback signals will reinforce instead of cancel each
other.

the r-f gain control

Very often, the level, or amplitude, of the output signal from an r-f voltage amplifier must be capable of being *manually controlled*. This permits relatively constant-amplitude output signals to be obtained even though the different input signals to which the amplifier is tuned may vary widely in amplitude.

Manual control of the output level is provided by the r-f gain control. The gain control is practically always a *variable resistor*, which can accomplish its function in two ways, depending on where it is used in the circuit. In one of these ways, the gain control affects the *signal itself*, either by shunting a portion of the signal to ground, or otherwise attenuating the signal. This method is generally unsatisfactory because of the very low strength of r-f signals. The other way in which the gain control can work is to leave the signal itself alone and change the gain of the r-f amplifier. By reducing the amplifier gain, the amplitude of the output signal is correspondingly lowered, and vice versa.

Some commonly used methods by which the r-f gain control reduces amplifier gain are illustrated. In A, variable resistor R is the gain control. It can be located in the cathode circuit *or* the screen grid circuit. When it is used in the cathode, it varies the *cathode bias* of the stage. With R at its minimum setting, the cathode bias is at its lowest value, being supplied only by resistor R_1. The gain of the stage is, therefore, maximum. Increasing the resistance of R causes the bias to increase, with a resulting decrease in stage gain. This type of gain control is used with *remote-cutoff* (variable-mu) *tubes*, since varying the grid bias of these tubes causes a smooth change in gain.

When the gain control is placed in the screen grid circuits, the value of R determines the screen grid current and, therefore, the screen grid voltage. By varying R, the screen grid voltage and the gain of the stage are controlled. This, though, is not as effective as the previous gain control.

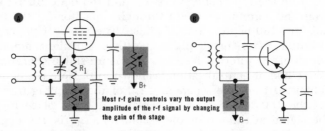

Most r-f gain controls vary the output amplitude of the r-f signal by changing the gain of the stage

In B, gain control R is used to vary the bias on the base of the stage. Increasing or decreasing the setting of R changes the base voltage and, therefore, the gain of the stage.

Frequently, the gain of r-f amplifiers is controlled automatically as well as, or instead of, manually. This is called *automatic gain control* (AGC), and is covered in Volume 7.

r-f traps

Sometimes, even with tuned circuits having the required bandwidth, unwanted large-amplitude signals are passed by the tuned circuits and are amplified along with the desired signal, causing interference and distortion. This occurs when the unwanted signals are *very strong* compared with the desired signal. Unwanted strong signals such as these can be removed from a receiver input before they can cause interference by circuits called *r-f traps,* or wave traps.

Basically, an r-f trap is a circuit that causes almost complete attenuation of the interfering signal without affecting any other signal frequency. Two common types of r-f traps are shown below. Since both of these traps are in the antenna circuit they eliminate the undesired signal before it can reach the r-f amplifier.

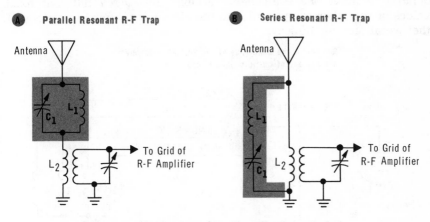

R-f traps provide almost complete attenuation of an undesired
signal frequency with little effect on other frequencies

In A, the trap consists of a parallel resonant circuit in series with the antenna and the antenna coil. The trap is tuned by capacitor C_1 to the frequency of the undesired signal. It thus offers a very high impedance at this frequency, preventing the signal from being developed across antenna coil L_2 and being coupled from there to the input of the r-f amplifier. To all other frequencies, though, the trap offers a low impedance, so appreciable currents of all but the unwanted frequency can flow in the antenna circuit.

The trap shown in B is a series resonant circuit that shunts the antenna coil. It is tuned to the frequency of the interfering signal, so it has minimum impedance at this frequency and a high impedance at all other frequencies. It thus shunts the unwanted signal currents around the antenna coil, but allows currents of all other frequencies to flow through L_2 and develop a signal voltage across it. Quite often, combinations of series and shunt traps are used.

bandswitching

In many equipments, an r-f amplifier must be capable of operating over a *very wide frequency range*. This means that the tuned circuits must be able to be tuned to any frequency within this wide range. Furthermore, the tuned circuits have to maintain the desired bandwidth regardless of the frequency to which they are tuned.

Usually, only one component (either L or C) of a tuned circuit is *variable*. When the circuit must be tunable over a very wide range, the variable component has to be adjustable over an almost impractical range of values. This difficulty could be avoided by making both components of the tuned circuit variable. However, when more than one tuned circuit is used, this would cause significant problems in tuning all of the circuits to the same frequency. Instead, what is usually done is to make one component variable and *switch* different fixed values of the other component into the circuit for different portions of the overall tuning range.

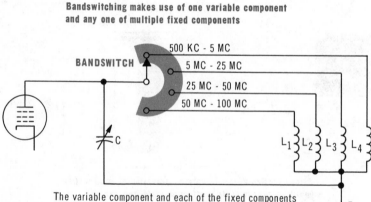

Bandswitching makes use of one variable component and any one of multiple fixed components

The variable component and each of the fixed components can be tuned over a band of frequencies. All of the individual bands together make up the overall tuning range

For example, assume the case of a parallel resonant circuit in the output of any r-f amplifier that operates over the frequency range of 500 kilocycles to 100 megacycles. A variable capacitor could be used for the capacitive circuit element, and four separate coils for the inductive element. The capacitor and all four coils are connected to a switch, called a *bandswitch*, which allows either one of the coils to be connected in parallel with the capacitor. Thus, if the overall tuning range is divided into subranges, or bands, of 500 kc–5 mc, 5 mc–25 mc, 25 mc–50 mc, and 50 mc–100 mc, the appropriate coil is switched into the circuit for each range.

When bandswitching is used, the variable component, say the capacitor, only has to have a limited range. This is because the same values of the variable capacitor produce different resonant frequencies when combined with the values of the different coils.

cascade r-f voltage amplifiers

R-f voltage amplifiers perform a variety of functions, depending on the type of equipment they are used in. In all cases, though, two of their most important functions are to produce signal amplification, or *gain*, and to have a good degree of frequency discrimination, or *selectivity*.

Both of these characteristics are directly related to the *number* of r-f amplifier stages used and can be improved or increased by connecting a number of amplifier stages in *cascade*. Essentially, this means that similar-type amplifiers are used in series, with the output of one connected to the input of the next, and so on. For practical purposes, the total gain of cascaded amplifiers can be considered to be the *product* of the gains of the individual stages. Thus, if three stages are used, each having a gain of 50, the overall gain is 50 × 50 × 50, or 125,000.

You should understand here that although gain is increased by cascading individual amplifiers, it does not mean that any extremely weak signal can be amplified to a usable level merely by adding stages. Noise received at the antenna along with the signal, as well as noise generated by the amplifier stages themselves, is amplified together with the signal. If this noise level is such that the *signal-to-noise ratio* at the output of the last amplifier stage is below a certain level, the signal will be unusable regardless of how much it has been amplified.

Cascading individual stages improves selectivity by increasing the number of tuned circuits. As shown, increasing the number of tuned circuits does not greatly affect the peak of the amplifier response curve, but significantly steepens the sides of the curve. This means that the response is much *sharper*, with the signal output decreasing greatly for small changes in frequency above and below resonance.

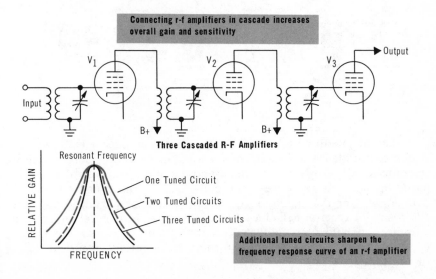

Connecting r-f amplifiers in cascade increases overall gain and sensitivity

Three Cascaded R-F Amplifiers

Additional tuned circuits sharpen the frequency response curve of an r-f amplifier

ganged tuning

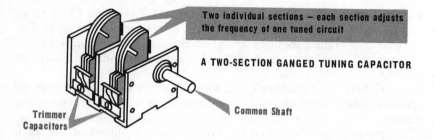

Two individual sections — each section adjusts the frequency of one tuned circuit

A TWO-SECTION GANGED TUNING CAPACITOR

Common Shaft

Trimmer Capacitors

Although cascading r-f amplifiers improves overall gain and selectivity, it also increases the number of tuned circuits that must be tuned to the same frequency. Each time a new signal is to be received, every tuned circuit must be *simultaneously* retuned to the new signal frequency.

This simultaneous tuning is generally accomplished by having all of the tuned-circuit capacitors mounted on a *common shaft*. When the shaft is rotated, the plates of each capacitor move into or out of mesh by the same amount, so the capacitance of each is changed equally. Such a capacitor is called a *ganged tuning capacitor* and has as many individual sections as there are tuned circuits. In effect, then, the sections of the ganged tuning capacitor make up individual but identical capacitors whose values are changed equally by rotating the common shaft. When the shaft is rotated, the capacitance value, and, therefore, the resonant frequency of each tuned circuit is changed equally.

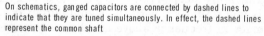

On schematics, ganged capacitors are connected by dashed lines to indicate that they are tuned simultaneously. In effect, the dashed lines represent the common shaft

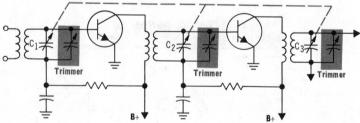

In actual practice, it is impossible to mass-produce electronic components with identical values. Thus, variations caused by manufacturing tolerances exist between the supposedly identical sections of a ganged capacitor, as well as between the coils used in the tuned circuits. To compensate for these differences, every section of a ganged capacitor has a small capacitor called a *trimmer capacitor* in parallel with it. The trimmer capacitors are adjusted so that each section of the ganged capacitor has the required value to provide essentially identical tuning of the tuned circuits.

cascode r-f amplifiers

A somewhat special but very common type of r-f amplifier is called a *cascode* r-f amplifier. A tube-type cascode circuit consists of a *grounded-cathode* stage driving a *grounded-grid* stage, while in a transistor cascode circuit, a *grounded-emitter* stage drives a *grounded-base* stage. This could be done with capacitor coupling, but a cascode circuit usually employs *direct coupling* between stages, with the signal coupled directly from the plate or collector of the first stage to the cathode or emitter of the second stage. In effect, the two stages are connected in *series*, with the input circuit of the second stage acting as the output load for the first.

When tubes are connected in cascode, triodes can often be used without neutralization. This is because both tubes form a voltage divider across the B+ supply, so the plate voltage and, therefore, the gain of the first stage are relatively low. As a result, the feedback voltage through the plate-to-grid interelectrode capacitance is not, in many cases, sufficient to cause oscillation. As the second stage is connected in the grounded-grid configuration, it does not require neutralization under any circumstances. By using triodes, therefore, a cascode r-f amplifier has the low-noise characteristics inherent in triode amplifiers. At the same time, the total gain of the two stages is about the same as would be obtained with a single pentode stage.

When transistors are connected as a cascode r-f amplifier, neutralization is also generally not needed. This is because of the stabilizing effect that the very low input impedance of the grounded-base stage has on the grounded-emitter stage.

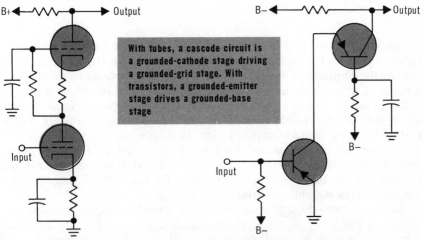

With tubes, a cascode circuit is a grounded-cathode stage driving a grounded-grid stage. With transistors, a grounded-emitter stage drives a grounded-base stage

In the tube version, the grid of the output stage is at ground potential for the r-f signal. In d-c terms, though, the grid is returned to the plate of the first stage. If this were not done, the high voltage on the cathode of the output stage would cut the stage off

circuits for cascode r-f amplifiers

A typical, tube-type cascode r-f amplifier is shown in A. V_1 is a grounded-cathode stage, and V_2 is a grounded-grid stage. The input signal is coupled through transformer T_1 to the series-tuned circuit consisting of coil L_1 and variable capacitor C_1. The signal is developed across C_1 and applied to the grid of V_1. Stage V_1 operates class A, with cathode bias supplied by resistor R_1 and capacitor C_2.

A   Tube-Type Directly-Coupled Cascode R-F Amplifier

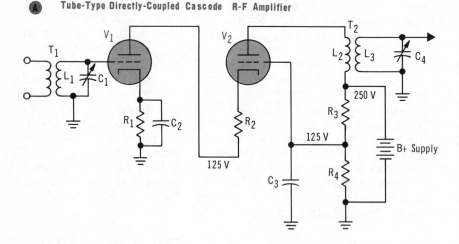

The plate current of V_1 flows to the B+ supply through stage V_2. This means that the *entire* output current of V_1, both the r-f component and the d-c component, flows through R_2, which functions as the cathode resistor of stage V_2. The r-f component of the voltage drop across R_2 is the input to the stage, while the d-c component of the voltage drop, which is 125 volts in this circuit, creates a large cathode voltage. If the grid of the stage were connected *directly* to ground, a large bias would result and cut off the stage. To prevent this, the grid is kept at r-f ground potential by capacitor C_3, and is returned at the same time to a 125-volt tap on the B+ supply. The bias for the second stage is then dropped across R_2, and so is the signal voltage.

Since the cathode fluctuates with the signal voltage, and the grid voltage is fixed, the signal is then amplified in tube V_2. The amplified output of stage V_2 is developed across coil L_2 and transformer-coupled to a tuned circuit serving as the input to a following stage. The cascode amplifier is tuned to the desired frequency by ganged capacitors C_1 and C_4. The trimmers for these capacitors are not shown.

circuits for cascode
r-f amplifiers (cont.)

B Transistor-Type Directly-Coupled Cascode R-F Amplifier

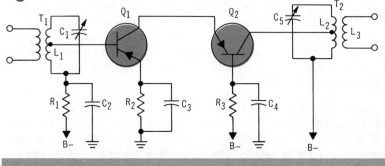

C Capacitor-Coupled Cascode R-F Amplifier

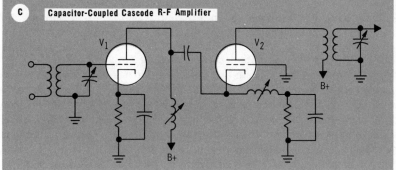

In the transistor cascode amplifier shown in B, transistor Q_1 is connected as a grounded-emitter stage, and Q_2 is connected as a grounded-base stage. The input to the base of Q_1 is from the tuned circuit consisting of tapped coil L_1 and capacitor C_1. Capacitor C_2 bypasses the r-f signal around bias resistor R_1 so that the maximum input signal is developed across the tuned circuit. Temperature and bias stability for Q_1 are provided by resistor R_2 and capacitor C_3. The emitter-collector circuit of Q_1 and the base-emitter circuit of Q_2 form a series circuit, providing Q_1 with excellent stability. Capacitor C_4 keeps the base of Q_2 at r-f ground potential to avoid degeneration. The output signal from Q_2 is developed across a tapped tuned circuit and transformer-coupled to the succeeding stage.

Diagram C shows how the cascode amplifier can be *capacitor-coupled.* It works similarly to ordinary cascoded stages, except that the output of V_1, which is a grounded-cathode stage, is coupled to the cathode of V_2, which is a grounded-grid stage. You can see that since the two stages are isolated from one another, they both can use the same B+ voltage.

summary

☐ The bandwidth of an r-f amplifier is the range between the two frequencies at which the amplified output voltage falls to a value 0.707 times its value at the frequency to which the amplifier is tuned. ☐ Amplifiers with a narrow bandwidth have good selectivity; those with a wide bandwidth have poor selectivity. ☐ For single-tuned amplifier circuits, bandwidth is equal to f_R/Q. ☐ In various r-f amplifier circuits, such as a triode grounded-cathode stage, positive feedback occurs, which can cause the stage to oscillate. To prevent oscillation, an external signal is fed back to the input to cancel the unwanted feedback. This is called neutralization. ☐ Pentodes or grounded-grid amplifiers do not require neutralization.

☐ A variable resistor in either the cathode or screen circuit can be used to provide r-f gain control. ☐ R-f traps, or wave traps, remove unwanted strong signals before they reach the r-f amplifier. ☐ When an r-f amplifier must be tunable over a wide range, the use of a single tuned circuit is impractical. In this case, one component is made variable, and different fixed values of the other component are switched into the circuit for different portions of the overall tuning range. This is bandswitching.

☐ Very high gain can be obtained by cascading amplifier stages. ☐ While cascading improves overall gain and selectivity, it has a disadvantage in that all stages must be gang tuned. To reduce this problem, trimmer capacitors are used to ensure identical tuning. ☐ A tube-type cascode amplifier consists of a grounded-cathode stage feeding a grounded-grid stage. A transistor cascode amplifier consists of a grounded-emitter stage feeding a grounded-base stage. ☐ Neutralization is generally not required in cascode amplifiers. ☐ Direct coupling is usually employed between the stages of a cascode amplifier.

review questions

1. How do cascaded and cascoded amplifiers differ?
2. Why is neutralization required for triode r-f amplifiers?
3. What are r-f traps and why are they used?
4. What is meant by the *signal-to-noise ratio*?
5. If the gain of each stage of a three-stage cascaded amplifier is 10, what is the overall gain?
6. A gain of 9000, minimum, is required. How many cascaded stages are required if each stage has a gain of 20?
7. Draw an r-f amplifier with a gain control.
8. What is meant by the *selectivity* of an amplifier?
9. Why are trimmer capacitors used in cascaded r-f amplifiers?
10. What is meant by *bandswitching*?

the r-f buffer amplifier

Although r-f buffer amplifiers are used in many kinds of electronic equipment, it is in high-power radio transmitters that their use is most extensive. As you know, in a transmitter, a *low-level* r-f signal is produced by an oscillator. This low-level signal is usually then increased in frequency and power level by succeeding stages. If the oscillator in a transmitter was to feed the output to a stage that required a large amount of *input driving power*, such as an intermediate or power amplifier, the oscillator would be loaded down and would *shift* from its natural frequency. This is especially true if the stage fed by the oscillator was keyed. Each time the transmitter was keyed, the load on the oscillator would change and its output frequency would shift. To prevent this loading of the oscillator, a buffer amplifier is placed in the circuit *directly after* the oscillator.

R-F Buffer Amplifier

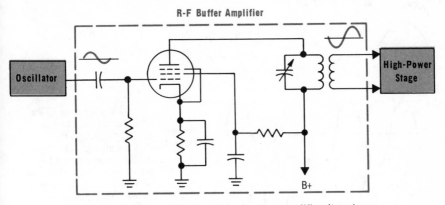

Ideally, an r-f buffer amplifier is a class A voltage amplifier. It produces no loading on the oscillator, and delivers as an output a voltage-amplified version of its input signal. Its purpose is to isolate stages

Ideally, the buffer amplifier is a *class A* r-f *voltage* amplifier. The high-input impedance of such a stage has no loading effect on the oscillator, and the amplified output contains sufficient power to drive the following stage easily. Very often, though, the luxury of an ideal buffer amplifier cannot be afforded, so less efficient but more practical circuits are used. For example, the buffer might be operated as a low-level class B or C power amplifier. It would produce some loading of the oscillator, but would be performing the added function of power amplification at the same time. As another example, the buffer might also be used as a frequency multiplier. Again, it would be operated class B or C, and would produce some loading on the oscillator.

You can see from the above that buffer amplifiers are really not a separate type of amplifier as far as *circuit configuration* is concerned. Many different types of circuits can perform the buffering function, and so, strictly speaking, are buffer amplifiers.

the frequency-multiplier stage

A frequency-multiplier stage receives as its input a sinusoidal signal, usually from an oscillator or buffer amplifier, and delivers as its output a sinusoidal signal from a tank circuit having a frequency that is some *multiple* of the input signal frequency. If the output has *twice* the frequency of the input, the stage is called a *frequency doubler;* if the output is *three times* the input, it is a *frequency tripler;* and so on.

Frequency multipliers are used extensively in AM radio transmitters that operate in the VHF region and higher. At these high frequencies, it is difficult to design oscillators that are stable. With frequency multipliers, oscillators can be used that have frequencies many times less than the transmitter output frequency. For example, if an oscillator having a frequency of 4 megacycles was used with two triplers and one doubler, its frequency would be multiplied eighteen times to a final frequency of 72 megacycles.

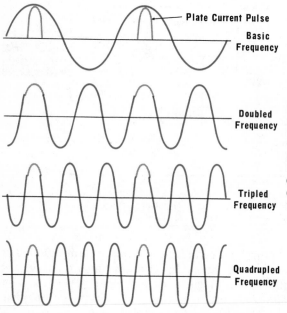

Plate Current Pulse

Basic
Frequency

Doubled
Frequency

Tripled
Frequency

Quadrupled
Frequency

In frequency multipliers, the plate current pulses for the basic frequency reinforce the tank circuit oscillations. In a doubler, they reinforce the peak of every other sine wave; in a tripler, they aid the peak of every third sine wave; in a quadrupler, they aid every fourth sine wave; and so on

Frequency multipliers are also widely used in FM transmitters. When the FM carrier is shifted in frequency by the modulation, the deviation is quite small. However, by sending the signal through a frequency multiplier, both the center frequency and the deviation are increased. For example, a center frequency of 10 megacycles that shifts to 10.001 megacycles, for a shift of 1 kilocycle, can be converted to a center frequency of 90 megacycles with a shift to 90.009 megacycles by being sent through two tripler stages. The shift is thus increased nine times, from 1 kilocycle to 9 kilocycles.

the frequency-multiplier stage (cont.)

Frequency Doubler Waveforms

Plate Current Pulse

Input

Output

Tank Current

B+

With no resistance in the tank circuit, the oscillatory currents would continue indefinitely at the tank's tuned frequency

The oscillatory currents would gradually diminish if energy was not supplied by the plate current pulses to replace that dissipated by the resistance

Frequency multipliers are essentially class C r-f amplifiers that have a parallel resonant circuit, or tank circuit, as their plate load. Plate current flows only during the positive peaks of the input signal, but because of the oscillatory or flywheel current produced in the tank circuit, a *sinusoidal output* is produced. The frequency of the output signal is determined by the resonant frequency of the tank circuit.

In theory, oscillatory currents can be set up in the tank circuit, and a sinusoidal output produced, at any multiple (or harmonic) of the circuit input frequency. In practice, though, the oscillatory currents, and, therefore, the amplitude of the output signal, decrease for each increase in harmonic. For example, if the tank circuit is tuned to the second harmonic of the input frequency, the output is 65 percent of what it would be if the tank was tuned to the input frequency. If the tank is tuned to the third harmonic, the output is 40 percent of what it would be if it was tuned to the input frequency. Because of this reduction in output, a frequency-multiplier stage is rarely tuned beyond the *fifth* harmonic of its input frequency.

You should understand here that if the tank circuit of a multiplier is tuned to any frequency other than a multiple of the input, oscillatory currents cannot flow in the tank. The output of the stage is therefore not sinusoidal.

In tube circuits, triodes with their high plate efficiency can be used for frequency multipliers without the necessity for neutralization. This is because the grid and plate signals have *different frequencies*.

A one-tube multiplier circuit is shown in A on the next page. The r-f input signal is applied to the grid of the stage through capacitor C_1 and developed across coil L_1, which has a large reactance at the r-f frequency. The stage is biased well beyond cutoff by the fixed bias battery, so the tube conducts only on the positive peaks of the input signal. The resulting pulses of plate current are rich in harmonics, since they are a distorted version of the input signal.

frequency-multiplier circuits

The frequency of the plate tank circuit is set to the desired harmonic by setting switch S for the desired tank coil and then fine-tuning capacitor C_2. The output of this type of circuit is usually RL or RC coupled to the following circuit, which may be another frequency multiplier or some type of power amplifier. Although fixed bias is shown for the circuit, a combination of grid-leak and cathode bias is often used.

A circuit that can be used for the efficient production of even-order harmonics in its output is the *push-push multiplier* shown in B. When used as a doubler or quadrupler, this circuit has a greater power output and higher plate efficiency than a single-tube multiplier. As shown, the *grids* of a push-push stage are connected in *push-pull*, and the *plates* are connected in *parallel*. As a result, the signals applied to the grids of the two tubes are 180 degrees out of phase, so that a pulse of plate current flows in one tube on the positive peaks of the input signal, and a pulse of plate current flows in the other tube on the negative peaks of the input signal. Two pulses of current are therefore delivered to the tank circuit during each full cycle of the input signal, instead of only one pulse as in the one-tube multiplier.

If both the inputs and outputs of two tubes are connected in push-pull, the circuit can be used as an efficient tripler, since such a circuit produces only odd-harmonic frequency multiplication.

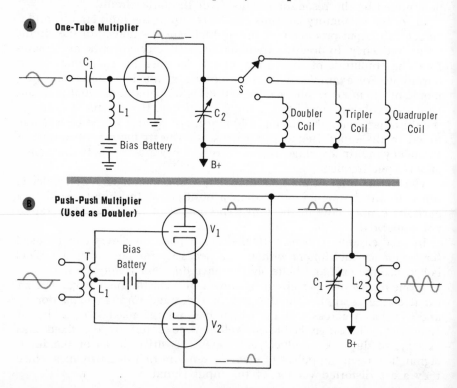

r-f power amplifiers

R-f power amplifiers are used to increase the power level of an r-f signal applied to their input. Their principal application is in electronic transmitters, where they boost the r-f carrier signal to the high power levels required to drive transmitting antennas. R-f power amplifiers can be classified in various ways: by their relative output levels, their class of operation, the type of tubes used, or their circuit configuration. In practically all cases, though, they require relatively large input driving power and use tuned circuits as their output load.

R-f power amplifiers operate either class B or C, which means that plate current flows for only a *portion* of the input signal cycle. The output is *sinusoidal*, nevertheless, because of the flywheel action of the tuned circuit in the output. Since *grid current* flows in a class B or C amplifier when the input signal drives the grid positive, grid-leak bias is used extensively in r-f power amplifiers. However, a certain amount of fixed or cathode bias is usually also provided, inasmuch as the grid-leak bias is lost when there is no input to the stage; for example, when the transmitter is keyed. Without this additional bias, excessive current would flow through the tube when the grid-leak bias was lost and damage would result.

Some of the various types of power amplifier circuits are shown.

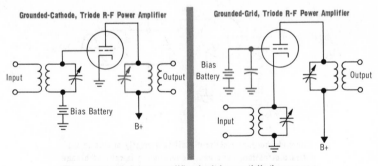

The grounded-cathode power amplifier circuit is essentially the same as a frequency multiplier circuit. The basic difference is that the output tank circuit is tuned to the input frequency rather than to a harmonic of that frequency. Although not shown, this circuit must be neutralized

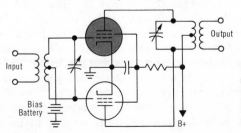

In the grounded-grid circuit, the grid acts as a shield between the input and output circuits, preventing feedback. Therefore, a triode can be used without the need for neutralization

tube vs. transistor
r-f power amplifiers

Although both tubes and transistors can be used as r-f power amplifiers, they are significantly different in their electrical capabilities. Tubes have been used for many years, and it is a relatively easy matter to design and construct tube-type r-f amplifiers that can operate at VHF, UHF, and higher frequencies and deliver hundreds and even thousands of watts of output power.

Transistors, on the other hand, still have *frequency* and *power* limitations that make their use as r-f power amplifiers fall far short of that of tubes. Special transistors have been developed that can deliver a few hundred watts of output power at useful r-f frequencies; but in most cases, the cost of the transistor is much greater than that of a comparable tube circuit. Consequently, transistor r-f amplifiers are for the most part limited to special applications involving low power requirements, such as walkie-talkie transmitters, or applications where the greatly-decreased size and weight of transistor circuits are more important than the additional cost. An example of this would be the transmitters used in satellite telemetry systems.

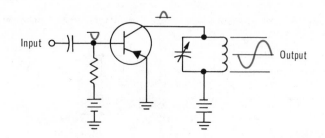

Although the base-emitter circuit is normally biased in the forward direction, for class C operation it is reverse-biased. This is necessary to bias the stage well beyond cutoff

If a transistor is used as an r-f power amplifier, it is usually operated class C. For most of the input cycle, therefore, only a small amount of "cutoff" current flows in the collector circuit. For the grounded-emitter circuit shown, this means that the transistor only conducts in bursts, and these bursts occur during the positive peaks of the input signal. But, as in tube circuits, the bursts of collector current are converted into a sinusoidal output by the action of the tank circuit in the collector output. A unique feature of the class C transistor amplifier is that in order to achieve a bias point considerably beyond cutoff, the emitter must be biased the *reverse* of what is considered normal. Thus, in the circuit shown, the emitter is biased positive with respect to the base.

effect of modulation

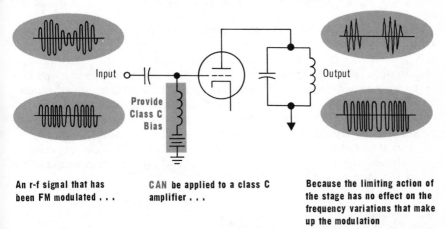

Once an r-f signal has been AM modulated . . .	It CANNOT be applied to a class C amplifier	If it were, the limiting action of the stage would greatly distort the signal

| An r-f signal that has been FM modulated . . . | CAN be applied to a class C amplifier . . . | Because the limiting action of the stage has no effect on the frequency variations that make up the modulation |

In many transmitters, a series of cascade r-f power amplifiers is required to produce the necessary output power. The last stage is called the *final* power amplifier, or merely the power amplifier, and the preceding stages are called *intermediate* amplifiers, or *drivers*. If the r-f signal is to be *modulated* (either AM or FM), the modulation can be introduced at various places in the transmitter.

For AM modulation, the point at which the modulation occurs has an important effect on the type of r-f power amplifier circuits that are used. This is because the modulation varies the instantaneous peak-to-peak *amplitude* of the r-f signal. These variations, which make up the modulation envelope, must be preserved once modulation takes place. Any stage that amplifies the signal after it has been modulated has to be *linear,* which means class A, or class B push-pull. The *unmodulated* r-f signal, though, can be amplified by a class C stage. Since class C amplifiers have the highest efficiency, high-power AM transmitters are most efficient when the modulation takes place at the output of the final power amplifier. All of the stages, including the last, can then be operated class C.

In FM transmitters, modulation takes place *before* any of the power amplifier stages. Every power amplifier therefore amplifies the modulated signal. However, the FM signal has no envelope that can be distorted by the characteristics of a class C stage. The modulation is merely a shift in the frequency of a constant amplitude r-f signal, and these frequency variations can be reproduced in a class C amplifier without distortion. Class C amplifiers, with their high efficiencies, are therefore generally used for the power stages of FM transmitters.

AM vs. FM r-f power amplifiers

You have already seen one of the differences between r-f power amplifiers used for AM signals and those used for FM. In addition, there is one other significant difference. This is the Q or *selectivity* of the tuned input and output circuits.

Tuned circuits used with power amplifiers in AM transmitters generally have higher Q's and, therefore, greater selectivity. The reason for this is that in AM transmitters the tuned circuits usually only process the unmodulated r-f signal. There are no *side bands*, so the circuits can be *sharply* tuned to the r-f frequency. In FM transmitters, on the other hand, the r-f power amplifiers and their tuned circuits process the modulated signal. This signal contains side bands both above and below the center frequency, and these side bands must be passed *equally* by the tuned circuits if the signal is not to be distorted. The response of these tuned circuits, therefore, must be broad enough to accommodate all of the side bands.

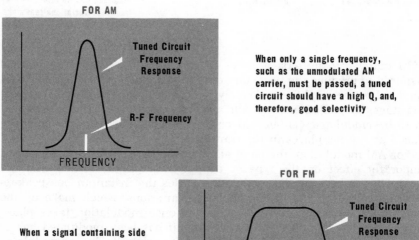

FOR AM

Tuned Circuit
Frequency
Response

R-F Frequency

FREQUENCY

When only a single frequency, such as the unmodulated AM carrier, must be passed, a tuned circuit should have a high Q, and, therefore, good selectivity

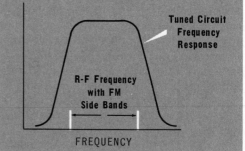

When a signal containing side bands must be passed, a tuned circuit requires a low enough Q so that all the side bands will be passed equally

FOR FM

Tuned Circuit
Frequency
Response

R-F Frequency
with FM
Side Bands

FREQUENCY

The need for lower Q's in the r-f amplifier tuned circuits of FM transmitters has the effect of making triodes, in general, less desirable for FM than for AM power amplifiers. This is because of the relatively large *output capacitance* of triodes. The shunting effect of this capacitance on the plate tank circuit tends to increase the Q of the circuit, resulting in too narrow a bandpass.

input circuits

Since an r-f tube-type power amplifier is operated class C or class B push-pull, its input impedance is not extremely high like that of a class A amplifier. For efficient power transfer, therefore, there must be an impedance match between the grid input impedance of the r-f power amplifier and the plate output impedance of the previous stage. There are many circuit arrangements that can be used to provide this impedance match, with the one used chosen on the basis of the particular requirements of the application. Some of these circuit arrangements are illustrated here.

In this capacitance-coupled arrangement, L and C make up the output tank circuit of V_1. Coil L is tapped to step up the signal voltage from V_1 and present the power amplifier input circuit with the proper impedance

This capacitance-coupled arrangement is similar to A, except that the tuned circuit is in the grid circuit of the power amplifier

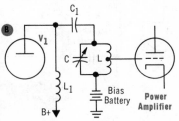

The signal is taken from the top of the tank and coupled to the grid of the power amplifier through C_1. This circuit is used to match a lower output impedance to a higher input impedance

The tapped tank coil steps the signal voltage down and presents a lower impedance to the input of the power amplifier. This circuit is used to match a higher output impedance to a lower input impedance

This capacitance-coupled arrangement is somewhat similar to A. However, by applying plate voltage for V_1 through the tap of the coil, the voltage at the bottom of the tank circuit has the correct phase for neutralization

In this arrangement, the signal is link-coupled from a tuned output circuit to a tuned input circuit. Essentially, the link is just a few turns of wire on either end joined by a length of transmission line

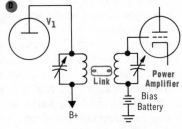

A triode can therefore be used for V_1 and a neutralizing voltage fed back to the grid of V_1 through capacitor C_n. This is not possible with the circuits of A or B. Neutralization is covered in more detail later

The link has a very small inductance, so the impedance of the coupling circuit is low, and power losses are minimized. An advantage of link coupling is that it allows the power amplifier to be located some distance from its driving stage

output circuits

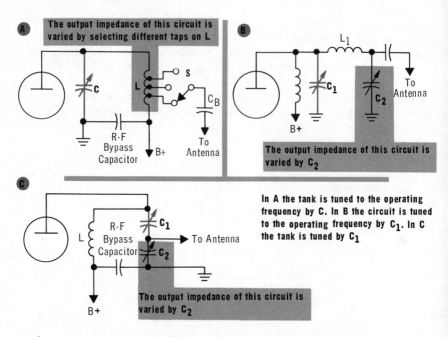

When an antenna is fed directly from the r-f amplifier output tank circuit, which is commonly done in small portable transmitters, impedance matching is the main requirement. The tank circuit in the amplifier output must match the output impedance of the amplifier *directly* to the antenna impedance, which can vary over a wide range during operation. Therefore, a tank circuit must be used that can compensate for a wide range of impedance. Three basic circuits that can do this are shown.

In A, the coil of the output tank circuit has various taps, any of which can be selected by switch S. The bottom of the tank circuit is at ground potential for the r-f signal, so the bottom tap on the coil has a very low impedance, and each higher tap has a greater impedance. The desired impedance is selected by switch S, and the output is coupled to the antenna through capacitor C_B, which prevents the B+ supply voltage from reaching the antenna.

In B, a commonly-used output circuit, called a pi-network, is shown. Effectively, capacitor C_1 and C_2, with inductor L_1, make up the output tank circuit. L_1 and C_2 form an impedance-matching voltage divider with the relative voltage drops determined by the setting of C_2. C_1 is also variable and is used to tune the circuit to resonance at the operating frequency.

The circuit shown in C is a variation of the pi-network in which one of the capacitors is not grounded. The two capacitors (C_1 and C_2) make up the impedance-matching voltage divider, with the output taken from across C_2.

the antenna tuning unit

Quite frequently, a separate piece of equipment, called an *antenna tuning unit*, is used between the final power amplifier of a transmitter and the antenna. The antenna tuning unit performs two functions: (1) it provides a means of making the antenna *resonant* at any frequency over a relatively large range, thus making the antenna *purely resistive* at the operating frequency; and (2) it also provides a means of *matching* the antenna resistance to the output impedance of the r-f power amplifier.

Antenna circuits are covered in Volume 7. Now, though, you should understand that when an antenna is purely resistive at its operating frequency, maximum power transfer and radiation are achieved. By means of an antenna tuning unit, a transmitter can efficiently drive any one of many different antenna types having a wide variety of electrical characteristics.

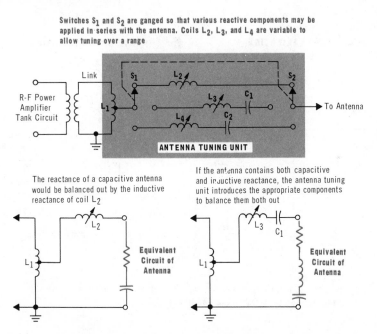

Switches S_1 and S_2 are ganged so that various reactive components may be applied in series with the antenna. Coils L_2, L_3, and L_4 are variable to allow tuning over a range

The reactance of a capacitive antenna would be balanced out by the inductive reactance of coil L_2

If the antenna contains both capacitive and inductive reactance, the antenna tuning unit introduces the appropriate components to balance them both out

A basic antenna tuning unit is shown. In this circuit, switch S connects various capacitors and coils in *series* with the antenna circuit. These components are then adjusted to resonate with the reactive properties of the antenna. This makes the antenna a series resonant circuit, and, therefore, purely resistive.

The output of the r-f power amplifier is inductively (link) coupled to coil L_1 in the antenna tuning unit. L_1 has a variable tap that is set so that the resistance of the antenna is reflected back as the optimum load on the power amplifier tank circuit.

neutralization

You recall that when triodes are used as grounded-cathode r-f amplifiers, the reactance of the grid-to-plate interelectrode capacitance is often low enough to cause a significant amount of undesired feedback. This feedback is in phase with the input signal, and if it is not eliminated by neutralization, it can cause the stage to oscillate, thus producing unstable operation and distortion. In r-f tube-type voltage amplifiers, this problem is generally solved by using tubes or circuit configurations in which the unwanted feedback is not present. But in r-f power amplifiers, grounded-cathode triode stages are often desirable. When they are used, neutralization must be provided.

As you know, neutralization is merely the feeding back from *output* to input a voltage that is *equal* in *amplitude* to but *opposite* in *phase* with the undesired internal feedback through the tube interelectrode capacitance. The two voltages cancel each other and regeneration is eliminated.

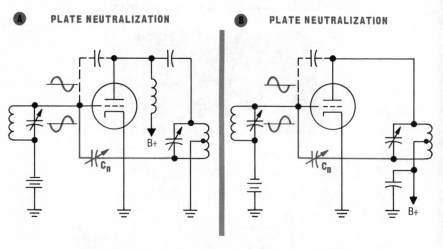

A PLATE NEUTRALIZATION   **B** PLATE NEUTRALIZATION

The voltage fed back to the grid through the external neutralization path
(in color) cancels the voltage fed back through the grid-to-plate
interelectrode capacitance (dashed lines)

The two basic methods of neutralization are called *plate neutralization* and *grid neutralization*. In plate neutralization, shown in A and B, the coil in the plate tank circuit is tapped to ground with respect to the r-f signal. This makes the r-f voltage at the bottom of the tank 180 degrees out of phase with the r-f signal at the top of the tank, again with respect to ground, and also, therefore, with respect to the grid. By connecting a capacitor (C_n) between the bottom of the tank and the grid, a voltage is fed back to the grid that is 180 degrees out of phase with the voltage fed back through the interelectrode capacitance.

neutralization (cont.)

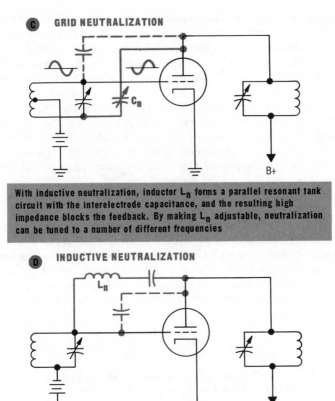

GRID NEUTRALIZATION

With inductive neutralization, inductor L_n forms a parallel resonant tank circuit with the interelectrode capacitance, and the resulting high impedance blocks the feedback. By making L_n adjustable, neutralization can be tuned to a number of different frequencies

INDUCTIVE NEUTRALIZATION

C_n is variable so that the neutralizing voltage can be made equal in amplitude to the undesired feedback voltage.

In grid neutralization, shown in C, the tapped coil is in the grid circuit. The unwanted feedback voltage is applied to the top of the tapped coil, and the neutralizing voltage is applied, through C_n, to the bottom of the coil. Since the coil is tapped, both voltages are again 180 degrees out of phase and cancel each other.

In a somewhat different method of neutralization, shown in D, a small coil (L_n) is connected between the plate and grid. The reactance of this coil is equal to the reactance of the grid-to-plate interelectrode capacitance at the signal frequency, so a parallel resonant circuit is formed between grid and plate. Such a resonant circuit has a high impedance at resonance, which prevents the undesired feedback voltage from being coupled back to the grid. The capacitor in series with the coil prevents the d-c plate voltage from reaching the grid. This method of neutralization is called *inductive neutralization* and is effective only at a *single* frequency, as determined by the reactance of the coil.

parasitic suppression

R-f power amplifiers are susceptible to what are called *parasitic oscillations*. These are oscillations that are *unrelated* and usually far removed from the frequency to which the amplifier is tuned. Parasitic oscillations can reduce the power output of the amplifier, cause excessive current that can shorten the life of the tube, and produce radiation of spurious signals that interferes with nearby electronic equipment.

The cause of parasitic oscillations is the development of *unwanted resonant circuits* that interact with each other in such a way that sufficient feedback is produced to sustain oscillation. These unwanted resonant circuits may be produced by the stray circuit capacitances interacting with the inductance of the circuit wiring, component leads, and tube elements, or they might be produced by a combination of these things and the actual circuit components themselves. In any case, the specific causes of parasitic oscillations vary from circuit to circuit. Because of this, the methods for eliminating parasitic oscillations, called parasitic suppression, also vary widely from circuit to circuit.

Generally, however, parasitic suppression involves the incorporation of small components in the circuit to: (1) detune one of the unwanted resonant circuits causing the parasitic oscillations; or (2) provide attenuation in the feedback path. Some of the circuits used for parasitic suppression are shown.

Small resistors or r-f chokes in series with the grid or plate connection provide parasitic suppression

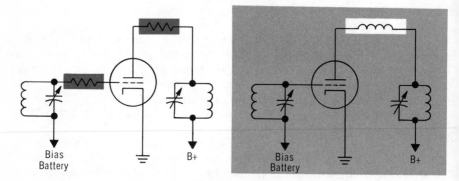

Resistors provide attenuation in the feedback path, while r-f chokes change the resonant frequency of one of the unwanted tuned circuits causing the parasitic oscillation

summary

☐ An r-f buffer amplifier is used to isolate, or act as a buffer for, one circuit from another. It gets its name from its function rather than its configuration. Ideally, a buffer amplifier is a class A, r-f voltage amplifier, although low-level class B or C amplifiers are sometimes used. ☐ In a radio transmitter, the buffer amplifier prevents loading of the oscillator by the succeeding amplifiers. ☐ Frequency multipliers are essentially class C r-f amplifiers. Frequency multipliers do not require neutralization because their input and output frequencies are different. ☐ R-f power amplifiers are used to increase the power level of an r-f signal. They operate either class B or C. ☐ For very high power requirements, tube-type r-f power amplifiers are used, but for low power applications, transistorized ones are being used increasingly.

☐ The last stage of a transmitter is the final power amplifier. ☐ In high-power AM transmitters, modulation takes place at the output of the final power amplifier. This allows all amplifier stages to be operated class C. ☐ In FM transmitters, modulation takes place before any of the power amplifier stages. ☐ Tuned circuits used with the r-f power amplifiers in AM transmitters generally have higher Q's and, therefore, greater selectivity than those in FM transmitters. ☐ For efficient power transfer, impedance-matching circuits must be used between cascaded r-f power amplifiers.

☐ Impedance-matching circuits must be used to match the output of an r-f power amplifier to any transmission line or antenna that it feeds. ☐ An antenna tuning unit is a separate unit that performs as an impedance-matching device between an r-f power amplifier and an antenna. ☐ Parasitic suppression is necessary in r-f power amplifiers to eliminate parasitic oscillations caused by unwanted resonant circuits.

review questions

1. What causes parasitic oscillations?
2. Why do frequency multipliers not require neutralization?
3. Why are buffer amplifiers used?
4. Why do FM r-f amplifiers require lower Q's than AM amplifiers?
5. What is an antenna tuning unit?
6. What are the two basic types of neutralization?
7. Are transistors ever used in power amplifiers?
8. Draw a frequency multiplier. Explain its operation.
9. In AM transmitters, modulation usually takes place in the output of the final power amplifier. Why?
10. Draw the circuit for a class C transistor amplifier.

i-f amplifiers

Intermediate-frequency (i-f) amplifiers are used in equipment such as superheterodyne receivers, where all input signals are converted to a single frequency (i-f frequency) for further processing after some degree of amplification. The i-f amplifiers provide the major portion of the *signal amplification* that takes place in an equipment and, at the same time, provide the necessary degree of *selectivity* so that adjacent-channel signals do not interfere with the desired signal. You will recall from Volume 2 that some equipments employ *double conversion*, in which two i-f frequencies and, therefore, two groups of i-f amplifiers are used. Essentially, though, the i-f amplifiers function in the same way. Only their frequencies are different.

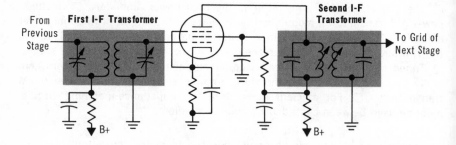

A basic tube-type i-f amplifier consists of a pentode class A voltage amplifier with double-tuned coupling circuits in both its input and output

An i-f amplifier is similar to an r-f voltage amplifier in that it is a tuned class A voltage amplifier. However, an r-f amplifier can be tuned to any frequency over its operating range, but an i-f amplifier is permanently tuned to a *single frequency*. Another difference is that r-f amplifiers rarely use *double-tuned coupling circuits* between stages, but with i-f amplifiers, double-tuned coupling is very common, especially with tube circuits.

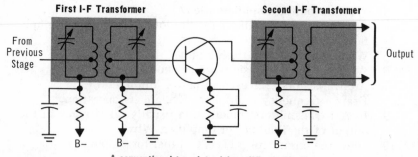

A conventional transistor i-f amplifier is similar to its tube counterpart in many respects

bandwidth

The *selectivity*, and, therefore, the *bandwidth* requirements of an i-f amplifier are somewhat contradictory in nature. A good degree of selectivity must be provided to prevent interference from adjacent channel signals. At the same time, however, the bandwidth must be sufficiently wide so that a signal and all its side-band frequencies are amplified equally.

The required bandwidth of an i-f amplifier depends on the frequency range of the side bands contained in the signal. This, in turn, depends on the type of signal, as well as on the degree of acceptable distortion. For example, an i-f amplifier for use in an AM broadcast receiver needs a bandwidth of 10 kilocycles, since such AM signals contain an upper and a lower side band, both 5 kilocycles wide.

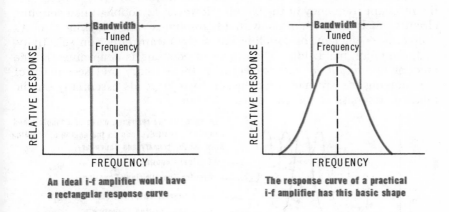

An ideal i-f amplifier would have a rectangular response curve

The response curve of a practical i-f amplifier has this basic shape

For some applications, such as voice communication, distortion of the signal is acceptable as long as it does not destroy the intelligibility. In these cases, the i-f amplifier could have a bandwidth as narrow as, say, 2500 cps. The signal would still be intelligible, and the increased selectivity would provide better discrimination against adjacent channel signals. The i-f amplifiers used for wide-band FM and television require relatively wide bandwidths since these signals contain a broad spectrum of side-band frequencies.

You can see from the above that although all i-f amplifiers perform essentially the same function, their selectivity and bandwidth requirements vary widely according to the type of equipment in which they are used. In all cases, though, their frequency-response curve is similar in shape to that shown.

The relatively flat peak of the curve indicates that all frequencies within the required bandwidth are amplified about equally. The steeply sloping sides indicate adequate discrimination against frequencies outside of the bandwidth.

effect of coupling on selectivity and bandwidth

In most electronic equipment, the necessary degree of selectivity cannot be achieved with a single i-f amplifier. You saw that selectivity in r-f voltage amplifiers was directly related to the *number* of tuned circuits used. The more tuned circuits, the greater the selectivity. The same thing is true for i-f amplifiers. For this reason, two or more i-f amplifier stages, each with tuned input and output circuits, are usually used for i-f amplification.

You will also recall from the discussion of r-f voltage amplifiers that the *shape* of the response curve of a single-tuned coupling circuit depends essentially only on the Q of the circuit, and the bandwidth of such a circuit is given by the equation: Bandwidth $= f_R/Q$, where f_R is the resonant frequency of the circuit. However, in double-tuned coupling circuits, such as those used with i-f amplifiers, the coupling circuit's *degree,* or coefficient, of coupling has a significant effect on selectivity, and, therefore, bandwidth. The degree of coupling is determined by the amount of *mutual inductance* between the primary and secondary of the coupling transformer, and this, in turn, depends essentially on the relative closeness of the two coils.

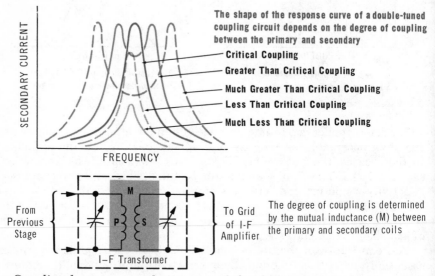

The shape of the response curve of a double-tuned coupling circuit depends on the degree of coupling between the primary and secondary

— Critical Coupling
— Greater Than Critical Coupling
— Much Greater Than Critical Coupling
— Less Than Critical Coupling
— Much Less Than Critical Coupling

The degree of coupling is determined by the mutual inductance (M) between the primary and secondary coils

Coupling between tuned circuits is defined in terms of what is called *critical coupling.* This is the degree of coupling, as shown, at which the resonant current in the secondary circuit reaches its maximum value. If the coupling is less than critical (undercoupling), the secondary current has a lower value, and the circuit has a narrower bandwidth. When the coupling is greater than critical (overcoupling), the response curve widens (greater bandwidth), but displays two humps.

effect of coupling on selectivity and bandwidth (cont.)

You can see from the response curves that the various degrees of coupling possess both advantages and disadvantages as far as the selectivity and bandwidth requirements of an i-f amplifier are concerned. The curves for greater than critical coupling have steeply sloping sides, which means good frequency discrimination. They can also provide a relatively wide bandwidth. However, the humps indicate unequal response to difference frequencies within the bandwidth, and this is unacceptable since it would mean distortion of the signal. For critical and slightly less than critical coupling, good response within the bandwidth would be obtained, but the bandwidth is too narrow for most practical applications. Coupling much less than critical is generally undesirable because of both its narrow bandwidth and low response amplitude.

The frequency response of i-f amplifiers can be made to provide the necessary selectivity and bandwidth in one of two basic ways. One way is to use greater than critical coupling in the tuned coupling circuits, and then modify the circuit to produce a more linear response over the bandwidth. As shown in A, this can be done by placing *resistors* in *parallel* with the L and C components of the tuned circuits. These shunt resistors have the effect of adding resistance in series with the coils and thus lower the Q of the tuned circuits. The result is a flatter response, although at some sacrifice in amplitude.

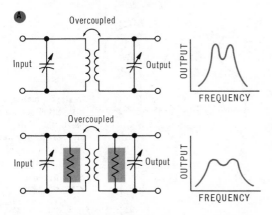

By adding shunt resistors across the tuned circuits, the dip in the overcoupled frequency response curve can be smoothed out. Some loss in gain results, however

Another method of making the response more linear (shown in B) is to *overcouple* one i-f transformer to obtain the required bandwidth and then use another i-f transformer with a *single-peak* response curve to "fill in" the dip in the response. The single-peak response can be provided by either a single-tuned coupling circuit, or a double-tuned circuit with critical or slightly less than critical coupling.

practical i-f coupling circuits

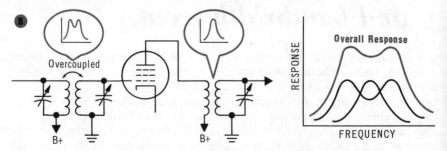

The desired response can be obtained by using a coupling circuit with a single-peak response to fill in the dip produced by an overcoupled circuit

The other common method of obtaining the required response is to use different tuned circuits that are tuned to slightly *different* frequencies. The circuits then all have single-peak response curves slightly displaced in frequency from each other. Since the overall response is the product of the individual responses, both the required bandwidth and an essentially flat response are obtained. This method is called *stagger tuning* and is illustrated in C. While stagger tuning can also be used with transformer coupling, it is more frequently used with LC coupling circuits. This is known as *impedance coupling*, where each coil resonates with its interwinding capacitances, and a capacitor couples the signal to the next stage. The circuit shown uses six tuned coils, with each pair tuned to one frequency. If all six were tuned to different frequencies, an even flatter overall response would be obtained.

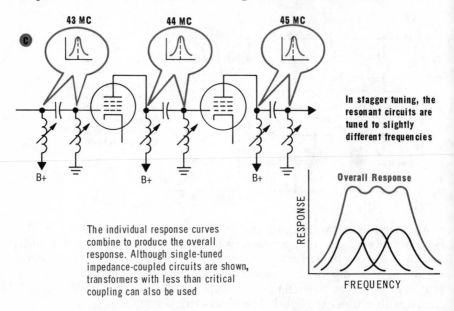

In stagger tuning, the resonant circuits are tuned to slightly different frequencies

The individual response curves combine to produce the overall response. Although single-tuned impedance-coupled circuits are shown, transformers with less than critical coupling can also be used

frequency response of television i-f amplifiers

So far, all of the i-f frequency response curves shown have been *symmetrical* about the tuned frequency. This is a requirement for i-f amplifiers that must process *double side-band* signals. Since the side bands on either side of the carrier of a double side-band signal contain equal intelligence, both side bands must be amplified equally, or else the signal will be distorted.

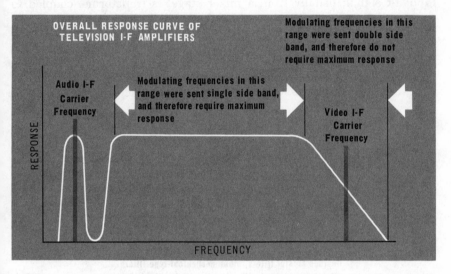

In i-f amplifiers used in television receivers, though, the situation is different. You recall from Volume 1 that *vestigial side-band* AM transmission is used for the video portion of the television signal. All frequencies in the lower side band more than 0.75 megacycles from the carrier are rejected and not transmitted. This means that modulating frequencies greater than about 0.75 megacycles are transmitted as single side-band signals, and those less than 0.75 are transmitted as double side-band signals. Since the modulation energy in both side bands is ultimately combined to reproduce the original intelligence, a symmetrical response in the receiver i-f section would result in a demodulated signal output twice as great for video signals below 0.75 megacycles as for signals above 0.75 megacycles. This would cause an unacceptable degree of distortion.

To compensate for the lower amplitudes of the video modulation frequencies above 0.75 megacycles, the response of the i-f amplifiers is not symmetrical about the video carrier frequency. Instead, the response is adjusted so that frequencies above 0.75 megacycles are amplified more than those below 0.75 megacycles, with the result that the relative amplitudes of all the original modulating frequencies are restored.

filter selectivity

Although tuned coupling circuits are the most common way of providing i-f amplifier selectivity, in some equipments practically all of the i-f selectivity is provided by a single *selective filter* at the input to the first i-f amplifier. One of the most frequently used selective filters is a *piezoelectric crystal*. Such a crystal is essentially a *series* LCR circuit, with its thickness, shape, and material determining the resonant frequency. In the circuit shown, a crystal filter is connected between two conventional tuned circuits in the input to the first i-f amplifier. The input i-f signal, usually from a mixer stage, is transformer-coupled to the parallel resonant circuit consisting of coil L_1 and capacitor C_1. To frequencies within its resonant bandwidth, the crystal offers a very low resistance, and these signal frequencies are coupled through capacitor C_3 to the tuned circuit of the first i-f amplifier (L_2C_4). To frequencies outside of its resonant bandwidth, the crystal offers a very high resistance, and these frequencies are effectively attenuated.

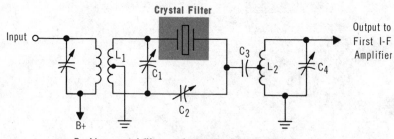

Besides crystal filters, other mechanical-type filters are sometimes used with i-f amplifiers to provide the required selectivity and bandwidth

Capacitor C_2 is called the crystal-phasing capacitor. It is adjustable and is used to neutralize the capacitance that exists between the crystal and its holder. Coil L_2 is tapped to provide an impedance match between the crystal and the input circuit of the first i-f amplifier.

By using a crystal filter for i-f selectivity, the requirements of the coupling circuits between i-f amplifiers are greatly reduced. Basically, all these circuits have to do is preserve the frequency response established by the crystal filter. Sometimes, tuned coupling is even eliminated, and adequate RC or LC coupling can be used.

In many communications receivers, a crystal filter can be switched in and out of the circuit. For reception of CW signals, the crystal is connected in the i-f circuits and provides a very narrow i-f bandwidth (as narrow as 50 to 100 cps) and sharp discrimination against frequencies outside of this band. For modulated signals, such as voice, the crystal is switched out of the circuit, and the i-f selectivity and bandwidth are provided by conventional tuned coupling circuits.

gain

Normally, the gain of an i-f amplifier cannot be adjusted manually. However, in many applications, such as radio and television receivers, the i-f gain is automatically adjusted to compensate for changes in the strength of the received signal

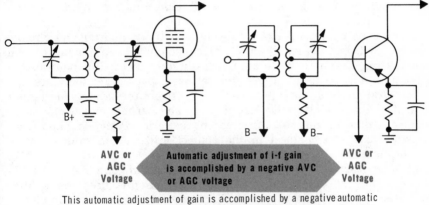

AVC or AGC Voltage

Automatic adjustment of i-f gain is accomplished by a negative AVC or AGC voltage

AVC or AGC Voltage

This automatic adjustment of gain is accomplished by a negative automatic volume control (AVC) or automatic gain control (AGC) voltage produced at a later stage in the equipment. The AVC or AGC voltage varies the grid voltage, and, therefore, the stage bias in tube i-f amplifiers, and usually the base voltage, and, therefore, the base-emitter bias in transistor amplifiers

As was pointed out previously, i-f amplifiers provide by far the largest portion of the overall signal gain in equipments in which they are used. Generally, their inputs are in microvolts or millivolts, and they must deliver an output signal of a few volts to a detector stage. To supply this gain, it is usually necessary to connect two or more i-f amplifier stages in cascade. In tube circuits, pentodes, with their high gain, are most commonly used for i-f amplifiers. Transistors, because of their lower gain, normally require more cascaded stages than do tubes to provide the required overall gain. In some tube circuits, even though a certain number of stages can supply the required gain, they cannot provide the necessary selectivity and bandwidth. Additional stages and their accompanying tuned circuits are then used for *response purposes,* with their gain being of secondary importance.

The high gains of i-f amplifiers increase the chance of *stray coupling* between stages when a cascade arrangement is used. The greater the number of cascaded stages, the more chance there is of feedback through the stray coupling. This can cause instability and oscillation, and result in distortion and a decrease in gain. As a result, careful shielding, good circuit layout, and effective *decoupling* networks are important in cascaded i-f amplifiers. This problem is somewhat lessened when *double conversion* is used, since all of the i-f stages do not then operate at the same frequency.

neutralization

Normally, tube-type i-f amplifiers do not require neutralization, since they use *pentodes*. However, at FM and higher frequencies, high-gain pentode i-f amplifiers have a tendency to oscillate because of feedback through the tube interelectrode capacitance. These capacitances are very small, but the combination of *large gain* and *high frequency* can cause sufficient feedback to cause oscillation.

When such conditions exist, conventional triode neutralizing circuits can be used, but the small values of capacitance involved make such neutralizing circuits hard to adjust. A different method of neutralizing a pentode stage is to use a *common* bypass capacitor for the plate and screen grid circuits. Such a capacitor effectively forms a *bridge circuit* with the tube interelectrode capacitances and cancels any regenerative feedback that would otherwise reach the grid. Parasitic suppressor resistors can also be used in the control grid, screen grid, or plate circuit, as with r-f amplifiers.

Most transistor i-f amplifiers are neutralized to eliminate partially the internal collector-to-base feedback. The circuits used are similar to those employed for the neutralization of r-f transistor amplifiers. However, the neutralization requirements for i-f stages are less severe because of the lower frequencies involved and the fact that an i-f amplifier always operates at the same frequency. Frequently, transistor i-f amplifiers are designed so that they do not require neutralization. Almost always, though, this is done at some sacrifice in gain. Methods that can be used for this include an *intentional mismatch* between the outputs and inputs of succeeding cascaded stages and the use of *shunt damping resistors* in collector-tank circuits.

Often, oscillation takes place in i-f sections because the signal from one of the later stages is fed back to an earlier stage through the B+ line. To prevent this, the plate circuit of each i-f stage is filtered by an *RC decoupling network* to keep the i-f signal out of the power supply.

C_4 is a common bypass capacitor for the plate and screen grid circuits. As shown at the right, it forms a bridge circuit with the tube interelectrode capacitances. Any feedback voltages that would otherwise be coupled back to the grid (1) from the plate (2) and the screen grid (3) are canceled by the lower arms of the bridge (C_3 and C_4)

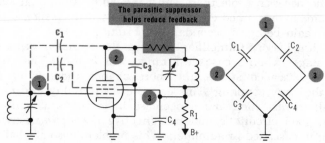

The parasitic suppressor also helps reduce feedback within the tube. C_4 and R_1 form an RC decoupling network that prevents the signal from being fed through the B+ line to another stage

typical i-f amplifiers

A two-stage, transistor i-f amplifier of the type used in FM receivers is shown in A. The required FM bandwidth is obtained by using double-tuned coupling circuits that are slightly overcoupled. The dip in the response curve caused by overcoupling is eliminated by providing a degree of mismatch between the tuned coupling circuits and the transistor inputs and outputs. This mismatch dampens or lowers the Q of the tuned circuits, thereby flattening out their response. The primary of each i-f transformer is mismatched to its respective transistor output by being connected directly in the collector circuit. The secondary of each transistor is mismatched to its transistor input by means of a capacitive voltage divider.

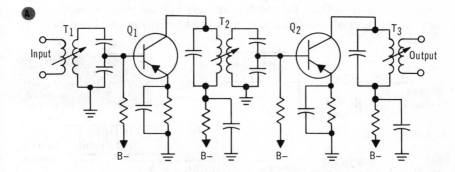

Very often, the individual stages of cascaded i-f amplifiers are identical. A careful analysis of the operation of one stage can provide a good understanding of the operation of the complete i-f section

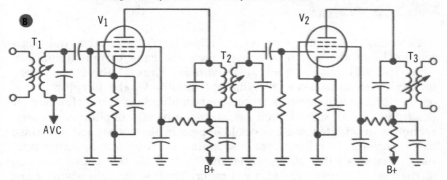

A typical two-stage, tube-type i-f amplifier is shown in B. Again, double-tuned coupling circuits are used throughout. In this amplifier, though, the necessary bandwidth is achieved by stagger-tuning i-f transformers T_1, T_2, and T_3. Aside from the coupling circuits, each stage operates as a conventional class A voltage amplifier. Plate decoupling networks keep the i-f signal out of the B+ line.

i-f limiters

I-f limiters are used in *FM* receivers between the last i-f stage and the detector. The purpose of an i-f limiter is to deliver to the detector a *constant-amplitude* i-f signal. This eliminates any amplitude variations that have been imposed on the signal by noise or other interference. If these amplitude variations are passed on to certain types of detectors, they will appear in the demodulated signal as distortion or as annoying sounds.

The type of detector used generally determines whether a limiter is necessary. Some types of detectors, such as the Foster-Seeley discriminator, are sensitive to amplitude variations in their inputs, and therefore *must* be preceded by a limiter. Other detectors, such as the ratio detector and the gated-beam detector, do not readily respond to amplitude variations in their inputs. So, limiters are not required when these detectors are used, but are sometimes used to ensure good results.

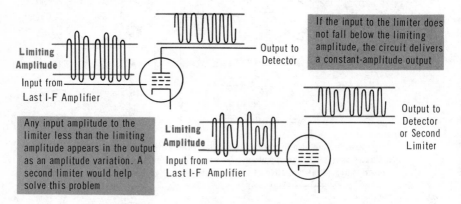

Limiting Amplitude

Input from Last I-F Amplifier

Output to Detector

If the input to the limiter does not fall below the limiting amplitude, the circuit delivers a constant-amplitude output

Any input amplitude to the limiter less than the limiting amplitude appears in the output as an amplitude variation. A second limiter would help solve this problem

Limiting Amplitude

Input from Last I-F Amplifier

Output to Detector or Second Limiter

Essentially, a limiter removes, or clips, both the positive and negative *peaks* of the signal whenever they exceed a certain amplitude, which we will call the *limiting amplitude*. Thus, if the input to the limiter never falls below the limiting amplitude, the clipping action of the limiter will produce a constant-amplitude output. However, if the input signal should drop below the limiting amplitude, a corresponding amplitude variation would appear in the output and be passed to the detector. In other words, the limiter is *ineffective* against amplitude variations *below* the limiting amplitude. This fact constitutes one of the basic requirements of any limiter. That is, that the signal must be amplified sufficiently by the i-f stages so that when it reaches the limiter its minimum amplitude is equal to or greater than the limiting amplitude. In some receivers, where there might be a problem, more than one limiter is used in cascade, so the second limiter can take care of what the first one missed.

The two basic types of limiters are explained on the following pages. Quite often, both of these techniques are used in one stage.

the plate limiter circuit

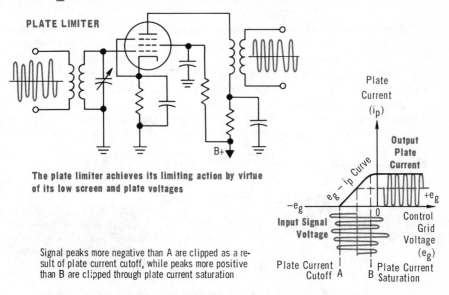

PLATE LIMITER

The plate limiter achieves its limiting action by virtue of its low screen and plate voltages

Signal peaks more negative than A are clipped as a result of plate current cutoff, while peaks more positive than B are clipped through plate current saturation

One basic type of limiter is the plate limiter. The bias and operating voltages for the stage are set so that the positive and negative values of the limiting amplitude correspond to *plate current saturation* and *plate current cutoff,* respectively. When a peak of the input signal exceeds the *positive* limiting amplitude, the grid voltage causes plate current saturation. No additional *plate* current can flow no matter how much further the signal swings positive, so the output signal is clipped at the limiting value. When a peak of the output signal exceeds the *negative* limiting value, it is sufficiently negative to cut off the *plate* current, so again the output is clipped at the limiting value.

To achieve this limiting action, the stage is operated with very low screen grid and plate voltages. The low screen and plate voltages cause the positive signal peaks to drive the tube into saturation very easily. Because of the low plate and screen voltages used, the bias must also be low to allow current to flow. However, because of the low voltages, very little additional bias is needed to cut off the tube. The negative swings of the signal do this easily.

In tube circuits, *sharp cutoff* pentodes are normally used for plate limiters, because there is a small range between cutoff and saturation. Transistor versions of the plate limiter operate in essentially the same manner as described above. The transistor bias is set so that excessive amplitude peaks are clipped in the collector output.

Because of its low screen and plate voltages, which may be 30 volts or less, a plate limiter produces very little gain of the i-f signal. In some applications, this is a disadvantage. Where gain as well as limiting are desired, the *grid limiter* can be used. This is described on the following page.

the grid limiter circuit

The grid limiter circuit uses higher operating voltages than the plate limiter, so it can provide gain as well as limiting. The typical grid limiter shown in A operates essentially as a class C amplifier using *grid-leak bias*. The bias is developed by capacitor C_1 charging when the grid draws current on the positive peaks of the input signal and then discharging through resistor R_1 when the signal amplitude drops to cause negative voltage drop, which serves as the bias. As shown in B, the larger the amplitude of the input signal, the farther the stage is biased beyond cutoff.

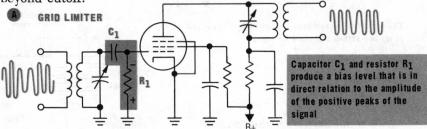

A   GRID LIMITER

C_1

R_1

B+

Capacitor C_1 and resistor R_1 produce a bias level that is in direct relation to the amplitude of the positive peaks of the signal

Because of the action of C_1 and R_1, the input signal, regardless of its amplitude, produces an equal pulse of plate current. The plate tank circuit then converts these pulses to a constant-amplitude FM output

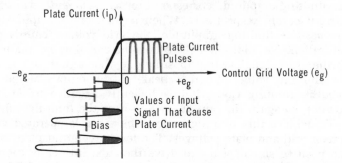

B

Plate Current (i_p)

Plate Current Pulses

$-e_g$

0    $+e_g$ Control Grid Voltage (e_g)

Values of Input Signal That Cause Plate Current

Bias

Since the shift in the bias point is directly proportional to signal amplitude, each cycle of the input signal will cause plate current to flow for an approximately *equal* period of time. Thus, the output voltage has a constant amplitude.

The *RC time constant* must be long with respect to the time of one cycle of the i-f frequency. This is necessary to maintain the bias constant as long as the input signal amplitude is constant. At the same time, the time constant should be short compared with one cycle of the lowest frequency amplitude variations that are to be clipped. If it is not, the bias will be determined by the lower-frequency amplitude variations, and the higher-frequency variations will not be limited at all.

When various types of AM interference must be removed from a signal by limiting, sometimes two limiters are connected in cascade, and each has a different time constant for its grid-leak bias circuit.

summary

□ The required bandwidth of an i-f amplifier depends on the frequency range of the side bands contained in the signal. □ With double-tuned coupling, which is common in i-f amplifiers, the degree of coupling has a significant effect on selectivity. □ Undercoupling results in a narrower bandwidth than does critical coupling, while overcoupling produces a wider bandwidth, but with two humps in the response curve. □ Stagger tuning provides a very flat frequency response with a large bandwidth.

□ Television i-f amplifiers have nonsymmetrical frequency-response curves to compensate for the vestigial side-band transmission used for the video signal. □ Crystal filters, which operate on the piezoelectric effect, are very selective, and are sometimes used to provide all of the i-f selectivity in an equipment. □ Because of the high gain of cascaded i-f amplifiers, effective decoupling networks are important to prevent instability and oscillation.

□ At lower frequencies, i-f amplifiers do not require neutralization because they use pentodes. However, at FM and higher frequencies, high-gain i-f amplifiers tend to oscillate as a result of feedback, and neutralization is required. □ Most transistor i-f amplifiers are neutralized to partially cancel internal collector-to-base feedback. □ I-f limiters clip the amplitude extremes of a signal. □ Plate limiters clip by means of plate current saturation and plate current cutoff. □ Grid limiters clip by means of an automatically varying grid bias.

review questions

1. What is *stagger tuning*?
2. Where gain, in addition to limiting action, is desired, should a plate or grid limiter be used?
3. Must tube-type i-f amplifiers be neutralized?
4. Why do television i-f amplifiers have unsymmetrical response curves?
5. What is meant by *critical coupling*? *Overcoupling*? *Undercoupling*?
6. For each type of coupling, draw a typical response curve.
7. In cascaded i-f amplifiers, why is effective decoupling important?
8. What is *double conversion*? Why is it used?
9. What is the equivalent circuit of a crystal filter?
10. Draw a grid limiter circuit. Explain its operation from a waveform standpoint.

electronics
six

oscillators

An oscillator is a circuit that generates a continuously-repetitive output signal. The output signal may be ac or fluctuating dc. You should note here that an oscillator *generates* its particular output signal; many other circuits can deliver the same type of output as an oscillator, but for these circuits, the output is an amplified or reshaped version of the input signal to the circuit. An oscillator does not have to receive an *input signal*. It develops its output using only the d-c power provided by a power supply. Thus, an oscillator can be considered as a circuit that *converts* d-c power into an a-c or fluctuating d-c signal.

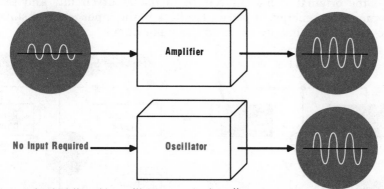

The output signals delivered by oscillators are not unique. However, oscillators require no input signal to produce their output. They convert their d-c input power into the output signal

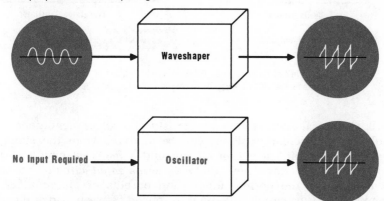

There are literally hundreds of different types of oscillators, if all of the basic oscillator circuits and their many variations are considered. However, they all can be divided into two broad groups: *sinusoidal* oscillators and *nonsinusoidal* oscillators. By thoroughly understanding the operation of the basic oscillator types within each group, you will be able to analyze the operation of practically all modifications of the basic circuits that you will encounter.

conditions required for oscillation

A sinusoidal oscillator is essentially an *amplifier* in which a small amount of the output signal is *fed back* to the input circuit. The oscillator thus provides its own input, as well as a usable output. The first two conditions required for oscillation, therefore, are that the circuit amplify, and that a portion of the output be fed back to the input. For oscillation to occur and be sustained, two additional conditions must be satisfied. First, the feedback voltage must be positive. That is, it must be *in phase* with the original excitation voltage in the input circuit. And second, the amount of energy, or power, fed back to the input must be sufficient to overcome the energy losses in the input circuit.

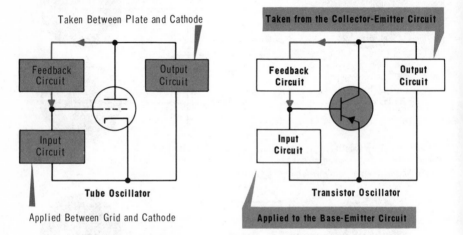

A sine-wave oscillator is an amplifier in which feedback of the correct polarity and amplitude takes place between the output and input circuits

All sinusoidal oscillators must satisfy the above conditions. As a result, any particular oscillator can be analyzed from the standpoint of an input circuit, an output circuit, and a feedback circuit or path. You should understand here that the terms *input circuit* and *output circuit* refer to the normal inputs and outputs of an *amplifier*. For example, in a tube circuit, the input is applied between grid and cathode and the output is taken between plate and cathode. Similarly, in a grounded-emitter transistor circuit, the input is applied to the base-emitter circuit and the output is taken from the collector-emitter circuit. As you will learn, although the output circuit provides the feedback required for oscillation, the *usable output signal* of an oscillator is often taken from the input circuit.

Positive feedback is also known as *regenerative* feedback.

sinusoidal oscillators

Sinusoidal oscillators, as the name implies, produce *sine-wave outputs*. The output waveform of some of these oscillators is a perfect sine wave. The waveforms produced by others contain various amounts of distortion; but the distortion is small enough that they can be considered as perfect sine waves for practical purposes.

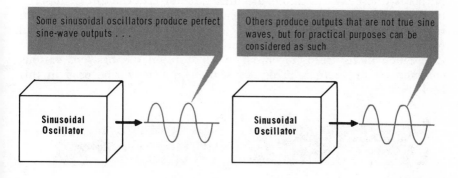

An important characteristic of a sine-wave oscillator is the frequency of its output. Not only must an oscillator produce the desired frequency, but it must maintain that frequency within certain limits. In other words, the output frequency must not drift appreciably during operation. An oscillator whose output frequency drifts very little is said to be *stable*. One whose frequency varies widely is termed *unstable*. Certain oscillator types are inherently more stable than others.

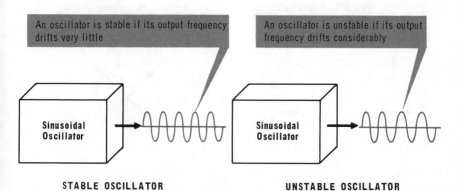

An oscillator consists of one or more electron tubes or transistors, and associated circuit components. Tubes and transistors are not oscillators in themselves. But when certain interactions are made to take place between their inputs and outputs, they behave as oscillators, and deliver continuous sinusoidal output signals.

types of sinusoidal oscillators

Sinusoidal oscillators can be classified in a variety of ways. One classification is *output frequency;* for example, audio-frequency (a-f) oscillators, radio-frequency (r-f) oscillators, ultra-high-frequency (UHF) oscillators, etc. Another classification is *function;* for example, local oscillators, beat-frequency oscillators, etc. Although useful for certain purposes, these classifications are unsatisfactory from a circuit description standpoint. They tell nothing about how a particular oscillator works, inasmuch as many different circuit configurations can be used for an a-f oscillator, a local oscillator, etc. For circuit analysis purposes, it is much more useful to classify oscillators on the basis of various *common circuit features*. This is the method that will be used in this book.

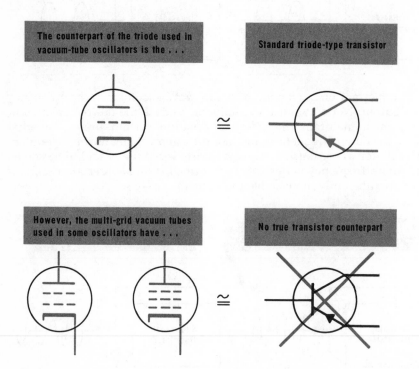

Both electron-tube and transistor oscillator circuits will be described on the following pages. You will see that for many oscillator types there is both a tube and a transistor version, the two being quite similar in operation. However, all common transistor oscillators use standard three-terminal transistors (base-emitter-collector), so there is no true transistor counterpart for electron-tube oscillators that use tubes having more than three elements.

the basic two-tube oscillator

The basic oscillator is nothing more than an amplifier circuit that regenerates its own signal. A simple circuit that shows this is a two-stage amplifier, in which the first stage feeds the second stage, and the second stage *feeds back* to the first stage. If you consider any signal on the first stage's control grid as the zero degree reference, the first tube will shift the signal 180 degrees, and this signal, in turn, will be shifted another 180 degrees by the second stage. The output of the second stage, then, is in phase with the signal on the grid of the first stage, so that the two tubes will oscillate.

Here's the way it works. When the tubes are first energized, capacitors C_1 and C_2 charge to B+. One tube, let's say V_1, will conduct slightly more since no two tubes are exactly the same. As V_1 conducts, its plate voltage goes down, so capacitor C_1 discharges through R_4 to drive the grid of V_2 negative. The plate current of V_2 goes down, causing its plate voltage to rise. This rising plate voltage is coupled as a positive-going signal by capacitor C_2 to the grid of V_1. This causes the plate current of V_1 to rise some more and V_1 plate voltage goes down again, driving the V_2 grid more negative. The plate voltage of V_2 goes up some more, driving V_1 still more positive. This regenerative action continues until V_1 approaches saturation and V_2 approaches cutoff. This completes one half cycle.

The plate voltage of V_1 then stops dropping and C_2 discharges less. The negative voltage on the grid of V_2 is then reduced so the current through V_2 goes up and its plate voltage drops. This causes C_2 to discharge through R_1, driving V_1 negative. V_1 plate current goes down and its plate voltage goes up to drive V_2 positive. This regenerative action continues until V_1 approaches cutoff and V_2 approaches saturation. This completes one full cycle, which is then repeated continuously.

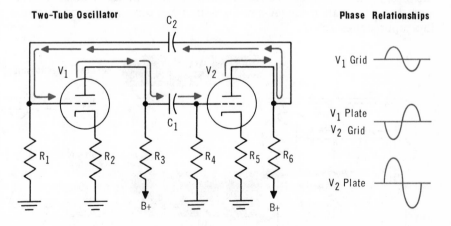

Two-Tube Oscillator

C_2

V_1

V_2

C_1

R_1 R_2 R_3 R_4 R_5 R_6

B+ B+

Phase Relationships

V_1 Grid

V_1 Plate
V_2 Grid

V_2 Plate

The two tubes shift the signal 360°, so that the feedback to the grid of V_1 is positive

the basic transformer oscillator

Actually, since the purpose of the second main tube is to shift the signal another 180 degrees to get positive feedback, a transformer can be used in its place to do the same thing. If we use a transistor circuit like this, when the circuit is first energized, collector current through the transistor starts to rise. The current through the primary of the transformer then induces a positive-going voltage in the secondary that is capacitor-coupled in phase with the base. This increases the forward bias to cause the collector current to go up again. More voltage is thus induced in the secondary, driving the base with still more forward bias. This regenerative action continues until the transistor approaches saturation. This completes one half cycle.

The collector current then rises more slowly, and the transformer flux lines induce less of a voltage in the secondary. Less positive voltage is coupled to the base, and the overall forward bias goes down. The collector current starts dropping, and now the transformer couples a negative voltage to the base that reduces the forward bias even more. This regenerative action continues until the transistor approaches cutoff. This completes the second half cycle. The rate of collector current drop slows down, so that less negative voltage is coupled back to the base, and the next, full sine-wave cycle starts.

Quite often, instead of using the transistor's (or tube's) saturation or cutoff characteristics to end each half cycle, the flux saturation and cutoff characteristics of the transformer's magnetization curve can be used to bring about the same action. For this to happen, the transformer must have a narrower operating range than the transistor. So, as current through the transformer rises regeneratively to produce more flux, as saturation is reached, flux increase becomes less, and the induced voltage in the secondary goes down. Less positive voltage is applied to the base, which reduces collector current through the transformer to start the next half cycle. A similar action happens as the transformer flux approaches zero.

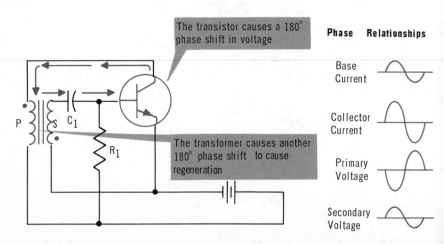

frequency, feedback, and phase

The frequency at which the previous circuits will oscillate is determined by the frequency that will cause a 360-degree phase shift. This is accomplished by the active parts themselves, so no phase shift should be produced by the coupling networks. Since RC networks will shift phases of certain frequencies according to their time constants, only frequencies that cause zero degree shifts will cause oscillations. Also, transformers can be designed to work better at some frequencies than at others, which can aid the frequency control.

Actually, although the previous examples use a 360-degree feedback signal, it does not have to be exactly that. A difference of a few degrees either way will still cause oscillation. Of course, right on 360 degrees the amplitude of feedback needed to sustain oscillation is much less, and the further off phase the feedback signal is, the greater its amplitude **must be.**

At exactly 360°, only a little feedback is needed to overcome circuit losses and sustain oscillations. More feedback is needed off 360°

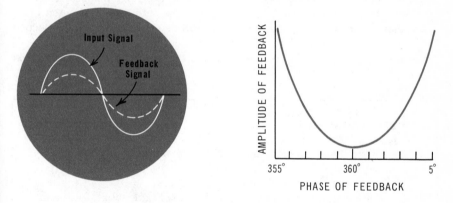

Too much feedback will allow frequency drift

Actually, to keep the circuit oscillating, the amount of feedback need only be just enough to overcome the signal losses in the circuit, tube, or transistor. With too much feedback, the oscillating frequency will drift considerably, and with too little feedback, the oscillations will be erratic. They could cut out repeatedly and vary in amplitude.

The time constants of the RC networks in the basic oscillators should be long to prevent phase shifting, but they should not be long enough to build up grid-leak bias. The basic oscillators must be operated class A to make use of the saturation and cutoff characteristics. More is explained about these oscillators later under the discussion on RC oscillators.

summary

☐ An oscillator consists of one or more tubes or transistors and associated circuit components, which, together, generate a repetitive a-c or fluctuating d-c output. ☐ Oscillators do not receive an input signal. They generate an output using only the d-c power provided by a power supply. ☐ All oscillators can be divided into two basic groups: sinusoidal and nonsinusoidal. ☐ Sinusoidal oscillators produce sine-wave outputs, the frequency of which must be stable within certain limits. ☐ Although sinusoidal oscillators could be classified by output frequency or function, they are usually classified according to their circuit features.

☐ Three conditions required for oscillation in a sinusoidal oscillator are: (1) that the circuit amplify; (2) that positive feedback occur; and (3) that the energy fed back overcome the energy losses (I^2R losses) in the input circuit.

☐ In a basic two-stage sinusoidal oscillator, a portion of the second stage output is fed back to the first stage. ☐ The frequency of oscillation is the frequency that will cause the feedback signal to arrive in phase (plus or minus a few degrees) at the first-stage input. ☐ Basic two-stage sinusoidal oscillators must be operated class A to make use of the saturation and cutoff characteristics of the stages. ☐ A transformer can be used in place of the second stage of a two-stage oscillator. The transformer, then, instead of a tube or transistor, provides the 180-degree phase shift required for positive feedback.

review questions

1. What distinguishes oscillators from amplifiers, wave-shapers, etc.?
2. What are the two basic oscillator types?
3. For oscillation to occur and be sustained, what four conditions must be satisfied?
4. What is another term for *positive feedback*?
5. In this text, sinusoidal oscillators are classified by which of the following: (a) output frequency; (b) function; or (c) common circuit features?
6. In a basic two-stage oscillator, each stage shifts the signal by what amount?
7. Draw a basic two-stage sinusoidal oscillator and describe its operation.
8. How will excessive feedback affect oscillator stability?
9. What is the optimum amount of feedback in an oscillator?
10. Why must basic two-stage sinusoidal oscillators be operated class A?

LC oscillators

You can see that some problems exist with these basic oscillators. They drift in frequency easily and a slightly distorted sine wave is generated because of the cutoff and saturation characteristics that are used. One of the most widely used methods of overcoming these problems is to use *LC tuned circuits*. In most of these LC oscillators, the tuned inductor-capacitor combination is in the form of a parallel resonant, or *tank*, circuit connected in the input of a tube or transistor stage. In this type of oscillator, the resonant circuit generates the sinusoidal signal. The principal function of the tube or transistor is to provide the necessary gain and feedback to sustain the oscillations in the resonant circuit. The LC tank is more frequency selective and so minimizes oscillator drift. As the tank itself generates the signals, perfect sine waves can be produced.

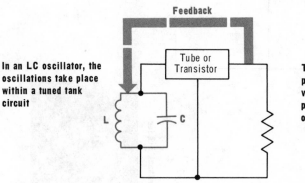

In an LC oscillator, the oscillations take place within a tuned tank circuit

Feedback

Tube or Transistor

L   C

The tube or transistor provides a feedback voltage of the proper polarity to sustain the oscillations in the tank

You recall from your studies of electricity that a tank circuit consists of an inductor and a capacitor connected in parallel. If a voltage pulse is initially applied to such a circuit, a large circulating current is set up within the tank. The circulating current is caused by the alternate storage and release of energy by the inductor and capacitor. The frequency of the current is determined by the *resonant* frequency, $f = 1/(2\pi\sqrt{LC})$, of the tank, and the amplitude of the current is determined by the quality, $Q = X_L/R$, of the tank. As a result of the circulating current, an a-c voltage is developed across the tank capacitor. In addition, an alternating magnetic field is produced around the inductor. Every tank circuit contains some resistance, due primarily to the d-c resistance of the inductor. Consequently, although the initial circulating current produced in the tank by an applied voltage pulse is large, it gradually diminishes, or damps out. To maintain the circulating current, and, therefore, the a-c voltage across the capacitor and the alternating magnetic field around the inductor, additional energy has to be periodically added to the tank circuit. This is provided by the tube or transistor portion of the oscillator.

feedback

The circulating current in the tank circuit of an LC oscillator is maintained by voltage feedback to the tank from the output of the tube or transistor. This feedback voltage must satisfy two conditions, as was previously mentioned: it must have a sufficient *amplitude* to compensate for the I²R losses in the tank circuit, and its *polarity* must be such that it adds to the instantaneous voltage developed by the tank circuit.

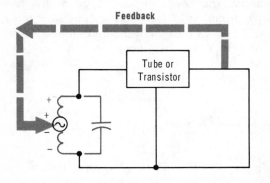

Feedback

Tube or Transistor

The feedback voltage induced in the coil is effectively in series aiding with the voltage developed across the coil by the tank circuit

The higher the Q of the tank, the less the feedback has to be to sustain oscillation

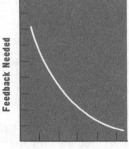

Feedback Needed

Q of Tank

The I²R loss depends on the d-c resistance of the tank circuit, and, therefore, can generally be related to the Q of the tank. If the Q is high, it means that the resistance is relatively low. Consequently, the I²R loss in the tank is low, and only a small regenerative feedback voltage is required to sustain oscillations. Conversely, a low Q means high resistance, large I²R loss, and a requirement for a fairly large, positive feedback voltage.

The polarity of the feedback voltage must be such that it *aids* the circulating tank current. This can be accomplished in a variety of ways. The simplest method is to have the feedback voltage induced in the tank coil so that it *adds* to the instantaneous voltage developed across the coil by the tank current. This is shown above, with the feedback voltage represented by an a-c generator in series with the tank coil.

the armstrong oscillator

One of the earliest electron-tube oscillators is named the *Armstrong oscillator* in honor of the man who devised it. (You will find that naming oscillators after the person who originally designed them is quite common.) It is essentially the transformer-feedback oscillator you learned about earlier.

The basic Armstrong oscillator circuit is shown. It consists of a triode amplifier, with the only input to the stage being the B+ voltage provided by the power supply. The tuned tank (L_1 and C_1) connected between the grid and cathode serves as the oscillating portion of the circuit. The values of L_1 and C_1 determine the frequency at which the circuit oscillates.

The Armstrong oscillator is also called the tickler feedback oscillator because of the loose coupling that exists between transformer coils L_1 and L_2

The closer the coupling, the greater the feedback and vice versa

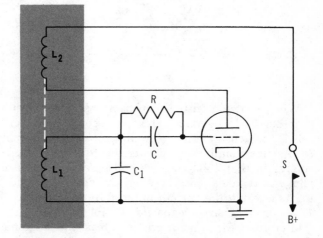

The oscillations in the tank apply an a-c voltage to the grid of the triode, and thus appear in amplified form in the plate circuit. A portion of the varying signal in the plate circuit is coupled back to the tank circuit by the mutual induction that exists between plate coil L_2 and tank coil L_1. The amount of energy fed back is determined by the degree of coupling existing between L_1 and L_2, which form a transformer. This is adjusted so that the feedback is sufficient to overcome the losses in the tank circuit. The feedback voltage is in phase with the grid, or tank, voltage as a result of a 180-degree phase shift introduced by the tube, and another 180-degree shift introduced by the transformer action of L_1 and L_2.

Capacitor C and resistor R provide grid-leak bias for the tube. As you will see, this type of bias is required if the oscillator is to be *self-starting* when switch S is initially closed.

operation of
the armstrong oscillator

Feedback to start oscillation and feedback to sustain oscillation occur
only during the time that the plate current is increasing

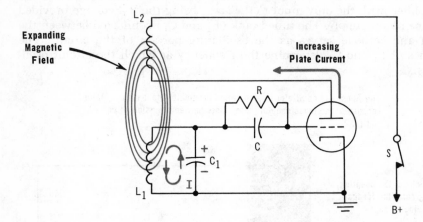

When switch S in the Armstrong oscillator circuit is first closed, the
tube begins to conduct. This produces a rising current through plate
coil L_2, which, in turn, generates an *expanding* magnetic field around
L_2. As this magnetic field cuts the turns of tank coil L_1, it induces a
voltage in that coil. The two coils are so positioned that a 180-degree
phase shift takes place between the emf of L_2 and the induced emf in
L_1. As a result, the current induced in the tank has the direction shown.
This current charges capacitor C_1 in a direction that makes the triode
grid positive. Since, with grid-leak bias, the stage has *zero bias* initially,
the positive voltage on the grid causes the tube to conduct more. This
builds up the magnetic field around L_2 even more, causing a greater
voltage to be induced in L_1, and thereby driving the grid further positive.
Such action continues until the tube effectively reaches saturation. At
this point, plate current stops increasing, and the magnetic field around
L_2 no longer expands. No feedback voltage is induced in L_1, and, as a
result, capacitor C_1 starts to discharge.

Effectively, this begins the oscillatory action of the tank, with the
charge on C_1 driving the grid of the stage alternately positive and negative. As you will see on the next page, feedback is applied to the tank to
sustain its oscillations only during a small portion of the oscillation
cycle when the grid side of capacitor C_1 is positive. This is because of
the action of the grid-leak bias.

the effect of grid-leak bias

The Armstrong oscillator, and most other tube LC oscillators, is operated *class C* to allow maximum power to be developed. This means that the grid must be biased well beyond cutoff. The required negative bias could be supplied by a fixed-bias source, but this would make it impossible to start the circuit oscillating by merely closing switch S. The fixed negative bias would prevent the tube from initially conducting. But with grid-leak bias, the tube initially has zero bias; so when switch S is closed, as described previously, the tube conducts, and oscillations in the tank circuit begin.

Once the oscillations start, the tube draws grid current every time the top of the tank circuit goes positive. The grid current charges grid capacitor C, which discharges through resistor R when the tank voltage reverses polarity. As in normal grid-leak bias, resistor R has a large value, so capacitor C loses only a small amount of its charge during each cycle and is fully charged again by the succeeding flow of grid current because of the low resistance of the conducting grid path through the tube. The net result is that a relatively large negative bias is maintained by C and R.

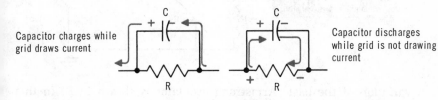

Capacitor charges while grid draws current

Capacitor discharges while grid is not drawing current

As a result of the negative bias, once it has been established, the tube is only driven into conduction by the positive peaks of the tank voltage. Feedback, therefore, also only occurs during the positive peaks of the tank voltage.

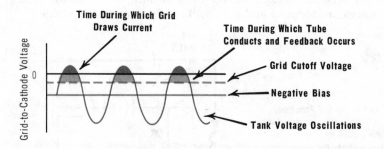

Once oscillations begin in the tank circuit, the negative grid-leak bias quickly builds up to the point where it keeps the tube cut off except during the positive peaks of the tank voltage

circuit variations of the armstrong oscillator

The basic Armstrong oscillator described on the previous pages oscillates at the natural, or *resonant*, frequency of the tank circuit. This frequency, of course, is determined by the values of the tank capacitor and coil. When both of these components have *fixed* values, oscillation can occur at only a single frequency. If either the coil or capacitor is made variable, the frequency of oscillation can be varied by changing the value of the variable component. Usually, the capacitor is the variable component, as shown in A.

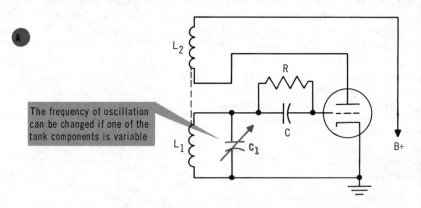

The frequency of oscillation can be changed if one of the tank components is variable

A variation of the basic Armstrong oscillator is shown in B. In this circuit, only the a-c component of the tube's plate current flows through tickler coil L_2. Capacitor C_2 blocks the d-c component of the plate current, but couples the a-c signal to the next circuit. The d-c component flows to the B+ supply through the r-f choke, which also prevents the a-c component from following this path. An oscillator of this type is called a *parallel-fed* Armstrong oscillator. By keeping dc out of the tank circuit, I^2R losses are reduced and the oscillator becomes more stable.

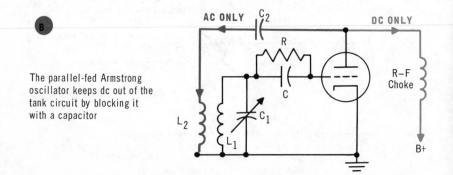

The parallel-fed Armstrong oscillator keeps dc out of the tank circuit by blocking it with a capacitor

output of
the armstrong oscillator

The output from the Armstrong oscillator must be taken from the *tank circuit*. It cannot be taken elsewhere, since the plate voltage is only a series of pulses because the stage is operated class C. There are three ways in which the output can be coupled from the tank circuit. In one of these (shown in A), the load is connected *directly* across the tank. This method significantly lowers the Q of the tank, and is therefore generally undesirable.

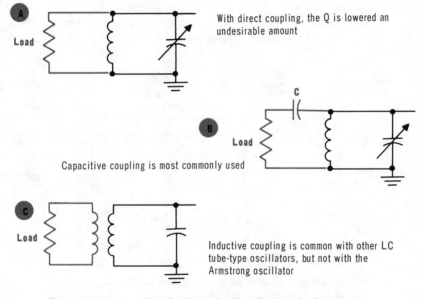

With direct coupling, the Q is lowered an undesirable amount

Capacitive coupling is most commonly used

Inductive coupling is common with other LC tube-type oscillators, but not with the Armstrong oscillator

The more power a coupling circuit transfers from the tank circuit, the greater is the loading effect on the tank, and the poorer is the frequency stability of the oscillator

Capacitive coupling, shown in B, is commonly used. The larger the value of the coupling capacitor, the more the energy that is coupled out of the tank. However, as the coupling capacitor is increased in size, the Q of the tank is lowered proportionately. The value of capacitance used, therefore, is a compromise between the desired degree of coupling and the permissible amount of loading of the tank.

Both direct and capacitive coupling can be used not only in the Armstrong oscillator, but in most other tube-type LC oscillators as well. Another method of coupling, which, although not often used with the Armstrong oscillator, is frequently employed with other LC oscillators, is called *inductive coupling*. This is shown in C. In inductive coupling, the tank circuit coil serves as the primary winding of a coupling transformer.

the tuned-base oscillator

As shown, the tuned-base oscillator uses a grounded-emitter stage, with an LC tank in the base circuit and tickler-coil feedback between the collector and base. Operation is similar to that of the parallel-fed, tube-type Armstrong circuit. One exception is that the tank voltage is coupled to the base by capacitor C_2, instead of directly. This is necessary to isolate the low resistance of the tank coil from the base-emitter bias circuit. Also, the transistor oscillator cannot generally be operated class C because the swings of the signal voltage must be great enough to recharge the grid-leak capacitor each cycle. Such large signal swings could also drive the transistor into its reverse or zener breakdown region, since class C operation would require a reverse bias close to that region. The transistor could be operated class B or beyond cutoff to some point as long as the signal swing does not reach reverse breakdown.

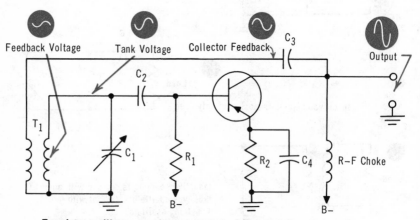

Transistor oscillators are often operated class A so that the output can be taken from most points in the circuit

When d-c power is applied to the circuit, the rise in collector voltage is coupled to the tank circuit by capacitor C_3 and transformer T_1. This starts the tank circuit oscillating. These oscillations then cause an a-c voltage to be coupled to the base through capacitor C_2, and this feedback voltage alternately varies the forward bias regeneratively. The resulting changes in collector voltage are fed back to the tank circuit by capacitor C_3 and T_1 to sustain the oscillations. The voltage fed back is regenerative as a result of the 180-degree phase shift that takes place between the base and collector, and the additional 180-degree phase shift introduced by the transformer, T_1.

You can see from the above description that feedback can occur during more than just the positive peaks, as class C bias is not used. This is a characteristic difference between most tube and transistor LC oscillators.

summary

□ In LC oscillators, a parallel resonant, or tank, circuit is connected to the input of a tube or transistor stage. The oscillator oscillates at the natural, or resonant, frequency of the tank. □ The resonant circuit of an LC oscillator generates the sinusoidal signal and the tube or transistor provides gain and feedback. □ The voltage feedback in an LC oscillator is induced in the tank coil in series aiding with the tank voltage. □ The frequency of oscillation can be controlled by making the tank capacitor or inductor variable.

□ The Armstrong oscillator is a transformer-feedback type of oscillator. □ Positive feedback is produced by transformer coupling a portion of the output back to the input. The secondary of the coupling transformer is the tank circuit coil. □ Grid-leak bias is required for the Armstrong oscillator to be self-starting. □ Once oscillation begins, tube conduction, and therefore feedback, occur only during the positive peaks of the tank voltage. □ In transistor LC oscillators, feedback occurs during more than just positive peaks of the tank voltage. This is because class C bias is not used.

□ There are three ways to couple the output from the tank of an LC oscillator: (1) direct coupling, (2) capacitive coupling, or (3) inductive coupling. □ Direct coupling is generally undesirable, since it lowers the Q of the tank significantly.

review questions

1. What are the primary advantages of LC oscillators when compared to the basic two-stage oscillator?
2. The sinusoidal signal is generated by what part of the LC oscillator?
3. In a tank circuit, what determines: (a) the current frequency, and (b) the current amplitude?
4. How is the Q of the tank related to oscillator feedback requirements?
5. Why are the Armstrong and most other tube LC oscillators operated class C?
6. Why is grid-leak bias used in the Armstrong oscillator?
7. How can the frequency of an Armstrong oscillator be varied?
8. What methods can be used to couple the signal from an LC oscillator?
9. Draw an Armstrong oscillator. Explain its operation.
10. What is one characteristic difference between most tube and transistor LC oscillators?

the hartley oscillator

A Hartley oscillator is a modified version of the tickler-type feedback oscillator. In the Hartley circuit, the oscillating tank uses a *tapped coil.* One part of the coil is in the input circuit of the tube or transistor, and the other part is in the output circuit. This makes it possible for a single tank coil to supply the a-c voltage from the tank to the tube or transistor, and at the same time develop the regenerative feedback signal to sustain oscillation.

A basic transistor Hartley oscillator circuit is shown. The resonant frequency of the tank circuit, consisting of capacitor C_1 and tapped coil L_1, determines the frequency of the oscillator. The two sections of L_1 are designated L_{1a} and L_{1b}. L_{1a} is effectively in the base circuit of the transistor, and L_{1b} is in the collector circuit. When B+ is applied to the stage, collector current begins to flow. The resulting drop in collector voltage is coupled through capacitor C_3 and developed across L_{1b}. This serves as the initial excitation for the tank and causes circulating current to begin to flow in the tank. The circulating current produces a voltage across L_{1a}, which is coupled by capacitor C_2 to the base of the transistor. The amplified signal at the collector is coupled back to the tank circuit by capacitor C_3, and developed across L_{1b}. The feedback voltage developed across L_{1b} is in phase with the input voltage across L_{1a}, and so maintains the tank circuit oscillations.

A Parallel (Shunt-Fed) Hartley Oscillator

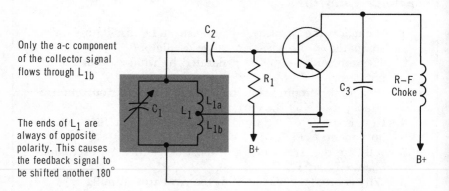

Only the a-c component of the collector signal flows through L_{1b}

The ends of L_1 are always of opposite polarity. This causes the feedback signal to be shifted another 180°

C_2

R_1

C_3

R–F Choke

C_1 L_1 L_{1a} L_{1b}

B+

B+

Two factors are responsible for the correct phase of the feedback voltage. One is the 180-degree phase shift between base and collector of the grounded-emitter stage. The other factor is that the two ends of coil L_1 are always of *opposite polarity.* So, since the centertap of L_1 is grounded, the feedback voltage is, in effect, shifted an additional 180 degrees. Effectively, L_1 acts as an autotransformer in coupling the feedback voltage, and so works similar to the Armstrong oscillator.

circuit variations of the hartley oscillator

A series-fed Hartley oscillator circuit is shown in A. This is essentially the same as the parallel-fed Hartley oscillator, except that both the a-c and d-c components of the emitter current flow in L_{1b} of the tank circuit. Capacitor C_3 provides the feedback path from the collector through ground to the tank circuit. The series-fed arrangement has the disadvantage, especially in a tube circuit, that the tank components must be insulated to withstand the d-c voltage, and the d-c current lowers the Q of the coil and increases I^2R losses.

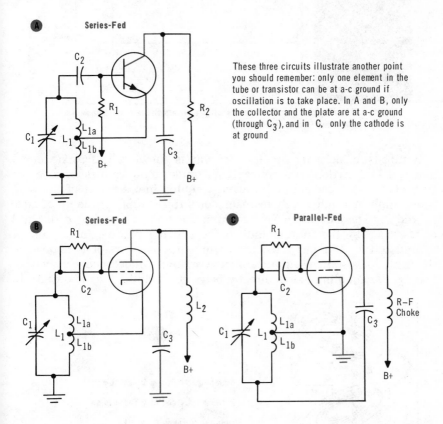

These three circuits illustrate another point you should remember: only one element in the tube or transistor can be at a-c ground if oscillation is to take place. In A and B, only the collector and the plate are at a-c ground (through C_3), and in C, only the cathode is at ground

Both series and parallel-fed, tube-type Hartley oscillators are shown in B and C. Their operation is the same as the transistor versions, except that the tube circuits are biased for *class C* operation by their grid-leak bias components, R_1 and C_2. This means that feedback occurs only during a portion of the tank cycle when the tube grid is sufficiently positive to cause plate current to flow.

LC OSCILLATORS (CONT.)

the meissner oscillator

The Meissner oscillator is a variation of the basic Armstrong circuit. The principal difference in the Meissner oscillator is that the tank circuit is *floating;* that is, it is not connected directly to the tube or transistor.

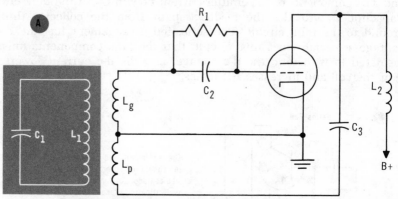

The Meissner oscillator is essentially an Armstrong oscillator with a "floating" tank circuit

A tube-type Meissner oscillator circuit is shown in A. Capacitor C_1 and coil L_1 function as a conventional tank circuit and determine the frequency of the oscillator. However, coupling into and out of the tank is accomplished inductively by means of a transformer made up of coils L_g and L_p. The a-c output voltage from the tank is coupled to the grid of the tube by the mutual inductance existing between a portion of L_1 and coil L_g. Similarly, feedback from the plate circuit is applied to the tank to sustain oscillation by the mutual inductance between L_p and L_1. No coupling exists directly between L_p and L_g, as shown in B.

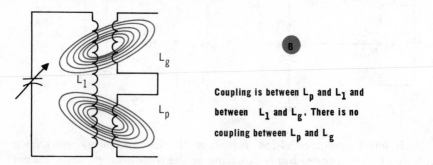

Coupling is between L_p and L_1 and between L_1 and L_g. There is no coupling between L_p and L_g

The circuit shown here is of the parallel-fed type. In practice, a series-fed circuit could be used as well. In essence, the Meissner oscillator tunes the mutual inductance of the feedback transformer, L_g–L_p.

the reinartz oscillator

A Reinartz transistor oscillator is shown. In this circuit, regenerative feedback takes place between the *collector* and *emitter* of a common-base circuit. The frequency of the feedback and, therefore, the output frequency of the oscillator are determined by the L_1-C_1 tank circuit, which is inductively coupled to both collector coil L_2 and emitter coil L_3. The three coils are positioned so that the feedback voltage developed across L_3 is in phase with the voltage produced across L_2 by the collector current. As a result of the regenerative feedback, the transistor current varies sinusoidally at the tuned frequency.

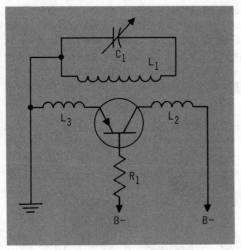

Oscillation is produced by the feedback between collector and emitter

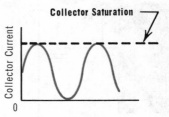

In another version of this circuit, coil L_1 and capacitor C_1 can be eliminated, and a tuning capacitance used across either L_2 or L_3, instead. Feedback would then be through the mutual inductance between L_2 and L_3, with the frequency determined by the values of the parallel capacitor and coil. Such an arrangement, however, results in a decrease in the frequency stability of the oscillator because d-c current will flow through the tank.

Since this is a common-base circuit, the signals in the collector and emitter are already in *phase,* so the feedback path should *not* shift the phase of the feedback signal.

the colpitts oscillator

The Colpitts oscillator is similar to the parallel-fed Hartley oscillator, except that *two capacitors* are used in the tank circuit instead of a tapped coil. A tube-type Colpitts circuit is shown in A. The two tank capacitors, C_1 and C_2, make up the total capacitance of the tank circuit. They are connected so that C_1 is in the grid circuit and C_2 is in the plate circuit. The a-c tank voltage produced by the circulating current divides between the two capacitors. That portion developed across C_1 is applied to the grid of the tube by coupling capacitor C_3 and grid resistor R_1. The resulting plate signal is coupled back to the tank circuit by capacitor C_4 and developed across tank capacitor C_2. The feedback is in phase with the grid voltage as a result of the 180-degree phase shift introduced by the tube, and the 180-degree shift caused by the ground tap between C_1 and C_2. You can see that since opposite polarities always exist across the tank, the polarity at the top plate of C_1 is always opposite to the polarity at the bottom plate of C_2. In relation to ground, then, the feedback voltage applied to C_2 is shifted in phase across C_1 to produce regeneration in the tank.

The output frequency of a Colpitts oscillator is determined by the value of the tank inductance and the total capacitance of the two SERIES capacitors

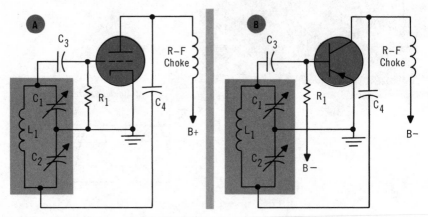

Feedback is produced by the divider network, C_1–C_2, which taps down the amplitude needed and reverses the phase in relation to ground

Grid-leak bias is used to allow the oscillator to be self-starting. This bias is provided by capacitor C_3 and resistor R_1. The grid-leak resistor is connected in parallel with the grid circuit, instead of in series with it, to provide a d-c path for the grid current.

A transistor Colpitts oscillator circuit is shown in B. Its operation is similar to that of the Hartley oscillator, except for the use of class C bias, as described above for the tube circuit.

the clapp oscillator

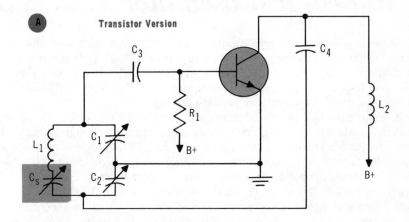

The Clapp oscillator is a modification of the basic Colpitts oscillator. The only difference between the two is that the Clapp oscillator has a capacitor, C_s, added in *series* with the tank coil. This series capacitance is generally made small compared to the total value of tank capacitors C_1 and C_2. As a result, it is the values of C_s and the tank coil that effectively determine the oscillator frequency. This significantly improves the frequency stability of the oscillator by minimizing the effects of variations in transistor parameters that would otherwise be reflected as changes in the effective values of C_1 and C_2.

As shown, capacitor C_s can be made variable to provide for oscillation over a range of frequencies. Capacitors C_1 and C_2 are also variable. However, they are varied to set the desired levels of feedback voltage and transistor input voltage. They are not frequency adjustments.

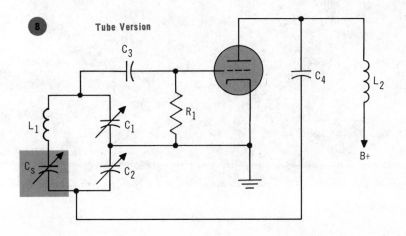

the tuned-plate, tuned-grid oscillator

A *tuned-plate, tuned-grid oscillator* is a tube-type oscillator that uses tuned tanks in both the grid and plate circuits. The feedback necessary to sustain oscillation is coupled from the plate to the grid circuit through the grid-to-plate *interelectrode capacitance* of the tube. Grid-leak bias is used so that the oscillator is self-starting.

A basic tuned-plate, tuned-grid oscillator, or TPTG oscillator, as it is called, is shown. The interelectrode capacitance through which the feedback takes place is shown by broken lines. The amount of feedback must be sufficient to overcome the losses of the grid tank. The feedback, of course, must be in phase with the grid voltage. Since the tube introduces a 180-degree phase shift, the feedback must be shifted another 180 degrees if it is to be regenerative at the grid. This is accomplished by making the *grid tank* satisfy two conditions. The first condition is that the grid tank be tuned to, or resonate at, a frequency *slightly higher* than the oscillator's operating frequency. You recall from your studies of resonant circuits that at the oscillator frequency this makes the tank appear as an inductance. The second condition is that the inductive reactance of the tank be greater than the capacitive reactance of the plate-to-grid interelectrode capacitance of the tube.

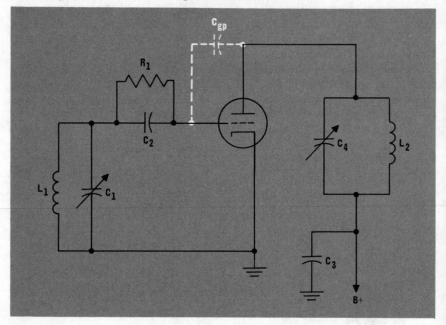

In the TPTG oscillator, regenerative feedback takes place through the grid-to-plate interelectrode capacitance of the tube

the tuned-plate, tuned-grid oscillator (cont.)

With these two conditions met, variations in plate voltage cause a *capacitive current* to flow through the tube interelectrode capacitance and the equivalent inductance of the tank. This means that the current leads the plate voltage by 90 degrees. Across the equivalent inductance of the tank, the current produces a voltage drop that, as in any inductance, leads the current by 90 degrees. Thus, this voltage across the inductance, which is effectively the grid voltage, leads the plate voltage by 180 degrees. The feedback voltage is thus shifted 180 degrees with respect to the plate voltage, and is therefore in phase with the original grid voltage.

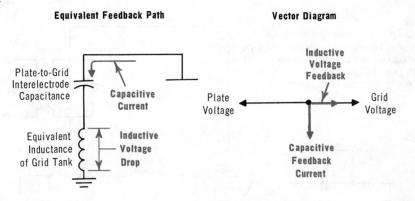

Equivalent Feedback Path

Plate-to-Grid Interelectrode Capacitance

Capacitive Current

Equivalent Inductance of Grid Tank

Inductive Voltage Drop

Vector Diagram

Inductive Voltage Feedback

Plate Voltage

Grid Voltage

Capacitive Feedback Current

The plate tank in the TPTG oscillator, as the grid tank, is tuned slightly higher than the operating frequency of the oscillator. This causes the feedback voltage to have the same frequency as the grid voltage produced by the grid tank. The tanks are tuned so slightly off the desired frequency that often the amount is negligible. However, since the TPTG oscillator can operate off resonance, it is subject to drift and is unstable.

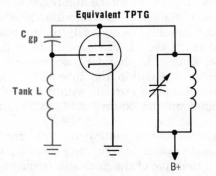

Equivalent TPTG

C_{gp}

Tank L

B+

The capacitive current in the interelectrode capacitance leads the plate voltage by 90°. The voltage across the tank inductance leads that current by another 90°, so the voltage from the plate is shifted 180° to cause oscillation

the electron-coupled oscillator

An electron-coupled oscillator is actually an *oscillator* and a *buffer amplifier* combined in a single stage, usually a pentode. The oscillator portion of the circuit is coupled to the amplifier portion by means of the electron stream within the tube. The output taken off at the plate produces little loading effect on the oscillator, and results in excellent frequency stability.

In the typical electron-coupled oscillator shown, the cathode, control grid, and screen grid are connected in a conventional Hartley oscillator circuit. The screen grid acts as the plate of a parallel-fed Hartley circuit, with the variations in screen voltage coupled back to the grid tank by capacitor C_2. Actually, any other type of oscillator circuit can also be used between the cathode, control grid, and screen grid.

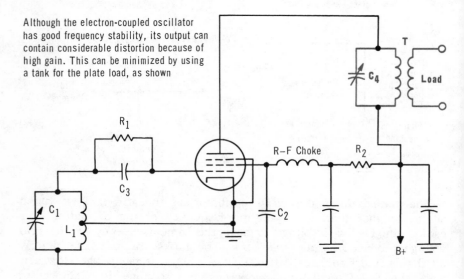

Although the electron-coupled oscillator has good frequency stability, its output can contain considerable distortion because of high gain. This can be minimized by using a tank for the plate load, as shown

The screen grid intercepts only relatively few of the electrons emitted by the cathode. The rest pass through the screen and travel to the plate. Enough current, however, flows in the screen grid circuit to provide the feedback required to sustain oscillation. The majority of the electrons pass through the screen and reach the plate. Coupling from the oscillator to the output, or plate, circuit is therefore accomplished entirely by means of the electron stream within the tube. This also permits a large output signal, since the plate current within the tube is amplified by the oscillating signal on the control grid, as in any conventional pentode amplifier.

In the electron-coupled oscillator, a frequency-multiplying tank circuit can be used as the plate load. This makes possible frequency doubling or tripling by tuning the plate tank to a multiple of the grid-tank frequency.

summary

☐ In the Hartley oscillator, a tapped tank coil supplies ac to the tube or tran-sistor and, at the same time, develops the feedback signal. The coil acts as an autotransformer in coupling the feedback voltage and shifting it 180 degrees. ☐ For oscillations to occur, only one element in a transistor or tube can be at a-c ground. ☐ In the Meissner oscillator, the "floating" tank circuit is transformer-coupled to the tube or transistor.

☐ The Colpitts oscillator is similar to the parallel-fed Hartley, except that it uses two series capacitors in the tank instead of a tapped coil. ☐ In the Clapp oscillator, which is a modified Colpitts, a third capacitor is connected in series with the tank coil to improve frequency stability and to adjust the oscillator frequency.

☐ Feedback in the tuned-plate, tuned-grid (TPTG) oscillator is coupled from plate to grid through the interelectrode capacitance of the tube. ☐ Both tank circuits in a TPTG oscillator are tuned to a frequency slightly higher than the oscillator's operating frequency. ☐ The cathode and first two grids of a multi-element tube are used as the oscillator in the electron-coupled oscillator. The oscillator signal is coupled to the output, or plate circuit, by the tube's internal electron stream.

review questions

1. In a Hartley oscillator, how is regenerative feedback pro-duced?
2. Draw a Meissner oscillator.
3. What distinguishes a Meissner oscillator from an Arm-strong oscillator?
4. Regenerative feedback takes place between which elements in the Reinartz transistor oscillator?
5. How does the Colpitts oscillator differ from the parallel-fed Hartley oscillator?
6. What is the purpose of the third series capacitor in the Clapp oscillator's tank circuit?
7. How is the regenerative feedback coupled from the plate to the grid circuit in the TPTG oscillator?
8. In the TPTG oscillator, the tube causes a 180-degree phase shift. How is the remaining 180-degree shift needed for the feedback to be regenerative accomplished?
9. What are the advantages inherent in the electron-coupled oscillator?
10. What elements of the pentode are ordinarily used as the oscillator in a typical electron-coupled oscillator?

crystal oscillators

LC oscillators, like those previously described, are used in a wide variety of applications. However, they are generally unsatisfactory when extreme *frequency stability* is required. This is because the effective values of the LC tank circuit components tend to change during operation. Also, the tank is shunted by the tube or transistor, which, as you learned, also has capacitances. These, too, tend to change. This, of course, causes the frequency of oscillation to *drift*.

The principal reasons for these changes are fluctuations in equipment temperature and loading of the oscillator by succeeding circuits. When a high degree of frequency stability is needed, *crystal oscillators* are generally used. These oscillators use crystal slices, usually made of quartz, as the main frequency-determining element.

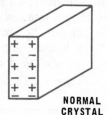

NORMAL
CRYSTAL

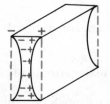

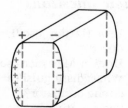

COMPRESSED CRYSTAL   STRETCHED CRYSTAL

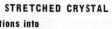

Crystals convert mechanical vibrations into alternating electrical voltages, and vice versa

You recall from your studies of electricity that quartz crystals, as well as many other crystal materials, exhibit the *piezoelectric effect*. If mechanical pressure is put on such a crystal, opposite electrical charges appear across its faces. If an opposite pressure is put on the crystal, the charges on its faces reverse polarity. Thus, by alternately twisting the crystal *mechanically*, an a-c voltage can be generated. Conversely, if an a-c voltage is applied across the crystal faces, the crystal will vibrate mechanically. Due to mechanical inertia, these vibrations will be damped or gradually die out when the a-c voltage is removed. But if enough electrical energy is supplied to overcome the inertia losses, the crystal will continue to vibrate, and in doing so generate an a-c voltage similar to an LC tank circuit.

crystal resonant frequency

The amplitude of a quartz crystal's vibration depends on the natural mechanical frequency of vibration of the crystal, and the electrical excitation frequency. If a crystal is excited by an a-c voltage of the *same* frequency as the crystal's natural frequency, large amplitude vibrations are set up, and the crystal generates a significant a-c voltage. But if the frequency of the exciting voltage is even *slightly different* than the crystal's natural frequency, little mechanical vibration is produced. A crystal, therefore, has extremely sharp frequency-selective characteristics. It is this property that makes crystals highly useful in oscillator circuits.

The particular characteristics of any crystal depend on a variety of factors, such as type of material, how it is cut, and its physical dimensions. In general, however, the natural frequency of a crystal, which is also called the resonant frequency, is determined mainly by its *thickness*. The thinner the crystal, the higher its resonant frequency. The mechanical difficulties involved in working with extremely thin crystals places an upper limit on the frequencies at which crystals can be used.

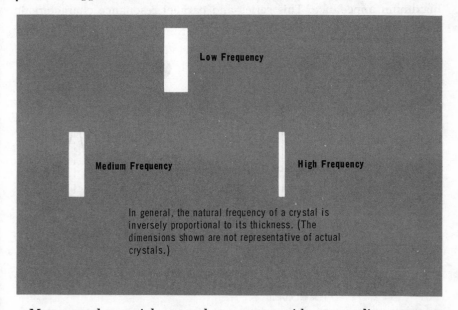

Low Frequency

Medium Frequency   High Frequency

In general, the natural frequency of a crystal is inversely proportional to its thickness. (The dimensions shown are not representative of actual crystals.)

Most crystal materials expand or contract with surrounding temperature changes. This change in dimensions changes the natural frequency of the crystal, which is undesirable in oscillator circuits. Such a shift in crystal frequency can be avoided by using a crystal material that has practically a zero temperature coefficient, or by taking steps to keep the crystal at a constant temperature. In many oscillator circuits, the crystal is contained in a temperature-controlled oven so that its temperature does not change.

crystal equivalent circuit

As a crystal behaves like a series resonant circuit, it can be represented by a series LCR circuit, as shown in A. This equivalent circuit
is modified, however, when the crystal is mounted in a crystal holder.
In the holder, the crystal is effectively placed between two metallic
electrodes, thus forming a capacitor, with the crystal acting as the dielectric. As a result, the equivalent circuit of the crystal is modified to that
shown in B, where C_p represents the capacitance introduced by the
crystal holder. This equivalent circuit, and therefore the crystal, behaves
as a parallel resonant circuit at a frequency at which the series LCR
branch has an inductive reactance equal to the capacitive reactance of C_p.
In effect, therefore, a crystal can act as either a series or a parallel
resonant circuit, depending on the frequency of the applied voltage.
At the crystal's natural mechanical frequency, it behaves as a series
resonant circuit, with the series LCR combination offering minimum
impedance. At a slightly higher frequency, the crystal behaves as a
parallel resonant circuit, with the series LCR combination acting as an
inductance in parallel with C_p, and the parallel combination offering
maximum impedance. This series and parallel resonance characteristic
is illustrated by the frequency-vs.-impedance characteristic curve of a
crystal, shown in C.

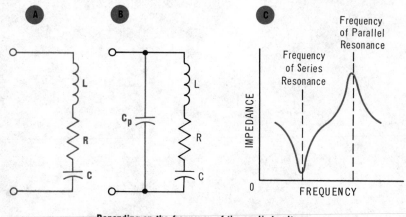

Depending on the frequency of the applied voltage,
a crystal can act as either a series or parallel
resonant circuit

You can see from the above that the behavior of a crystal is determined by the frequency at which it is operated. In oscillator circuits,
a crystal can be operated at its parallel resonant frequency and used
in place of an LC tank circuit for generating the required a-c voltage.
Or, it can be operated at its series resonant frequency and placed in
the feedback path. The crystal then acts as a sharp filter, permitting
feedback only at the desired frequency.

the pierce oscillator

The Pierce oscillator is analogous to the Colpitts oscillator, except that a crystal is used in place of the tank circuit coil. This is shown in A. The crystal is essentially the tuned circuit, and so determines the frequency of oscillation. Capacitors C_1 and C_2 form a voltage divider between the collector and emitter. Their relative reactances determine the *amount* of feedback from collector to emitter, and, therefore, the amount of crystal excitation. Because of its extremely sharp resonance characteristic, the crystal will vibrate, or oscillate, only over a very narrow frequency range. The frequency output of the oscillator is therefore very stable in spite of changes in circuit characteristics that would cause a conventional Colpitts oscillator to change frequency.

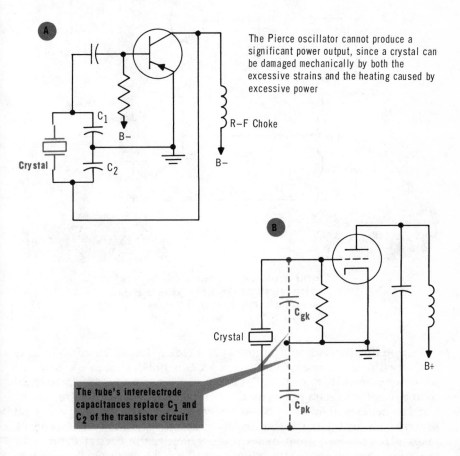

The Pierce oscillator cannot produce a significant power output, since a crystal can be damaged mechanically by both the excessive strains and the heating caused by excessive power

A tube version of the Pierce oscillator is shown in B. In this circuit the tube's plate-to-cathode and grid-to-cathode interelectrode capacitances are used in place of capacitors C_1 and C_2 of the transistor circuit.

the crystal-controlled hartley oscillator

You have seen how crystals can be operated at their parallel resonant frequencies and used in place of LC tank circuits. As was mentioned before, crystals can also be operated at their *series* resonant frequencies and inserted in the feedback path of an oscillator to control the frequency at which feedback takes place. An example of this is the crystal-controlled Hartley oscillator shown.

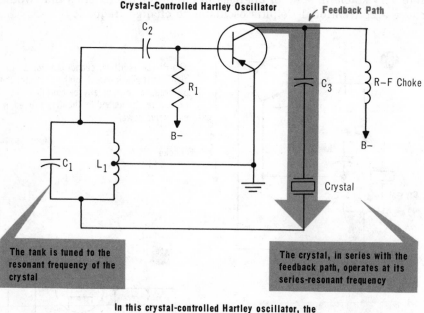

Crystal-Controlled Hartley Oscillator

C₂ — (C_2)

R₁ — (R_1)

B–

C₃ — (C_3)

R–F Choke

B–

Feedback Path

C₁   L₁ — (C_1) (L_1)

Crystal

The tank is tuned to the resonant frequency of the crystal

The crystal, in series with the feedback path, operates at its series-resonant frequency

In this crystal-controlled Hartley oscillator, the crystal controls the frequency at which feedback can take place and, therefore, determines the frequency of the oscillator

Essentially, this is a conventional parallel-fed Hartley circuit. The only difference is the use of a crystal in series with the feedback path. At its series resonant frequency, the crystal presents minimum impedance to the feedback voltage, so oscillation takes place at this frequency. For frequencies above and below its series resonant point, the crystal presents a very high impedance. As a result, essentially no feedback takes place at these frequencies. Consequently, the crystal determines the frequency at which the circuit oscillates by limiting feedback to the desired frequency. The tank, of course, is tuned to the resonant frequency of the crystal, but if the tank tends to drift, the crystal keeps the frequency of oscillation steady.

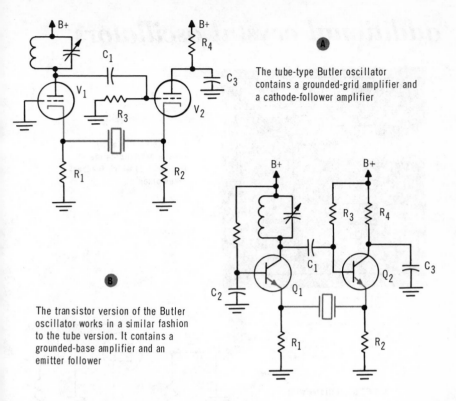

A

The tube-type Butler oscillator contains a grounded-grid amplifier and a cathode-follower amplifier

B

The transistor version of the Butler oscillator works in a similar fashion to the tube version. It contains a grounded-base amplifier and an emitter follower

the butler oscillator

The *Butler oscillator* is a two-tube oscillator in which the second tube is used to provide the proper phase signal for regenerative feedback. However, instead of the feedback signal being coupled from plate to grid, it is coupled from cathode to cathode. Since the phase at the cathode of V_2 is the same as the phase on the grid of V_2, the second stage, then, does not actually provide the needed additional 180-degree phase shift. However, since the feedback signal is coupled to the *cathode* of V_1, it affects V_1 the same as a signal 180 degrees out of phase with it would at the *grid* of V_1, so the circuit regenerates. For example, if the grid of V_1 was swinging negative, its plate would swing positive. This positive swing is coupled to the grid of V_2, which causes the cathode to swing positive. The positive swing is crystal-coupled to the cathode of V_1, which produces the same effect as if the V_1 grid were driven more negative, which is positive feedback. The tank in the plate of V_1 oscillates and is regenerated by V_1 plate current. The crystal is series resonant and so only passes feedback at its resonant frequency.

A big advantage of the Butler oscillator is that very small voltages exist across the crystal, and so it is exposed to little potential strain and gives stable operation.

additional crystal oscillators

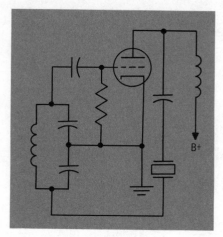

Colpitts oscillator with
crystal determining the
frequency at which feedback
takes place

B+

A TPTG oscillator with
crystal serving as grid tank

A Colpitts oscillator with
common-base circuit and
crystal as frequency-
determining resonant circuit

B+

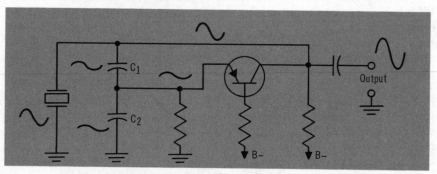

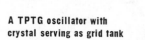

C_1

C_2

Output

B−   B−

Collector-to-emitter feedback is developed across C_2 to sustain oscillation.
The feedback is not shifted in phase, as in the common-emitter circuit, since
the common-base configuration does not cause a 180° phase shift from
emitter to collector

summary

☐ When a high degree of frequency stability is required, quartz crystals are used as the frequency-determining elements in oscillators. ☐ By means of the piezoelectric effect, crystals generate a-c voltages of highly stable frequency when a-c voltages are applied across their faces. ☐ The natural, or resonant, frequency of crystals, which are highly frequency selective, is determined mainly by their thickness.

☐ A crystal reacts only to a-c voltages whose frequencies are close to its own natural frequency. ☐ The largest amplitude vibrations are set up when the crystal resonant frequency and applied a-c voltage frequency are the same. ☐ Depending on the frequency of the applied voltage, a crystal can act as either a series or a parallel resonant circuit. ☐ As a series resonant circuit, the crystal can serve as a sharp feedback filter. As a parallel resonant circuit, a crystal can be used in place of an LC tank circuit.

☐ The Pierce oscillator, which is very stable, uses a crystal as its tank circuit. ☐ In the crystal-controlled Hartley oscillator, the crystal acts as a filter, controlling the frequency at which feedback takes place. For frequencies outside the resonant band of the crystal, the crystal has a high impedance, and thus obstructs feedback. At resonance, the crystal has a low impedance and so allows feedback to cause oscillation. ☐ The Butler oscillator crystal-couples the cathodes of its two tubes to control the feedback frequency. The crystal essentially serves the same function as in the crystal-controlled Hartley; it passes only the feedback at the desired frequency.

review questions

1. Explain how a quartz crystal operates.
2. Why do LC oscillators drift slightly during operation?
3. The natural, or resonant, frequency of a crystal is determined mainly by what factor?
4. What is the resonant frequency of a crystal?
5. At a crystal's natural mechanical frequency, it behaves as a series resonant circuit. How does it behave at slightly higher frequencies?
6. When operated at its series resonant frequency, a crystal can be used as what kind of device?
7. Draw a Pierce oscillator and explain its operation.
8. Draw a crystal-controlled Hartley oscillator and explain its operation.
9. Draw a Butler oscillator and explain its operation.
10. What is one main advantage of the Butler oscillator over other crystal-controlled oscillators?

RC sine-wave oscillators

The basic two-tube oscillator you studied on page 6-5 is an RC sine-wave oscillator. Feedback in this kind of oscillator does not always have to be from plate to grid. Cathode coupling can also be used, as shown. Essentially, V_1 is a grounded-grid amplifier and V_2 is a cathode follower that provides feedback of the proper phase. When the circuit is energized, V_1 initially conducts more heavily than V_2. As the conduction of V_1 increases, its plate voltage falls, and a negative-going voltage is applied to the grid of V_2. This causes the conduction of V_2 to decrease, and, as a result, the voltage drop across cathode resistor R_2 becomes less positive. The fall in voltage across R_2 is coupled to the cathode of V_1 by capacitor C_2. This makes the cathode of V_1 less positive, which is the same as making the grid more positive. As a result, current through V_1 increases further. This action is cumulative and continues until V_1 reaches plate current saturation.

When V_1 reaches saturation, a negative-going signal is no longer coupled to the grid of V_2. So V_2 begins to conduct more heavily. The resulting increase in its cathode voltage is coupled by C_2 to the cathode of V_1. This has the same effect as making the grid of V_1 more negative, and causes a decrease in the conduction of V_1 and an increase in its plate voltage. The increase in the plate voltage of V_1 is coupled to the grid of V_2, causing more of an increase in the conduction of V_2 and a corresponding increase in the voltage across R_2. The rise in cathode voltage of V_2 is coupled to the cathode of V_1 and has the same effect as making the grid of V_1 more negative. As a result, the conduction of V_1 again decreases further.

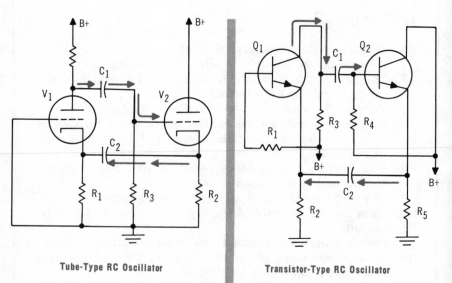

Tube-Type RC Oscillator   Transistor-Type RC Oscillator

RC sine-wave oscillators (cont.)

This process continues until V_1 reaches cutoff. At this time, the plate voltage of V_1 is maximum and no longer rises. Therefore, the grid of V_2 stops going positive and drops to zero. The conduction of V_2 goes down and the drop across R_2 goes down, so that a negative-going signal is coupled to the cathode of V_1. Since this is the same as making the grid positive, V_1 comes out of cutoff and the entire cycle is repeated. The net result is that the conduction of V_1 varies between saturation and cutoff in such a way that a near sinusoidal output voltage is developed.

The emitter feedback in the transistor circuit works the same as the cathode feedback in the tube circuit. Actually, capacitor coupling does not even have to be used. A common-emitter resistor for the transistors, or a common-cathode resistor for the tubes, will act as direct coupling for feedback.

The frequency of oscillation of such RC circuits is difficult to predict, since it is determined by the RC relationships of the coupling circuits and the distance between cutoff and saturation of the tubes. Generally speaking, since the tubes themselves provide the full 360-degree phase shifts, the circuit will oscillate at a frequency where the coupling networks will *not* shift the phase of the signal. This is where the X_C of the coupling capacitors is much lower than the resistance of the coupling circuit, so that essentially only resistive current flows. This means that this circuit can oscillate over a *range* of frequencies and it usually does. It is a very unstable oscillator.

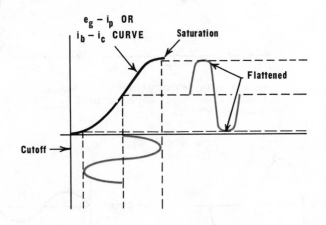

Because RC oscillators rely on the nonlinear effects that occur close to cutoff and saturation to end one-half of the cycles, somewhat flattened sine waves are produced

the crystal-controlled RC oscillator

A modification of the RC oscillator described on the previous pages uses a crystal as the coupling element between the two cathodes. Such a circuit, shown below, is similar to the Butler LC oscillator. The crystal is operated at its series resonant frequency, so sufficient feedback to maintain oscillation is produced only at that frequency. Above and below the series resonant frequency, the crystal is effectively a high impedance in the feedback path. A circuit such as this is much more stable than the one shown earlier in which a capacitor is used to provide coupling between the two cathodes. The same technique would be used to stabilize the basic two-tube RC oscillator you first studied.

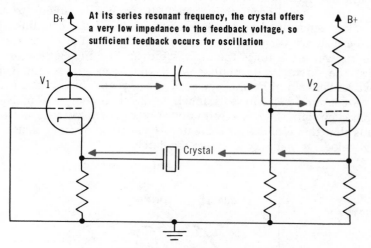

At its series resonant frequency, the crystal offers a very low impedance to the feedback voltage, so sufficient feedback occurs for oscillation

Above and below the resonant frequency, the high impedance of the crystal prevents appreciable feedback to the cathode of V_1

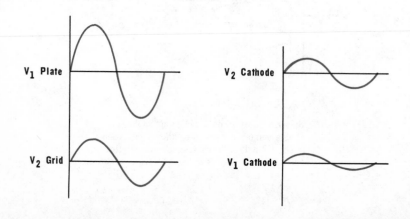

the phase-shift oscillator

One popular type of RC oscillator uses three or more RC networks instead of a second stage in the feedback path, with each network providing a *portion* of the 180-degree phase shift required for the feedback to be regenerative. The feedback path consists of three phase-shift networks: R_1C_1, R_2C_2, and R_3C_3. The values of these components are such that each network shifts the feedback voltage 60 degrees, so that the feedback applied to the base has been shifted a total of 180 degrees.

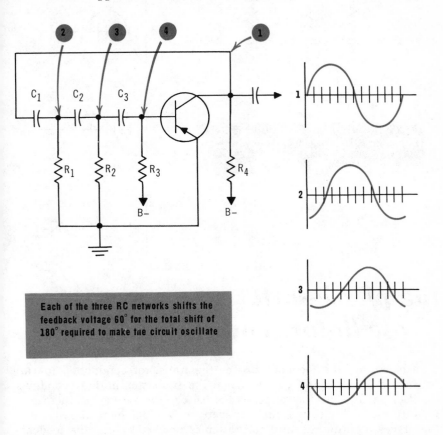

Each of the three RC networks shifts the feedback voltage 60° for the total shift of 180° required to make the circuit oscillate

Each phase-shift network is an RC circuit in which the current leads the voltage by 60 degrees. Therefore, the feedback voltage developed across R_1 leads the collector voltage by 60 degrees. Since the voltage across R_1 is the input to the R_2C_2 phase-shift network, the voltage across R_2 leads the voltage across R_1 by 60 degrees. Or, in other words, it leads the collector voltage by 120 degrees. The same thing is true of the R_3C_3 network. The feedback voltage developed across R_3 leads that across R_2 by 60 degrees, that across R_1 by 120 degrees, and the collector voltage by 180 degrees. The feedback is therefore regenerative.

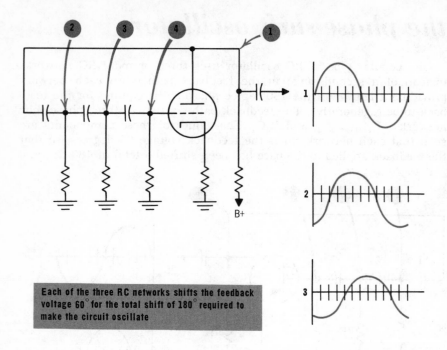

Each of the three RC networks shifts the feedback voltage 60° for the total shift of 180° required to make the circuit oscillate

the phase-shift oscillator (cont.)

In operation, the feedback causes the transistor conduction to vary between saturation and cutoff. When the transistor initially conducts, the decrease in collector voltage is fed back to the base as an increasing forward bias. This causes the transistor to conduct more heavily, with the process continuing until saturation is reached. Then, the feedback begins to decrease the forward bias on the base, with the process continuing until collector current cutoff is essentially reached. This process is continually repeated, and, as a result, the collector voltage varies in an approximately sinusoidal way, as in the other RC oscillator circuit you just learned about.

Since the three phase-shift networks must each produce a 60-degree phase shift, the circuit will naturally tend to oscillate at or near the frequency where these phase shifts occur. The proper RC values must be chosen to bring this about at the desired frequency.

the wien-bridge oscillator

A Wien-bridge oscillator is a two-stage circuit in which the frequency of oscillation is determined by an *RC bridge network*. The second stage provides the 180-degree phase shift necessary for regenerative feedback. The feedback path is from the collector of Q_2, through capacitor C_3, to the bridge circuit. The feedback voltage is developed across the various elements of the bridge circuit, with the portion developed across the parallel combination of C_2 and R_2 providing regenerative feedback for the base of Q_1. As you will see on the next page, the bridge will provide the correct feedback to support oscillation only at one frequency (actually a very narrow frequency range). Above and below this frequency, the bridge prevents the circuit from oscillating.

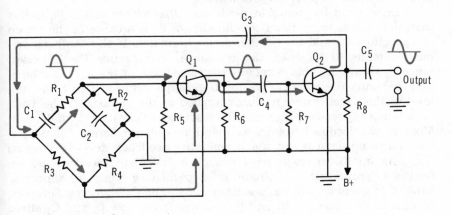

The Wien-bridge oscillator utilizes two stages to provide the required 180° phase reversal of the feedback, and a special bridge network to control the frequency of oscillation

As a result of the regenerative feedback, transistor Q_2 operates between saturation and cutoff, and generates an essentially sinusoidal output voltage in the process. The sequence of operation is as follows. When the circuit is initially energized, Q_1 and Q_2 begin to conduct. The resulting decrease in the collector voltage of Q_1 is coupled to the base of Q_2, causing the current through Q_2 to decrease. This produces an increase in the collector voltage of Q_2, which is coupled by capacitor C_3 back to the bridge circuit and applied to the base of Q_1. The feedback thus causes Q_1 to conduct even more. This action is cumulative, with current in Q_1 steadily increasing and current through Q_2 decreasing. Eventually Q_1 reaches saturation and Q_2 reaches cutoff. The feedback then reverses, and the opposite action occurs, as with the other RC oscillators. The net effect is that a sine-wave voltage is developed at the collector of Q_2.

operation of the bridge network

The bridge network of the Wien-bridge oscillator consists of two *parallel* branches, each of which acts as a voltage divider for the feed-back voltage. One branch contains R_3 and R_4, and the other contains R_1C_1 and R_2C_2. The portion of the feedback voltage developed across R_4 of the R_3R_4 branch is applied to the cathode of V_1, and the portion of voltage across R_2C_2 of the R_1C_1–R_2C_2 branch is applied to the grid of V_1. Since the branches of the bridge are in parallel, both the cathode and grid always *tend* to receive feedback of the *same polarity*. Since the polarity of the feedback applied to the grid is such that it is *regenerative,* the feedback applied to the cathode, then, tends to be *degenerative.* For the circuit to oscillate, of course, the regenerative feedback must be greater than the degenerative feedback.

At the desired frequency of oscillation, the voltage across R_4 is less than that across the parallel combination of R_2C_2 because of the action of capacitors C_1 and C_2. So the circuit oscillates. If the feedback frequency tends to increase, the reactance of capacitor C_2 decreases. Since C_2 shunts R_2, this decreases the impedance of the R_2C_2 combination, reducing the regenerative feedback applied to the grid below the level of the degenerative feedback applied to the cathode. If the feedback frequency tends to decrease, the reactance of capacitor C_1 increases. More of the feedback voltage is therefore dropped across C_1, with a corresponding decrease in the regenerative feedback developed across R_2C_2. Again, the regenerative feedback is less than the degenerative feedback, preventing the circuit from oscillating. Only at a narrow band of frequencies will the reactances of C_1 and C_2 allow regeneration. Of course, the values of R_1 and R_2 also determine how C_1 and C_2 affect the frequency of oscillation.

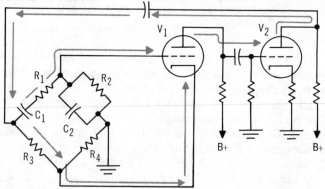

The bridge network provides both regenerative and degenerative feedback

The degenerative feedback is constant, while the regenerative feedback varies with frequency, being greater than the degenerative feedback at only a single frequency. This is because the resistance of C_1 goes up at the lower frequencies and that of C_2 goes down at the higher frequencies

negative-resistance oscillators

One of the basic characteristics of a normal *resistance* is that it remains constant so that the current through it increases as the voltage across it is increased, according to Ohm's Law. When operated in a certain way, some devices exhibit just the *opposite* characteristic; that is, the resistance goes up sharply as the voltage is increased, so that the current goes down. These devices are therefore said to have a *negative-resistance* characteristic.

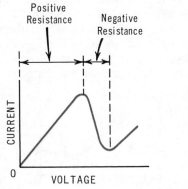

The voltage current characteristic of some devices exhibits both a positive and a negative resistance portion

Negative resistance can be used in an oscillator circuit to provide regenerative feedback to an LC tank. The negative resistance is connected in such a way that it produces a circulating current in the tank. As long as the negative resistance is larger than the tank's d-c resistance, oscillations will continue in the tank, with the negative resistance, in effect, overcoming the d-c resistance of the tank. For this to happen, the resistance of the device should go up by a proportionately larger amount than the increase in voltage.

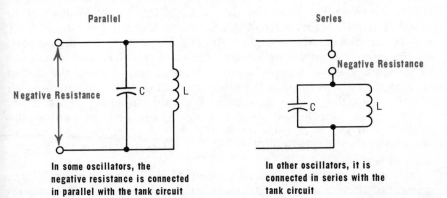

In some oscillators, the negative resistance is connected in parallel with the tank circuit

In other oscillators, it is connected in series with the tank circuit

the tunnel-diode oscillator

One type of negative-resistance oscillator uses a tunnel diode to provide the required negative resistance. You recall from Volume 4 that a tunnel diode has a voltage-current characteristic curve similar to that shown. The portion of the curve shown in color represents negative resistance, since as the voltage is *increased,* the resistance of the diode goes up by a proportionately larger amount to *reduce* the current through the diode. The action of the tunnel diode in producing oscillation can be explained on the basis of the simple circuit shown.

The battery voltage is chosen so that it biases the tunnel diode for operation over its negative resistance region. When switch S is closed, current flows in the circuit, producing voltage drops across the resistor and the tunnel diode. The voltage drop across the tunnel diode equals the battery voltage minus the drop across the resistor; and the sum of the drops across the diode and resistor equals the battery voltage.

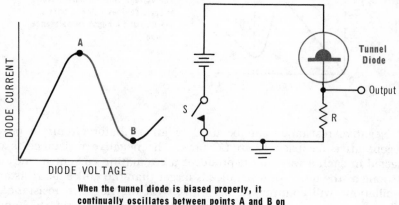

When the tunnel diode is biased properly, it
continually oscillates between points A and B on
its voltage-current curve

When the circuit is first energized, current in the circuit starts to rise to the value determined by the total resistance of the tunnel diode and R. The voltage drops across the diode and R match the ratio of their resistances. But, as the voltage across the diode starts passing point A on the curve, it enters the negative resistance region. The resistance of the diode goes up sharply, so that the total resistance of the circuit reduces the current through the diode and R. Since the current through R went down, the voltage drop across R goes down so that more of the source voltage appears across the diode. Again, because of this, the resistance of the diode goes up sharply to reduce circuit current and lower the drop across R still further to further increase the voltage across the diode.

This action continues until the current in the circuit and the voltage across the diode reach point B, which is the end of half of the regenerative cycle.

the tunnel-diode oscillator (cont.)

Then, as the voltage starts to increase, the diode starts into the positive resistance region. The resistance goes down to lower the overall circuit resistance and raise the current. This increases the drop across R so that less voltage is left for the diode. The drop in diode voltage moves the operation back in the negative resistance region in the opposite direction. The reduced voltage reduces the resistance of the diode to increase circuit current, so that the drop across R goes up again to lower the diode voltage again; this action continues until point A is reached to complete the second half cycle.

As the voltage tends to drop past A into the other positive resistance region, the diode resistance goes up to lower current, reduce the drop across R, and raise the diode voltage to swing the operation back into the negative resistance region to start the next cycle. This continues with the voltage and current swinging back and forth between A and B in a near-sinusoidal manner. The sinusoidal current is dropped across R as a voltage output.

Although the circuit described on the previous page is useful for describing the action of the tunnel diode, it is not practical as an oscillator for a variety of reasons. In r-f tunnel-diode oscillators, the diode is placed in series with an LC tank. The tank oscillates, and the diode voltage varies in the opposite direction to the tank voltage swings to regenerate its action and compensate for its losses.

A practical tunnel-diode oscillator circuit is shown. For the circuit to operate efficiently and stable, resistors R_1 and R_2 are added to set the proper bias current and voltage for the diode. R_1 sets the voltage level for the diode and tank, and the shunting effect of R_2 establishes the current level through the diode. The values of R_1 and R_2 compared to the resistance of the diode also determine how the negative resistance affects the circuits. The diode current is set to operate in the center of the negative resistance region.

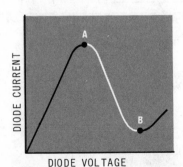

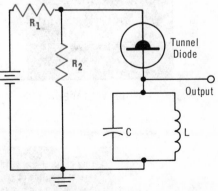

In an oscillator circuit, the tunnel diode is biased to operate at the center (linear) portion of its negative-resistance characteristic

the tunnel-diode oscillator (cont.)

When the circuit is energized, the tank begins oscillating as the diode enters the negative resistance region. This is caused by the capacitor initially charging, and then discharging when the current through the diode decreases after point A. The oscillating current that flows in the tank produces a sinusoidal voltage across the tank that alternately drives the diode voltage above and below its bias point. As a result, the diode voltage varies sinusoidally about the center of its negative resistance region.

When the top of the tank is going positive, the diode voltage, and thus its resistance, is decreased, and the total circuit current increases. This increase in current adds to the charge on the tank capacitor, and aids, or reinforces, the circulating tank current. When the top of the tank is going negative (or less positive), the diode voltage, and thus its resistance, is increased, so the circuit current decreases. This decrease in current aids the discharge of the tank capacitor and its recharging in the opposite direction. So, again, the circulating tank current is reinforced.

The same action is repeated during each oscillating cycle of the tank circuit. The net effect is that the current changes produced by the negative resistance of the diode always reinforce the circulating tank current and, in doing so, overcome the tank circuit losses and sustain oscillation. Also, since the tank oscillations determine the sine-wave swings, the circuit can be designed so that the current never reaches points A and B, and *pure* sine waves are produced.

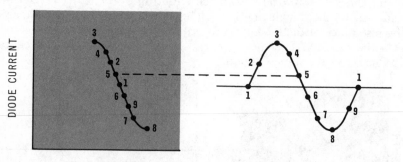

This diagram shows how the diode current varies along the negative resistance region to produce a sine wave

the dynatron

A tetrode, you recall from Volume 3, exhibits negative resistance when the plate voltage is lower than the screen-grid voltage. This is sometimes called the *dynatron effect*. When it is used to produce oscillations, the circuit is called a dynatron negative-resistance oscillator.

Energy of the correct phase to sustain oscillations in the tank is supplied from the plate as long as the negative plate resistance is less than the resistance of the tank at resonance. The value of the negative plate resistance is determined by the plate-current, plate-voltage characteristic of the tube. It is set at the proper value by adjusting the potential on the control grid to make the plate operate in the center of the negative-resistance region.

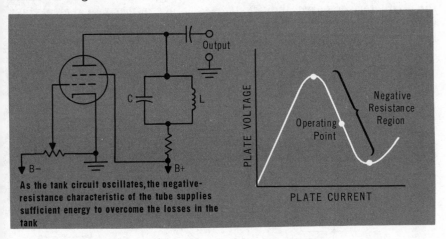

As the tank circuit oscillates, the negative-resistance characteristic of the tube supplies sufficient energy to overcome the losses in the tank

When the circuit is first energized, plate current starts to flow, and the tank starts oscillating. Since the tank is a parallel resonant circuit, it acts as a high impedance at resonance and drops a sinusoidal voltage at the resonant frequency. As the signal goes positive, it adds to the B+ to increase the plate voltage. As the plate voltage goes up, the plate current goes down because of negative resistance. So, there is less of a drop across the tank, and plate voltage goes up higher to add to the tank's positive swing. The higher plate voltage again reduces the plate current to continue the regenerative action. This continues until the tank signal swings negative. This opposes the B+ to reduce the plate voltage so that the plate current starts rising. The increased plate current causes a larger drop across the tank to add to its negative swing, reducing plate voltage still more to continue regeneration. This continues until the tank swings again to start the next cycle.

When the circuit is properly designed, the tank swings will control the action to keep the operation on the linear portion of the curve. If a resistor is used instead of the tank, the plate current will oscillate between the top and bottom of the negative-resistance region to produce a somewhat flattened sine wave.

other
negative-resistance oscillators

There are various other types of negative-resistance oscillators besides the tunnel diode and the dynatron. Most of them are essentially similar in principle, with the major difference being the manner in which the negative resistance is produced. A transistor-type negative-resistance oscillator is shown in A. It is a common-base circuit, with an LC tank connected to the base. The transistor is manufactured in such a way that the collector exhibits a negative-resistance characteristic over a portion of its voltage-current curve. A point-contact transistor exhibits this characteristic. When the transistor is operated on this portion of the characteristic curve, the negative-resistance property of the collector supplies energy of the proper phase to the tank to support oscillation in the same fashion as the negative-resistance tetrode.

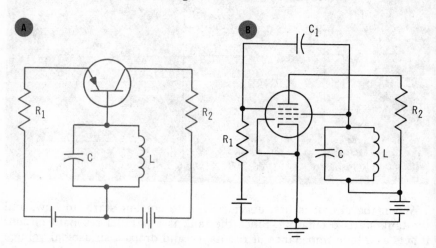

The basic difference between negative-resistance
oscillators is the manner in which the negative-
resistance characteristic is produced

Another type of negative-resistance oscillator is called the *transitron*. Such a circuit is shown in B. In the transitron, the negative resistance is supplied to the tank by the screen grid of a pentode. The screen acquires its negative-resistance characteristic by being connected to the suppressor grid through a capacitor (C_1). When the screen voltage increases, screen current would normally also increase. However, C_1 couples the rise in screen voltage to the suppressor grid, so the suppressor attracts more electrons towards the plate. Consequently, the screen current decreases in spite of the increase in screen voltage.

summary

☐ RC sine-wave oscillators use coupling between stages to keep the first stage varying between saturation and cutoff. These oscillators are very unstable, as their frequency of oscillation is determined by the RC relationships of the coupling circuits and the distance between tube saturation and cutoff. ☐ RC oscillators can be stabilized somewhat by using a crystal as the coupling element.

☐ In the phase-shift oscillator, three or more RC networks are used instead of a second stage. Each network shifts the feedback a portion of the required 180 degrees. Generally, three RC phase shift networks are used, with each network providing a 60-degree shift. ☐ The Wien-bridge oscillator uses two conventional stages, with an RC bridge network controlling the frequency of oscillation. The bridge network provides degenerative feedback that is independent of frequency and regenerative feedback that varies with frequency. Oscillation occurs only at the frequency at which the regenerative feedback is larger than the degenerative feedback.

☐ Devices with a negative-resistance characteristic can be used to provide regenerative feedback to an LC tank. The tunnel diode is such a device. ☐ When a tunnel diode is biased so that it operates in its negative-resistance region, it will reinforce circulating tank current and sustain oscillations. ☐ A tunnel-diode oscillator can produce perfect sine waves. ☐ The negative-resistance characteristic of tetrodes is used in the dynatron oscillator. In the transitron oscillator, a pentode is used with voltages such that the screen grid exhibits negative resistance. ☐ A point-contact transistor's base has a negative resistance region that can also be used to cause oscillations.

review questions

1. Why are RC oscillators unstable?
2. Describe the waveforms produced by a typical RC oscillator.
3. How is a crystal used to stabilize the basic RC oscillator?
4. In a phase-shift oscillator containing four RC networks, how many degrees must each network shift the feedback signal?
5. What determines the frequency of oscillation in a Wien-bridge oscillator?
7. What is meant by *negative resistance*?
8. How is negative resistance used in an oscillator?
9. When used in an oscillator, how is the tunnel diode biased?
10. Name three negative-resistance oscillators.

quenched oscillators

Quenched oscillators are oscillators that deliver outputs periodically rather than continuously. Their oscillations are intermittently cut off, or *quenched*. Two basic types of quenched oscillators are used: self-quenching, and externally quenched. A self-quenching oscillator cuts *itself* off after one or more output cycles, and then automatically begins oscillating again after a set time. This pattern is continually repeated, so that the output can be considered as a series of evenly-spaced *pulses*, with each pulse consisting of one or more sine waves. One type of self-quenching oscillator consists of a conventional LC oscillator circuit with a special *biasing* arrangement. The bias initially allows the stage to conduct and produce oscillations. During each output cycle, the bias gradually increases, until after a certain number of cycles it is sufficient to cut off the stage. While the stage is cut off, the bias then automatically decreases to the point where conduction can again take place.

In the circuit shown, a conventional series-fed Hartley oscillator is used. Quenching action is accomplished by the grid-leak bias circuit consisting of resistor R_1 and capacitor C_1. In the standard Hartley oscillator, the time constant of R_1 and C_1 is selected so that the tube is biased class C. But in *this* circuit, R_1 and C_1 have a considerably *longer* time constant, so more charge is gained by C_1 when the grid is positive than is lost through R_1 when the grid is negative. During each output cycle, therefore, the grid becomes increasingly negative, until finally the tube is completely cut off. While the tube is cut off, C_1 discharges through R_1 to keep the tube cut off. When C_1 loses enough charge, the tube again begins to conduct.

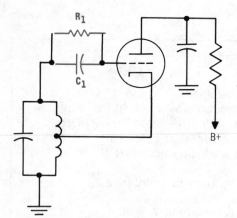

The output of the self-pulsing blocking oscillator consists of periods of oscillation and periods of rest

OUTPUT VOLTAGE

The grid-leak network builds up enough bias, because of its long RC time constant, to keep the tube cut off for longer periods than it oscillates

externally quenched oscillators

In externally quenched oscillators, quenching is caused by a voltage or signal applied to the oscillator from some *external* source. The rate or pattern of the quenching action therefore depends on the external source rather than on the oscillator itself.

Practically any standard oscillator can be operated as an externally quenched oscillator. All that is required is that the quenching voltage be applied in such a way that it prevents the oscillator from oscillating when it is present. One type of externally-quenched oscillator is shown in A. It is a conventional Colpitts oscillator in which the quenching voltage is in the form of negative pulses applied to the grid. When the quenching voltage is present, the tube is cut off. No feedback is returned to the grid, so oscillation cannot take place. In this circuit, the output is taken from the tank. When the quenching voltage is applied, oscillation does not stop immediately because of the circulating current that continues to flow in the tank. Instead, oscillation *gradually diminishes,* or damps out, because of the resistance of the tank.

The circuit shown in B is a transistor Armstrong oscillator, in which the quenching signal overcomes the forward base-emitter bias to cut off the transistor.

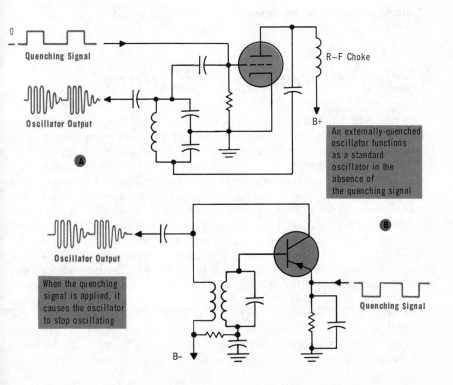

Quenching Signal

Oscillator Output

R–F Choke

B+

An externally-quenched oscillator functions as a standard oscillator in the absence of the quenching signal

A

Oscillator Output

When the quenching signal is applied, it causes the oscillator to stop oscillating

B

Quenching Signal

B–

Lead Inductance, Junction Capacitances, and High-Frequency Cutoff

Interelectrode Capacitance, Transit Time, and Inductive Reactance of Electrodes

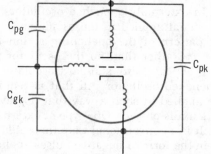

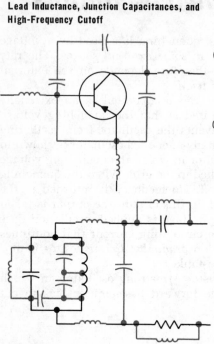

Many of the electrical properties of a circuit and its components can be ignored at low and medium frequencies even though they are present. At high frequencies, however, these properties have a significant effect on circuit operation

Capacitance Between Wiring and Inductance of Wiring

high-frequency oscillators

As frequency increases, you will find that some tubes or transistors will not work well. This is because the interelectrode capacitances in tubes start shunting the high-frequency signals, and the same is true for the junction capacitances in transistors. Also, a tube's *transit time* limits frequency response, as does a transistor's *carrier mobility*. You will find that tubes and transistors have an upper operating limit. So, generally, you have to be careful with the ones you choose at VHF and higher frequencies. Also, at the higher frequencies, even if the proper tubes are used, interwinding capacitances of inductors will have to be considered and certain resistors will develop inductance as do capacitors' plates. The induction of circuit wiring will have an effect, as well as the capacitances between the wiring. Around 200 megacycles and higher, even the placement of parts is critical. All of these factors become progressively significant at higher and higher frequencies, with the result that standard oscillators for use at these frequencies are very often considerably different than those used at the lower radio frequencies. Some of these oscillators are described on the following pages.

the ultra-audion oscillator

The ultra-audion oscillator is essentially a *Colpitts* oscillator modified for use at high frequencies. The tank circuit for the oscillator consists of coil L_1, capacitor C_1, and the tube's grid-to-cathode and plate-to-cathode interelectrode capacitances, C_{gk} and C_{pk}. The series combination of capacitances C_{gk} and C_{pk} is effectively in parallel with C_1, and these three make up the total capacitance of the tank. C_{gk} and C_{pk} also serve to tap the tank circuit to ground, with C_{gk} providing the grid voltage for the tube, and C_{pk} providing the feedback path from the plate. Capacitor C_2 and resistor R_1 make up a grid-leak bias circuit, and blocking capacitor C_3 keeps the d-c component of the plate voltage out of the grid tank. Both C_2 and C_3 are made large so that they have negligible reactance at the oscillation frequency. They therefore do not affect the frequency at which the circuit oscillates. C_1 is made small enough so that C_{gk} and C_{pk} will have an effect.

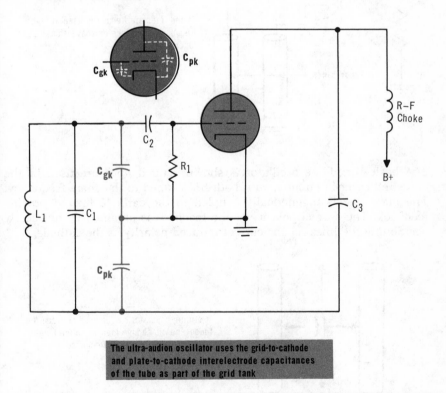

The ultra-audion oscillator uses the grid-to-cathode and plate-to-cathode interelectrode capacitances of the tube as part of the grid tank

The ultra-audion oscillator is an example of how tube interelectrode capacitances can be used to advantage in circuit design at high frequencies. This type of oscillator can be used effectively up to about 500 megacycles with tubes designed for that purpose.

tuned-line oscillators

At high frequencies, sections of *transmission line* are often used in place of conventional LC tuned circuits. These sections of transmission line are *frequency selective*. They will develop significant currents and voltages at a single frequency (actually a narrow range of frequencies). This single frequency is called the resonant frequency of the line and depends on the physical length of the line. Another characteristic of these tuned lines is that voltages can be magnetically coupled from one line to another by placing the lines relatively close together. The characteristics and theory of tuned transmission lines are described in Volume 7.

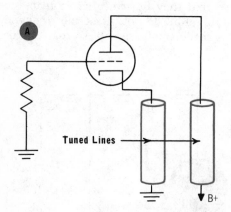

Tuned lines are frequently used at high frequencies in place of conventional LC tuned circuits

A basic tuned-line oscillator is shown. Tuned lines are used in the plate and cathode circuits, with both lines tuned to the *same* frequency. The plate line is magnetically coupled to the cathode line to provide feedback. The correct polarity of the feedback is obtained by physically positioning the lines for the correct induced polarity at the cathode.

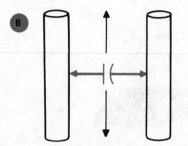

A sliding capacitor can be used between the tuned lines to change their effective length, and, thus, their resonant frequency

Other types of oscillator circuits can also utilize tuned lines. For example, tuned lines can be used in the plate and grid circuits, with the lines positioned to produce the required feedback polarity.

the microwave tube

For frequencies up around 1000 megacycles, special-purpose tubes are designed to minimize interelectrode and circuit capacitances. Also, the spacing of the tube elements is made close to reduce transit time, and there are no connecting leads, to minimize wiring inductances. The envelopes of such tubes are connecting rings that make direct contact with special tuned-line structures, which actually form the socket to contain the tube. The tube and tuned-line structure form *coaxial* elements, in which one circuit element is contained within the other, so that the outer elements enclose and shield the inner ones from outside effects. Examples of such tubes are the *acorn, lighthouse,* and *pencil* tubes, so named because of their shapes.

An example of a lighthouse tube circuit is shown. The plungers set the length and, thereby, the resonant frequency of the tuned lines, and capacitive coupling between the lines provides feedback. The circuit oscillates like a TPTG oscillator.

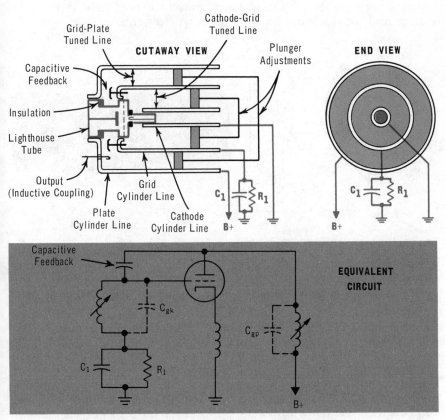

This lighthouse tube and the coaxial tuned lines form a TPTG oscillator

the barkhausen-kurz oscillator

Although it is not used frequently for commercial applications, the Barkhausen-Kurz oscillator illustrates the principle of *electron oscillation* and its use in oscillator circuits. In this oscillator, the grid is operated at a relatively high positive potential, and the plate is made slightly negative. Both the grid and plate circuits contain tuned lines, which serve as resonant circuits.

The feedback required for oscillation is produced by electrons oscillating back and forth past the control grid. This oscillation is produced by the grid and plate potentials. As electrons travel from the cathode, some strike the positive grid and are absorbed. Most of them, however, pass through the grid wires and continue toward the plate, which, because of the grid and plate potentials, they never reach. Instead, they reverse direction and travel back towards the grid, which some strike and are absorbed. But most pass through the grid wires into the space between the grid and cathode, where the majority once more reverse direction and are attracted back towards the grid. The oscillation continues in this fashion, its frequency determined primarily by the grid voltage and the distances between the tube electrodes.

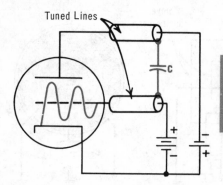

Tuned Lines

Capacitor C is used to set the frequency at which the tuned lines resonate. Oscillations in the tuned-line tank are regenerated by the energy received from the electrons oscillating past the grid as they go back and forth between the cathode and plate

In this description of electron oscillation there is no a-c component to the grid voltage. Actually, when the circuit is energized, oscillations begin in the grid resonant circuit. This adds an a-c component to the grid voltage. Some of the electrons then oscillate in *synchronism* with the grid voltage and *give up* energy to the grid circuit before eventually striking the grid wires and being absorbed. These electrons maintain the oscillations in the grid circuit. Those electrons that are not in synchronism with the grid voltage oscillate with larger and larger amplitudes, until they strike the plate. Whether or not an electron is in synchronism with the grid voltage depends on the instantaneous phase of the grid and plate voltages at the instant the electron leaves the cathode. This oscillator can work up to about 2000 megacycles, but is not too stable and cannot produce a signal with very much power.

the magnetron oscillator

A magnetron oscillator is capable of producing thousands of watts of output power at frequencies as high as ten thousand or more megacycles. As shown, a magnetron consists essentially of a cylindrical cathode surrounded by an anode, usually in the form of a copper block. A series of holes are cut in the anode, with radial slots leading from each hole to the inner surface of the anode. The holes are called *resonant cavities*, and are the electrical equivalents of LC resonant circuits. The frequency at which the cavities resonate is determined by their physical *dimensions*. If electrons are made to pass a cavity slot with a velocity that corresponds to the resonant frequency of the cavity, the electrons will give up energy to the cavity. This will either start the cavity oscillating, or sustain oscillation once it has begun.

Usually, the anode of a magnetron is kept at ground potential and the cathode is made negative. The anode is thus positive with respect to the cathode. A powerful magnetic field is set up in the magnetron, either by a permanent magnet or an electromagnet, with the direction of the field *parallel* to the cathode. Electrons emitted by the cathode are attracted to the anode, since it is more positive than the cathode. However, the magnetic field causes the electrons to follow spiral paths, and in doing so they pass the cavity slots. Under the proper conditions of anode voltage and magnetic field strength, the velocity of the electrons corresponds to the resonant frequency of the cavities. Powerful oscillations are then set up and sustained in the cavities. The output of the magnetron is magnetically coupled from the cavities. Generally, a magnetron is pulsed with a voltage between the cathode and anode to produce oscillations. Between pulses, then, the magnetron is at rest.

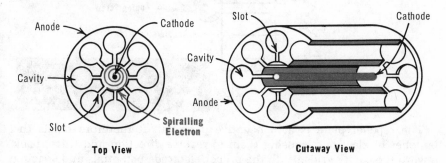

Top View   Cutaway View

The magnetron is an extremely high-frequency, high-power oscillator

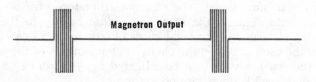

Magnetron Output

the klystron oscillator

You recall from Volume 3 that klystrons are a class of tubes used as high-frequency amplifiers or oscillators. For oscillator use, a special type of klystron, called a *reflex klystron*, is generally used. A basic reflex klystron contains a cathode, an accelerating grid, two cavity grids, and a repeller plate, as shown. A resonant cavity is connected between the cavity grids.

Electrons emitted by the cathode are attracted toward the accelerating grid, which has a positive potential. Most of the electrons pass through the accelerating grid, and in the process are formed into beams. The beams of electrons then pass through the cavity grids, which are also at a positive potential. Electron flow past these grids starts the cavity oscillating, and this oscillation produces a sinusoidally varying *electric field* between the cavity grids. As the electric field varies, it alternately speeds up and slows down the electrons, so that the electrons leave the area of the second cavity grid in bunches.

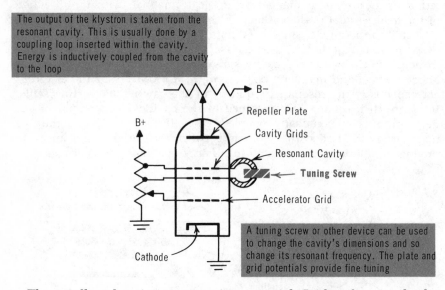

The output of the klystron is taken from the resonant cavity. This is usually done by a coupling loop inserted within the cavity. Energy is inductively coupled from the cavity to the loop

B–

B+

Repeller Plate

Cavity Grids

Resonant Cavity

Tuning Screw

Accelerator Grid

Cathode

A tuning screw or other device can be used to change the cavity's dimensions and so change its resonant frequency. The plate and grid potentials provide fine tuning

The repeller plate is at a negative potential. It therefore repels the bunches of electrons, causing them to *reverse* direction and travel back toward the cavity grids. With the proper electrode potentials and spacing between electrodes, each bunch of electrons arrives back at the cavity grids when the electric field between the grids has a polarity that causes the electrons to *slow down*. The electrons therefore give up energy to the electric field. This is the same as *adding* energy to the resonant cavity, so the electron bunches add energy to the resonant cavity, thereby sustaining the oscillations in the cavity. The potentials of the accelerator grid and the repeller plate can be adjusted to synchronize the electron bunching action with the cavity oscillation.

shock-excited oscillators

Shock-excited oscillators produce short bursts of damped, sinusoidal oscillations. They do this by setting up a heavy d-c current flow through an LC tank circuit and then *suddenly interrupting* that current flow. A basic shock-excited oscillator circuit is shown. Because the grid is connected to the B+ supply through a large value resistor, it is positive, causing a heavy current flow in the circuit. The tube is in series with an LC tank, so the tube current flows through the tank and builds up an appreciable magnetic field around L. By suddenly applying a large negative voltage to the grid, the tube is abruptly cut off. This shocks the tank circuit into oscillation. The oscillations are started by the collapsing magnetic field, which charges the tank capacitor.

The tank is allowed to oscillate as long as the negative input voltage on the grid is present. However, since no energy is added to the tank once it begins oscillating, the oscillations gradually diminish because of the tank's resistance. If the tube were cut off for a long enough period, the oscillations would die out completely. In practice, the Q of the tank is made high enough to sustain an appreciable oscillation amplitude during the time that the tube is cut off.

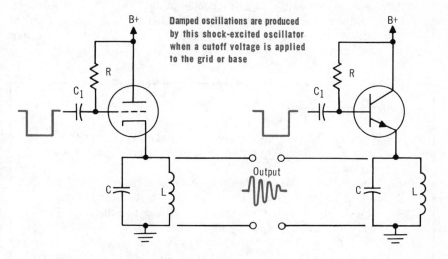

Damped oscillations are produced by this shock-excited oscillator when a cutoff voltage is applied to the grid or base

When the negative voltage is removed from the grid, the tube again begins conducting heavily. The large d-c current that this causes through the tank quickly damps the tank oscillations. Pure d-c current again flows through the tank, building up the magnetic field around the coil to be used for the next shock-excited oscillations.

In other versions of this circuit, the tube is kept cut off, and a sharp positive pulse starts it conducting only momentarily. The burst of current through the tank initiates LC oscillations, which continue until they damp out.

summary

☐ In quenched oscillators, the tube or transistor is cut off intermittently to produce periodic rather than continuous outputs. ☐ Quenched oscillators can be self-quenching or externally quenched. ☐ The self-quenching oscillator cuts itself off and begins oscillations again after a set period. The externally-quenched oscillator is cut off by an externally applied signal. ☐ Practically any oscillator can be quenched by applying an external cutoff voltage or signal.

☐ Standard oscillators used at high frequencies differ considerably from those used at lower radio frequencies. This is because of the characteristics exhibited by circuit components at high frequencies. ☐ The ultra-audion oscillator is a Colpitts oscillator modified for high-frequency use. It uses the grid-to-cathode and grid-to-plate interelectrode capacitances as part of the grid tank. ☐ Sections of frequency-selective transmission line are often used in high-frequency oscillators in place of LC tuned circuits.

☐ At frequencies around 1000 megacycles, special-purpose tubes such as the acorn and lighthouse tubes are used to minimize the effect of interelectrode and circuit capacitances. ☐ The Barkhausen-Kurz, magnetron, and klystron oscillators are all extremely high-frequency oscillators. ☐ Shock-excited oscillators produce short bursts of damped, sinusoidal oscillations. They do this by setting up heavy d-c current flow through an LC tank circuit and then suddenly interrupting that current flow.

review questions

1. What are the two basic types of quenched oscillator?
2. Draw one type of quenched oscillator and describe its operation.
3. Explain why many radio-frequency oscillators do not work well at higher frequencies.
4. How is the Colpitts oscillator modified to function effectively as a high-frequency oscillator?
5. What characteristics of transmission line sections enable them to be used at high frequencies in place of conventional LC tuned circuits?
6. At what frequency ranges are acorn, lighthouse, and pencil tubes used in oscillators?
7. How is feedback produced in the Barkhausen-Kurz oscillator?
8. Describe the magnetron oscillator.
9. Describe how a klystron oscillator works.
10. What initiates the oscillations in the tank circuit of a shock-excited oscillator?

nonsinusoidal oscillators

You have seen the various types of oscillator circuits that can be used to generate sinusoidal outputs. These circuits vary widely in configuration and operation, but they have the common characteristic of a sine-wave output. You will now learn about another broad class of oscillator circuits, called *nonsinusoidal oscillators*. As their name implies, these oscillators deliver outputs that are *not* sine waves.

No one output waveshape is characteristic of all nonsinusoidal oscillators. In fact, there is no one specific characteristic that applies to all of the circuits that are generally classified as nonsinusoidal oscillators. They are actually a collection of circuits, each of which has its own characteristic output waveshape. In all cases, though, the output wave-shape is independent of the circuit input. Some nonsinusoidal oscillators require no input, and deliver a continuous output of their characteristic waveshape. Others must be triggered by an input pulse or voltage before they will deliver their output.

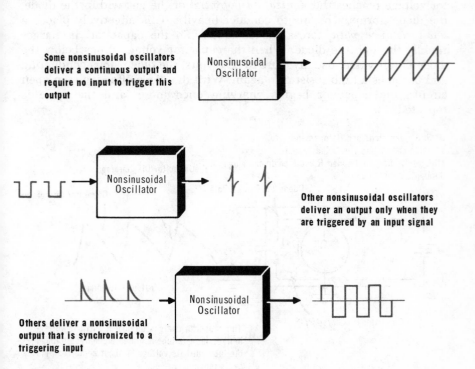

Some nonsinusoidal oscillators deliver a continuous output and require no input to trigger this output

Nonsinusoidal Oscillator

Other nonsinusoidal oscillators deliver an output only when they are triggered by an input signal

Nonsinusoidal Oscillator

Others deliver a nonsinusoidal output that is synchronized to a triggering input

Nonsinusoidal Oscillator

Nonsinusoidal oscillators are frequently referred to as *relaxation oscillators*. This is because in producing their output waveshape they generally have a period of conduction as well as a period of noncon-duction.

the gas-diode oscillator

The basic gas-diode oscillator consists of a resistor and capacitor connected in series across a source of d-c power, and a gas diode in parallel with the capacitor. Diode conduction is controlled by the capacitor, since the capacitor voltage is directly across the diode. You recall that a gas diode does not conduct until a definite voltage is applied across it. Once this voltage is applied, though, the diode conducts heavily, so it has a very low resistance. The diode will continue to conduct heavily until the voltage across its terminals is reduced to almost zero.

When the gas-diode oscillator circuit is initially energized, there is no charge on the capacitor. Consequently, there is no voltage across the diode; it is *cut off*, and represents a very high resistance. Current flow in the circuit is therefore through the capacitor and resistor, charging the capacitor. As the capacitor becomes charged, its voltage, and, therefore, the voltage across the diode, increases. When the capacitor voltage reaches the *ionization potential* of the gas within the diode, the diode abruptly begins to conduct heavily. This effectively places a *low-resistance path* across the capacitor. So the capacitor discharges rapidly through the diode. When the capacitor voltage drops below the diode cutoff value, usually close to zero volts, the diode stops conducting and becomes a high resistance again. With the diode effectively an open circuit, the capacitor begins charging once more, and the cycle is repeated.

Once the gas diode oscillator is energized, it
operates continuously with the capacitor
alternately charging through R and then discharging
through the diode

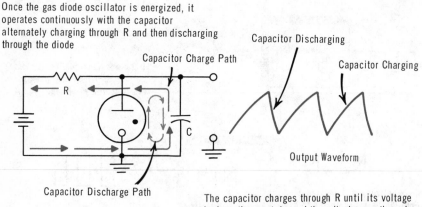

Capacitor Charge Path

Capacitor Discharging

Capacitor Charging

Output Waveform

Capacitor Discharge Path

The capacitor charges through R until its voltage
ionizes the gas tube and then discharges through
the tube until its voltage is about zero. Then the
cycle repeats

The output of the oscillator is the charge and discharge voltage of the capacitor, which resembles a sawtooth wave. The rise in charging voltage is slow because of the relatively high resistance of resistor R; and the discharge cycle of the capacitor is rapid because of the low resistance of the ionized gas tube.

the gas-diode used as a linear-sawtooth generator

The leading and trailing edges of the waveform produced by the gas-diode circuit on the previous page follow the *exponential* charging and discharging of the capacitor. Very often, the same circuit is used to produce a *linear sawtooth* output waveform. Theoretically, you recall, a sawtooth wave has a *linearly* increasing leading edge, and a trailing edge that decreases practically *instantly*.

The basic gas-diode oscillator can be made to deliver a sawtooth output by using suitable values for the circuit components. With such values, the capacitor never fully charges nor does it ever fully discharge. In fact, the capacitor operates over only a *small portion* of its possible charging range. The extreme exponential characteristics of the capacitor's charging and discharging are, therefore, not present in the circuit, and for practical purposes the capacitor voltage can be considered to follow a true sawtooth pattern. This is shown on the graph. The broken-line curves show how the capacitor voltage would vary if the capacitor was allowed to charge fully and discharge fully. The solid lines show how a sawtooth wave can be produced by using only a small portion of the capacitor voltage range. This is usually accomplished by using a B+ range much greater than that which will cause the diode to conduct and a diode that will cut off not too far below its ionization potential.

The sawtooth output frequency depends on the values of resistance, capacitance, and B+ voltage. For a given value of C, increasing the value of B+ voltage or decreasing the value of R causes C to charge faster. This raises the output frequency. Similarly, decreasing the B+ voltage or increasing the value of R causes a decrease in output frequency.

This circuit is usually referred to as a sawtooth generator, since it delivers a continuous output of sawtooth waves

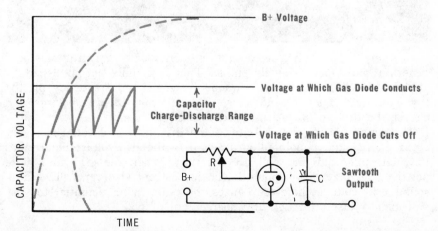

B+ Voltage

Voltage at Which Gas Diode Conducts

Capacitor
Charge-Discharge Range

Voltage at Which Gas Diode Cuts Off

CAPACITOR VOLTAGE

TIME

R   B+   C   Sawtooth Output

the thyratron sawtooth generator

A thyratron, you recall, is a *gas-filled triode*, in which the grid exerts a considerable degree of control over the ionization potential of the gas within the tube. The more negative the grid is made, the higher is the potential that must be applied to the plate to cause the tube to conduct. Once the gas is ionized and the tube conducts, though, the grid no longer has any control. The tube can only be cut off by reducing the plate potential to zero.

The thyratron can be used in an oscillator circuit similar to that previously described using a gas diode. An advantage of using a thyratron is that the output frequency can be changed by merely adjusting the grid voltage. In addition, the thyratron is more stable than the gas diode.

The basic thyratron oscillator can be used as a sawtooth generator, the same as shown previously for the gas-diode oscillator. All that is required is the use of the proper component and voltage values.

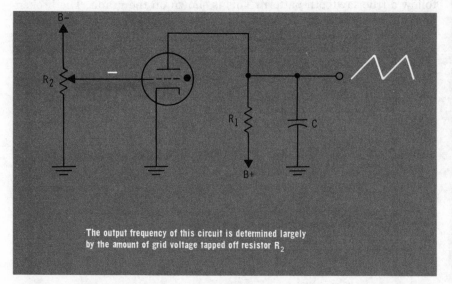

The output frequency of this circuit is determined largely by the amount of grid voltage tapped off resistor R_2

In many applications, the output frequency of a thyratron sawtooth generator must be extremely stable. This is usually accomplished by applying a small sinusoidal voltage of the desired frequency on the thyratron grid. Such a voltage is called a *synchronizing voltage* and causes the tube to *fire* at the synchronized frequency.

The synchronizing voltage causes the thyratron grid voltage to vary *sinusoidally*. And, as pointed out previously, the grid voltage determines the plate potential that will fire the tube. When the grid goes more positive, the plate firing potential decreases and vice versa. The sinusoidal grid voltage therefore causes the plate firing potential to vary sinusoidally also, although 180 degrees out of phase.

the thyratron
sawtooth generator (cont.)

In actual circuits, the synchronizing voltage has the desired sawtooth frequency. The natural frequency of the thyratron oscillator is made slightly lower than the desired frequency. Without synchronization, the sawtooth output would be as shown below in black. But with the synchronizing voltage, the tube will fire as shown in color, when the sinusoidally varying firing potential coincides with the capacitor voltage. In this way, the firing of the tube, and, therefore, the output sawtooth frequency, cannot vary appreciably from the synchronizing frequency. The output frequency is then said to be "locked on" to the synchronizing frequency.

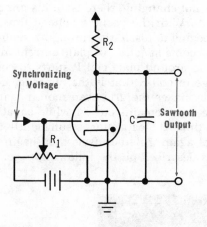

With synchronization, the frequency of the sawtooth output can be made extremely stable. R_1 is set to choose the right frequency and the synchronizing voltage controls the firing of the tube to lock its oscillations to the synchronizing frequency

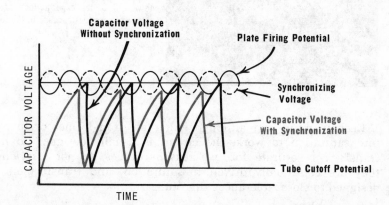

the blocking oscillator

A blocking oscillator is a special type of self-quenching oscillator that keeps itself cut off during most of each cycle. A basic tube-type blocking oscillator is shown. When the circuit is energized, plate current begins to flow through plate coil P, which forms a transformer with grid coil S. This causes a voltage to be induced in coil S, with a polarity such that it acts as a *positive-going* grid voltage. Tube conduction therefore increases, producing a still greater induced voltage across coil S, and driving the grid even more positive. With the grid being driven positive, grid current flows, and a charge is developed on capacitor C, as in a normal *grid-leak bias* circuit. Tube conduction continues to increase and the charge on capacitor C continues to rise until the tube or the transformer core approaches *saturation*. At saturation, since the transformer flux is not changing, there is an instant at which no voltage is induced in coil S. With the positive voltage thus removed from the grid, capacitor C begins to discharge through resistor R. This discharge causes the grid to become *negative*, so plate current in the tube decreases. As a result, the field around plate coil P starts to *collapse;* in doing so, it induces a voltage in coil S that is the opposite of the polarity previously induced. This makes the grid even more negative, and drives the tube to cutoff. The tube remains cut off while capacitor C continues to discharge. After a time, the capacitor is sufficiently discharged to allow the tube to conduct again. Another cycle then begins. The output taken from this circuit is described on the following page.

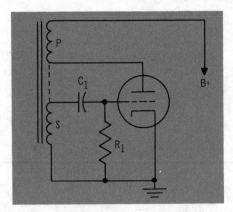

The blocking oscillator delivers single cycles of output voltage separated by durations during which the tube is cut off. The tube is kept cut off by the grid-leak network R_1C_1 for longer periods than it is allowed to conduct because of the long RC time constant

Keep in mind that although either the transformer or tube can go into saturation to work, the circuit is usually designed to have the transformer saturate for two reasons: tubes do not last long when they are continually driven to saturation, and transformers can be designed to closer tolerances than tubes.

blocking-oscillator waveforms

A transistorized blocking oscillator is shown in A. Its operation is the same as that of the tube type just described. The voltage waveforms at the base and collector for two cycles of operation are shown in B. At T_1, the base voltage rises above cutoff, and the transistor starts to conduct. The collector voltage, which is the B+ voltage minus the voltage across coil P, therefore starts to drop and a positive voltage is fed back to the base. At T_2, saturation is reached. As a result, feedback stops and C_1 discharges through R_1; the base voltage becomes less positive and the collector voltage more positive. At T_3, the base voltage starts to cut off the transistor. Collector current is therefore zero, so the collector voltage equals the B+ voltage. The collector voltage, however, continues to rise, since the field around coil P is still collapsing, and induces a voltage in P that adds to the B+.

At T_4, the field of coil P is completely collapsed. No further collector current flows, and the collector voltage stays equal to the B+ voltage. Right after T_3, although the base voltage has no effect on the collector voltage, the base continues to go further negative because of the collapsing transformer field. As the discharge of C_1 slows down, the base voltage becomes less and less negative, until at T_5 it rises above cutoff again. Another cycle then occurs. Since the time the circuit is cut off is determined by the RC time constant of C_1R_1, R_1 can be adjusted to change the time constant and thus the frequency.

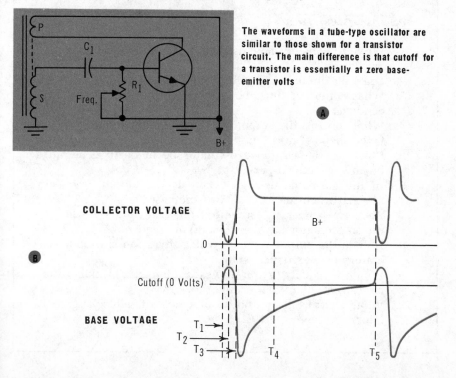

The waveforms in a tube-type oscillator are similar to those shown for a transistor circuit. The main difference is that cutoff for a transistor is essentially at zero base-emitter volts

Ⓐ

Ⓑ

COLLECTOR VOLTAGE

B+

0

Cutoff (0 Volts)

BASE VOLTAGE

T_1

T_2

T_3

T_4

T_5

summary

☐ Nonsinusoidal oscillators, whose output waveshape is independent of the circuit input, if there is an input, are also called relaxation oscillators because they have a period of conduction as well as a period of nonconduction. ☐ The output of the gas-diode oscillator resembles a sawtooth wave.

☐ A capacitor in parallel with the gas diode controls its conduction and supplies the circuit output through its charge and discharge cycle. ☐ By choosing component values that limit the charging range of the capacitor, a gas-diode oscillator can be made to produce a linear sawtooth wave. ☐ The output frequency of the gas-diode oscillator can be varied by changing the values of the resistor, capacitor, or B+ voltage. ☐ A thyratron oscillator is similar to the gas diode oscillator, with a thyratron used in place of the gas diode. ☐ The frequency of the sawtooth output of a thyratron oscillator can be made extremely stable by firing the tube with a sinusoidal synchronizing voltage applied to the grid.

☐ The output frequency of the thyratron oscillator can be varied by adjusting the grid voltage. ☐ The blocking oscillator, by self-quenching, is cut off during most of each cycle. ☐ The long cutoff time of the blocking oscillator and, thus, its frequency, are controlled by an adjustable RC network.

review questions

1. Why are nonsinusoidal oscillators referred to as "relaxation oscillators"?
2. Draw the circuit of a basic gas-diode oscillator.
3. What condition must be reached before a gas diode will conduct?
4. What controls the output of the gas-diode oscillator? What is the shape of this output?
5. How can the gas-diode oscillator be made to generate a linear sawtooth output?
6. In the gas-diode oscillator, how is the output frequency affected when the value of R is increased?
7. What effect does adjustment of the grid voltage in the thyratron oscillator have on the output frequency? Why?
8. How is the output frequency of a thyratron sawtooth generator made extremely stable?
9. Which is usually driven into saturation in a blocking oscillator, the transformer or tube? Why?
10. What controls the duration of cutoff of a blocking oscillator?

multivibrators

Depending on how they are used, multivibrators can be considered as nonsinusoidal oscillators, pulse generators, or switching circuits. Regardless of how they are classified, they are one of the most widely used types of circuit in electronics. Basically, a multivibrator is a *two-stage* circuit, with each stage controlling the conduction characteristics of the other. Output pulses are delivered when the stages *reverse* conditions. That is, when one stage goes from conduction to cutoff while the other simultaneously goes from cutoff to conduction. From a functional standpoint, there are three basic kinds of multivibrators: *astable,* or *free-running,* multivibrators; *bistable* multivibrators; and *monostable* multivibrators.

Free-running multivibrators operate *continuously,* with first one stage conducting and the second cut off, and then the second conducting and the first cut off. This continuous switching action takes place automatically. No input is required, but synchronizing pulses are used.

Bistable multivibrators must be *triggered* in order to operate. Each time a trigger pulse is received, the two stages switch *once*. The conducting one cuts off, and the one that is cut off begins conducting. The stages remain in this condition until another trigger pulse is received.

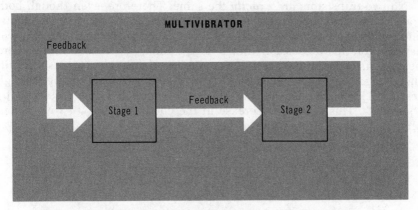

The output of each stage of a multivibrator is fed back to the other stage.
In this way, each controls the conduction characteristics of the other. When
one conducts it keeps the other cut off, and vice versa

Monostable multivibrators are similar to the bistable type, except that they have a *normal condition* to which they always return after being switched by a trigger pulse. For example, the normal condition might be that the first stage conducts and the second is cut off. When a trigger pulse is received, this condition reverses, with the first stage going into cutoff and the second into conduction. However, the stages automatically switch back to their normal condition after a period, and stay there until another trigger pulse is received.

the free-running multivibrator

A transistor, free-running, or astable, multivibrator is shown. It consists essentially of two RC coupled amplifier stages, with the output of each coupled to the input of the other. Each stage alternately conducts and is cut off, with only one conducting at a time. A tube version is shown on page 6-72.

This arrangement looks similar to the two-stage RC sine-wave oscillator you studied earlier, but there is a difference. The sine-wave oscillator does not go *into* cutoff, but the multivibrator does. This is controlled by the long time constant of the RC coupling networks. Both stages produce square-wave outputs, although at alternate times. So the output can be taken from *either* stage.

When B+ voltage is initially applied, both stages begin conducting heavily, since they have forward bias. In addition, coupling capacitors C_1 and C_2 charge close to the B+ voltage. The charging paths are from ground, through the transistors, to the bases, through the capacitors, and to the B+ supply. There is also some charging current through resistors R_1 and R_2, which causes positive voltage to be applied to the bases to make them conduct more; this lowers the collector voltage of both transistors.

No two transistors are *exactly* the same. Therefore, even though both stages have the same transistor types and the same value components, one transistor initially conducts slightly heavier than the other. We will assume for this discussion that it is Q_1. Since Q_1 is conducting more heavily, its collector voltage is lowered faster than that of Q_2. As a result, the voltage coupled to the base of Q_2 by capacitor C_2 discharging through resistor R_2 is more negative than the voltage coupled to the base of Q_1 by C_1 and R_1. This causes a decrease in the conduction of Q_2, with a consequent increase in its collector voltage.

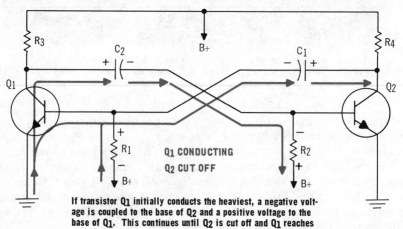

If transistor Q_1 initially conducts the heaviest, a negative voltage is coupled to the base of Q_2 and a positive voltage to the base of Q_1. This continues until Q_2 is cut off and Q_1 reaches saturation

the free-running multivibrator (cont.)

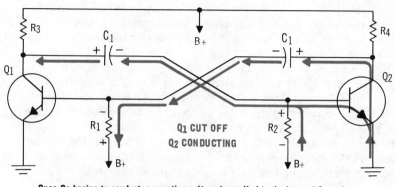

Once Q2 begins to conduct, a negative voltage is applied to the base of Q1 and a positive voltage to the base of Q2. This continues until Q1 is cut off and Q2 reaches saturation

The rise in the collector voltage of Q_2 is coupled back to the base of Q_1 as a positive voltage. So Q_1 conducts even more, causing its collector voltage to drop further, and the base of Q_2 to be driven more negative as C_2 discharges even more. This process continues until eventually Q_2 is cut off and Q_1 conducts in saturation. At this point, capacitor C_2 is still discharging through resistor R_2 to ground. Stage Q_2 remains cut off until C_2 has discharged sufficiently to allow the base of Q_2 to rise above cutoff. Q_2 then begins to conduct, starting the second half of the multivibrator cycle.

As Q_2 begins to conduct, its collector voltage falls, causing capacitor C_1 to begin discharging through resistor R_1, and in doing so, applying a negative voltage to the base of Q_1. Conduction through Q_1 therefore decreases, resulting in an increase in the Q_1 collector voltage. This is coupled to the base of Q_2 as a positive voltage, so Q_2 conducts even more. Like the previous half cycle of operation, this action is regenerative and continues until Q_1 is cut off and Q_2 conducts in saturation. Q_1 stays cut off until C_1 discharges enough to bring Q_1 out of cutoff. At this point, the complete cycle begins again.

The length of time each stage conducts depends on how long the other stage is cut off. This, in turn, depends on the RC time constants of C_1 and R_1, and C_2 and R_2. The shorter the time constant, the more rapid is the switching action, and therefore the higher is the output frequency of the multivibrator. In the circuit described here, both RC networks have the same time constant, both tubes conduct and are cut off for equal periods. This is called a *symmetrical* free-running multivibrator. In some applications, one RC coupling network has a longer time constant than the other. One tube therefore conducts for a longer period than the other. Typical waveforms are shown on page 6-72.

synchronization

The free-running relaxation oscillator is very unstable; its frequency drifts over a wide range if it is allowed to run free. To make it work at a fixed frequency, synchronization pulses are applied to either stage to control the times that the stages are driven into or out of cutoff or saturation. In other words, just as the capacitor discharge is about to switch the state of a stage, the sync pulse arrives to do it. And the pulse arrives at the same time at each cycle to maintain a fixed frequency.

The pulse polarity can be such that it drives a stage into *or* out of cutoff, and the pulse can be applied to either stage of a multivibrator. Usually, it is applied to the base, or control grid, to take the stage out of cutoff. A tube multivibrator with sync pulse inputs is shown in A; B shows how the blocking oscillator can be synchronized—either input can be used. The waveforms for the transistor circuit of page 6-70 when sync pulses are applied to the base of Q_1 are shown in C.

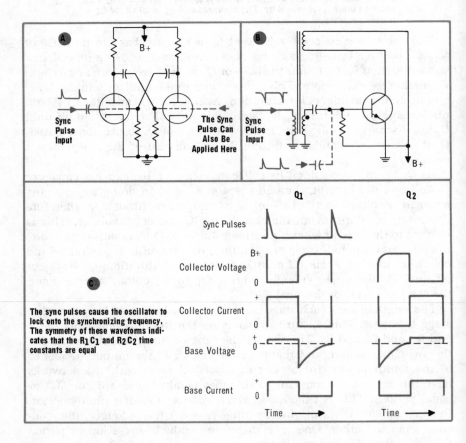

The sync pulses cause the oscillator to lock onto the synchronizing frequency. The symmetry of these waveforms indicates that the R_1C_1 and R_2C_2 time constants are equal

the bistable multivibrator (flip-flop)

A bistable multivibrator is somewhat similar to the free-running multivibrator, except that it does not run continuously. The circuit has *two stable states*. For the transistor type shown in A, these are Q_1 conducting and Q_2 cut off, and Q_2 conducting and Q_1 cut off. A *trigger pulse* applied to the circuit will cause it to switch from one state to the other. Another trigger pulse is then required to switch the circuit back to its original state. Coupling between the collector of one stage and the grid of the other is accomplished by *direct coupling*. Effectively, the coupling is done principally by the voltage-divider resistors (R_1 and R_2). The main purpose of capacitors C_1 and C_2 is to improve the switching characteristics of the circuit by passing the high-frequency components of the square-wave pulses. This allows fast rise and fall times, so that the square waves will not be distorted. C_1 and C_2 are thus called *commutating capacitors*.

Bistable multivibrators are generally referred to as *flip-flops*. The type shown is known as the Eccles-Jordan multivibrator.

The bistable multivibrator has two stable states. It will remain in whichever state it happens to be in until a trigger pulse causes it to switch to its other state. Direct coupling is used between the stages to bring this about

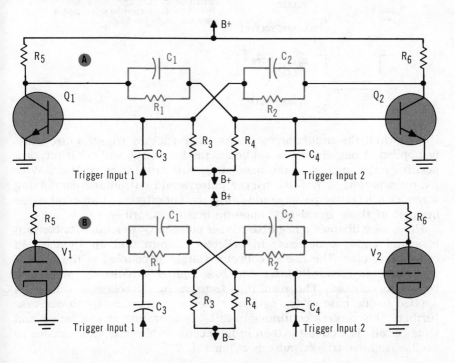

operation of the bistable multivibrator

When the circuit is first turned on, assume that Q_1 conducts the heaviest; its collector voltage will decrease faster than the collector voltage of Q_2. This decrease is directly coupled to the base of Q_2 by the voltage-divider action of R_1 and R_4 and reduces its base-emitter forward bias. Q_2 collector current therefore decreases and collector voltage increases. The rise in the collector voltage of Q_2 is directly coupled back to the base of Q_1 by R_2 and R_3 and increases its base-emitter forward bias. This increases the collector current and decreases the collector voltage of Q_1 even further. As a result, the collector of Q_1 reduces the base-emitter forward bias of Q_2 even more. This sequence continues until the collector current in Q_1 reaches saturation, causing its collector voltage to go down to close to zero volts. This puts almost zero volts on the base of Q_2, cutting it off. The circuit is then in one of its two stable states. The low collector voltage on Q_1 keeps Q_2 cut off.

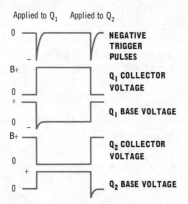

Negative trigger pulses initiate switching of the bistable multivibrator by reducing collector current in the conducting stage. This is true of n-p-n transistors. For p-n-p transistors, positive trigger pulses do the same thing

To switch the multivibrator to its other state, a trigger pulse must be applied. A negative pulse applied to the base of Q_1 will cut it off, or a positive pulse applied to the base of Q_2 will cause it to conduct. With p-n-p transistors, a positive trigger pulse would cut off the conducting stage, or a negative pulse would bring the cut-off stage into conduction because of these transistors' opposite biasing polarities.

Here, we will apply a negative trigger pulse to Q_1 to reduce its forward bias and cause a decrease in collector current and an increase in collector voltage. The rise in collector voltage is coupled to the base of Q_2, where it forward biases the base-emitter circuit. Q_2, therefore, begins to conduct. The resulting decrease in its collector voltage is applied to the base of Q_1, causing collector current in Q_1 to decrease further. This process continues until Q_2 is operating at saturation and Q_1 is cut off. The circuit is then in its second stable state and remains so until a negative trigger pulse is applied to Q_2.

trigger-pulse steering

In the previous circuit, *separate* trigger input lines were used for each stage of the bistable multivibrator. If only one of the two lines is used, succeeding trigger pulses have to be of *opposite polarity*. If it is desired that all trigger pulses have the same polarity, then the pulses must be applied *alternately* first on one line and then the other.

In some applications, it is desirable to trigger a bistable multivibrator with pulses of the same polarity and without the necessity of alternating between the separate input lines. This could be done by having one trigger common to both stages, and therefore applying the pulses to the two stages simultaneously. Although such an arrangement would cause the multivibrator to change states, as desired, it would increase the time required for switching. This is because the pulse would be attempting to change the condition (conducting or cutoff) of one stage, and at the same time be aiding the existing condition of the other. To overcome this problem, *pulse-steering circuits* are often used. These circuits receive pulses of one polarity and apply, or steer, them to the appropriate stage of the multivibrator.

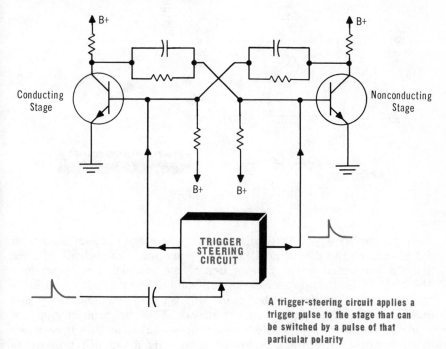

A trigger-steering circuit applies a trigger pulse to the stage that can be switched by a pulse of that particular polarity

The circuits used for trigger-pulse steering are essentially *diode-gate circuits*. Each steering circuit contains two diodes, one for each multivibrator stage. The diodes are arranged and biased in such a way that they will only pass a trigger pulse to the appropriate stage.

operation of trigger-pulse steering circuits

Steering circuits for the multivibrator shown on page 6-73 are shown below. A is the steering circuit for positive trigger pulses, and B is for negative pulses. Since n-p-n transistors are used, the base of the "on" transistor is positive and the base of the "off" transistor is negative. *Positive* trigger pulses must therefore be applied to the transistor that is "off," and *negative* pulses to the one that is "on."

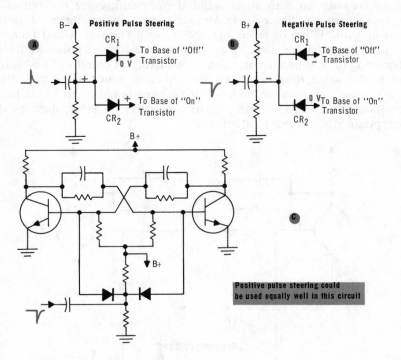

In the positive pulse-steering circuit, a voltage divider maintains the anodes of the diodes at a negative potential. The cathode of each diode is connected to the base of one of the multivibrator transistors. The "off" transistor applies almost zero volts to the cathode of its diode (CR_1), so the positive trigger pulse will forward bias the diode and find a low-resistance path to that transistor. The "on" transistor applies a *positive* voltage to the cathode of its diode (CR_2), so that it is biased in the reverse direction. Effectively, then, this diode will present an open circuit for the trigger pulse.

For negative steering (shown in C), the diodes are reversed, and their cathodes are kept at a constant positive potential. CR_2 is biased in the forward direction, as the trigger pulse is coupled to the "on" tran-sistor. CR_1 is reverse biased and blocks the trigger pulse.

the monostable multivibrator

The monostable multivibrator has only *one stable state*. A trigger pulse will cause the circuit to switch states, but after a certain time, it will automatically switch back to its stable state and remain there until another trigger pulse is received.

One type of monostable multivibrator is shown. Tube V_2 has zero grid bias, since its grid is connected to its cathode through resistor R_2. The plate current of V_2 flows through *common-cathode resistor* R_3, and the voltage drop it produces is sufficient to cut off tube V_1. This is the stable state of the circuit. No changes occur until a positive trigger pulse is applied to the grid of V_1; this overcomes the cathode bias, allowing V_1 to conduct. As V_1 starts to conduct, its plate voltage begins falling. So capacitor C_2, which had been charged to the B+ voltage, begins to discharge through resistor R_2. This puts a negative voltage on the grid of V_2, decreasing its plate current. As a result, the voltage drop across R_3 decreases, allowing more current to flow in V_1. This, in turn, lowers the plate voltage of V_1, causing the grid of V_2 to be driven more negative.

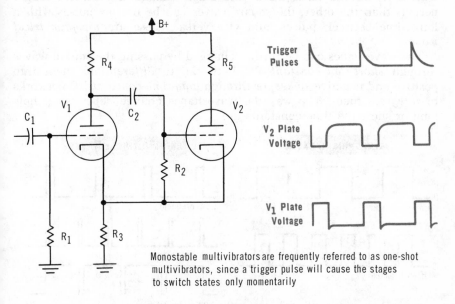

Monostable multivibrators are frequently referred to as one-shot multivibrators, since a trigger pulse will cause the stages to switch states only momentarily

The action is cumulative, and continues until V_2 is cut off and V_1 is conducting substantially. At this point capacitor C_2 is still discharging. V_2 remains cut off until C_2 has lost sufficient charge to allow the grid of V_2 to rise above cutoff. When V_2 begins conducting, it rapidly develops a large enough voltage drop across resistor R_3 to cut off V_1. The circuit is then back to its stable state, with V_2 conducting heavily and V_1 cut off. It remains this way until another positive trigger pulse is applied to the grid of V_1. The RC time constant of R_2C_2 determines how long V_2 will remain cut off after the trigger pulse is received.

frequency and waveshape of relaxation oscillators

It was mentioned earlier that since each cycle was determined by the RC time constants of the coupling networks, if the time constants were changed, the tube cutoff time would be changed, and so would the period of each cycle and thus the frequency. This is usually accomplished by using variable resistors in the RC networks. Less resistance will produce a shorter time constant and a higher frequency.

The output waveshape of relaxation oscillators can take many forms. For example, in the free-running multivibrators you studied, since the collectors or plates just rise and fall in a square-wave fashion, the output can be taken at one of these points to produce a *train* of square-wave pulses. If both stages of the oscillator are identical, they will conduct and be cut off for equal times, and the square waves and the time between them will be equal. These are known as *symmetrical waves.* If, on the other hand, one stage remains cut off for longer periods than the other, the square waves can be narrow pulses with a long time between pulses, and vice versa. These are *unsymmetrical waves.*

The waveshapes can be further changed by passing the square waves through *short-time-constant* RC networks to *differentiate* them into positive and negative *spikes;* or through *long-time-constant* RC networks to *integrate* them. The way the waveshapes change depends on how long or short the time constants are.

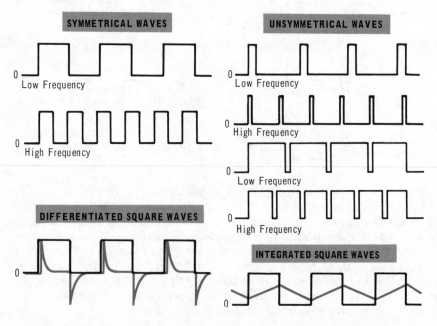

SYMMETRICAL WAVES

Low Frequency

High Frequency

DIFFERENTIATED SQUARE WAVES

UNSYMMETRICAL WAVES

Low Frequency

High Frequency

Low Frequency

High Frequency

INTEGRATED SQUARE WAVES

frequency and waveshape of relaxation oscillators (cont.)

Outputs from the multivibrators are usually capacitively or directly coupled, but the blocking oscillator can also be inductively coupled. Capacitive or direct coupling from the plate will produce unsymmetrical square-wave signals, but inductive coupling will produce sharp narrow pulses since plate current flows for only short periods.

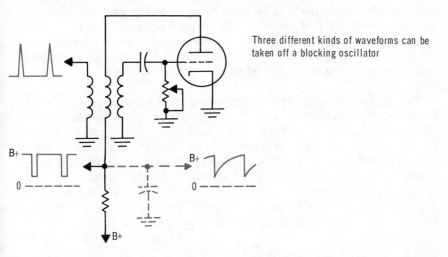

Three different kinds of waveforms can be taken off a blocking oscillator

In all of the relaxation oscillators, sawtooth waves can be produced instead of square waves by connecting charge capacitors from the collector or plate circuits to ground. Then the voltages on these circuits will not be able to rise and fall almost instantaneously. Instead they will have to follow the charge and discharge pattern of the capacitor.

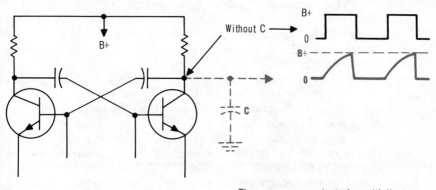

The square wave output of a multivibrator can be changed to a sawtooth by adding a charging capacitor

summary

☐ A multivibrator is essentially a two-stage circuit in which each stage controls the conduction characteristics of the other. ☐ The free-running multivibrator operates continuously and automatically. Its square-wave output can be taken from either stage. ☐ The length of time each stage conducts in a free-running multivibrator is controlled by the time constants of the RC networks that couple the output of each stage to the input of the other.

☐ The bistable multivibrator, which is also called a flip-flop, must be switched from one of its stable states to the other by an externally-applied trigger pulse. The two stages are direct-coupled. ☐ Trigger pulses to a bistable multivibrator may be negative or positive. In some multivibrators, the trigger pulses are applied on a single input circuit to both stages. ☐ Diode-gate circuits are sometimes used to steer the trigger pulse to the proper stage.

☐ The monostable multivibrator always returns to its one stable state after being switched by a trigger pulse. ☐ In one popular type of monostable multivibrator, feedback is accomplished by means of a common cathode resistor. ☐ The output waveshapes of relaxation oscillators are controlled by the RC time constants of their coupling networks. The output waveshapes can be altered by changing the value of the resistors in the RC networks. ☐ The method of output coupling used also alters the output waveshape of a relaxation oscillator. Unsymmetrical RC time constants produce unsymmetrical square waves; inductive coupling produces sharp narrow pulses.

review questions

1. When are the output pulses of a multivibrator delivered?
2. What are the three basic kinds of multivibrator?
3. Draw a free-running multivibrator and describe its operation.
4. From which stage is the output from a free-running multivibrator taken?
5. What is a flip-flop?
6. What form of coupling is used between the two stages of a bistable multivibrator?
7. What is the purpose of the pulse-steering circuits used with some bistable multivibrators?
8. Draw a monostable multivibrator and describe its operation.
9. How can the square-wave output of a multivibrator be changed to a sawtooth?
10. How are symmetrical output waveshapes produced in multivibrators?

modulators

Modulators are circuits that add the *intelligence* to r-f carriers. They do this by varying some characteristic of the carrier in accordance with a modulating signal. The *modulating signal*, you will recall, is a relatively *low-frequency* electrical signal whose variations, usually in amplitude, correspond to the voice, picture, or other intelligence to be transmitted. In the modulator, these variations of the modulating signal cause the amplitude, frequency, or phase of the carrier to fluctuate in such a way that there is a direct correspondence between the intelligence and the carrier variations. For pulse modulation, the amplitude, width, position, or some other characteristic of the individual pulses in a pulse train is made to vary in accordance with the modulating signal.

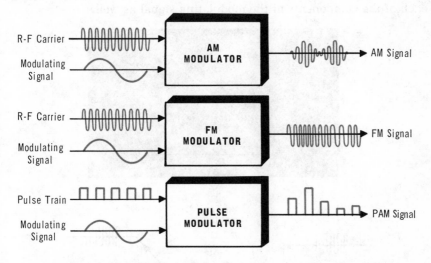

Modulators vary some characteristic of an r-f carrier (or a pulse train for pulse modulation) in accordance with the variations of the modulating signal

Probably the simplest type of modulation is that used to produce *interrupted CW signals*. This is done by using a handkey that operates as a *switch* to open or close some circuit in a CW transmitter. When the key is closed, the path through the transmitter for the CW signal is complete, and the transmitter delivers an output. When the key is open, the signal path through the transmitter is open, so no output is delivered. In this way, the CW signal is broken up into a series of pulses that corresponds to some code, such as the Morse code.

Although CW keying is simple in theory, in actual practice there are many methods and a wide variety of circuits that can be used to accomplish it. However, due to the relative limited use of commercial interrupted CW transmission, the circuits used for this type of modulation will not be covered in this book.

AM modulators

Amplitude modulators vary the *amplitude,* or strength, of an r-f carrier in accordance with the modulating signal. You recall from Volume 1 that an amplitude-modulated signal contains *side bands,* which actually contain the signal intelligence. These side bands are produced when the r-f carrier and the modulating signal are both applied to a *nonlinear* device, such as a tube or transistor. The *heterodyning* of the two signals in the nonlinear device causes a complex signal to be produced as an output. The complex signal contains as components the two original signal frequencies, plus their *sum* and *difference* frequencies. If the modulating signal itself is complex and contains many frequencies, the output signal from the modulator contains the sum and difference frequencies of the r-f frequency and each of the components of the modulating signal as well.

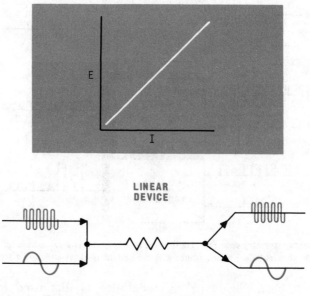

If two signal frequencies are applied to a linear device, the output contains as components only the two input frequencies.

Any of the frequency components of the modulated signal can be filtered out and either rejected or used separately. For standard AM signals, the modulating signal is removed from the output of the modulator by filtering, and only the r-f carrier and the side bands are used. This is easily done, since the modulating signal frequencies are usually very much lower than the carrier and side-band frequencies. For various types of side-band transmission, one of the side bands, and sometimes the carrier, are also removed.

AM modulators (cont.)

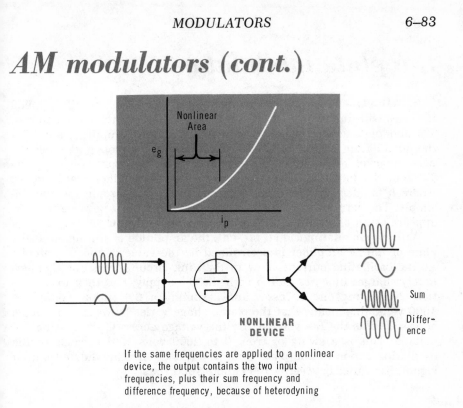

If the same frequencies are applied to a nonlinear
device, the output contains the two input
frequencies, plus their sum frequency and
difference frequency, because of heterodyning

The strength of the side-band components of an amplitude-modulated signal depends on how much the amplitude of the modulated carrier varies above and below its unmodulated amplitude. Since the side bands contain all of the signal intelligence, it is generally desirable that they contain as much power as possible. This means that the amplitude of the modulated carrier should vary as much as possible. How much the amplitude of the modulated carrier varies is expressed by the *percent modulation* of the signal. Percent modulation can be calculated from the equation:

$$\text{Percent modulation} = \frac{e_{MAX} - e_{MIN}}{2e_0} \times 100$$

where e_{MAX} and e_{MIN} are the maximum and minimum amplitudes of the modulated carrier, and e_0 is the amplitude of the unmodulated carrier.

One hundred percent modulation occurs when the modulated carrier varies between twice its unmodulated amplitude and zero. Modulation in excess of 100 percent is generally undesirable, since it causes distortion of the signal intelligence.

Remember that amplitude modulation uses heterodyning to take place, and so must occur in a nonlinear device. All tubes or transistors have certain portions of their operating curves nonlinear, but some have more nonlinear portions than others. Tubes specially designed for modulation will provide a wide nonlinear range for the modulating signal to work on.

the plate modulator

In AM *plate modulation*, the modulating signal is usually applied in series with the plate tank of a class C r-f power amplifier, as shown. The modulator stage, which is generally a class A amplifier, amplifies the modulating signal to the level required to produce the desired percentage of modulation. The signal is then transformer-coupled by T_1 from the modulator stage output to the r-f amplifier plate circuit, where it is effectively in *series* with the plate tank circuit and the B+ supply. The carrier, amplified to a high level by the r-f power amplifier, appears as an alternating voltage across plate tank $L_1 C_1$.

With no modulating signal present, the amplitude of the signal at the plate of the r-f amplifier is determined by the value of the B+ supply. As the oscillating currents flow in the tank circuit, capacitor C_1 alternately charges in *series aiding* with the B+ supply, and then in *opposition*. Neglecting circuit losses and assuming a B+ supply voltage of 1000 volts, this means that the plate voltage varies between the voltage across C_1 *plus* the B+ voltage and the voltage across C_1 *minus* the B+ voltage. This is a swing of from 0 to 2000 volts, and because of the oscillating action of the plate tank, represents an unmodulated output signal that varies between +1000 and −1000 volts.

Effectively, plate modulation varies the B+ supply voltage of an r-f amplifier in accordance with the amplitude variations of the modulating signal

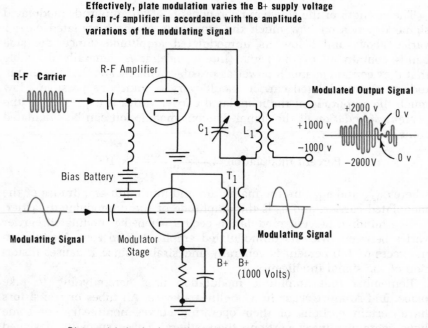

Plate modulation is also called high-level modulation, since it is accomplished at a point in the r-f amplifier circuit where high voltage levels exist

the plate modulator (cont.)

When a modulating signal is applied through T_1, it adds or subtracts, depending on its polarity, from the B+ voltage of the r-f amplifier. If the signal varies between +1000 and −1000 volts, neglecting circuit losses, the effective B+ supply voltage varies between 0 and 2000 volts at a rate determined by the frequency of the signal. Capacitor C_1 therefore charges to a maximum of 2000 volts when the modulating signal is at its *largest positive* value and to 0 volts when the modulating signal is at its *largest negative* value. At times, therefore, when the modulating signal is maximum and C_1 is in series aiding with the B+ supply, the plate voltage of the r-f amplifier is 4000 volts. When the modulating signal is maximum negative, the plate voltage is zero.

The output signal across the tank circuit therefore has a 4000-volt swing of from zero to 4000 volts peak-to-peak. In between the times of these maximum and minimum values, the modulating signal voltage and the B+ voltage add and subtract to produce a changing plate voltage for the r-f amplifier that corresponds to the changing amplitude of the modulating signal. As the plate voltage swings with the modulating signal, the e_g–i_p curve of the stage fluctuates with it, so that the plate current rises with the plate voltage and falls with it as well. The amplitude of the carrier, then, changes accordingly to get the modulation envelope. Because the e_g–i_p curve of the modulator is constantly changing with the modulation signal, the stage is exceedingly nonlinear so that the two signals heterodyne well to produce the modulated carrier.

In the above example, 100 percent modulation was achieved, since the modulated signal varied between zero and twice its unmodulated value. If the modulating signal voltage was made less than the B+ voltage, the percent modulation would be less than 100 percent.

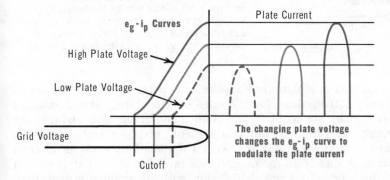

A plate modulator must use class C operation to be efficient because the stage becomes more dependent on the plate voltage when the grid bias is so far in the cutoff region. Thus, the modulating signal has a greater effect on the plate current for more efficient operation. The main disadvantage of the plate modulator is that a large modulating signal is needed to swing the plate voltage.

the grid-bias modulator

The modulating signal is frequently applied to r-f amplifiers at the *control grid*. This is called grid-bias, or low-level, modulation. Effectively, grid-bias modulation causes the grid bias of the r-f amplifier to vary in accordance with variations of the modulating signal.

A basic grid-bias modulator circuit is shown. The modulating signal is coupled by transformer T_1 to the grid circuit of the r-f amplifier so that it is in series with the grid-bias battery. As the modulating signal changes in amplitude, it adds and subtracts from the bias voltage, and thus varies the effective input level of the r-f signal. The power output of the amplifier therefore follows the amplitude variations of the modulating signal. Because the modulating signal must vary the bias while the stage is conducting at all times, this type of modulator must be operated class A or class AB, so that the modulating signal does not cause the tube to cut off or saturate; otherwise, part of the modulating signal will be clipped, causing distortion.

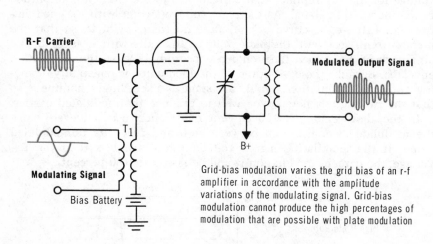

R-F Carrier

Modulated Output Signal

T_1

Modulating Signal

Bias Battery

B+

Grid-bias modulation varies the grid bias of an r-f amplifier in accordance with the amplitude variations of the modulating signal. Grid-bias modulation cannot produce the high percentages of modulation that are possible with plate modulation

Since grid-bias modulation is applied at a point where the r-f signal voltages are relatively low, lower values of modulating signal voltages can be used than are required for plate modulation. This reduces the space, weight, and input power requirements of the modulator circuit, and makes it highly suitable for special applications such as aircraft transmitters. A disadvantage of grid-bias modulation is that it cannot provide a high percentage of modulation without producing distortion. One of the reasons for this is that the modulating signal cannot be large enough to drive the amplifier grid to zero bias. With no bias, excessive plate current would flow in the tube, producing not only distortion, but possibly also damage. Also, since this type of modulator must be operated close to class A, it is not as efficient as the plate modulator, which is operated class C.

other AM modulators

Although grid-bias and plate modulation are the two most widely used methods of producing AM signals, other methods, in which the modulating signal is applied to the *screen grid,* the *suppressor grid,* or the *cathode,* are also used. Typical circuits for these three modulation methods are shown.

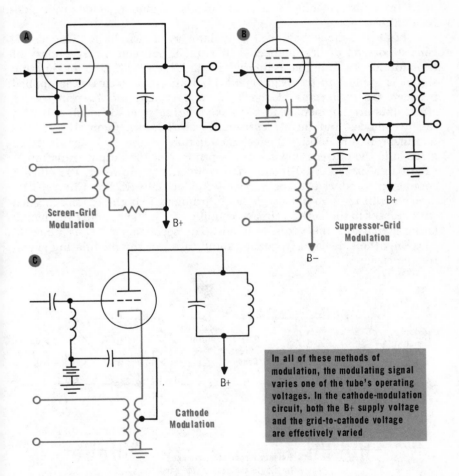

Screen-Grid
Modulation   B+

Suppressor-Grid
Modulation

B–

Cathode
Modulation   B+

In all of these methods of modulation, the modulating signal varies one of the tube's operating voltages. In the cathode-modulation circuit, both the B+ supply voltage and the grid-to-cathode voltage are effectively varied

In A, the modulating signal is coupled in series with the screen grid and the screen supply voltage. In B, the modulation is applied in series with the suppressor grid and a negative bias voltage for the suppressor. In C, the modulation is applied in series with the cathode. All of these methods are essentially similar in that they cause one of the tube's operating voltages to vary in accordance with the instantaneous amplitude of the modulating signal. This, in turn, causes the output of the r-f amplifier to vary in the same way.

balanced modulators

For *suppressed-carrier* transmission, balanced modulators are used. With these modulators, the carrier frequency is *cancelled* in the output, leaving only the sum and difference frequencies (side bands) and the modulating signal. The modulating signal is usually removed by a simple tuned circuit, so only the side bands remain. For single side-band transmission, one of the side bands is then rejected by a side-band filter.

A basic two-diode balanced modulator is shown in A. The circuit consists of two diodes connected in *parallel* between the secondary of transformer T_1 and the primary of transformer T_2. The modulating signal is applied to the primary of T_1, while the r-f carrier is applied between the centertaps of the T_1 secondary and the T_2 primary. In effect, this arrangement places the *modulating signal* in push-pull with the two diodes and the *r-f carrier in parallel* with them. Due to the nonlinear nature of the diodes, modulation of the two signals takes place, and the current flowing in the primary of the output transformer (T_2) contains the usual modulation components. However, the current component produced at the carrier frequency always flows in *opposite directions* in the two halves of the T_2 primary. It is therefore cancelled with respect to the entire primary winding of T_2, leaving only the modulating signal and the two side bands. The secondary of T_2 is tuned to pass only the side-band frequencies and to reject the modulating signal frequencies.

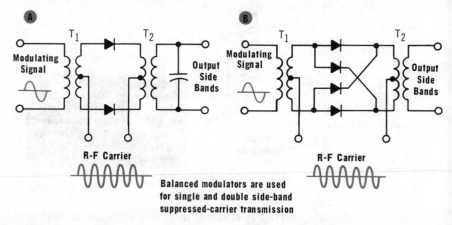

Balanced modulators are used
for single and double side-band
suppressed-carrier transmission

Another balanced modulator that uses four diodes instead of two is shown in B. In this circuit, the modulating signal as well as the r-f carrier is eliminated from the output without the need for a filter circuit. This is accomplished by the diodes, which act as switches, causing the modulating signal to be *bypassed* around the output transformer. As a result, only currents corresponding to the sum and difference frequencies produce output signals across the primary of T_2.

FM modulators

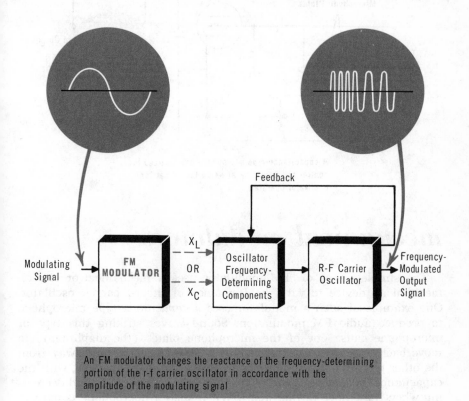

An FM modulator changes the reactance of the frequency-determining portion of the r-f carrier oscillator in accordance with the amplitude of the modulating signal

Frequency modulators vary the *instantaneous frequency* of an r-f carrier in accordance with the amplitude of a modulating signal. Essentially, an FM modulator consists of a stage or device whose *reactance* is varied by the modulating signal. This change in reactance is then used to vary the frequency of oscillation of the oscillator that generates the r-f carrier. Unlike amplitude modulation, which is accomplished after the r-f carrier has been amplified, sometimes to a very high level, frequency modulation is carried out at a *low* power level. All amplification of the output signal takes place after modulation.

Practical FM modulators cannot provide a large *deviation* of the r-f oscillator frequency. It is necessary, therefore, that frequency multipliers be used after the FM modulator to produce the frequency swing required for efficient demodulation.

Like AM modulation, FM modulation produces side-band frequencies above and below the center frequency. These side-band frequencies contain the transmitted intelligence, and, with the center frequency, make up the overall output signal.

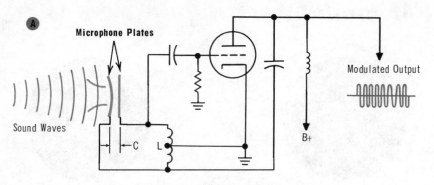

A capacitance-type microphone can be used to
control the frequency at which the r-f carrier
oscillator operates

mechanical modulators

The simplest type of FM modulator uses a mechanical or electro-mechanical device to vary the frequency of the r-f carrier oscillator. One example of such a modulator uses a *capacitance-type* microphone to produce audio FM modulation. Sound waves striking this type of microphone cause one of the microphone plates (the diaphragm) to move back and forth, making it either closer to or further away from the other plate. The two microphone plates act as a capacitor, with the capacitance increasing as the plates come closer together, and decreasing when they move farther apart. When such a microphone is used in place of the capacitor in the tank circuit of, say, a Hartley oscillator, the *separation* of the plates, and, therefore, the input sound waves, determines the instantaneous frequency at which the oscillator oscillates. This is, of course, because the resonant frequency of the tank circuit determines the frequency of oscillation.

In general, mechanical modulators are used only in a limited number of special applications. They do not have the versatility of the more widely used types of electronic FM modulators.

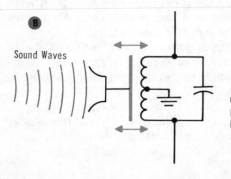

Another way a microphone can change the
resonant frequency is to have it cause a metal
plate to vibrate near the coil, thereby changing
its inductance

reactance-tube modulators

A reactance-tube modulator injects inductive or capacitive current into the frequency-determining tank circuit of the r-f carrier oscillator. This has the same effect as connecting an additional coil or capacitor across the tank and changes the tank circuit's resonant frequency. The amount of reactive current that is injected is proportional to the amplitude of the modulating signal, causing the oscillator frequency to vary in accordance with the modulation.

One type of basic reactance-tube modulator is shown. Capacitor C_4 and coil L_1 make up the tank circuit of the oscillator, and capacitor C_5 couples the signal developed across the tank to the oscillator grid. With no modulating signal applied to the modulator tube, the r-f oscillations in the oscillator tank circuit cause current to flow between the top of the tank circuit and ground. The signal is coupled through capacitor C_3 and resistor R_2. At the center frequency of the FM signal, the reactance of C_3 is large in comparison with the resistance of R_2. As a result, the signal current through C_3 *leads* the tank voltage by close to 90 degrees. This current produces a voltage drop across R_2, therefore, which also leads the tank voltage by 90 degrees. Since the voltage across R_2 is applied to the grid of the modulator tube, it causes r-f variations in the tube plate current that also lead the tank voltage by 90 degrees. These current variations are coupled to the tank circuit through capacitor C_2, where they act as if they were supplied by an additional *capacitor* across the tank circuit. The no-signal, or center, frequency of the oscillator is therefore determined by the amount of this capacitive current injected into the tank with no modulating signal present.

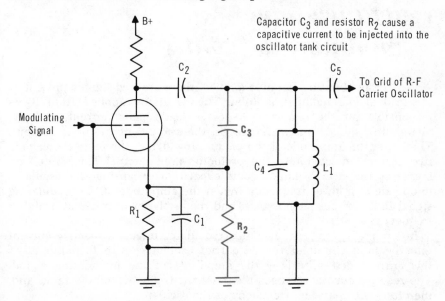

Capacitor C_3 and resistor R_2 cause a capacitive current to be injected into the oscillator tank circuit

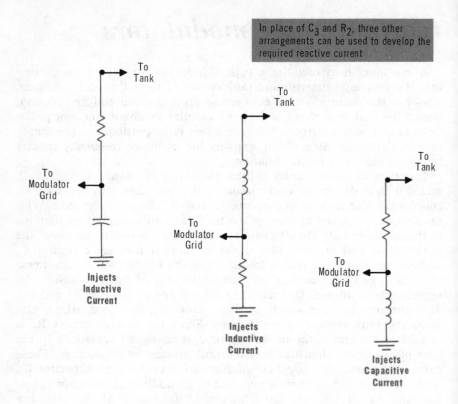

In place of C₃ and R₂, three other arrangements can be used to develop the required reactive current

To Tank

To Tank

To Tank

To Modulator Grid

Injects Inductive Current

To Modulator Grid

Injects Inductive Current

To Modulator Grid

Injects Capacitive Current

reactance-tube modulators (cont.)

When a modulating signal is applied, there are *two* signals present at the grid of the modulating tube. The r-f signal applied from R_2 is responsible for the reactive (90-degree lead) plate current, and the modulating signal causes changes in the *amount* of the plate current. The larger the amplitude of the modulating signal, the more the capacitive current injected into the oscillator tank circuit. This, in effect, increases the overall tank circuit capacitance, causing the oscillator to operate at a lower frequency. When the amplitude of the modulating signal falls, the converse is true, and the oscillator operates at a higher frequency.

In summary, the reactance-tube modulator injects a reactive current into the tank circuit of the r-f carrier oscillator, with the amount of this current determined by the amplitude of the modulating signal. The reactive current changes the resonant frequency of the tank, and, therefore, the operating frequency of the oscillator.

phase modulators

Phase modulators produce modulated output signals identical to those developed by FM modulators. They do this, however, by using *fixed-frequency* crystal oscillators, and passing the r-f carrier through a *phase-shifting circuit* containing resistance and reactance. The amount of phase shift produced is made proportional to the amplitude of the modulating signal by causing the resistance of the shifting network to vary in accordance with the modulating signal.

A simple phase modulator is shown. The r-f carrier from the crystal oscillator is coupled to the output through capacitor C and a vacuum-tube triode. The value of C is fixed, but the *plate resistance,* R_p, of the triode varies in proportion to its conduction, which is determined by the amplitude of the modulating signal. The phase-modulated output is taken from across the tube, which is the resistance of this RC circuit. Since the phase angle between the applied voltage and the output depends on the relative values of X_C and R_p, the phase of the output is proportional to the amplitude of the modulating signal, which controls the plate resistance (R_p) of the triode.

Although not shown, the modulating signal is shifted 90° in phase by a correction network (usually a simple, series RC network) before it is applied to the phase modulator

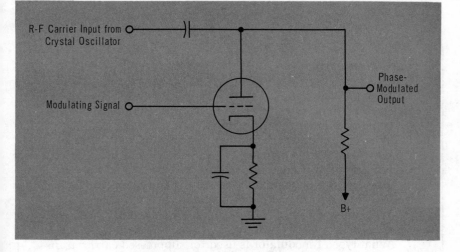

The 90° phase shift is necessary, you recall from Volume 1, so that the output phase variations of the modulated signal correspond to the phase of an equivalent FM signal

summary

☐ Modulators change the amplitude, frequency, or phase of an r-f carrier in accordance with a modulating signal whose variations correspond to the intelligence to be transmitted. ☐ AM modulation must occur in a nonlinear device, as it uses heterodyning to produce the modulated signal. When a signal modulates a carrier, it produces upper and lower side bands.

☐ In AM plate modulation, the modulating signal is applied in series with the plate tank of a class C r-f amplifier. The modulating signal varies the plate supply voltage of the r-f amplifier. ☐ A main disadvantage of the plate modulator is that a large modulating signal is needed to produce the required swing in plate voltage. ☐ In grid-bias modulation the modulating signal varies the bias of the r-f amplifier's control grid. ☐ The grid-bias modulator must be operated class A or class AB. ☐ Other methods of AM modulation apply the modulating signal to the screen grid, the suppressor grid, or the cathode of the r-f amplifier. ☐ Balanced modulators are used for suppressed-carrier transmission.

☐ FM modulators vary the instantaneous r-f carrier frequency in accordance with the modulating signal. In the reactance-tube modulator the reactance of the frequency-determining tank circuit is varied by injecting inductive or capacitive current into the tank. ☐ Phase modulators pass the r-f carrier through a circuit that shifts the phase of the signal in proportion to the amplitude of the modulating signal.

review questions

1. How are side bands produced in an amplitude modulator?
2. In AM, what is meant by 100 percent modulation? 50 percent modulation? Overmodulation?
3. Why is amplitude modulation in excess of 100 percent undesirable? Draw a sine wave and show what happens to it because of overmodulation.
4. Draw an AM plate modulator and explain its operation.
5. Why is the plate modulator operated class C?
6. Why must the grid-bias modulator be operated class A or class AB?
7. What type of modulator is used for suppressed-carrier transmission?
8. Why are frequency multipliers used with FM modulators?
9. Describe the basic operation of a reactance-tube modulator.
10. Draw a phase modulator and explain its operation.

mixers and converters

In a receiver, r-f signals are generally first converted to i-f signals by circuits called mixers and converters. Essentially, a mixer operates like a *low-level modulator* connected between the last r-f amplifier and the first i-f amplifier. The mixer receives two input signals: one from the r-f amplifier, and the other from an oscillator stage called the *local oscillator*. Both the r-f amplifiers and the oscillator are tuned simultaneously, usually by ganged tuning capacitors, with the oscillator frequency always separated from the r-f signal frequency by the *same* amount. Normally, the oscillator frequency is the higher of the two.

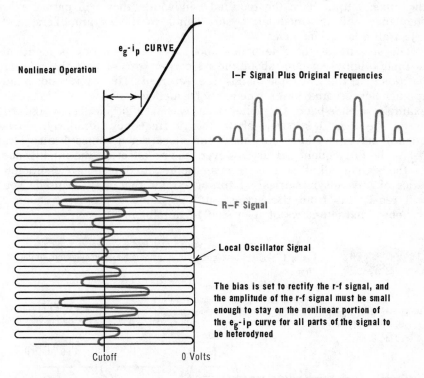

e_g-i_p CURVE

Nonlinear Operation

I–F Signal Plus Original Frequencies

R–F Signal

Local Oscillator Signal

The bias is set to rectify the r-f signal, and the amplitude of the r-f signal must be small enough to stay on the nonlinear portion of the e_g-i_p curve for all parts of the signal to be heterodyned

Cutoff   0 Volts

The tube or transistor used for the mixer stage must be a *nonlinear* device. The required nonlinearity is usually obtained by biasing mixer stages at or close to cutoff, as in class B operation. This allows the r-f signal to work on the nonlinear portion of the tube's e_g–i_p curve. It is important that the r-f signal operate completely in the nonlinear region of the curve. If the r-f signal amplitude is too great and rises to the linear part of the curve, poor heterodyning will take place there, causing distortion. Because of this nonlinear operation, the oscillator and r-f signals are *heterodyned* within the stage. As you know, this produces sum and difference frequencies, as well as the two original frequencies, in the output.

mixers and converters (cont.)

Tuned circuits between the output of the mixer and the first i-f amplifier are tuned to the *difference frequency*, and this is used as the *i-f frequency*. When the r-f signal contains modulation side bands, difference frequencies are produced in the mixer not only between the oscillator and r-f carrier frequencies, but between the oscillator and side-band frequencies as well. These difference frequencies resulting from the side bands are spaced above and below the fundamental difference (i-f) frequency the same as the original side-band frequencies were spaced above and below the r-f carrier. So if the tuned circuits in the mixer output have the required bandwidth, they will pass the i-f frequency and the modulation side bands to the i-f amplifiers, and reject all other frequencies.

The spacing of the side bands about the i-f frequency is identical to their original spacing about the r-f carrier, except that the *relative positions* of the two side bands are *reversed*. The upper side-band frequencies become lower side-band frequencies, and vice versa. For example, a side-band frequency that was 1 kilocycle below the r-f carrier becomes 1 kilocycle above the i-f frequency. Similarly, a frequency that was 4 kilocycles above the r-f carrier becomes 4 kilocycles below the i-f frequency. This, however, has no effect on the intelligence of the signal. All it does is reverse the required response characteristics of any unsymmetrical i-f tuning circuit that may be used. You will recall this from the discussion in Volume 1 on the frequency response characteristics of television i-f amplifiers.

TRIODE MIXER STAGE — From the signal at the plate, you can see that the mixer rectifies the input signals. The output tank circuit then restores the sinusoidal form of the i-f frequency

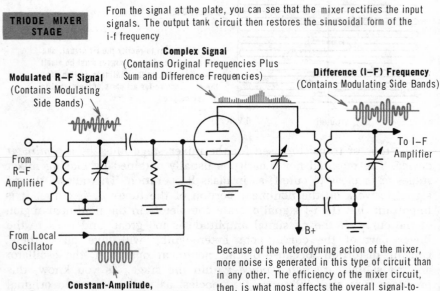

Modulated R–F Signal (Contains Modulating Side Bands)

Complex Signal (Contains Original Frequencies Plus Sum and Difference Frequencies)

Difference (I–F) Frequency (Contains Modulating Side Bands)

From R–F Amplifier

From Local Oscillator

Constant-Amplitude, Single-Frequency Oscillator Signal

To I–F Amplifier

B+

Because of the heterodyning action of the mixer, more noise is generated in this type of circuit than in any other. The efficiency of the mixer circuit, then, is what most affects the overall signal-to-noise ratio of the receiver

mixers and converters (cont.)

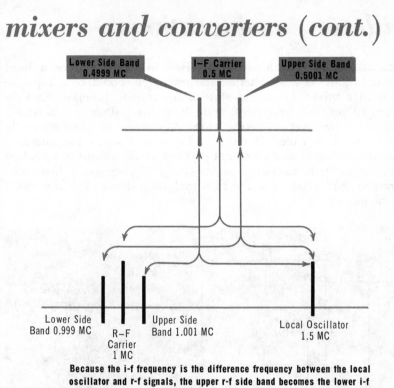

Because the i-f frequency is the difference frequency between the local oscillator and r-f signals, the upper r-f side band becomes the lower i-f side band, and vice versa

Mixers and converters work the same way for AM, FM, phase modulators, pulse modulation, and so on. The r-f signal is beat with a local oscillator signal to produce an i-f signal that carries the modulation. AM mixers are covered in the following pages. The other types of signals are mixed in the same way, however.

Converters perform exactly the same function as mixers. The only difference is that a *mixer* uses a *separate* stage for the oscillator, while in a *converter* the oscillator and mixer are contained in a *single stage*.

Very often, the mixer or converter in a superheterodyne receiver is called the *first detector* or *demodulator*. This is because the stage is often thought of as taking the modulation off the r-f carrier and then reinserting it on the i-f carrier. In essence, any time modulation is removed from a carrier, detection or demodulation is considered to take place. In spite of this, you should realize that a mixer or converter is essentially a modulator rather than a detector or demodulator. Its purpose is to change the frequency of the signal on which the intelligence is carried, not to recover the intelligence.

Since the mixer is not used strictly for gain, and the output frequency is different from the input frequency, the gain of the mixer stage is the ratio of the output i-f amplitude over the input r-f amplitude. This is known as *conversion gain*.

oscillator considerations

There are many considerations involved in the design of a local oscillator. One of these is whether the oscillator should be a separate stage, as in a mixer, or combined with the mixing function, as in a converter. In general, converters, with their single stage, are desirable for economy. However, the oscillators in converters are frequently subject to what is called "pulling." This occurs when the coupling between the oscillator and r-f signal portions of the circuit is sufficient to cause the oscillator to *change in frequency.* The oscillator then tends to operate at the frequency of the r-f signal, even though it is not tuned to that frequency.

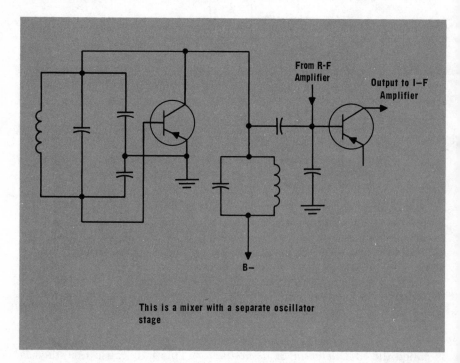

From R-F
Amplifier

Output to I–F
Amplifier

B–

This is a mixer with a separate oscillator
stage

Pulling depends in large part on the *difference* between the oscillator and r-f signal frequencies. The greater this difference is, the less tendency there is for pulling. Thus, if the oscillator operates *above* the r-f signal frequency, pulling can be minimized by using a *high oscillator frequency,* or, in other words, a high i-f frequency. However, very high i-f frequencies result in decreased gain in the i-f amplifiers, while the high oscillator frequency can cause the oscillator to be unstable. As a result, high r-f signal frequencies often require that a mixer instead of a converter be used, or that the oscillator operate *below* the r-f signal frequencies. Sometimes, both of these measures are necessary.

oscillator considerations (cont.)

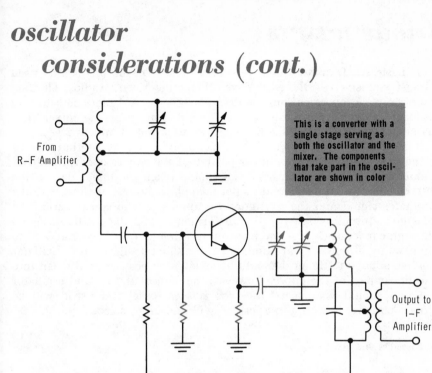

This is a converter with a single stage serving as both the oscillator and the mixer. The components that take part in the oscillator are shown in color

From R–F Amplifier

Output to I–F Amplifier

B+

A local oscillator must also have a relatively constant output amplitude over its frequency range and be free from frequency drift caused by factors such as heating of components. Although it is important to keep the local oscillator output relatively constant, the mixer can tolerate some amplitude variations if the oscillator signal is large enough to swing into the linear part of the mixer's operating curve. There, since heterodyning is poor, the amplitude changes will have little effect. Only the r-f signal need operate completely in the nonlinear part of the curve. In addition, the oscillator should produce little or no harmonics that might interfere with the r-f signal and be well laid-out or shielded to minimize radiation that can cause interference with nearby electronic equipment.

One of the most important requirements of the local oscillator is that it always be separated from the r-f signal by the *same frequency difference*, regardless of what r-f frequency is selected. This is called *tracking*, and is accomplished by using specially shaped ganged tuning capacitors for the oscillator and the r-f amplifiers. Small adjustable capacitors, called *padders,* are connected in series with each section of the ganged capacitors to compensate for differences between capacitor sections and thus ensure proper tracking.

triode mixers

A basic triode mixer stage is shown. This type of mixer was used almost exclusively in the early days of superheterodyne radios. The fact that the stage operates somewhat similarly to an AM plate detector (to be covered later) led to the name "first detector" for the mixer. The name has persisted, and is still sometimes used for all mixer stages.

The triode mixer is biased approximately at cutoff so that the r-f signal will work on the nonlinear portion of the stage's operating curve. Remember, no part of the r-f signal should reach the linear part of the curve as heterodyning there does not take place too well. Below, both the oscillator signal and the r-f signal are applied to the control grid: the r-f signal through single-tuned transformer T_1 and the oscillator signal through capacitor C_1. For the maximum usable output i-f signal, and to nullify any amplitude variations on the oscillator signal, the oscillator voltage applied to the grid should be as large as possible and reach into the linear part of the curve. However, the sum of the r-f and oscillator voltages should *not* exceed the *bias voltage,* or else the grid will be driven positive, resulting in a loss of gain and input selectivity.

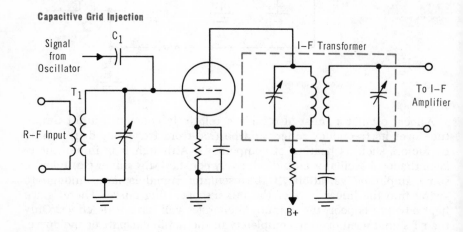

Capacitive Grid Injection

When the combined r-f and oscillator positive voltages exceed the cutoff voltage, the tube conducts and plate current flows. The current contains variations caused by both the r-f signal voltage and the oscillator voltage. These variations beat together to produce the sum and difference frequencies. The plate tank circuit, which is tuned to the difference, or i-f, frequency, presents a high impedance at this frequency and a low impedance at all other frequencies. Consequently, a significant output voltage is developed only at the i-f frequency. The bandwidth of the i-f transformer, of which the plate tank is the primary, is wide enough to pass the i-f frequency and its side bands to the first i-f amplifier.

triode mixers (cont.)

Two other ways in which the oscillator signal can be injected into the mixer are shown in A and B. In A, inductive coupling to the cathode is used; in B, inductive coupling to the grid is used. The cathode method has the advantage of injecting the oscillator signal at a low-impedance point. This causes less loading of the oscillator and tends to increase its stability.

Triode mixers provide good gain and have a relatively low noise level. However, they are generally unsuitable at very high frequencies because of interaction between the oscillator and mixer that results in frequency instability.

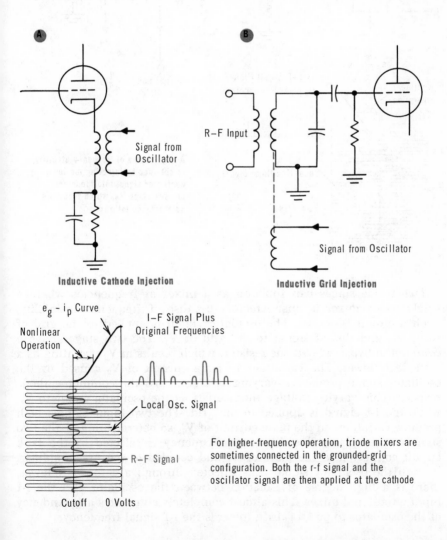

Inductive Cathode Injection

Inductive Grid Injection

For higher-frequency operation, triode mixers are sometimes connected in the grounded-grid configuration. Both the r-f signal and the oscillator signal are then applied at the cathode

the cathode-coupled triode mixer

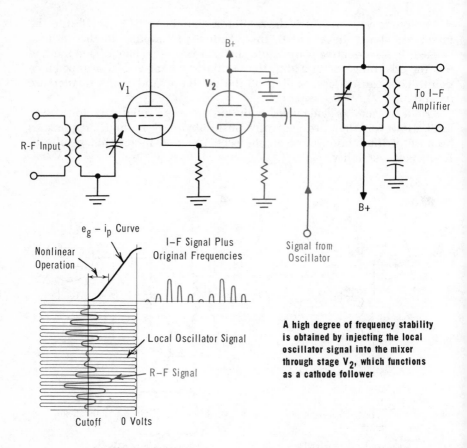

Two triode stages can function as a mixer at frequencies where a single triode mixer is unsatisfactory because of frequency instability. Such a circuit is shown. The oscillator signal is applied to the grid of stage V_2, and the r-f signal to the grid of V_1. The two stages have a *common* unbypassed cathode resistor, which results in V_2 operating as a cathode follower. The variations in plate current of V_2 caused by the oscillator signal produce a varying voltage across the common-cathode resistor. This varying voltage then serves as the oscillator input to V_1, while the r-f signal is applied to the grid. The two input signals both produce variations in the plate current of V_1, so heterodyning of the two signals takes place. The difference frequency is selected by the tank circuit connected to the plate of V_1 and coupled to the first amplifier.

With the oscillator signal thus injected through a cathode follower, there is a high degree of isolation between the oscillator and the r-f input circuit and mixer. This almost completely eliminates any tendency of the oscillator to pull, or drift, towards the r-f signal frequency.

pentode mixers

Pentode mixers have better *high-frequency* characteristics than triode mixers. One of the high-frequency advantages of pentode mixers is that they do not require *neutralization*. At their lower operating frequencies, triodes do not have to be neutralized either. But at high frequencies, the oscillator and r-f signal frequencies are relatively close together. This results in a large high-frequency content in the plate current, and causes the plate-load impedance to be significant at the r-f frequency. Tuned-plate, tuned-grid oscillation can then take place unless the stage is neutralized by conventional means. This problem does not exist in pentode mixers because of their low values of interelectrode capacitance.

The operation of pentode mixers is the same as that of triode mixers. Pentodes permit higher *gain* than triode mixers but at the same time produce more tube *noise*. The noise performance of a pentode mixer is best if the oscillator signal is injected at the grid rather than at the cathode. As with the other mixers, the r-f signal should operate completely in the nonlinear region of the curve.

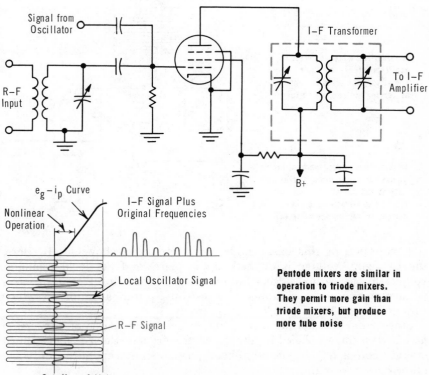

Pentode mixers are similar in operation to triode mixers. They permit more gain than triode mixers, but produce more tube noise

diode mixers

At the extreme upper end of the VHF band (300 megacycles and higher), diode mixers are usually used, since they have good characteristics at these high frequencies. A basic diode mixer circuit is shown in A. Both the oscillator and r-f signal voltages are applied to the cathode, and a bias voltage keeps the plate of the diode negative with respect to the cathode. The diode conducts only when the positive peaks of the oscillator signal overcome the bias. When the diode does conduct, its plate current contains variations corresponding to both the oscillator and the signal voltages. Heterodyning therefore occurs, and the i-f signal is selected by the tuned plate circuit.

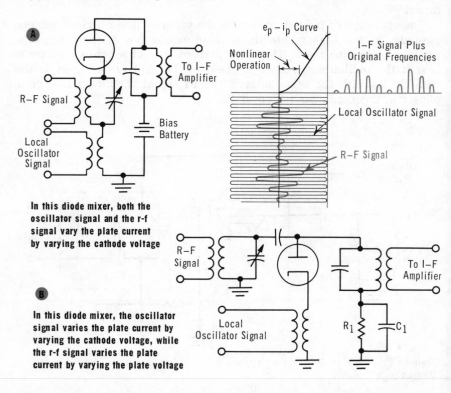

In this diode mixer, both the oscillator signal and the r-f signal vary the plate current by varying the cathode voltage

In this diode mixer, the oscillator signal varies the plate current by varying the cathode voltage, while the r-f signal varies the plate current by varying the plate voltage

A variation of this basic diode mixer circuit is shown in B. Here, the r-f signal voltage is applied to the plate, and the local oscillator voltage to the cathode. Bias for the diode, in the form of a negative voltage on the plate, is supplied by resistor R_1 and capacitor C_1, which function much like a grid-leak bias circuit.

Since a diode is not an amplifying device, some degree of *conversion loss* always takes place. In the diode mixer, too, the r-f signal must operate completely in the nonlinear portion of its operating curve to allow heterodyning.

semiconductor diode mixers

The good high-frequency characteristics of tube-type diode mixers can be achieved and *better noise performance* obtained by the use of diode mixers utilizing semiconductors as the diode element. These semiconductor diodes are made of *silicon* or *germanium* crystals and can operate satisfactorily at frequencies of 3000 megacycles and higher. You recall from Volume 4 that the resistance of a silicon or germanium diode depends on the *direction* of conduction. If a voltage is applied in the *forward direction,* the diode conducts heavily, since its resistance in this direction is low. In the *reverse direction,* though, the resistance is high, and little current flows. Essentially, a semiconductor diode has a portion of its curve *nonlinear* in the same way that tube-type diodes are nonlinear. This makes their use as mixers possible.

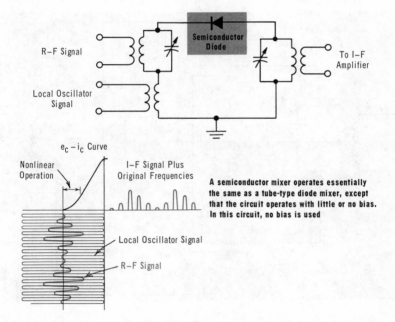

A semiconductor mixer operates essentially the same as a tube-type diode mixer, except that the circuit operates with little or no bias. In this circuit, no bias is used

As shown, a semiconductor mixer is very similar to a tube-type diode mixer. The basic difference is that semiconductor mixers are usually operated with little or no bias and no filament voltage. This keeps the noise introduced by the circuit to a minimum. It also reduces the amount of *reverse current* that flows through the diode when the plate is negative with respect to the cathode. Reverse current is not a problem in tube-type diode mixers, since with practical operating voltages current will not flow from plate to cathode. In a semiconductor diode, though, although the resistance in the reverse direction is high, it still allows some current to flow. Too much such current would seriously affect the operation of the mixer.

balanced mixers

Balanced mixers are frequently used in high-frequency radar, navigation, and FM equipment. There are many variations of balanced-mixer circuits, but they all operate essentially the same as a *balanced modulator*, which was discussed previously. Essentially, a balanced mixer heterodynes the local oscillator and r-f signals, and at the same time *cancels* one or both of these signal frequencies in its output. This cancellation results in an improved signal-to-noise ratio of the output signal and good frequency stability for the oscillator and mixer.

In a balanced mixer, a signal applied to the mixer stages in push-pull is cancelled in the common-plate circuit. This cancellation, though, has no effect on the sum and difference frequency components of the output signal

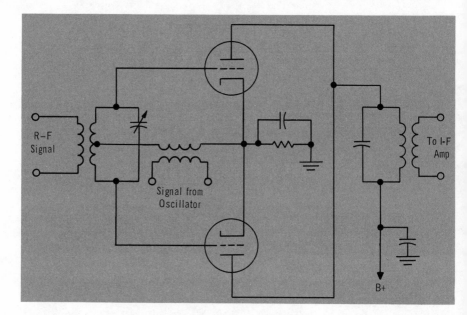

In the balanced mixer shown, the r-f signal is applied in *push-pull* to the grids of two triodes, while the oscillator signal is applied to the two grids in *parallel*. The two input signals are heterodyned in both tubes to produce the usual sum and difference frequencies. However, since the r-f inputs at the grids of the stages are 180 degrees out of phase, the r-f signal components of the two plate currents are also 180 degrees out of phase. Inasmuch as the plates are connected in parallel, the two r-f components cancel each other, leaving only the oscillator frequency and the sum and difference frequencies. The common-plate tank then selects the difference frequency in the usual way. If both the r-f and oscillator signals are applied in push-pull to the grids, they are both cancelled in the common-plate circuit.

pentagrid mixers

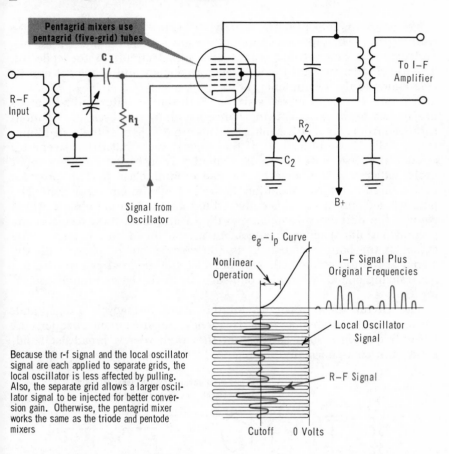

Pentagrid mixers use pentagrid (five-grid) tubes

C_1

R-F Input

R_1

Signal from Oscillator

To I-F Amplifier

R_2

C_2

B+

$e_g - i_p$ Curve

Nonlinear Operation

I-F Signal Plus Original Frequencies

Local Oscillator Signal

R-F Signal

Cutoff   0 Volts

Because the r-f signal and the local oscillator signal are each applied to separate grids, the local oscillator is less affected by pulling. Also, the separate grid allows a larger oscillator signal to be injected for better conversion gain. Otherwise, the pentagrid mixer works the same as the triode and pentode mixers

Most often, pentagrid tubes are used in converter circuits. Sometimes, however, they are also employed as mixers. A *penta*grid mixer has *five grids*, in addition to its cathode and plate. The oscillator signal is applied to the first grid (closest to cathode), and the r-f signal to the third grid. The second grid is a screen grid, which provides shielding between the oscillator and the signal grids. The fourth and fifth grids function as the screen and suppressor grids in a conventional pentode.

A typical pentagrid mixer circuit is shown. In some circuits, the point of injection of the two input signals is reversed. Heterodyning of the two signals takes place in the common electron stream flowing through the tube. The positive voltage on the first screen grid isolates the oscillator grid from the signal grid. Similarly, the second screen grid isolates the signal grid from the plate.

Pentagrid mixers have a fairly high gain, but due to their many grids they introduce a considerable amount of noise.

transistor mixers

Transistor mixers perform exactly the same function as their tube counterparts. They receive as inputs the local oscillator and r-f signals, and deliver a heterodyned output to a tuned circuit in the collector. The tuned circuit selects the difference frequency and couples it and its side bands to the i-f amplifier.

A typical transistor mixer is shown. Both the oscillator and r-f signals are applied to the base. For impedance-matching purposes, the r-f input is tapped from a capacitive voltage divider that is part of the tuned input circuit. The base-emitter bias of the stage is such that the base-emitter circuit is reverse biased for only a small portion of the oscillator input cycle. Otherwise, the stage is operated around class B. This provides the required nonlinear operation, as well as maximum mixer gain. The heterodyned output signal is delivered to the tuned output circuit, which couples the difference frequency to the i-f amplifier. As a result of the grounded split-capacitor arrangement in the tuned output circuit, the signal at the bottom of coil L_1 is 180 degrees out of phase with the signal at the top of the coil. This provides the required polarity for the neutralizing signal, which is coupled back to the base through capacitor C_n.

The circuit shown operates on the 30–60 megacycle range, and, because of the high operating frequency, requires neutralization. At lower frequencies, such as those of the standard AM broadcast band, neutralization is normally not required.

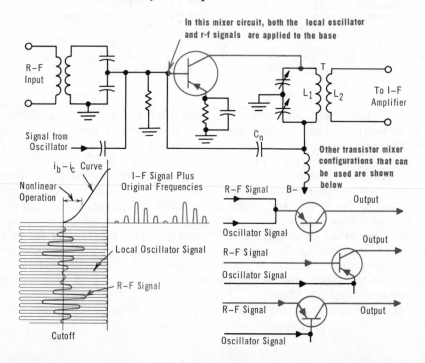

summary

☐ In receivers, mixer and converter circuits convert r-f signals to i-f signals by heterodyning the r-f signal with a local oscillator signal. ☐ The tube or transistor used as a mixer is operated on the nonlinear portion of its characteristic curve. ☐ The efficiency of the mixer has a significant effect on the signal-to-noise ratio of a receiver. ☐ In a converter, the oscillator and mixer are contained in a single stage.

☐ With good tracking, the local oscillator signal must differ from the incoming r-f signal by the same frequency difference, regardless of the r-f frequency selected. ☐ Triode mixers provide good gain and have low noise level but are quite unstable at very high frequencies. ☐ The high-frequency instability of triode mixers can be overcome by using two triode stages. The second stage functions as a cathode follower. ☐ Pentode mixers have better high-frequency characteristics than triodes, but produce more tube noise.

☐ At 300 mc and above, diode mixers are preferred. ☐ Semiconductor diodes have excellent noise performance, as they are operated with little or no bias voltage. ☐ Balanced mixers operate essentially the same as balanced modulators, cancelling one or both of the input signal frequencies. ☐ Pentagrid mixers have high gain, but introduce considerable noise as a result of their many grids.

review questions

1. What are the sources of the two input signals received by a receiver mixer?
2. What is the essential difference between a converter and a mixer?
3. The mixer or converter in a superheterodyne receiver is often called the first detector. Why?
4. What is *conversion gain*?
5. Why do high r-f signal frequencies often require use of a mixer instead of a converter?
6. What is *tracking* and how is it accomplished?
7. In the triode mixer, why must the sum of the i-f and oscillator voltages be kept below the bias voltage?
8. What advantages do pentode mixers offer at high frequencies in comparison with triode mixers?
9. Describe the circuit configuration and operation of a diode mixer in which the oscillator and r-f signal are applied to the cathode.
10. Why is the noise performance of semiconductor diode mixers better than that of tube-type diode mixers?

converters

Converters are essentially mixers that perform the local oscillator function as well as the mixer function. The most widely used type of tube converter is the *pentagrid converter*. These converters are special multigrid tubes that are basically the same as those used for pentagrid mixers.

In the typical pentagrid converter circuit shown, the r-f signal is applied to the third grid. The oscillator signal is generated by the cathode, the first grid, and the second grid, which together with their associated components function as a *series-fed Hartley oscillator*. The oscillator causes variations in the electron stream within the tube, and so also does the r-f signal. Heterodyning therefore takes place the same as in mixer circuits. Actually, except for the fact that the local oscillator is part of the circuit, the operation of the pentagrid converter is basically the same as that of a mixer.

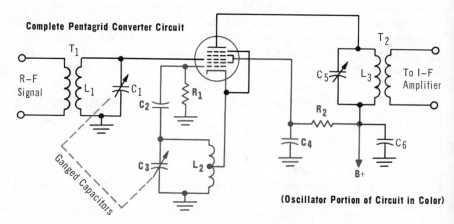

Complete Pentagrid Converter Circuit

(Oscillator Portion of Circuit in Color)

The oscillator portion of a pentagrid converter consists of the cathode, the first and second grids, and their associated components. The entire circuit works exactly the same as the pentagrid mixer, except that the local oscillator (in color) is self-contained

In the converter circuit shown, the oscillator is shown in color. It is a conventional series-fed Hartley circuit, with the first and second grids of the converter tube acting as the control grid and plate, respectively, of a triode stage. The feedback path for the oscillator is thus from the second grid of the converter, through the split coil (L_2), to the first grid. Capacitor C_2 and resistor R_1 provide grid-leak bias for the oscillator. They also supply the bias for the whole converter circuit.

Various types of oscillators are used in pentagrid converters. However, any type used must be inherently stable, since there is a relatively large degree of interaction between the oscillator and the r-f input circuit in a converter.

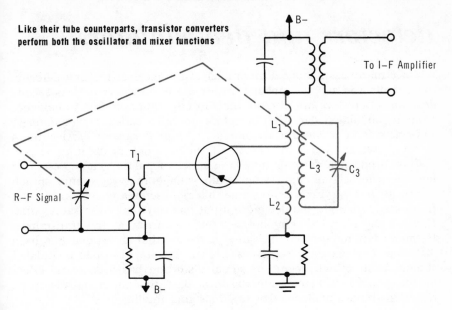

Like their tube counterparts, transistor converters perform both the oscillator and mixer functions

transistor converters

Transistor converters are also frequently used, especially for AM receivers that operate in the broadcast band. A simplified version of one of the most commonly used types of transistor circuit is shown. The r-f signal is applied to the transistor base through transformer T_1, which steps down the r-f voltage to match the low input impedance of the transistor.

The oscillator circuit consists essentially of coils L_1 and L_2, connected in the collector and emitter circuits, respectively, and the tuned circuit made up of coil L_3 and capacitor C_3. Oscillation takes place as a result of feedback from L_1 to L_2 caused by the mutual induction between the two coils. Both L_1 and L_2 are also mutually coupled to coil L_3, so that the reflected impedance from L_3 determines the degree of mutual inductance that exists between L_1 and L_2. The reflected impedance, in turn, is determined by the resonant frequency of L_3 and C_3. At the resonant frequency, the mutual inductance between L_1 and L_2, and, therefore, the feedback, is maximum. At other frequencies, the feedback is negligible. Thus, variable capacitor C_3 determines the frequency at which collector-to-emitter feedback takes place. It therefore serves as the oscillator tuning capacitor.

As a result of the oscillator feedback, both the oscillator signal and the r-f signal are applied in series between the base and emitter. The circuit is biased for nonlinear operation, so the two signals are heterodyned in the output. The difference frequency is selected by the tuned-plate tank and coupled to the i-f amplifier through another impedance-matching transformer.

detectors and demodulators

Since many designers call the mixer of the receiver the first detector, the circuits you are now about to study are often referred to as *second detectors*. *Detectors* are circuits that, in effect, *remove* the intelligence from a modulated carrier. (Detectors are also called *demodulators*.) They do this by converting the modulated high-frequency carrier into a varying voltage that corresponds to the original modulating signal.

The output of a detector may be a series of pulses that represents a teletypewriter signal, a varying audio voltage that represents speech or music, or a varying video voltage that represents a television picture. In all cases, though, the detector output has essentially the same *variations* as the signal that modulated the r-f carrier at the transmitter. If the variations are not the same, it means that the signal has been distorted. Of course, in some cases, such as for pulse-code modulated signals, even a high degree of signal distortion has little or no effect on the signal intelligence. For the most part, though, signal distortion results in some impairment or loss of signal intelligence.

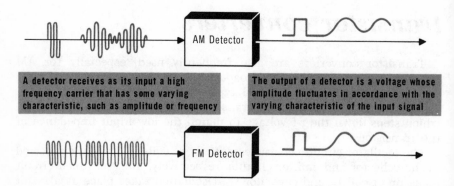

A detector receives as its input a high frequency carrier that has some varying characteristic, such as amplitude or frequency

The output of a detector is a voltage whose amplitude fluctuates in accordance with the varying characteristic of the input signal

For proper operation, all detectors require a definite level of input signal strength. The stages in an equipment that precede the detector must amplify the signal to this required level. Usually, most of this amplification is provided by i-f amplifiers.

There are two major classes of detectors: those used for the detection of AM signals and those used for the detection of FM signals. Although both AM and FM detectors perform the same function, their principles of operation are quite different due to the dissimilar characteristics of AM and FM signals.

When analyzing any type of detector it is often convenient to think of the modulated signal not in terms of a carrier (or center frequency for FM) and side bands, but in terms of a high-frequency signal that varies either in amplitude (AM) or frequency (FM). If the detector responds to all of these variations and produces an output voltage that varies in accordance with them, it automatically recovers all the intelligence that was contained in the side bands.

AM detectors

An AM detector produces an output voltage that corresponds to the variations in peak-to-peak amplitude of its input signal. It does this essentially in two steps. First, it *rectifies* the input signal, leaving only the positive or negative portion. Then, by means of a suitable filter network, it produces a voltage that follows the *envelope* of the rectified signal. The i-f carrier must be rectified because the modulation envelopes on the positive and negative sides are 180 degrees out of phase. If the signal were merely filtered, the positive and negative envelopes would cancel each other, and the intelligence would be lost. In most applications, it is unimportant whether the detector removes the positive or the negative portion of the AM signal, since both halves have the same variations. But in certain video applications, or sync pulse applications, as you will learn later, this polarity is an important consideration.

There are various types of AM detectors, with the one used for a particular application depending on the desired characteristics. Some of the most important detector characteristics are linearity, sensitivity, signal-handling capability, and selectivity.

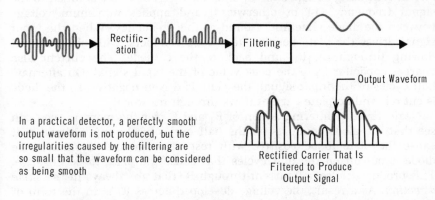

An AM detector rectifies the input high-frequency carrier and by filtering action produces a varying voltage that follows the envelope of the rectified carrier

Output Waveform

In a practical detector, a perfectly smooth output waveform is not produced, but the irregularities caused by the filtering are so small that the waveform can be considered as being smooth

Rectified Carrier That Is Filtered to Produce Output Signal

Linearity is a measure of how accurately the detector output follows the variations in the input signal. If the output amplitude is *proportional* to the input amplitude, the detector is said to be *linear*.

The sensitivity of a detector is determined by the amount of useful output delivered by the detector for a given input signal level. Signal-handling capability is a measure of the signal amplitudes that a detector can accept without producing distortion. The selectivity of a detector actually describes the effect of the detector on the selectivity, or Q, of the tuned circuit usually used in the detector input.

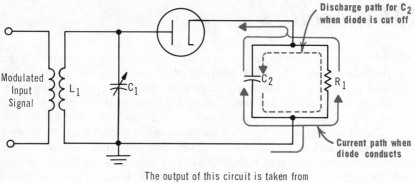

The output of this circuit is taken from
across resistor R$_1$

the diode detector

The simplest type of AM detector is the basic diode detector shown. The diode rectifies the modulated signal, and resistor R$_1$ and capacitor C$_2$ filter the rectified signal to produce the detected output. Semiconductor diodes can be used for this type of circuit as well as tube diodes. In either case, the operation is essentially the same, so we will limit the discussion to the tube circuit.

The modulated signal is transformer coupled to the tuned input circuit consisting of capacitor C$_1$ and coil L$_1$. The circuit is tuned to the signal frequency (i-f or otherwise), and applies maximum voltage between the diode plate and ground at this frequency. When the input signal drives the plate positive, the diode conducts, with plate current flowing through L$_1$, R$_1$, and back to the cathode. The current also charges capacitor C$_2$ to the peak value of the input signal. On alternate half cycles of the input signal, the plate is driven negative, so the diode is cut off, and no plate current flows through resistor R$_1$.

Neglecting the filtering action of R$_1$ and C$_2$ for the moment, you can see that the diode conducts on the half cycles of the input signal that cause the plate to be positive with respect to ground. Similarly, the diode is cut off on the half cycles that cause the plate to be negative. This produces pulses of current through R$_1$ that are always in the *same direction*. As a result, the voltage developed across R$_1$ is in the form of rectified pulses that follow the amplitude variations of the input signal. This is the situation that would exist without capacitor C$_2$.

If a semiconductor diode is substituted for the tube in the above circuit, the circuit operation is essentially the same. Semiconductor diode detectors are widely used in both tube and transistorized equipments

the diode detector (cont.)

Without capacitor C_2 in the circuit, the voltage across R_1 would be a series of pulses whose amplitudes varied in accordance with the amplitude of the input signal

Rising portions of waveform are produced by plate current flowing through R_1 when tube conducts

Falling portions of waveform are produced by C_2 discharging through R_1 when tube is cut off

With capacitor C_2 in the circuit, the voltage across R_1 can never fall below the charge on C_2

With C_2 in the circuit, the voltage across R_1 cannot drop to zero when the input signal cuts off the diode. Since C_2 charges to the *peak value* of the input signal when the diode conducts, it begins to discharge when the input signal begins to fall.

The discharge path for C_2 is through R_1, and the discharge current maintains the voltage across R_1 during the time that the input signal falls to zero and goes through its negative half cycle. The time constant of R_1C_2 is long compared to one cycle of the input signal, so the capacitor has lost very little of its charge by the time the next positive peak of the input signal causes the diode to conduct. Actually, the diode does not conduct until the input signal makes the plate voltage *greater* than the remaining charge on C_2. When the diode does conduct, plate current again flows through R_1, and C_2 charges to the peak value of the input signal.

Diode detectors have linear input-output characteristics and can handle relatively large input signals with little distortion. However, they have low sensitivity, since they provide no gain. In addition, a diode detector draws a comparatively large current from the tuned input circuit, which substantially reduces the selectivity of the stage. Therefore, equipments that use diode detectors must have a sufficient number of tuned circuits before the detector to compensate for the detector's poor selectivity.

the grid-leak detector

A grid-leak detector provides signal *amplification* as well as *detection*. Although triodes or pentodes can be used for grid-leak detectors, we will base our discussion here on the triode circuit shown. In some respects, the grid and cathode of this circuit, together with capacitor C_2 and resistor R_1, function like a diode detector. However, instead of producing the actual output voltage, this diode-like circuit merely develops the detection bias that rectifies the input signal. The rectified signal is then amplified and filtered in the plate circuit.

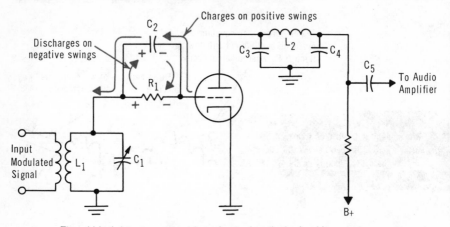

The grid-leak detector can best be understood on the basis of its waveforms

With no input signal, the grid-leak detector has essentially zero bias. Actually, it has a very small amount of contact bias, but this is so small that it can be considered negligible. When the modulated signal is coupled to the tuned input circuit, it drives the control grid alternately positive and negative. Each time the grid goes positive, it draws grid current, which flows through R_1 and L_1 and back to the cathode. In addition, the grid current also charges capacitor C_2 *almost* to the peak value of the input signal. Then, when the input signal falls, C_2 discharges through R_1; the time constant of R_1C_2 is long enough for the voltage across R_1 to follow the amplitude variations of the input signal. You should recognize this as the same type of filtering action that takes place in a diode detector.

As a matter of fact, the voltage waveform produced by C_2 and R_1 is similar to the output waveform of a diode detector. In this case, however, the voltage across R_1 is the bias for the stage. Since the bias is produced by the positive half of the modulated signal, it is approximately equal to it in amplitude and is opposite to it in polarity; the input signal is effectively rectified. The conducting grid clamps and cancels most of the positive half of the signal, and only the negative half produces significant variations in plate current.

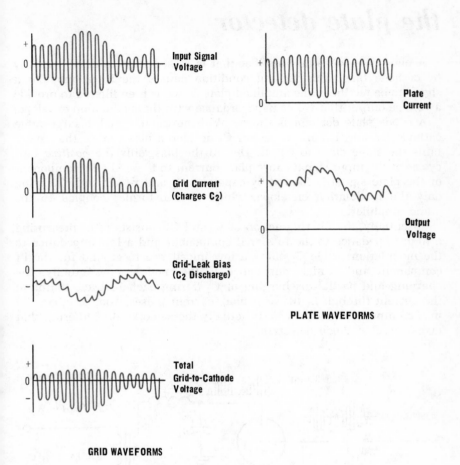

Input Signal
Voltage

Plate
Current

Grid Current
(Charges C$_2$)

Output
Voltage

Grid-Leak Bias
(C$_2$ Discharge)

PLATE WAVEFORMS

Total
Grid-to-Cathode
Voltage

GRID WAVEFORMS

the grid-leak detector (cont.)

The plate current consists of i-f (or r-f) variations, and these must be removed so that the output signal follows the modulation envelope. This is the purpose of r-f choke L_2 and capacitors C_3 and C_4 in the plate circuit. These components make up a filter that removes the r-f component from the output, and produces an output voltage that varies only in accordance with the modulation envelope. The output of the filter is coupled to the first audio amplifier by coupling capacitor C_5.

When the operating voltages of a grid-leak detector are such that it is operated as a square-law detector, the circuit has good sensitivity for weak input signals. Due to the nonlinear relationship between input and output, though, there is considerable distortion. Also, since the grid current flows through the input tuned circuit, the selectivity of the tuned circuit is relatively low.

the plate detector

A plate detector is an amplifier that is biased close to *cutoff,* usually by cathode bias. This biasing condition causes the input modulated signal to be rectified. The amplified plate signal is then filtered to provide a voltage output that varies in accordance with the modulation envelope.

A triode plate detector is shown. With no input signal, a large-value cathode resistor, R_1, and capacitor C_1 develop a bias voltage that maintains the stage close to cutoff. Due to the bias, only the *positive* half cycles of the input signal cause plate current to flow. The i-f component of the plate signal is filtered by capacitor C_2 and r-f choke L_1, leaving only the modulation envelope, which is transformer coupled to the audio amplifier.

Essentially, the filtering action of L_1 and C_2 consists of L_1 presenting a high impedance to the i-f signal component and a low impedance to the modulation, while C_2 offers a low impedance to ground for the i-f component and a high impedance to the modulation. Actually, the charging and partial discharging of C_2 during each i-f cycle maintain the current through L_1 between plate current pulses, and, in effect, fill in the output waveform. This is actually the same kind of filtering that takes place in diode detectors.

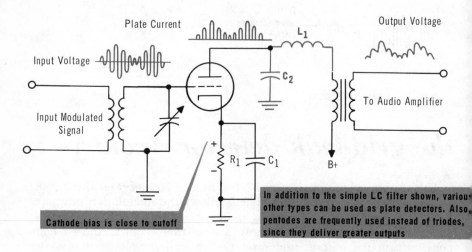

In addition to the simple LC filter shown, various other types can be used as plate detectors. Also, pentodes are frequently used instead of triodes, since they deliver greater outputs

A plate detector has good sensitivity and selectivity, provided that the input signal is not large enough to drive the grid positive with respect to the cathode. This would result in grid current and cause a decrease in sensitivity and selectivity. For weak signals, a plate detector is usually operated as a square-law detector on the nonlinear part of its e_g–i_p curve. For stronger signals, the tube is operated on the linear portion of its e_g–i_p curve, so the output is less distorted.

the infinite-impedance detector

The infinite-impedance detector is similar to the plate detector, except that its output is taken from the *cathode* instead of the plate. The plate of the stage is effectively grounded for both the i-f (or r-f) and modulation frequencies by capacitor C_3.

Cathode resistor R_1 and capacitor C_1 serve two purposes. They provide *automatic bias* for the stage near plate-current cutoff, and they develop and filter the output signal. These two functions are accomplished by using a value for C_1 so that its reactance is low at the i-f frequency but high at the modulation frequencies. For an unmodulated input signal, therefore, C_1 bypasses the i-f variations around R_1, and R_1 biases the stage close to cutoff. But, C_1 cannot bypass the modulation frequencies that correspond to the amplitude variations, so the bias voltage across R_1 *varies* with the modulation. This causes *degeneration* with the bias increasing when the modulation amplitude increases and vice versa. As a result, grid current can *never* flow no matter how large the positive amplitude of the input signal is.

The rectified plate-current pulses flow through the cathode circuit and are filtered by R_1 and C_1 in the same way as in a diode detector. The voltage across R_1 therefore varies as the modulation envelope of the input signal. It is capacitively coupled through C_2 to the audio amplifier.

The infinite-impedance detector has a high degree of selectivity, since it never draws grid current, and also has a highly linear output because of the degeneration. It produces a slight loss, though, and so has low sensitivity.

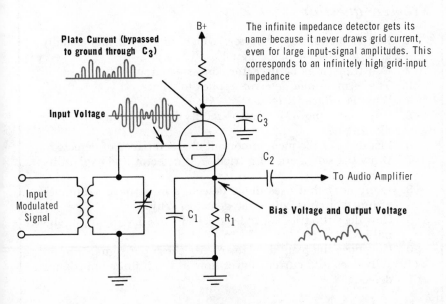

Plate Current (bypassed to ground through C_3)

Input Voltage

B+

C_3

C_2

To Audio Amplifier

Input Modulated Signal

C_1 R_1

Bias Voltage and Output Voltage

The infinite impedance detector gets its name because it never draws grid current, even for large input-signal amplitudes. This corresponds to an infinitely high grid-input impedance

summary

☐ In one popular type of pentagrid converter the oscillator signal is generated by the cathode and first and second grids, which function as a series-fed Hartley oscillator. ☐ Detectors remove the intelligence from the modulated carrier by converting it to a voltage whose variations correspond to the original modulating signal.

☐ The output voltage of an AM detector corresponds to the peak-to-peak amplitude variations of the input. ☐ The AM detector rectifies the input and filters the portion left to produce a voltage that follows the envelope of the rectified signal. ☐ Important detector characteristics are linearity, sensitivity, signal-handling capacity, and selectivity. ☐ Because they have poor selectivity, AM diode detectors use tuned circuits before the detector. ☐ The AM diode detector can handle large input signals with little distortion.

☐ The grid-leak detector amplifies as well as detects. It has low selectivity but good sensitivity for weak input signals. ☐ Plate detectors are amplifiers whose biasing condition rectifies the modulated input signal. A filter then produces the modulation envelope. ☐ The plate detector has good sensitivity and selectivity if the input signal is not relatively large. ☐ Infinite-impedance detectors never draw grid current and consequently have good selectivity. ☐ The output of the infinite-impedance detector is taken from the cathode.

---

review questions

1. In the pentagrid converter, which tube elements usually generate the oscillator signal?
2. Can transistors be used for converter circuits?
3. The term *second detector* applies to what?
4. What is a *linear detector*?
5. Why must the AM detector rectify the input signal before filtering it?
6. List three of the most important characteristics of detectors.
7. Draw the schematic of a triode AM detector and explain its operation.
8. Equipment that uses diode detectors must have a number of tuned circuits before the detector. Why?
9. How does the triode grid-leak detector rectify the input signal?
10. How does the plate detector rectify the input signal?
11. Why does grid current never flow in the infinite-impedance detector?

the regenerative detector

A regenerative detector is basically a grid-leak detector in which a portion of the output signal is fed back to the tuned input circuit *in phase* with the input signal. The in-phase feedback lowers the resistance of the tuned input circuit, therefore raising its Q. This substantially increases the strength of input signals at and near the resonant frequency of the tuned circuit, so that both the amplification and selectivity of the stage are raised, especially for extremely weak input signals.

A basic regenerative detector is shown. Resistor R_1, capacitor C_1, and the tuned input circuit function the same as in a grid-leak detector. Tickler coil L_2 in the plate circuit is coupled by mutual induction to the coil (L_1) of the tuned input circuit. When plate current flows, the magnetic flux produced in L_2 links L_1 and induces a voltage in it. The coils are arranged so that the polarity of the induced voltage has the same phase as the input voltage, thus making the feedback regenerative. The rest of the circuit operation is the same as a grid-leak detector, which has been discussed. The input signal is rectified by the action of R_1 and C_1 in the grid circuit, and the plate current pulses are filtered by r-f choke L_3 and capacitors C_2 and C_3.

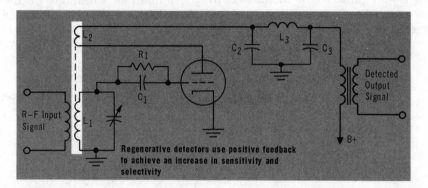

Regenerative detectors use positive feedback to achieve an increase in sensitivity and selectivity

A regenerative detector provides maximum sensitivity when the amount of feedback is *just below* that required to cause the stage to oscillate. There are various methods for adjusting the amount of feedback, the most basic one being to change the degree of coupling between the tickler and tank coils by varying the spacing between them. Another method is to vary the plate voltage, and, therefore, the amplification of the stage.

Regenerative detectors have several distinct disadvantages that limit their use. Their selectivity is so sharp that some of the outer side-band frequencies of a signal are eliminated or greatly attenuated. In addition, the amount of feedback must be changed each time a new input signal is received. Another disadvantage is that since the circuit operates just below the conditions necessary for oscillation, even random noise voltages send the circuit into oscillation.

the superregenerative detector

Essentially, a superregenerative detector is a regenerative detector that is continuously driven *in* and *out* of *oscillation*. Either an auxiliary circuit or components in the detector circuit *automatically* produce and then stop oscillation, usually at a low r-f rate of from 25 to 100 kilocycles. As a result, the circuit is called a *quenched oscillator*.

A basic superregenerative detector circuit is shown. The circuit is identical with that of the regenerative detector shown on the previous page with the exception of the plate supply voltage. Instead of a d-c plate supply, an *a-c supply voltage* with a quenching frequency of about 25 kilocycles is used. On the positive half cycles of the plate voltage, the tube conducts, feedback occurs, and the stage oscillates. On the negative half cycles, the tube cuts off and the oscillations in the tuned input circuit decay.

For proper operation, the oscillations must completely decay to zero before they begin building up again on the next positive half cycle of plate voltage. In effect, the r-f input signal, on its positive swings, keeps the circuit oscillating longer or shorter according to the amplitude of the r-f signal. These successive groups of oscillations are, then, amplitude and pulse-width modulated by the amplitude variations of the received signal, and are rectified and filtered by the detector action of the stage.

In this circuit, intermittent oscillations required for superregeneration are brought about by the use of an a-c plate supply voltage

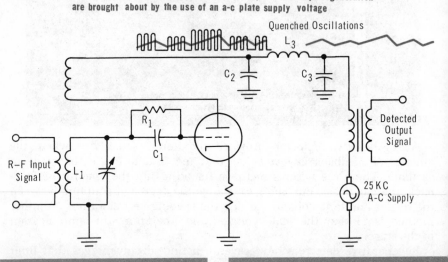

Another method of obtaining intermittent oscillations is to use a d-c plate supply and larger values for R_1 and C_1. When this is done, the grid-leak bias builds up beyond cutoff to a voltage determined by the amplitude of the input signal . . .

Oscillations are quenched and do not begin again until C_1 discharges to the point where the bias allows oscillation. This is known as self-quenching oscillation, and the quenching time follows the amplitude variations of the input signal

the beat-frequency detector

None of the detectors described so far is suitable for detecting the intelligence carried by *CW signals*. These signals have *constant amplitudes*, with the intelligence usually added by breaking the carrier up into a sequence of pulses. If such signals were applied to standard AM detectors, the filtering action of the detector would result in a *d-c output*, which is unsuitable for recovering the intelligence. What is usually desired is that the CW signal be *converted* to a lower (audio) frequency. Then, the signal pulses can be listened to by means of headphones or a loudspeaker.

Circuits that accomplish this frequency conversion of CW signals are called beat-frequency detectors, or *heterodyne detectors*, since they perform their function by heterodyning the CW signal with a locally-generated signal, known as the beat-frequency oscillator (*BFO*) signal. The BFO signal is always higher or lower than the CW signal by some audio frequency, such as 1000 cps. After heterodyning takes place, the two original frequencies, plus their sum, are removed by filtering or tuned circuits, and the difference beat frequency is applied to a loudspeaker or headphone.

One type of beat-frequency detector consists of a regenerative detector in which the feedback is adjusted so that oscillation takes place. The tuned grid circuit, therefore, contains two frequency components: the input CW signal frequency, and the frequency at which the stage is oscillating. Normally, the grid circuit is detuned just enough to produce an audible beat in the output. Thus, to tune in a CW signal, the detector is first tuned to the signal frequency, as indicated by a *zero beat* in the output. Then, the detector is slightly detuned until the desired audio beat frequency is heard in the output.

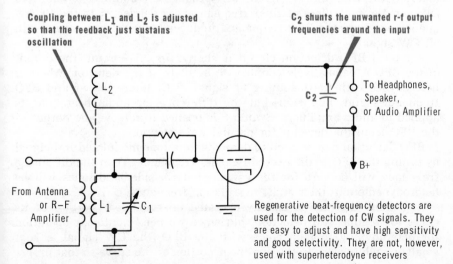

Coupling between L_1 and L_2 is adjusted so that the feedback just sustains oscillation

C_2 shunts the unwanted r-f output frequencies around the input

L_2

C_2 To Headphones, Speaker, or Audio Amplifier

From Antenna or R–F Amplifier

L_1 C_1

B+

Regenerative beat-frequency detectors are used for the detection of CW signals. They are easy to adjust and have high sensitivity and good selectivity. They are not, however, used with superheterodyne receivers

CW detection
in superheterodyne receivers

In AM superheterodyne receivers, BFO reception is made possible by the inclusion of a beat-frequency oscillator

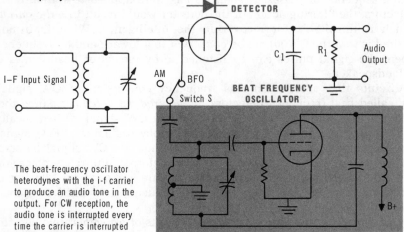

The beat-frequency oscillator heterodynes with the i-f carrier to produce an audio tone in the output. For CW reception, the audio tone is interrupted every time the carrier is interrupted

Superheterodyne receivers equipped for CW reception use a conventional AM detector for both AM and CW signals. However, when CW is being received, a special oscillator, called a *beat-frequency oscillator* (BFO), is switched into operation. The BFO has a basic frequency that is separated from the receiver i-f by some convenient audio frequency, such as 500 or 1000 cps. The BFO provides a signal that, when heterodyned with the i-f signal, will produce an audio beat note. All CW signals, regardless of their frequency, are converted to the i-f frequency, so the same BFO frequency produces identical beat notes with all CW signals.

A typical BFO detection circuit is shown. In this circuit, the output of the BFO is capacitively coupled to the plate of the detector, where it heterodynes with the incoming i-f signal. R_1C_1 filters the i-f and BFO frequencies and their sum, but the difference, or audio beat note, is applied to audio amplifiers. Switch S is opened to remove the output of the BFO from the detector for normal AM detection.

BFO detection can be used to demodulate a tone-modulated AM signal by tuning the BFO to the *exact* i-f carrier frequency. Then the difference frequency will be zero for the carrier, but the side-band tones will be heterodyned out at their audio modulation frequency.

The diode detector is usually operated on the linear portion of its curve for regular AM detection, but since we need nonlinear operation for heterodyning to take place with the BFO, the CW signal is kept small enough to work in the nonlinear portion of the curve so that proper mixing will take place.

the video detector

Detectors used for video signals, such as those encountered in radar and television, are of the same types as those previously described. However, there are two differences that you should be aware of. One of these is the *polarity* of the detected signal. In audio applications, it makes *no difference* which half of the AM signal is removed during detection, since both halves of the signal envelope have the same amplitude variations. But in video applications, an equipment is designed for a certain output polarity from the detector. For example, some television receivers require a positive output from the video detector, while others require a negative output. If the wrong polarity were used, although this is highly unlikely, the reproduced television picture would resemble a photographic negative. Areas that should be dark would be light and vice versa.

Whether or not a television receiver requires a positive or negative output from the video detector depends on the number of video amplifiers and where the video signal is applied (cathode or control grid) to the picture tube. As shown, a diode detector can be made to deliver either a positive or negative output merely by reversing its cathode and plate circuits.

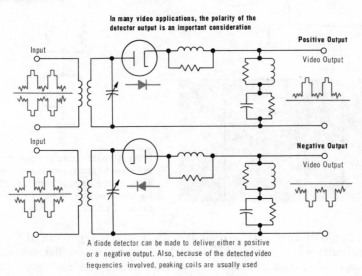

In many video applications, the polarity of the detector output is an important consideration

Input

Positive Output

Video Output

Input

Negative Output

Video Output

A diode detector can be made to deliver either a positive or a negative output. Also, because of the detected video frequencies involved, peaking coils are usually used

The second difference between video and other types of AM detectors is the *filters* and *loads* used to produce the output signal. Simple networks can be used when only audio modulation is involved, but with video modulation and pulse modulation, the filters and output loads must allow the higher video frequencies to be developed. Usually, series and shunt peaking coils are used. This was discussed earlier for the video amplifiers.

intercarrier detection

In television receivers, the video detector serves two functions: (1) it detects the video signal, and (2) it produces the intercarrier sound i-f signal. Remember that the main i-f section of the television receiver processes two signals: the video i-f carrier and the sound i-f carrier. The video i-f carrier is AM, and the sound i-f carrier is FM.

The video detector can demodulate the video signals, but it cannot demodulate the sound signals; also, we would not want the sound demodulated yet because it would interfere with the picture. Instead, since the video i-f carrier and the audio i-f carrier are always 4.5 megacycles apart, we beat the two carriers together in the detector diode and produce an FM intercarrier sound i-f signal that has a 4.5-megacycle carrier, which is the difference frequency. The response curve of the main i-f section is such that the curve gives only a little gain to the main audio i-f and a great deal of gain to the video i-f.

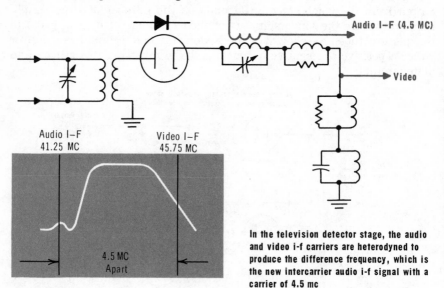

In the television detector stage, the audio and video i-f carriers are heterodyned to produce the difference frequency, which is the new intercarrier audio i-f signal with a carrier of 4.5 mc

The audio i-f amplitude is usually only from 2 to 5 percent of the video i-f amplitude when they reach the video detector stage. Because of this, the audio i-f carrier operates completely within the nonlinear portion of the diode's operating curve. This allows it to heterodyne with the video i-f carrier so that its modulation will be transferred to the difference frequency at 4.5 megacycles. The large amplitude video i-f carrier operates on the linear portion of the diode's curve so that its amplitude modulation will not take part in the heterodyning, and the video will not interfere with the sound. The 4.5-megacycle intercarrier sound i-f signal is removed at the output of the detector and sent to the audio i-f section.

single side-band detectors

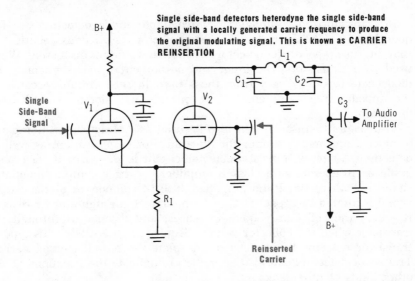

Single side-band detectors heterodyne the single side-band signal with a locally generated carrier frequency to produce the original modulating signal. This is known as CARRIER REINSERTION

When single side-band signals are transmitted with the full carrier, conventional AM detectors can be used to recover the intelligence. If the carrier is partially or completely *suppressed,* however, special detectors must be used. Actually, these detectors are really mixers, or modulators, since they *heterodyne* the single side-band signal with a locally generated carrier frequency. This is called *carrier reinsertion.* Essentially, the single side-band detector performs the *reverse* of the modulation operation that took place at the transmitter. The side-band signal is actually the sum frequency or difference frequency of the carrier and modulating frequencies. So, by heterodyning it with the reinserted carrier, the difference frequency produced corresponds to the original modulation.

There are numerous circuits used for single side-band detection. Many of them are essentially the same as, or variations of, the semiconductor-diode balanced modulators previously discussed. The low impedances of these diode circuits make them especially suitable for transistorized equipment. There are also many kinds of tube-type single side-band detectors in use. One of these, which employs dual triodes, is shown. You will recognize this circuit as being very similar to the cathode-coupled triode mixer previously described. The single side-band signal is applied to the grid of V_1, and the locally generated carrier frequency to the grid of V_2. The side-band signal is coupled to the cathode of V_2 by means of the voltage variations it produces across common-cathode resistor R_1. The heterodyne products produced at the plate of V_2 are then filtered by L_1, C_1, and C_2, leaving only the difference frequency, which is the original audio modulation. The audio output is coupled through capacitor C_3 to the first audio amplifier.

transistor AM detectors

In transistorized equipment, *semiconductor-diode* detectors are frequently used. The operation of these detectors is virtually identical to that of tube-type diode detectors, which have been discussed. When used with transistors, the input and output circuits of semiconductor diode detectors may vary from those used in tube circuits because of the impedance requirements. However, this does not alter their basic operation.

Transistors themselves can also be used as AM detectors. Compared to diode detectors, they offer the advantage of *amplification,* as well as detection. A simple transistor-detector circuit is shown in B. The stage is biased to operate as a class B amplifier, so the incoming modulated signal is both rectified and amplified. The i-f component of the output signal is filtered by capacitor C_1, which charges through emitter resistor R_1 when the collector voltage increases, and discharges through the transistor when the collector voltage decreases. Essentially, this type of transistor detector functions like the plate detector discussed earlier. Transistor detectors can also be made to duplicate the functions of the other kinds of tube detectors.

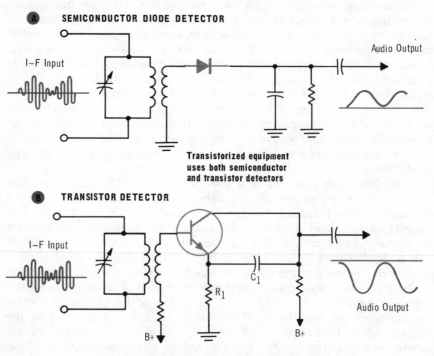

A   SEMICONDUCTOR DIODE DETECTOR

I–F Input

Audio Output

Transistorized equipment
uses both semiconductor
and transistor detectors

B   TRANSISTOR DETECTOR

I–F Input

C_1

R_1

B+   B+

Audio Output

The transistor detectors provide amplification as
well as detection. This transistor detector
operates class B to rectify the signal before
amplifying and filtering it

summary

☐ Regenerative detectors are grid-leak detectors that use positive feedback to increase their sensitivity and selectivity. The feedback raises the Q of the tuned input circuit. ☐ One limitation on the use of regenerative detectors is that the amount of feedback must be changed for each new input signal. ☐ The superregenerative detector is continuously driven in and out of oscillation by a quenched oscillator. The successive groups of oscillations are amplitude and pulse-width modulated by the amplitude variations of the received signal and are then rectified and filtered.

☐ CW detection in superheterodyne receivers is accomplished by an auxiliary beat-frequency oscillator that is switched into operation only for CW reception. The beat-frequency oscillator signal is heterodyned with the incoming CW signal and the audible difference frequency is applied to a loudspeaker. ☐ Two factors distinguish video detectors from audio detectors: (1) the polarity of the output signal is important in video detectors, and (2) video detectors use series and shunt peaking coils because of the higher frequencies involved.

☐ In television, the video detector produces the intercarrier sound i-f signal, as well as the video signal. ☐ When a carrier has been suppressed, single side-band detectors recover it by heterodyning the suppressed-carrier signal with a locally-generated carrier. The difference frequency produced corresponds to the original modulation.

review questions

1. What are some of the disadvantages that limit the use of regenerative detectors?
2. In what way is a regenerative detector modified to produce a superregenerative detector?
3. What is a beat-frequency oscillator?
4. Explain how a beat-frequency detector converts a CW signal to a lower frequency.
5. Why are peaking coils often used as filters and output loads in video detectors?
6. Is the output polarity of an audio detector important?
7. What signals are produced by the television video detector stage?
8. What is *carrier reinsertion*?
9. Single side-band detectors are quite similar to which of the circuits studied earlier in this volume?
10. Draw a transistor AM detector circuit and explain its operation.

FM detectors

An FM detector produces an output voltage that corresponds to the *frequency variations* of its input signal. Ideally, an FM detector should respond only to frequency variations. Amplitude variations that have been superimposed on the FM signal by noise, etc., should have *no effect* on the detector output. In practice, however, some FM detectors are sensitive to amplitude variations, and therefore must be preceded by a *limiter*. If a limiter is not used in these cases, or if a limiter is used but functions improperly, the detector output will be distorted.

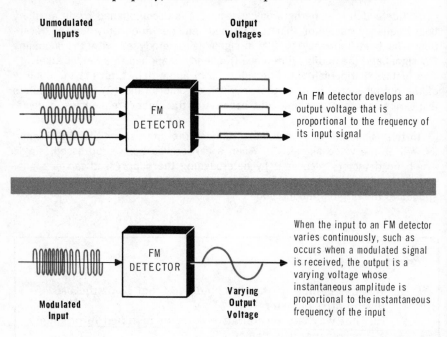

Unmodulated Inputs   **Output Voltages**

FM DETECTOR

An FM detector develops an output voltage that is proportional to the frequency of its input signal

FM DETECTOR

Modulated Input   **Varying Output Voltage**

When the input to an FM detector varies continuously, such as occurs when a modulated signal is received, the output is a varying voltage whose instantaneous amplitude is proportional to the instantaneous frequency of the input

Essentially, an FM detector operates by producing a d-c voltage at its output when an unmodulated signal is received. Then, when a modulated signal is received, the output varies above and below its d-c level in accordance with the frequency variations of the signal. As far as the signal intelligence is concerned, it makes no difference whether the detector is designed so that an increase in signal frequency causes a rise in output voltage and a decrease in signal frequency causes a drop in output voltage, or whether a decrease in frequency causes a rise in output voltage and an increase in frequency causes a drop. In either case, the output follows the *intelligence* contained in the input.

FM detectors are also called *discriminators*, since they discriminate, in terms of output amplitude, between different input frequencies.

the slope detector

One of the earliest developed and simplest FM detectors is the *slope detector*. As shown, the operation of a slope detector is based on the *frequency response curve* of an i-f amplifier. Normally, the highest point on the curve represents the resonant frequency of the amplifier tuned input and output circuits, which is the *same* as the i-f frequency. The i-f frequency thus receives maximum amplification, while frequencies *above* and *below* the i-f are amplified to a lesser degree.

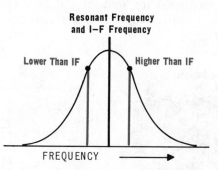

Resonant Frequency
and I–F Frequency

Lower Than IF   Higher Than IF

FREQUENCY ⟶

If a tuned circuit is tuned to the incoming i-f
frequency, frequencies above and below the i-f
receive less amplification than the i-f itself

Consider what happens if the amplifier is detuned, so that its resonant frequency is slightly higher than the i-f frequency. The i-f frequency now falls on the side, or *slope,* of the amplifier's frequency response curve. As a result, higher frequencies are *above* the i-f on the slope, and so receive *more amplification* than the i-f. Similarly, lower frequencies are *further down the slope,* and receive *less amplification.*

If a tuned circuit is tuned slightly off the i-f
frequency, frequencies above the i-f receive more
amplification, and frequencies below receive less

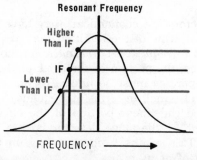

Resonant Frequency

Higher
Than IF

IF
Lower
Than IF

FREQUENCY ⟶

This is the basic principle on which the slope
detector works

the slope detector (cont.)

Since, in an FM signal, the i-f is the center frequency and the intelligence side bands are variations above and below the center frequency, this slope method satisfies the requirements of FM detection. The input frequency variations are converted to output amplitude variations. Actually, the output signal contains both frequency and amplitude variations, but when the signal is applied to a conventional AM detector, all of the i-f frequency components are filtered out, leaving only the audio signal.

A method sometimes used for achieving slope detection is to use a standard AM detector and detune its input circuit. A typical circuit for this is shown.

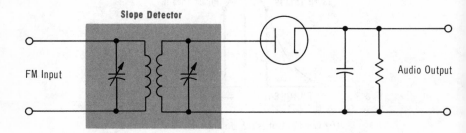

An AM diode detector with a detuned input circuit converts an FM input signal into an audio output by means of slope detection

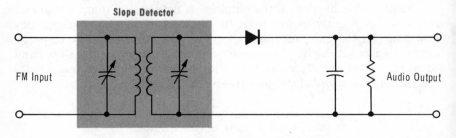

Although slope detectors are economical, they have many disadvantages that limit their use. One of these is that they are limited to input signals that have *small frequency variations*. For good reproduction of the signal intelligence, the portion of the slope of the response curve on which the circuit operates must be linear. In practical circuits, the linear portion is relatively small in terms of frequency range. Any input signals that are beyond the linear portion of the curve are distorted.

Another disadvantage of the slope detector is that it produces less than maximum gain. This results from operating on the slope of the response curve instead of at its peak.

the triple-tuned discriminator

Another type of FM detector that, although effective, is not used too extensively because of tuning difficulties, is the triple-tuned, or Travis, discriminator. As this circuit is sensitive to amplitude variations, it must always be preceded by a limiter.

A typical, triple-tuned discriminator is shown. Essentially, the circuit consists of two diodes, each with its own tuned input circuit and i-f filter network. The input to the discriminator is transformer coupled from a tuned circuit in the output of the limiter to the tuned input circuits of the diodes. The limiter output (L_1C_1) is tuned to the *center frequency* of the FM signal. One of the diode tuned input circuits, say L_2C_2, is tuned *above* the center frequency, and the other is tuned *below*. The resonant frequencies of both L_2C_2 and L_3C_3 differ from the center frequency by the *same amount*. So, when the FM signal is at the center frequency, relatively small, but equal, voltages are induced in L_2C_2 and L_3C_3 by transformer action. These voltages have the same polarity with respect to the two diodes, since the transformer is wound so that the top of L_2 and the bottom of L_3 always have like polarities. With equal input voltages, the two diodes therefore conduct an equal amount. This causes equal voltage drops across resistors R_1 and R_2, which are equal in value and serve as the loads for the respective diodes. Capacitors C_4 and C_5 filter the i-f components of the diode current.

The three tuned circuits at the input of the triple-tuned discriminator are all tuned to different frequencies

L_1C_1 is tuned to the signal center frequency, L_2C_2 is tuned some amount above the center frequency, and L_3C_3 is tuned below the center frequency by the same amount that L_2C_2 is above it

The output of each diode, therefore, changes as the input frequency shifts. At the center frequency, both diodes produce the same outputs, which cancel each other

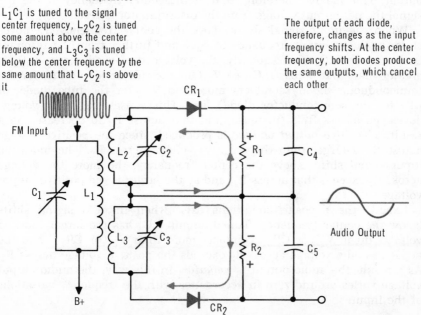

the triple-tuned discriminator (cont.)

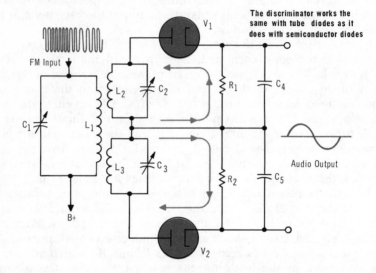

The discriminator works the same with tube diodes as it does with semiconductor diodes

Although the center frequency produces voltages of equal *amplitude* across R_1 and R_2, these voltages do *not* have the same polarity with respect to ground. Since the audio output is taken from across the two resistors, they are effectively in *series opposition* with respect to the output. This means, therefore, that at the center frequency of the FM signal the net output voltage from the discriminator is *zero*.

When the input signal shifts above the center frequency, it moves closer to the resonant frequency of L_2C_2 and further from the resonant frequency of L_3C_3. Consequently, the voltage developed across L_2C_2 is greater than that across L_3C_3, so V_1 (for the tube diode or CR_1 for the semiconductor diode) conducts more and V_2 (for the tube diode, or CR_2 for the semiconductor diode) less. This causes the audio voltage developed across R_1 to increase, and that across R_2 to decrease. As a result, a *positive output voltage* is produced, since the positive voltage across R_1 is larger than the negative voltage across R_2. The more the input signal shifts above the center frequency, the more the voltage across R_1 exceeds that across R_2, and so the larger is the positive output voltage.

Exactly the opposite conditions exist when the FM signal shifts below the center frequency. Tuned circuit L_3C_3 has the larger induced voltage, diode V_2 (or CR_2) conducts more than V_1 (or CR_1), and the negative audio voltage across R_2 exceeds the positive voltage across R_1. As a result, the audio output is *negative*. In this way, the audio output voltage varies around zero in accordance with the frequency variations of the input.

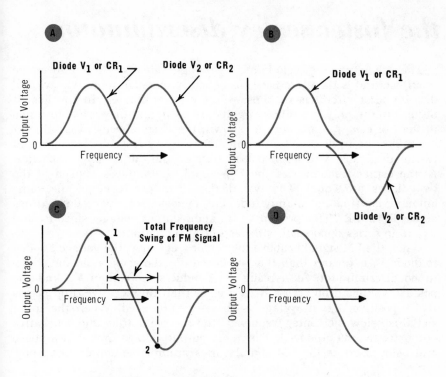

The frequency response of an FM discriminator is called an S curve, because of its inverted S shape

response curve

The two diode circuits of the triple-tuned discriminator have identical frequency responses, which *overlap* somewhat at the center frequency. This is shown in A. However, since one of the diodes delivers a negative output voltage, its response curve can be drawn in the *negative direction,* as shown in B. Inasmuch as the portions of the two curves that overlap cancel algebraically to produce zero output, the curves can be smoothly joined to produce one *continuous* response curve, as shown in C.

For the discriminator to deliver an undistorted output, it must operate on the *linear portion* of the overall response curve, which is essentially between points 1 and 2 in C. The frequency separation between these two points has to be great enough to accommodate the total frequency swing of the FM signal. If the separation is too narrow, large deviations will cause the diodes to operate in their nonlinear region, causing distortion of the output signal.

The useful portion of the discriminator response curve is shown in D. Because of its shape, it is frequently called an *S curve.* Such a curve is typical of the response of all FM discriminators.

the foster-seeley discriminator

The triple-tuned discriminator, although effective, is cumbersome to adjust, and is therefore used infrequently. A much more widely used discriminator circuit is the Foster-Seeley discriminator. In the Foster-Seeley circuit, only *two* tuned circuits are used, and they are both tuned to the FM *center frequency*. As shown, the Foster-Seeley discriminator resembles the triple-tuned discriminator in many respects. It consists of two diodes, each with its own load resistor and output filter capacitor. At the center frequency of the FM signal, the voltages applied to the two diodes are equal. The two diodes, therefore, conduct the same amount, causing equal-amplitude but opposite-polarity voltage drops across R_1 and R_2. This produces zero audio-output voltage, since R_1 and R_2 are in series opposition with respect to the output.

When the FM signal is above the center frequency, the voltage applied to diode V_1 is greater than that applied to V_2, the same as in the triple-tuned discriminator. As a result, V_1 conducts more than V_2, and the positive voltage drop across R_1 is greater than the negative drop across R_2. A positive output voltage is therefore produced. When the input signal is below the center frequency, the reverse is true, and a negative output voltage is produced. The audio output voltage thus varies above and below zero as the FM signal varies around the center frequency.

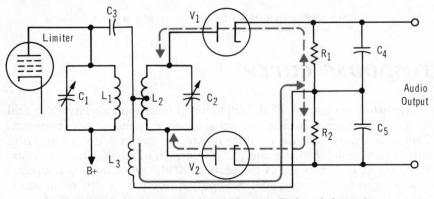

The Foster-Seeley discriminator is sensitive to amplitude variations and must therefore be preceded by a limiter, or an i-f amplifier that also serves as a limiter

You can see from this that the Foster-Seeley discriminator works the same as the triple-tuned discriminator, with the exception of the manner in which the input voltage is made to vary as the signal frequency varies. In the triple-tuned discriminator, the voltage input to the diodes varies with the signal frequency because of the *frequency response characteristics* of the separate tuned input circuits. In the Foster-Seeley circuit, though, the input voltage varies with the frequency as a result of a *phase shifting* of the input signal by tuned circuit L_2C_2, which is common to both diodes.

phase relationships in the foster-seeley discriminator

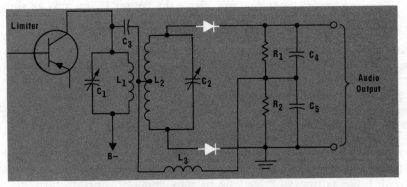

In many circuits, semiconductor diodes are often used in place of vacuum-tube diodes. The circuit functions the same, though, regardless of which type of diode is used

Each diode of the Foster-Seeley discriminator has *two voltages* applied to it. One of these is coupled *directly* from the limiter circuit by capacitor C_3 and the other is *transformer coupled* by the mutual induction existing between L_1 and L_2. The *vector sum* of these two voltages is the actual voltage that is applied to the diodes. To understand how this vector sum is developed, refer to the illustrations on the next page. These show the vector relationship between the voltage and current induced in the secondary of the input circuit (L_2C_2) and that in the primary (L_1C_1).

The voltage developed across the primary, E_p, is taken as the reference vector, and *leads* the primary current, I_p, by 90 degrees, as in any inductance. Because of the 180-degree reversal in polarity that always exists between the primary and secondary voltages in a transformer, E_i, which is the voltage induced in the secondary windings, lags E_p by 180 degrees. You should note that E_i is *not* the output voltage of the secondary, but must be considered as a voltage generated in series with the secondary winding. The induced voltage E_i causes secondary current, I_s, to flow through secondary winding L_2 and capacitor C_2.

At the *center frequency* of the FM signal, A on page 6-138, the secondary circuit is at resonance. The inductive and capacitive reactances effectively cancel each other, making the circuit *purely resistive*. As a result, the secondary current, I_s, is in phase with the induced voltage E_i. The flow of secondary current produces a voltage across C_2, which is the *output voltage, E_s,* of the secondary circuit. Since the voltage lags the current by 90 degrees in a capacitor, E_s lags I_s by 90 degrees. Thus, E_s also leads E_p by 90 degrees. In effect, then, at the center frequency of the FM signal, the voltage output of the secondary circuit produced by mutual induction leads the primary voltage by 90 degrees.

phase relationships in the foster-seeley discriminator (cont.)

When the input signal deviates *above* the center frequency, as shown in B, the secondary is no longer resonant at the signal frequency. X_L is larger than X_C, so the secondary is *inductive*. As a result, the secondary current is not in phase with the induced voltage E_i, but *lags* it by some amount. The exact amount of lag depends on how inductive the secondary is, and therefore on how much the signal is above the center frequency. Since the current through a capacitor *always* leads the voltage across it by 90 degrees, any shift in phase of I_s produces a *like shift* in E_s. This means that above the center frequency E_s leads E_p by an angle *less* than 90 degrees.

When the FM signal is *below* the center frequency (C) the phase relationships between E_i, I_s, E_s, and E_p are reversed. The secondary circuit is *capacitive*, so I_s leads E_i by some amount. This, in turn, causes the output voltage, E_s, to lead the primary voltage by *more* than 90 degrees.

On the following page, you will see how E_s and E_p combine to produce the required frequency-dependent input voltages for the discriminator diodes.

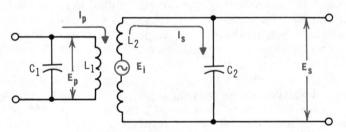

These are the currents and voltages in tuned transformers such as those used in the Foster-Seeley discriminator

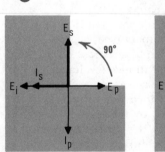

At Center Frequency

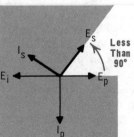

Above Center Frequency

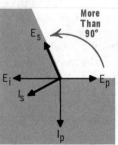

Below Center Frequency

phase relationships in the foster-seeley discriminator (cont.)

You saw on the previous page how the output voltage, E_s, of the secondary circuit (L_2C_2) leads the primary voltage by 90 degrees at the center frequency of the FM signal. However, since the secondary coil is centertapped, E_s is effectively divided into *two equal voltages* that are 180 degrees out of phase. At the center frequency, then, one of these voltages leads the primary voltage by 90 degrees, and the other lags by 90 degrees. This is shown in A. The total voltage applied to diode V_1 therefore consists of E_p, which is coupled through capacitor C_3 and developed across L_3, and E_{s1}, which is applied from the top of capacitor C_2. Similarly, the total voltage applied to diode V_2 consists of E_p and E_{s2}.

As shown in B, E_p and E_{s1}, combine vectorially to produce voltage e_1, which is the voltage for diode V_1, and E_p and E_{s2} combine vectorially to produce e_2, which is the voltage for diode V_2. Both E_{s1} and E_{s2} always have the same amplitude, and at the center frequency have equal phase relationships with E_p. At the center frequency, therefore, e_1 and e_2 are equal, causing equal diode currents, and zero audio output voltage.

As shown in C, above the center frequency E_{s1} shifts *closer* to E_p, while E_{s2} shifts *farther away*. Voltage e_1 is therefore larger than e_2, and a positive audio output voltage is produced. The reverse is true at frequencies below the center frequency (D). E_{s1} shifts *farther* from E_p, while E_{s2} shifts closer. As a result, e_2 is larger than e_1, and a negative audio output voltage is developed.

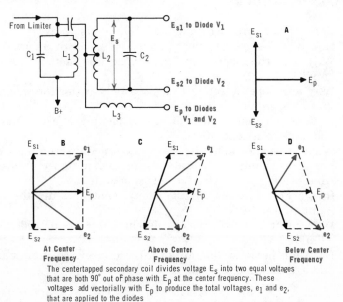

At Center Frequency   Above Center Frequency   Below Center Frequency

The centertapped secondary coil divides voltage E_s into two equal voltages that are both 90° out of phase with E_p at the center frequency. These voltages add vectorially with E_p to produce the total voltages, e_1 and e_2, that are applied to the diodes

summary

☐ An FM detector produces an output voltage whose amplitude variations correspond to the frequency variations of the input signal. ☐ In slope detection, the input circuit is tuned slightly higher than the i-f, or center, frequency. The FM side bands above and below the i-f, therefore, receive more or less amplification than the i-f. These variations are then converted to amplitude variations. ☐ Slope detectors are limited to inputs with small frequency variations. They also produce a limited amount of gain.

☐ The triple-tuned, or Travis, discriminator uses three input tuned circuits to convert frequency variations to voltage changes. The three tuned circuits are all tuned to different frequencies. When the response curves of the three tuned circuits are combined, they produce an S curve. ☐ At the center frequency of the AM signal, the output of the triple-tuned discriminator is zero. ☐ The triple-tuned discriminator operates on the linear portion of its S curve, which must be long enough to accommodate the total frequency swing of the FM signal.

☐ The Foster-Seeley discriminator has two tuned input circuits, both tuned to the FM center frequency. The input signal voltage to the two diodes of the circuit varies with frequency as a result of phase shifting. ☐ The Foster-Seeley discriminator is sensitive to amplitude variations and must be preceded by a limiter.

---

review questions

1. FM detectors are also called *discriminators*. Why?
2. How does a slope detector operate? What is an S curve?
3. Why does the slope detector produce less than maximum gain?
4. Why are slope detectors best used only with input signals that have small frequency variations?
5. Draw a schematic diagram of a triple-tuned discriminator and explain its operation.
6. What is another name for the triple-tuned discriminator?
7. For a discriminator to produce an undistorted output, on what portion of its S curve must it operate?
8. In the Foster-Seeley circuit, what frequencies are the two input circuits tuned to?
9. Why must a Foster-Seeley discriminator be preceded by a limiter?
10. Draw a schematic diagram of a Foster-Seeley discriminator and explain its operation.

the ratio detector

A commonly used FM detector that is relatively insensitive to amplitude variations of the input signal and therefore does not usually have to be preceded by a limiter stage is the ratio detector. Unlike the Foster-Seeley discriminator, the diodes in the ratio detector are connected in *series* with respect to the tuned input circuit L_2C_2.

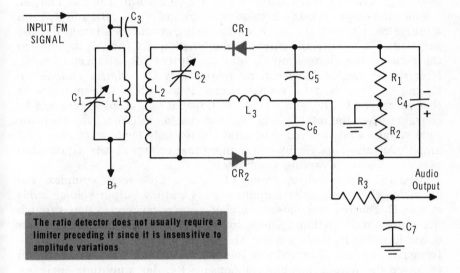

The ratio detector does not usually require a limiter preceding it since it is insensitive to amplitude variations

At the FM center frequency, both diodes have equal applied voltages, so they conduct equally. Conduction takes place on the half cycles of the input signal when the top of the input transformer secondary (L_2) is negative. The conduction path is through diode CR_1, resistors R_1 and R_2, diode CR_2, and back to the tuned circuit. During conduction, capacitor C_4 charges, with a polarity as shown, to the input signal voltage. During the half cycles of the input signal when the diodes are cut off, C_4 attempts to discharge through R_1 and R_2. However, the RC time constant of the combination is *long* in relation to both the i-f and audio-modulation frequencies. Consequently, C_4 loses very little of its charge. In effect, C_4 functions as a battery envelope voltage within which the output signal will vary.

While the diodes are conducting, still at the center frequency of the input signal, capacitors C_5 and C_6 also charge. Since they are connected directly across capacitor C_4, the *total* charge on C_5 and C_6 is the same as that on C_4. Both C_5 and C_6 have equal values, so when both diodes conduct, the total charge divides equally between them. As you can see, the audio output voltage is taken from the junction of C_5 and C_6, and is effectively the center voltage that exists across both C_5 and C_6. This means that at the center frequency, since the charges on C_5 and C_6 are equal, the voltage at their junction is effectively zero.

the ratio detector (cont.)

When the input signal shifts above or below the center frequency, one of the diodes *increases* in conduction, while the other *decreases*. This changes the charge balance between C_5 and C_6, but has no effect on the C_4, R_1, and R_2 circuit, since the total current does not change. When the charge on one of the capacitors is greater than the other, the voltage at their junction changes above or below zero according to the charges.

Since the output is taken in relation to ground, C_5, C_6, R_1, and R_2 form a bridge circuit, with the audio voltage being produced between the two junctions. Essentially, the output at the junction of C_5 and C_6 depends on the *ratio* of the charges on C_5 and C_6. Resistor R_3 and capacitor C_7 filter the i-f carrier. However, no matter how the *relative* charges on C_5 and C_6 vary, the *total* voltage across them both is still the same as that across the C_4, R_1, and R_2 circuit. Capacitor C_4 keeps it constant by charging when the total voltage tends to rise, and discharging when the total voltage tends to drop. The total voltage only tends to change with amplitude variations. So, by maintaining that voltage steady, C_4 counteracts the effect of a varying amplitude.

Actually, the overall operation of C_4 is a little more complex. For example, when the carrier amplitude rises and the output voltage tends to rise, C_4 charges and causes a higher average current to flow through the entire circuit, including the transformer. This loads the transformer down, lowering its Q. As a result, the phase-shift sensitivity of the transformer is reduced. This reduces the discriminator action of the circuit to lower the output to help compensate for the amplitude increase. The opposite happens when the amplitude of the carrier drops. In summary, then, C_4 acts as a limiter by both maintaining a relatively stable total drop and by adjusting the phase sensitivity of the transformer.

Capacitor C_4 is usually an electrolytic capacitor, so that even though it has a large value, it will not bypass the i-f signals. Electrolytics inherently are slow devices that only respond to low frequencies, such as audio frequencies.

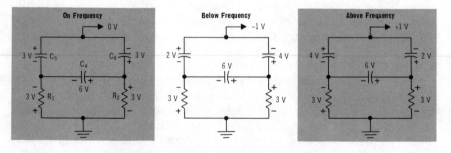

Since R_1 and R_2 are equal, they always have equal drops, as determined by the charge across C_4. However, the charges on C_5 and C_6 vary according to the FM signal. With this bridge circuit, the capacitor charges oppose the resistor drops, and the algebraic sum of each branch is the output. The algebraic sum of each branch is always the same, since the charges on C_5 and C_6 vary oppositely

the gated-beam detector

One of the latest approaches to FM detection is the gated-beam detector. This detector circuit provides both *limiting* and *detection* by means of the characteristics of a special type of tube, called a *gated-beam tube*. The gated-beam tube has a cathode, a plate, and three grids. The three grids are quite different in both design and function from the conventional control, screen, and suppressor grids used in a pentode. The gated-beam grids are called the *limiter* grid (grid 1), the *accelerator* grid (grid 2), and the *quadrature* grid (grid 3).

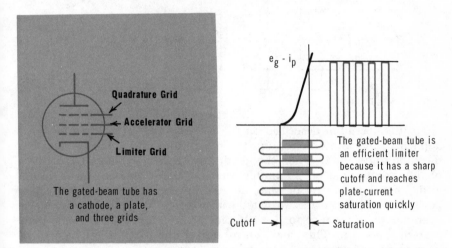

Quadrature Grid

Accelerator Grid

Limiter Grid

The gated-beam tube has a cathode, a plate, and three grids

$e_g - i_p$

The gated-beam tube is an efficient limiter because it has a sharp cutoff and reaches plate-current saturation quickly

Cutoff →   ← Saturation

In operation, both the limiter grid and the quadrature grid control the tube plate current *equally*. If either has a sufficiently negative voltage, plate current is cut off. However, when the plate current is cut off, *cathode current* still flows. This is because the internal structure of the tube is such that whenever one or both of the grids cut off the plate current, the cathode current is switched to the accelerator grid, which provides a return path to the B+ supply. Another characteristic of the gated-beam tube is that it reaches *plate-current saturation* very quickly. There is only a relatively small difference between the grid voltage that will just allow plate current to flow, and that which will cause plate-current saturation.

As a result of the above characteristics, a sinusoidal input to a gated-beam tube causes the plate current to be in the form of sharp rectangular *pulses*. The tube begins to conduct when the positive half cycle of the input reaches a certain value, and reaches saturation after only a small further increase in the amplitude of the input signal. The tube then continues to conduct at this saturation level until the input signal drops below the value required for plate current cutoff. This action occurs on every cycle of the input signal and provides the *limiting* required for FM signals.

operation of the gated-beam detector

GATED-BEAM DETECTOR

For the operation described on the previous page, the input signal is applied to the limiter grid, and the quadrature grid is biased to allow the tube to conduct. When the quadrature grid is sufficiently negative, plate current is cut off no matter what voltage is applied to the limiter grid. This *dual control* of plate current by the limiter and quadrature grids can be likened to two gates within the tube. *Both* gates must be open for plate current to flow. If one or both gates are closed, plate current is cut off. This dual control allows the gated-beam tube to be used as an FM detector, as you will now see.

In the typical gated-beam detector circuit shown, the FM input signal is applied to the limiter grid by tuned input circuit L_1C_1, which is tuned to the i-f, or center, frequency of the incoming signal. A parallel resonant circuit, L_2C_2, connected between the quadrature grid and ground, is also tuned to the signal center frequency. On positive half cycles of the input signal, the limiter grid is driven above plate current cutoff, so bunches of electrons flow through the tube towards the plate. As each bunch, or concentration, of electrons flows past the quadrature grid, electrostatic repulsion causes electrons to flow from the quadrature grid wire into tank circuit L_2C_2. These electrons make up a quadrature grid current that charges capacitor C_2 to a negative value.

When each bunch of electrons has passed the quadrature grid, C_2 discharges through L_2 and recharges in the opposite direction when the field around L_2 collapses in the normal tank-circuit flywheel action. These flywheel oscillations in L_2C_2 would eventually damp out, except that bunches of electrons pass the quadrature grid at the natural frequency of the tank circuit. Thus, energy is supplied to the quadrature tank circuit during each negative half cycle of its oscillation. The changing quadrature grid voltage caused by the tank-circuit oscillations alternately biases the quadrature grid in and out of plate-current cutoff.

operation of
the gated-beam detector (cont.)

The phase relationship between the quadrature grid voltage and the limiter grid voltage depends on the frequency of the input signal. If it is at the *center frequency*, the quadrature grid voltage *lags* the limiter grid voltage by *90 degrees*. This arises from two facts. First, the quadrature current lags the input voltage by 90 degrees, since quadrature current is maximum when the input voltage just begins to cause plate current, and zero when the input voltage is maximum. Secondly, the quadrature tank is at resonance, so it is *purely resistive* with respect to the quadrature current. This means that the quadrature voltage is in phase with the quadrature current, and so lags the input signal voltage by 90 degrees.

With this phase relationship between the two grid voltages, each grid tends to allow plate current to flow at a different time during the input signal cycle. However, plate current only flows when the voltages on both grids allow it. As shown, this occurs when the two grid conduction potentials overlap. In effect, each gate is open at a different time during the input signal cycle. But there is a period during which *both* gates are open. Plate current, in the form of equal-amplitude pulses, flows *only* during this period.

The above description applies to the operation of the gated-beam detector when the FM signal is at the *center frequency*. On the next page, you will see how the circuit responds to frequency variations in the input signal.

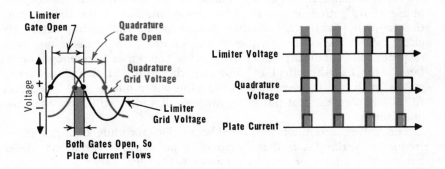

At the center frequency of the FM signal, the quadrature grid voltage lags the limiter grid voltage by 90°

For convenience, grid voltages in a gated-beam detector are often represented as pulses. At the center frequency of the FM signal, these voltages produce plate current pulses that have equal amplitudes and equal widths

operation of
the gated-beam detector (cont.)

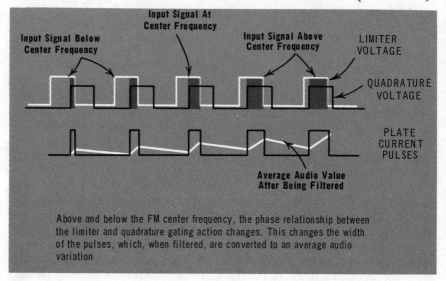

Above and below the FM center frequency, the phase relationship between the limiter and quadrature gating action changes. This changes the width of the pulses, which, when filtered, are converted to an average audio variation

When the FM input signal to the gated-beam detector varies around the center frequency, the electron bunches pass the quadrature grid at *varying* intervals rather than at the resonant frequency of the quadrature-grid tank circuit. However, the frequency variations continually pass through the center frequency, and in doing so supply enough energy to the quadrature tank circuit at its natural frequency to keep the phase of its gating action relatively constant. But at the limiter grid, the frequency variations change the phase of the gating action. In effect, above the center frequency the limiter gate opens *sooner* with respect to the quadrature gate, while *below* the center frequency it opens *later*. This has the effect of changing the *width* of the plate-current pulses, with higher frequencies producing wider pulses, and vice versa. All of the plate-current pulses, regardless of width, still have the same amplitudes.

The gating action of the gated-beam detector thus changes input-frequency variations into corresponding pulse-width variations. Referring to the schematic shown on page 6-144, the varying-width plate-current pulses are converted to a varying audio voltage by capacitor C_5. This capacitor is charged from plate to ground by the plate-current pulses, and attempts to discharge through resistor R_4 and the B+ supply when plate current is cut off. The RC time constant of C_5 and R_4, though, is long in relation to the i-f (or pulse) frequency. So the voltage across the capacitor is averaged to an audio voltage that varies in accordance with the average value of plate current, which is determined by the widths of the plate-current pulses.

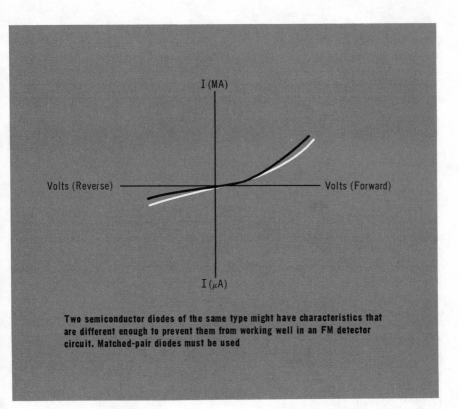

Two semiconductor diodes of the same type might have characteristics that
are different enough to prevent them from working well in an FM detector
circuit. Matched-pair diodes must be used

semiconductor matched pairs

In any of the FM detectors you studied, semiconductor diodes can
be used in place of the vacuum-tube diodes. However, because the circuit
requires that both diode sections perform almost exactly alike on and
off the center frequency, semiconductor diodes do present a problem.

Semiconductors cannot be controlled as well as vacuum tubes while
they are being manufactured. This is particularly true since semiconductors have a reverse current and their tube counterparts do not. So,
although two tube diodes of the same type will have close enough
characteristics to work in an FM detector circuit, two semiconductor
diodes probably will not work well even though they are the same type.
To get around this, manufacturers hand select semiconductor diodes
to find pairs that will match. These are called *matched pairs,* and they
are given a different designation to identify them. Matched pairs must
be used in a discriminator circuit. If one diode goes bad, both diodes
must be replaced with a matched pair.

summary

☐ Unlike the Foster-Seeley discriminator, the diodes used in the ratio detector are connected in series with the tuned input circuit. ☐ The ratio detector, which is not sensitive to amplitude variations in the input signal, need not be preceded by a limiter. ☐ The audio output voltage from the ratio detector is taken from the junctions of the detector's bridge circuit, at the output of the diodes. The output at this point depends on the ratio of the charges on the bridge circuit's two equal-value capacitors. The action of the electrolytic capacitor across the output circuit performs the limiting function.

☐ Since the gated-beam tube both limits and detects, its use as a detector also eliminates the need for a limiter. ☐ Two of the three grids of the gated-beam tube control the plate current in such a way that an FM input signal is converted into pulses whose width varies according to the input frequency variations. ☐ The output pulses of the gated-beam detector are converted to a varying audio voltage by an RC output network.

☐ When semiconductors are used in FM detectors, the two diodes are matched for almost identical characteristics. ☐ If one diode in a matched pair goes bad, both diodes must be replaced by another matched pair.

review questions

1. Draw a schematic diagram of a ratio-detector circuit and explain its operation.
2. Why isn't it necessary for a ratio detector to be preceded by a limiter?
3. What are the three grids in the gated-beam tube called?
4. What characteristics of the gated-beam tube make it an efficient limiter?
5. Draw a gated-beam tube detector circuit, and describe how the gated-beam tube works.
6. At the FM center frequency, what is the relationship between the quadrature grid voltage and the limiter grid voltage in the gated-beam detector?
7. Why does the width of the plate current pulses vary as the input frequency varies in the gated-beam detector?
8. In the gated-beam detector, how are the plate current pulse-width variations converted to a varying audio output voltage?
9. What are *semiconductor matched pairs*?
10. Why are semiconductor matched pairs necessary in FM detectors?

electronics
seven

auxiliary circuits

One of the major differences between an inexpensive table radio and a quality communications receiver is the degree to which auxiliary circuits are used

Both types use the required basic receiver stages, but the communications receiver also employs many auxiliary circuits, which account in large part for its quality performance

In the previous volumes, you studied the major classes of electronic circuits, such as amplifiers, oscillators, modulators, and demodulators. Because of their widespread use, you should thoroughly understand these circuits and their operation. In addition to these basic circuit types, there are many other circuits that you should understand as well. These other circuits, which perform a wide variety of *specialized functions*, can be grouped together under the broad category of *auxiliary circuits*.

Normally, auxiliary circuits are not used alone, but appear in combination or conjunction with a group of circuits. For this reason, many auxiliary circuits can be explained only on the basis of their interrelationship with some other circuit, or circuits. This is why the basic electronic circuit types have been covered first, before presenting the auxiliary circuits in this volume.

No attempt is made in this volume to describe all of the auxiliary circuits you are likely to encounter. This would be impossible due to the almost limitless number of such circuits. However, you will learn about the more common auxiliary circuits.

AVC and AGC circuits

In previous volumes, you learned about volume control and gain control circuits. In their simplest form, these are usually variable resistors that control either the gain or the input or output signal amplitude of an amplifier. The volume control of a radio receiver is the most common example of a volume or gain control. By *manually* adjusting such a control, the desired output level is obtained.

A disadvantage of manual gain control with a receiver is that it cannot provide a *constant* output under all conditions. If a receiver is tuned from a weak signal to a strong signal, its output might increase to an intolerable level. This would then require readjustment of the volume control. Similarly, when a receiver is tuned to a particular signal, the output level can vary widely if the input signal strength fluctuates as a result of fading and other similar transmission phenomena. Under such conditions, constant readjustment of the volume control would be necessary. This is obviously impractical, since such signal fluctuations are *rapid*.

To overcome these problems, *automatic volume control* (AVC) or *automatic gain control* (AGC) is frequently used in addition to the manual control. The manual control initially sets the receiver output at the desired level. The AGC circuit then automatically keeps the receiver output at this level in spite of variations in the input signal strength.

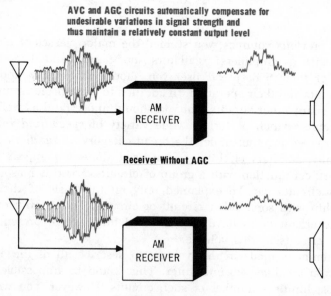

AVC and AGC circuits automatically compensate for undesirable variations in signal strength and thus maintain a relatively constant output level

AM RECEIVER

Receiver Without AGC

AM RECEIVER

Receiver With AGC

basic principles of AVC and AGC circuits

All AGC (and AVC) circuits perform two basic functions. The first of these is to develop a d-c voltage that is proportional to the receiver input signal strength at all times. This AGC voltage, as it is called, increases when the received signal strength increases and decreases when the signal strength decreases. The second function of the AGC circuit is to apply the AGC voltage to the r-f and i-f stages of the receiver, where it serves as a *bias* voltage. In this way, the AGC voltage controls the gain of the r-f and i-f stages, and, therefore, the overall gain of the receiver.

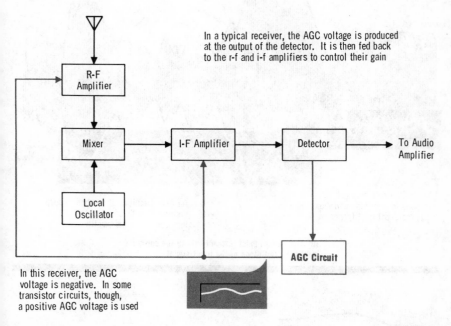

In a typical receiver, the AGC voltage is produced at the output of the detector. It is then fed back to the r-f and i-f amplifiers to control their gain

In this receiver, the AGC voltage is negative. In some transistor circuits, though, a positive AGC voltage is used

When the signal level at the receiver input increases, the AGC voltage increases a proportionate amount. Consequently, a larger bias is applied to the r-f and i-f stages, and their gain is reduced. The receiver output thus remains relatively constant, instead of increasing in accordance with the input signal strength.

When the receiver input signal decreases in strength, the *opposite* action occurs. The AGC voltage drops in amplitude, the bias of the r-f and i-f stages is reduced, and the receiver gain increases. Again, the receiver output level remains essentially constant.

response of AGC circuits

An AGC circuit must produce a d-c voltage that varies in amplitude in accordance with the signal strength variations caused by fading and other atmospheric conditions. However, the AGC circuit must not respond to the amplitude variations of the input signal that represent *intelligence*. If it did, the AGC voltage would tend to counteract the modulation envelope of the r-f carrier. This, of course, would result in *distortion* of the signal.

RECEIVER INPUT SIGNAL

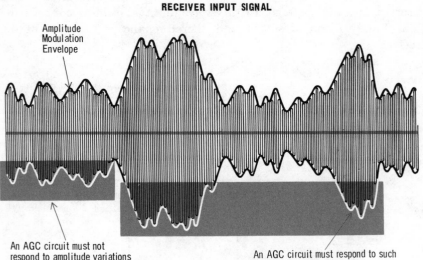

Amplitude
Modulation
Envelope

An AGC circuit must not
respond to amplitude variations
that represent intelligence

An AGC circuit must respond to such
variations as these unwanted
increases in signal amplitude

**An AGC circuit must respond only to the unwanted
amplitude variations of the input signal**

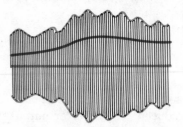

This diagram shows how the average level of the positive
alternations varies with signal strength. This is the
variation that produces the AGC voltage

The amplitude variations in a receiver input signal that are caused by fading are considerably *slower* than the amplitude variations that correspond to intelligence. So an AGC circuit must respond to relatively low-frequency amplitude variations, but not to high-frequency variations that represent intelligence.

the basic AGC circuit

In a receiver, the most convenient place to derive an AGC voltage is from the output of the *detector* stage. This is because the detector produces a fluctuating d-c output voltage that varies in proportion to the receiver input signal strength. The a-c component of the detector output serves as the receiver audio signal (or the video signal in a television receiver). But the d-c component, when properly filtered, is highly suitable as an AGC voltage.

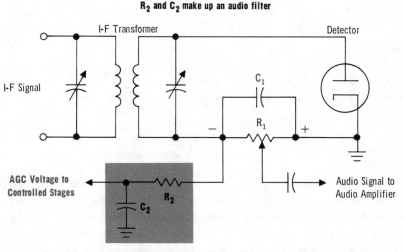

R$_2$ and C$_2$ make up an audio filter

R$_2$ and C$_2$ prevent the AGC voltage from following the audio variations present in the detector output signal

A basic AGC circuit is shown. The vacuum-tube diode is the receiver detector stage. The i-f signal is rectified by the diode and the i-f component is filtered by resistor R$_1$ and capacitor C$_1$. The voltage developed across R$_1$, therefore, varies in accordance with the audio modulation. However, its *average* d-c amplitude also changes in proportion to changes in the input signal strength. Resistor R$_2$ and capacitor C$_2$ remove the audio component from the voltage across R$_1$, leaving only the d-c component, which is the AGC voltage. The AGC voltage is then applied to the r-f and i-f amplifiers to control their gain. Usually, the AGC voltage is carried on a common wire, or line, called the *AGC bus*.

The AGC voltage shown is *negative,* since it is taken from the ungrounded side of resistor R$_1$. In tube-type receivers, the AGC voltage is always negative, since it must vary the negative bias on the grids of the controlled tubes. With transistor circuits that require a positive AGC voltage, the diode detector is reversed.

positive AGC

In transistorized receivers, semiconductor diodes are normally used as detectors. An AGC voltage can be derived from such detectors in exactly the same manner that it is derived from electron-tube detectors. This can be seen by comparing the circuit shown in A with that shown on the previous page. The only difference is that one uses a semiconductor diode and the other uses an electron-tube diode.

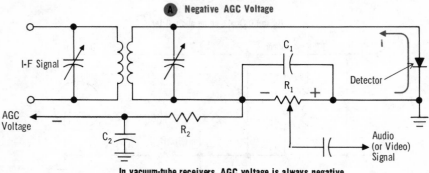

A Negative AGC Voltage

In vacuum-tube receivers, AGC voltage is always negative

An important difference between AGC circuits for tube and transistorized equipment is the polarity of the AGC voltage. In tube-type receivers, the AGC is *always* negative. But in transistorized receivers, the AGC can be either negative or positive. The polarity required depends on the type of transistors and the circuit configuration used for the r-f and i-f amplifiers. Generally, the same circuit can produce *either* a negative or a positive AGC voltage. The only difference is the point at which the voltage is taken from the detector circuit, or the diode polarity used. As an example, the circuit shown in A can be made to produce a positive AGC voltage by reversing the diode. The AGC voltage is then taken from the positive side of resistor R_1. This is shown in B.

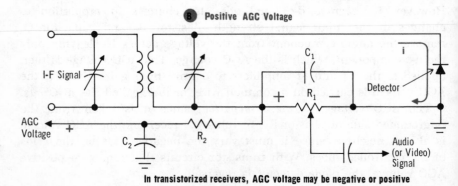

B Positive AGC Voltage

In transistorized receivers, AGC voltage may be negative or positive

other AGC circuits

Many variations of the basic AGC circuit just described are frequently used. All of them, however, are essentially similar. Sometimes, a *separate* diode is used for the AGC circuit. Such a circuit is shown in A. The AGC diode is used only to produce the AGC voltage. It does not serve as the detector stage for the receiver.

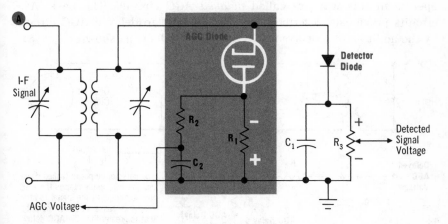

In the circuit shown, the detected signal voltage produced by the detector diode is *positive*. The AGC voltage produced by the AGC diode, however, is *negative*, since its plate is returned to ground. Resistor R_2 and capacitor C_2 filter the rectified i-f signal to produce a steady d-c voltage for the AGC. This type of circuit is used in receivers in which the output of the detector must be positive, although a negative AGC is needed.

Frequently, a single tube is used as an amplifier, a detector, triode and an AGC rectifier (as shown in B). These tubes contain small, subsidiary plates in addition to the regular plate. The small plates are used for the AGC circuit and the detector. Using a separate AGC diode minimizes the *interaction* between the detector and AGC circuits. This tube is a duo-diode triode.

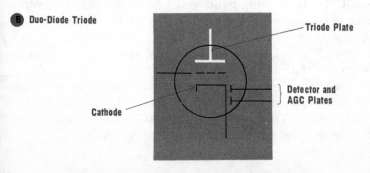

delayed AGC

The disadvantage of simple AGC is that it reduces the gain of even very *weak* input signals. This is undesirable, since weak signals require as much gain as possible. Ideally, therefore, an AGC circuit should produce *no AGC* voltage for weak signals, but function normally when the input signal rises above some certain minimum level. Circuits that operate in this way are called *delayed AGC* circuits. The basic AGC circuits previously described can be converted to delayed AGC circuits by the addition of a delayed AGC diode and voltage as shown.

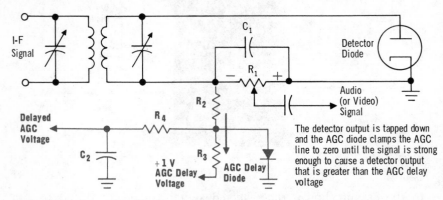

The detector output is tapped down and the AGC diode clamps the AGC line to zero until the signal is strong enough to cause a detector output that is greater than the AGC delay voltage

Resistors R_2 and R_3 are connected between the anode detector output and the delay voltage to control the delay diode. R_2 and R_3 are *equal* and drop equal voltages. When the d-c output of the detector is −1 volt, since the delay voltage is +1 volt, R_2 and R_3 will drop 1 volt so that the voltage at their junction, which is applied to the diode anode, is zero volts. The diode doesn't conduct, then, and there is zero AGC voltage. When the detector output is *less* than −1 volt because a weak signal is being received, the junction of R_2 and R_3 tends to go positive. The diode conducts and *clamps* the junction to ground (clamping is covered later), so there is still zero AGC voltage.

As a matter of fact, this condition continues for any weak signal that causes less than −1 volt at the detector. The diode conducts to prevent the AGC line from going positive as long as the negative output of the detector is *less* than the delaying voltage. Thus, the AGC is zero for all weak signals so that they can get maximum gain.

When a stronger signal is received, causing the negative detector output to be greater than the positive delay voltage, the voltage at the junction of R_2 and R_3 will be negative. The diode, then, will no longer conduct, and that negative voltage will be filtered by C_2 and R_4 and sent as the AGC voltage. The amplitude of the AGC will depend on how much greater the detector output is than the delay voltage.

amplified AGC

The AGC circuits previously discussed are suitable when the changes in signal strength that must be compensated for are not too large. When the signal strength varies widely, though, the AGC voltage variation is too small to give *full compensation*. As a result, some variations in signal amplitude still exist at the output of the receiver.

To keep the receiver output constant even for large variations in signal strength, a larger AGC voltage variation must be developed than is possible with a basic AGC circuit. This can be done by using an *amplified* AGC circuit.

A typical amplified AGC circuit is shown. It uses a separate amplifier stage to increase the level of the detected signal. This AGC amplifier receives the rectified signal from the detector through capacitor C_1. Its amplified output is rectified by the AGC rectifier and filtered by resistor R_5 and capacitor C_4. The resulting amplified AGC voltage is applied to the controlled stages along the AGC line. Variable emitter resistor R_3 permits adjustment of the gain of the AGC amplifier. In this way, the AGC voltage can be set at any desired level. If an AGC delay network similar to that described on the previous page is added at the output of the AGC rectifier, the circuit will provide a delayed AGC. Variable resistor R_3 then acts as a *threshold* control.

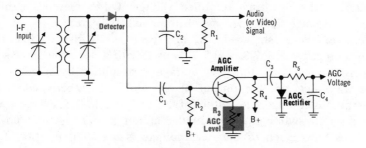

Essentially, an amplified AGC circuit contains an amplifier stage between the signal detector and the AGC rectifier and filter. An AGC level control sets the AGC action

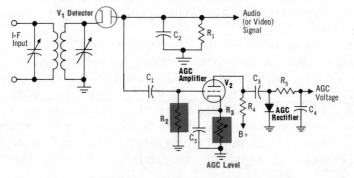

other amplified AGC circuits

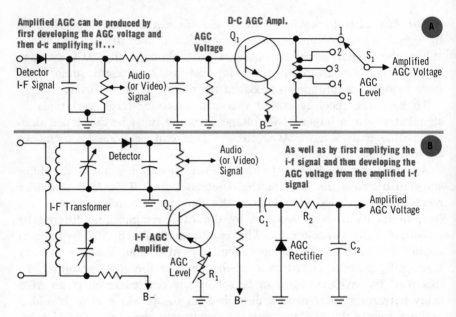

Amplified AGC can be produced by first developing the AGC voltage and then d-c amplifying it...

Detector I-F Signal

Audio (or Video) Signal

AGC Voltage

D-C AGC Ampl.

Q_1

S_1

Amplified AGC Voltage

AGC Level

B–

A

I-F Transformer

Detector

Audio (or Video) Signal

As well as by first amplifying the i-f signal and then developing the AGC voltage from the amplified i-f signal

B

Q_1

I-F AGC Amplifier

AGC Level

R_1

C_1

R_2

Amplified AGC Voltage

AGC Rectifier

C_2

B–

B–

You have seen on the previous page how amplified AGC can be produced by amplifying a portion of the detector output and then rectifying and filtering the resulting amplified voltage. Other methods can also be used to produce the same type of amplified AGC voltage.

In one of these, shown in A, any basic AGC circuit, like those described on pages 7-5, 7-6, and 7-7, is used with a *d-c amplifier* inserted in the AGC line. Thus, the AGC voltage is amplified by stage Q_1. For greater amplification, the output of Q_1 could be directly coupled to another amplifier stage. The output of Q_1 is applied to the AGC-controlled stages through switch S_1. The divider action at each switch position determines how much of the AGC voltage is used: in position 1, the full AGC is used, in 5, the AGC is disabled, and the other positions provide different levels of AGC. This method of amplified AGC has the advantage of providing an AGC voltage with good frequency-response characteristics.

Another type of amplified AGC circuit, shown in B, uses a *separate* secondary winding on the i-f transformer to produce the AGC. The i-f voltage developed across this winding is amplified by an i-f amplifier stage, Q_1, and coupled to the AGC rectifier by capacitor C_1. After being rectified, the AGC voltage is filtered by resistor R_2 and capacitor C_2. The AGC level is determined by the setting of variable emitter resistor R_1. This type of circuit can produce large AGC levels, but has the disadvantage of requiring a special i-f transformer.

keyed AGC

As explained previously, AGC circuits are designed so that they do not respond to amplitude variations that represent signal intelligence. This is done by making the RC time constant of the AGC filter circuit long in relation to the frequency of the signal variations. Ordinary AGC circuits are, therefore, relatively *slow acting* and cannot respond to rapid variations in signal strength.

In television receivers, the sluggishness required of the AGC circuit to keep it from responding to changes in the *average* level of the video signals would be particularly objectional. Therefore, AGC circuits are often used that can respond more rapidly to changes in signal strength, but at the same time do not respond to the average video levels of the picture signal. Such circuits are called *keyed,* and, sometimes, *gated,* AGC circuits.

A keyed AGC circuit operates only during the blanking portion of the composite television signal

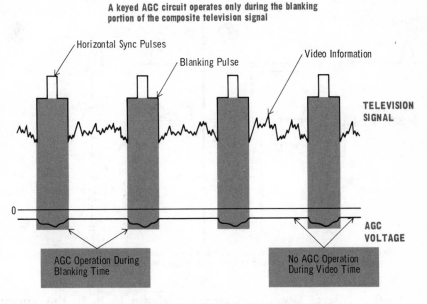

The circuit does not respond to the video variations of the signal

Essentially, a keyed AGC circuit is cut off during the video portion of the signal. It operates only during the blanking portion of the signal, when the blanking pulses, which have a relatively constant amplitude, are present. The circuit can thus be made to respond to rapid changes in the signal strength during blanking time, but not respond to the video variations.

keyed AGC circuits

One type of keyed AGC circuit is shown in A. It consists of a pentode stage with the video signal applied to the control grid. Plate voltage for the stage is *capacitively* applied in the form of a keying signal, or voltage, derived from the horizontal flyback pulse produced by the scanning circuits. The tube can conduct only when the keying signal provides plate voltage. This occurs at the same time that the horizontal blanking pulses appear at the control grid. The net result is that the tube is cut off during the video portions of the composite signal and conducts during the blanking portions in an amount corresponding to the amplitude of the blanking pulse. The average negative voltage developed across plate load resistor R_3 therefore varies in proportion to the blanking signal amplitude. This voltage is filtered by R_4 and C_3, and a steady AGC voltage is produced.

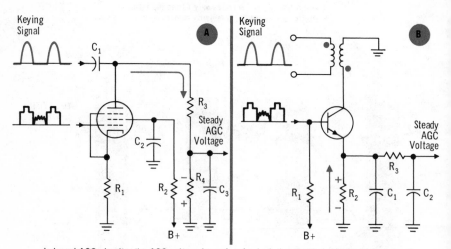

In keyed AGC circuits, the AGC voltage is produced only during the time that the keying signal is present. The average current that flows depends on the amplitude of the blanking pulse

Another type of keyed AGC circuit is shown in B. In this circuit, the keying signal is *inductively* coupled to the collector of the transistor. Except for the method of coupling the keying signal, the circuit operates essentially the same as that in A. Collector voltage is applied only when the keying signal is present. This coincides with the horizontal blanking pulses, so the stage only conducts during the horizontal blanking time. The stage operates as an emitter follower, with the AGC voltage developed across emitter resistor R_2 during conduction. A positive AGC voltage is filtered by resistor R_3 and capacitors C_1 and C_2 to provide a steady bias.

quiet AGC (squelch) circuits

With AGC, a receiver's sensitivity is *maximum* when *no signal* is being received. This condition occurs, for example, when the receiver is being tuned between stations. Because of the maximum sensitivity, the *background noise* picked up by the antenna between stations is greatly amplified by the receiver. This can be highly annoying, especially in radio receivers where the amplified noise is heard in the loudspeaker. To overcome this problem, a circuit called a *quiet AGC* circuit, or *squelch* circuit, is often used. Such a circuit cuts off the receiver output when no input signal is being received. It does this by blocking either the detector or audio amplifier when no signal is present.

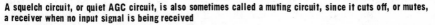

A squelch circuit, or quiet AGC circuit, is also sometimes called a muting circuit, since it cuts off, or mutes, a receiver when no input signal is being received

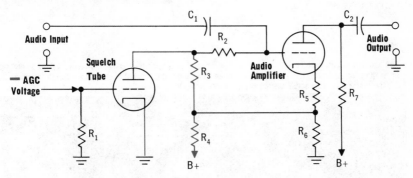

Here, the squelch circuit is activated by the absence of the AGC voltage

A basic squelch circuit is shown in A. The receiver AGC voltage is applied to the control grid of the squelch tube. When a signal is present at the receiver input, the AGC voltage it produces cuts off the squelch tube. The audio amplifier stage therefore operates normally, using cathode bias provided by resistors R_5 and R_6. With no signal at the receiver input, the squelch tube conducts, since no AGC voltage is produced. The plate current of the squelch tube then flows through resistor R_3, which is in the grid circuit of the audio amplifier. This reduces the positive voltage a great deal at that point, and effectively places a large negative bias on the grid of the audio amplifier, cutting off the stage and preventing background noise from reaching the loudspeaker.

quiet AGC
(squelch) circuits (cont.)

As an example of the circuit's operation, assume that there is an AGC input that cuts off the squelch tube. The values of R_4 and R_6 are such that their divider action puts $+10$ volts at the top of R_6. But, since both the grid and cathode are returned to the same point, the $+10$ volts have no effect. However, in between stations, when there is no AGC, the squelch tube conducts heavily and the plate current through R_3, which has a large value, causes the junction at R_2 and R_3 to be almost at ground. Now, the grid is returned to ground, but the cathode has $+10$ volts on it. This cuts off the audio amplifier.

You might notice that this circuit could not work off a delayed AGC, since no AGC voltage would be produced for weak signals and the receiver would be disabled. But it would work if a separate circuit were used to produce a d-c voltage from a signal in the audio section. In this case, the squelch circuit would be independent of the AGC circuit. Such a circuit is shown in B.

B

The squelch circuit here is activated by the absence of some positive voltage produced by the audio signal. When the positive voltage is applied to the base, it cancels the forward bias on the squelch stage, cutting the transistor off. The audio amplifier thus works normally

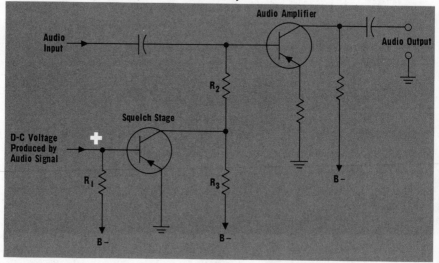

In between stations, when the positive voltage is not there, the squelch stage conducts heavily, putting the junction of R_2 and R_3 at ground. This removes the forward bias from the audio amplifier, cutting it off

summary

☐ The manual volume control must be readjusted to compensate for changes in signal levels. ☐ Automatic volume control (AVC) or automatic gain control (AGC) circuits are used in conjunction with the manual volume control to maintain a constant output regardless of variations in signal levels. These circuits develop a bias voltage that is applied to the r-f and i-f stages. ☐ When the strength of the input signal increases, the bias voltage increases and tends to reduce the output level. ☐ When the strength of the input signal decreases, the bias voltage decreases and tends to increase the output level.

☐ The AGC bias voltage is developed at the output of the detector circuit and is always negative for vacuum-tube circuits. ☐ For transistor circuits, the AGC voltage can either be positive or negative. ☐ The delayed AGC circuit prevents reduction in gain of weak signals. In this circuit, AGC voltages are developed only when the strength of the input signal exceeds a certain value. ☐ Standard AGC circuits cannot compensate for large variations in input signal strength. These variations can be compensated for by amplifying the AGC voltage.

☐ Slow-acting AGC circuits, although fine for standard receivers, should not be used in television receivers. Instead, fast-acting AGC circuits are used, but are cut off during the video portion of the signal. These circuits are called keyed, or gated AGC, circuits. ☐ The quiet or squelch AGC circuit prevents objectionable background noise when there is no signal input. When there is no signal input, a squelch tube cuts off the receiver.

review questions

1. What disadvantage of the manual volume control does the AGC circuit overcome?
2. What function does the manual volume control perform when AGC is used?
3. How does input signal strength affect the AGC circuit?
4. How are positive AGC voltages developed from a conventional AGC circuit?
5. Why must AGC circuits respond to low-frequency amplitude variations?
6. What does a delayed AGC circuit do?
7. What does a threshold control do?
8. When do keyed AGC circuits operate?
9. How does sensitivity affect background noise with no signal input?
10. How does a squelch tube operate?

limiter circuits

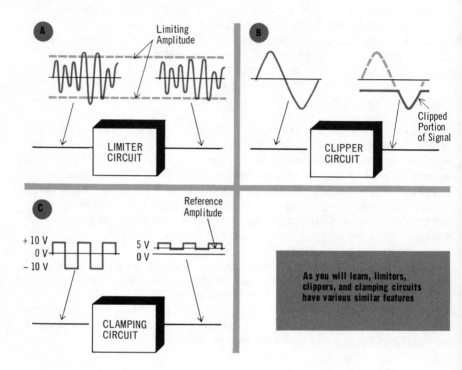

On the following pages, a class of circuits commonly called *limiters* will be described. As these circuits perform a variety of functions, it is difficult to establish an exact definition that includes them all. In this book, we will define a limiter as a circuit that eliminates those portions of a signal that *exceed* a certain amplitude. This is shown in A. Although the circuit in A removes *both* the positive and negative signal peaks, some limiters affect only the positive peaks, while others affect only the negative ones.

There are other circuits, called *clippers,* that perform functions somewhat similar to limiters. Actually, the term "clipper," or "clipper circuit" (B), is often used in place of "limiter." This is because limiting and clipping very often involve the same process. Both result in the removal of a portion of a signal waveform, although for different reasons. A limiter has *amplitude limitation* as its purpose, while a clipper is usually used for *waveshaping*. The term "clipper" is also used with separator circuits that *clip off* the desired part of the signal and reject the remainder.

the series diode limiter

The most basic limiter circuit consists merely of a diode in series with the load. The rectifying characteristic of the diode effectively *removes* either the positive or negative half cycles of an a-c input signal. You will recognize this, of course, as a basic *rectifier* circuit. But it also acts as a limiter circuit, since it prevents one-half cycle of the input signal from exceeding a certain amplitude, which, in this case, is ground (or 0 volts). Although such a simple circuit is not often used as a limiter, it demonstrates the fundamental principle of amplitude limiting.

Negative Signals Limited to Zero Amplitude

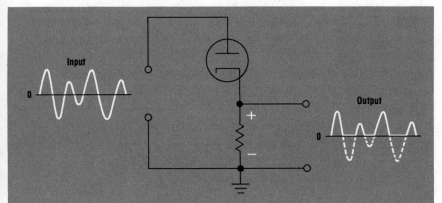

A basic rectifier circuit also serves the function of a basic limiter circuit

Positive Signals Limited to Zero Amplitude

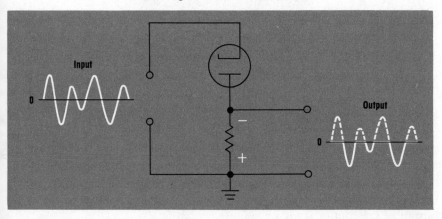

a practical series diode limiter

The basic series-diode limiter described on the previous page *completely* removes one-half cycle of the input signal. In practical applications, however, it is usually necessary to limit the positive or negative signal amplitude to some value other than zero.

This can be done by providing a *fixed bias* for the limiting diode, as shown. With this bias, the diode conducts even in the absence of an input signal, since the bias battery makes the diode cathode negative with respect to the plate. During the positive portions of the input signal, the diode anode becomes more positive, so the diode conducts more and the output signal follows the input signal. When the input signal goes negative, the diode anode becomes *less positive*. It is still positive with respect to the cathode, though, so the diode still conducts, although a smaller amount. But when the input signal goes sufficiently negative and the diode anode reaches the *same* potential as the cathode, the diode stops conducting. Any further increase in the negative amplitude of the input signal has no effect on the output signal, since the diode remains cut off. The negative signal amplitude is thus limited to the point at which the diode cuts off. This limiting amplitude can be changed by changing the value of the diode bias battery.

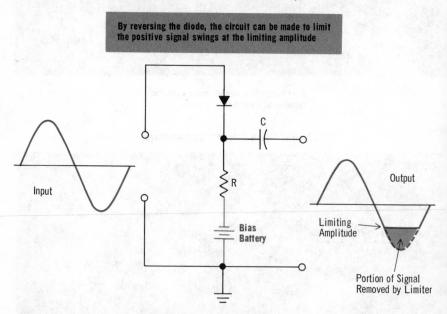

By reversing the diode, the circuit can be made to limit the positive signal swings at the limiting amplitude

Input

C

R

Bias Battery

Output

Limiting Amplitude

Portion of Signal Removed by Limiter

The voltage at the top of the diode cathode resistor is actually an a-c component riding on a d-c level. Capacitor C blocks the dc, so that the output of the limiter is an a-c signal.

the series noise limiter

Noise limiters are frequently used in high-quality radio receivers to remove *noise pulses* from amplitude-modulated signals. One common method of doing this is to limit the amplitude of the detector output before it is applied to the audio amplifiers. The noise pulses, which are of relatively *large amplitude,* are thus eliminated. A series diode limiter of the type shown can accomplish this.

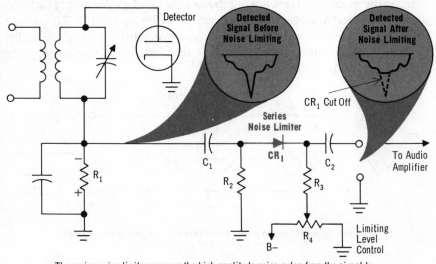

The series noise limiter removes the high-amplitude noise pulse from the signal by opening the path between the detector and audio amplifier for the duration of the noise pulse

Limiter diode CR_1 is connected between the detector output and the audio amplifier input. Resistor R_4 sets the *level* of limiting by making the cathode of the diode negative with respect to the anode by a certain amount. For normal signal amplitudes, CR_1 conducts and passes the signal to the audio amplifier. (Even though the signals are negative, they do not normally go negative enough to cut off diode CR_1.) But, when a large negative noise pulse is detected across detector load resistor R_1, it drives the anode of CR_1 negative with respect to the cathode. Consequently, CR_1 cuts off and does not pass the noise pulse. When the signal amplitude returns to a normal level at the end of the noise pulse, the diode begins conducting again.

In summary, the diode normally conducts to pass the signal to the audio amplifier. But, when the signal rises above a certain amplitude, the diode cuts off and does not pass the large-amplitude portion of the signal. The receiver is designed so that the desired signal does not reach the limiting level.

the parallel diode limiter

Series diode limiting is so called because the limiter diode is connected in series with the load. A diode can also be placed in *parallel* with the load to accomplish limiting. Such an arrangement is called a *parallel diode limiter*, and, often, a *shunt limiter*. As shown, the parallel diode can be connected to limit either the negative or positive signal alternation.

In A, the diode conducts during the positive half cycle, and practically the entire signal voltage is dropped across series resistor R. The output voltage delivered to the load is therefore essentially zero. Actually, there is a *small* output voltage during this half cycle due to the very low voltage drop across the diode.

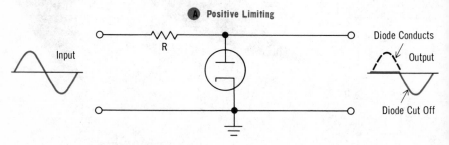

In parallel-diode limiting, the limiter diode is connected in parallel with the load.

During the negative half cycle, the diode is cut off, since its plate is negative with respect to its cathode. Consequently, the output voltage is equal to the full input voltage.

In the circuit shown in B, the diode is connected in the *opposite* manner. During the positive half cycle it is cut off, making the output voltage equal to the full input voltage. During the negative half cycle it conducts, limiting the output to the small voltage dropped across the diode.

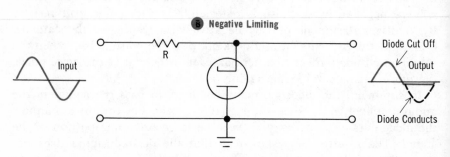

As discussed later, this is also called clamping

a practical parallel diode limiter

The basic parallel diode limiter described on the previous page essentially clips either the positive or negative half cycle from the input waveform. Usually, however, it is desired that limiting occur at some value *other* than zero. This can be done by providing a *bias voltage* for the limiter diode.

In the circuit shown in A, the bias battery makes the diode cathode positive with respect to the plate in the absence of an input signal. The diode, therefore, does not conduct until the input signal becomes sufficiently positive to drive the diode plate more positive than the cathode. When the diode does conduct, it shunts the signal and clips it as previously described. For all values of the input signal more negative than the bias voltage, the diode is cut off, so the output voltage is equal to the input.

By *reversing* the diode and the bias voltage, as shown in B, the circuit can be made to limit the negative half cycle of the input. In both of these circuits (A and B), the level at which limiting occurs is set by the value of the bias voltage.

Both half cycles of a signal can be limited by combining the circuits of A and B into a double diode limiter, as shown in C. In this circuit, CR_1 clips the positive half cycles and CR_2 clips the negative half cycles. Such an arrangement is a simple method of producing a usable square-wave output from a sine-wave input.

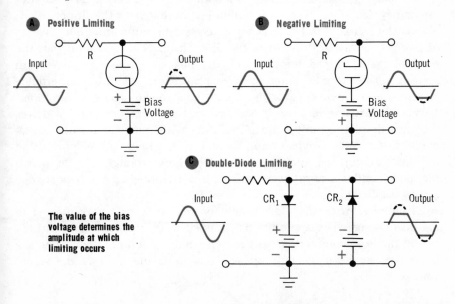

A Positive Limiting

Input R Output Bias Voltage + −

B Negative Limiting

Input R Output Bias Voltage − +

C Double-Diode Limiting

Input CR_1 CR_2 Output + − − +

The value of the bias voltage determines the amplitude at which limiting occurs

the parallel noise limiter

You saw previously how a series diode limiter can be used to remove unwanted noise pulses from the output of a receiver. A shunt diode limiter can also be used to accomplish the same thing. Such a circuit is called a *shunt noise limiter.*

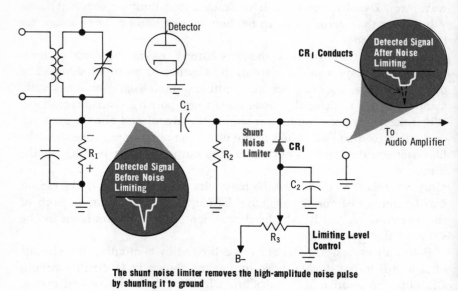

The shunt noise limiter removes the high-amplitude noise pulse by shunting it to ground

The shunt noise limiter shown is similar to the series noise limiter previously described. The basic difference is that here the limiter diode *shunts* the signal path between the detector and audio amplifier, instead of being in series with it. Also, the diode itself is *reversed,* so that the bias voltage developed across resistor R_3 makes the *anode* negative with respect to the cathode. Thus, under normal signal conditions, the diode is cut off and the detected audio signal is passed to the audio amplifier.

When a large noise pulse is detected across detector load R_1, it drives the cathode of the limiter diode more negative than the anode. Consequently, the diode conducts and C_2 shunts the noise pulse, preventing it from reaching the audio amplifier. The noise voltage level at which the diode conducts to produce limiting is determined by the *bias voltage* across the diode.

Essentially, when the diode conducts, the audio line is connected to the bias voltage. The audio line is *clamped* to that voltage level as long as the diode is conducting, so the noise pulse is eliminated. After the pulse passes, the diode cuts off and the audio line follows the signal voltage.

cutoff limiting

There are methods of amplitude limiting that do not use diodes. One uses the *cutoff characteristic* of a vacuum tube or transistor. A typical triode limiter circuit that works in this fashion is shown in A.

Cathode bias provided by resistor R_1 and capacitor C_1 sets the amplitude at which limiting takes place. Plate current in the circuit follows the input signal until the input goes sufficiently negative to cut off the tube. At this point, the plate current is *zero* and remains so until the input voltage rises above the cutoff value. Therefore, the output voltage waveform at the plate is an inverted replica of the input voltage until the tube cuts off. While the tube is cut off, the plate voltage remains at the full value of the B+ voltage and the negative peak of the *input* signal is clipped, or limited. Because of the 180-degree phase shift, this shows up in the positive peak of the output signal.

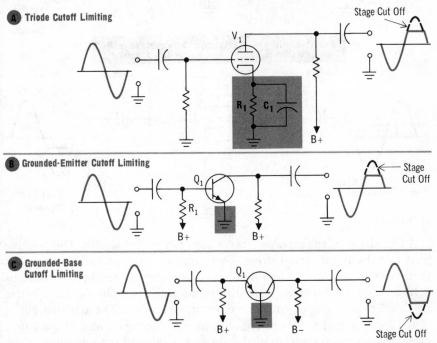

A Triode Cutoff Limiting   Stage Cut Off

B Grounded-Emitter Cutoff Limiting   Stage Cut Off

C Grounded-Base Cutoff Limiting   Stage Cut Off

Cutoff limiting occurs when a stage is driven into cutoff by the positive or negative extreme of the input signal

In a similar way, cutoff limiting can be produced in transistor circuits by the proper choice of bias voltages. The limiting action in the grounded-emitter stage (shown in B) is the same as for the triode. In the grounded-base stage (shown in C), polarity inversion does not take place between input and output, so the negative half cycle of the output is clipped rather than the positive half cycle.

saturation limiting

Cutoff limiting is made possible by the fact that when a tube or transistor is cut off, there is no *change* in its plate or collector current until the input signal drives it out of cutoff. This same condition of constant plate or collector current occurs when an input signal drives a stage into *saturation*. As a result, limiting can be accomplished by selecting operating parameters for a stage that will allow the input signal to drive the stage into saturation.

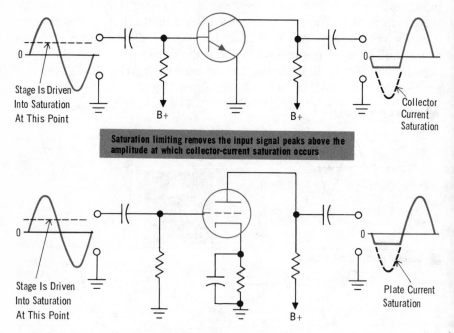

Saturation limiting removes the input signal peaks above the amplitude at which collector-current saturation occurs

A transistor stage employing saturation limiting is shown. The positive peaks of the input signal drive the transistor into saturation. Since no further collector current can flow once saturation is reached, the output voltage remains *constant* until the input signal amplitude falls below the level that produces collector current saturation. The positive peaks of the input signal are therefore clipped. For the remainder of the input cycle, the output waveform of the stage is a faithful reproduction of the input.

Since transistors have a forward-bias voltage at which runaway occurs, saturation limiting must be approached with care. The input signal swing must not be great enough to reach runaway, or the transistor will be damaged. With tubes, this not a severe problem, but the tube must be able to handle the grid current that will flow as a result of the positive peaks of the input signal.

the overdriven amplifier

On the previous pages you have seen how *cutoff* limiting can be used to clip the *negative* peaks of an input signal and how *saturation* limiting can clip the *positive* peaks. These two methods can be employed in a *single* stage to provide limiting of both the positive and negative peaks of a signal. A stage operated in this way is often called an *overdriven amplifier*, since it is alternately driven from saturation to cutoff to saturation, etc. An overdriven amplifier can take a sine-wave input and produce an output that approximates a square wave.

You have now seen how amplitude limiting of a signal can be accomplished both with various arrangements of diodes and with amplifying devices such as triodes and transistors. Diode limiting generally has the advantage of simplicity, yet amplifying devices can provide not only limiting, but amplification of the signal as well.

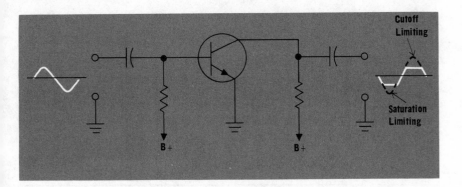

An overdriven amplifier combines saturation and cutoff limiting in a single stage

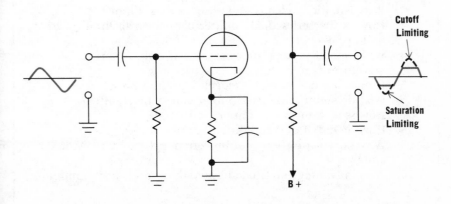

summary

☐ A standard diode, connected in series with the signal, will limit either the entire positive or negative half cycle. ☐ If a fixed positive or negative bias is placed in the cathode or anode circuit, then only a portion of either half cycle is limited. The amount of bias used determines how much limiting takes place.

☐ The series noise limiter is a typical application of a series limiter. ☐ Limiting can also be accomplished by connecting a diode in parallel with the load. This type of circuit is called a parallel diode limiter or shunt limiter. Like the series limiter, the portion of the waveform limited depends upon whether the waveform is connected to the anode or cathode. ☐ The shunt limiter can be used to limit a portion of the positive or negative half cycles by including a fixed bias in the cathode or anode. ☐ If two diodes are connected in parallel and properly biased, portions of both the positive and negative half cycles can be limited.

☐ Limiting can also be accomplished by using triodes instead of diodes. ☐ Cutoff limiting uses the cutoff characteristics of the triode to limit all or a portion of the negative half cycle. The portion limited depends upon the grid bias. ☐ Saturation limiting limits all or a portion of the positive half cycle. The triode operating parameters are set so that the tube saturates when the waveform reaches the desired positive value. ☐ Since positive voltages can cause runaway in transistor circuits, saturation limiting must be used with care. ☐ The effects of cutoff limiting and saturation limiting can both be combined in an overdriven amplifier.

review questions

1. What is the purpose of a limiter?
2. Why is a diode ideally suited for use as a limiter?
3. How is the series diode limiter connected to limit positive half cycles?
4. What modifications are necessary if only a portion of the waveform is to be limited?
5. How is a diode limiter connected to limit noise?
6. Why do shunt and series limiter connections differ?
7. How is a shunt noise limiter connected?
8. How do cutoff and saturation limiting differ?
9. Why isn't saturation limiting often used in transistor circuits?
10. What advantage do triode limiters have over diode limiters?

clamping circuits

Positive Clamping   **Negative Clamping**

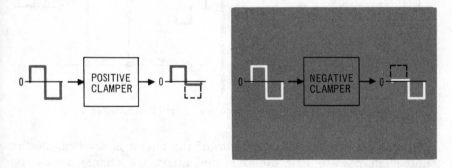

Some clamping circuits, known as d-c restorers, add a d-c reference
level to the signal, while others act as limiters on one polarity

It is often necessary to take a signal that varies above and below a
zero-volt reference level and change or restrict it to a signal that varies
around some fixed *d-c reference level*. A circuit that does this is called a
clamping circuit. In effect, such a circuit adds a d-c component to an
a-c signal, often without changing the basic waveshape of the signal.
Because they add a d-c component, some clamping circuits are also
called *d-c restorers*.

Another important clamping circuit application is to hold either the
positive or negative amplitude extreme of a waveform to a given reference level. Usually, this clamping circuit is used to prevent the signal
from going in one polarity, and does this by clamping the signal to
ground. Thus, the shunt limiters shown on page 7-20 are also clampers.

the diode clamper

A diode can be made to produce either positive or negative clamping, depending on how it is connected. A basic negative clamper is shown in A. You will notice that both of the circuits shown are similar to those shown on page 7-20. The difference, though, is that a charging capacitor is used here. During the initial positive half cycle of the input, the diode conducts and charges capacitor C to the peak value of the input. When the input reverses polarity, the diode cuts off. Capacitor C then attempts to discharge through resistor R. However, the *time constant* of R and C is long in relation to the negative alternation, so very little charge is lost from the capacitor.

Once stable operating conditions are attained, the diode conducts just enough to replace the charge on the capacitor that is lost during each cycle

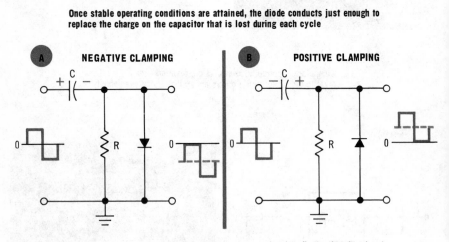

NEGATIVE CLAMPING   POSITIVE CLAMPING

Essentially, these circuits changed a pure a-c signal to fluctuating d-c signals

At this point, the stable condition of the circuit is reached. During subsequent positive half cycles of the input, the charge across the capacitor opposes the input voltage. The output voltage is therefore essentially zero. During the negative half cycles, the capacitor voltage adds to the input voltage, and the output voltage across R is twice the value of the input. Because the capacitor doubles one alternation and cancels the other, the complete cycle is reproduced as a fluctuating d-c voltage. The diode conducts slightly during each positive half cycle to replace the charge on the capacitor that is lost through the resistor when the input is negative.

By reversing the diode, as in B, positive clamping can be obtained in the same way. You can see that without the capacitor the diodes would merely clamp one alternation to ground and only pass the other alternation.

the triode clamper

A *triode* can also be used for clamping. Such a circuit offers the advantage of providing signal amplification as well as clamping. However, it has the limitation that it can provide only *positive* clamping.

In the circuit shown in A, the grid-cathode circuit of the triode is a diode clamper of the type described on the previous page. The charge on the capacitor that is lost during each negative half cycle is replenished when the grid draws current during positive half cycles of the input.

Because of the clamping action, the waveform at the grid of the triode is similar to that of a negative diode clamper circuit. The plate waveform, which is the output of the stage, is *amplified* and *inverted*. As a result of the polarity inversion, the circuit provides positive clamping.

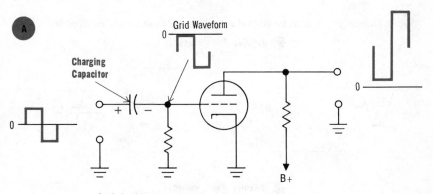

A triode clamper provides amplification as well as clamping

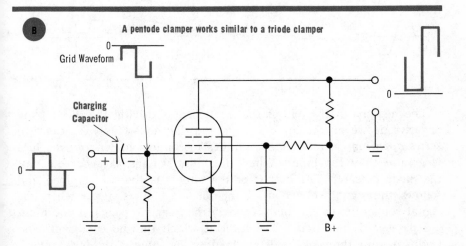

A pentode clamper works similar to a triode clamper

separator circuits

You saw previously how limiter circuits can remove the positive or negative peaks of a waveform (or both). Sometimes, though, only the *peaks* are wanted and the rest of the waveform is to be removed. A circuit that does this is usually called a *separator,* or *clipper,* circuit.

A diode separator that passes only the *negative peaks* of the input signal is shown in A. You will notice that the circuit is similar to a parallel limiter. However, in the limiter the bias voltage cuts the diode off in the absence of an input signal, but the bias voltage here causes the diode to *conduct* with no input. When an input is applied, the diode continues to conduct during the positive half cycle, since the signal drives the diode plate even more positive with respect to the cathode. Effectively, therefore, the entire input voltage is dropped across series resistor R, and the separator output is *clamped* to the bias voltage, E.

Separator circuits retain the peaks of a signal and eliminate the rest of the signal

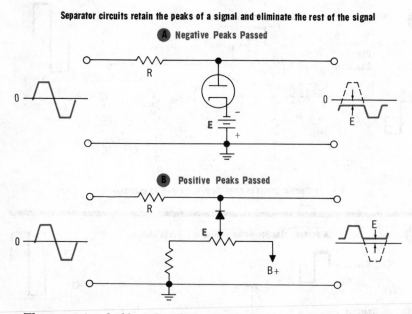

The negative half cycle of the input begins driving the diode plate negative. However, the input voltage and the diode bias voltage are in *series opposing,* so the diode continues to conduct as long as the bias is greater than the input. When the input voltage *exceeds* the bias, the diode cuts off. The output of the circuit is then unclamped and follows the signal voltage until the diode conducts again when the signal voltage drops. In this way, only the negative peaks of the input are passed by the circuit. The level at which the diode cuts off and begins passing the peaks is determined by the value of the bias voltage.

separator circuits (cont.)

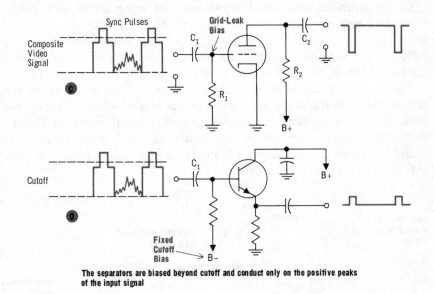

The separators are biased beyond cutoff and conduct only on the positive peaks of the input signal

A diode separator that passes only *positive* peaks is shown in B. Because of the polarity of the bias voltage, the diode shunts the entire negative half cycle of the input and a portion of the positive half cycle. It cuts off on the positive signal peaks and passes them to the output. This circuit also shows how a control can be used to set the bias voltage. By changing the control setting, the bias voltage will clip more or less of the signal peaks.

In place of diodes, separator circuits can also use electron tubes or transistors. This makes it possible for the circuit to *amplify* as well as separate. One such circuit used in television receivers for separating the *sync pulses* from the composite video signal is shown in C.

The triode is biased beyond cutoff and has a relatively low plate voltage. The tops of the sync portion of the video signal take the tube out of cutoff and drive it into *saturation*. This causes an amplified and inverted version of the sync pulses to appear at the output of the stage. Grid-leak bias is often used to keep the tube cut off between sync pulses. This is provided by capacitor C_1 and grid-leak resistor R_1.

If a positive output is needed from the separator, it can be arranged as a *cathode follower,* or an *emitter follower,* like that shown in D. The circuit operates the same as that in C, except fixed cutoff bias is provided and the output is taken from across the emitter resistor. The emitter-follower circuit has the disadvantage that it provides *less* than unity gain.

the television sync separator

On the previous page you saw circuits that separate the sync pulses from the composite video television signal. In every television receiver, these sync pulses are then processed by another circuit that is usually called a *sync separator*. In this case, though, the word *separator* denotes the separation of the vertical sync pulses from the horizontal sync pulses.

This sync separator must operate not on the basis of amplitude differences, like the other separator circuits you have seen, but on the basis of *pulse repetition rate*. This is because, as you learned in Volume 1, the horizontal sync pulses are individual 5.08-microsecond wide pulses, while each vertical pulse is made up of separate pulses that are also used as horizontal sync pulses.

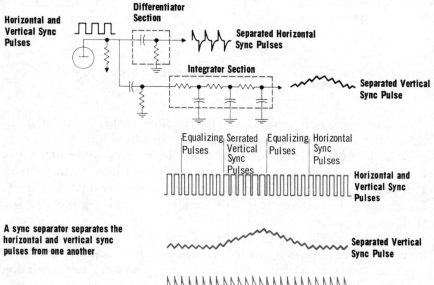

A sync separator separates the horizontal and vertical sync pulses from one another

You also learned in Volume 1 that *integrator* and *differentiator* circuits are used to separate the two types of sync pulses. Together, these make up a sync separator, as shown. The sync pulses are applied to both the *short time-constant* differentiator section and the *long time-constant* integrator section. Because of its short time constant, the differentiator section delivers one positive spike and one negative spike for every sync pulse. The integrator section, because of its long time constant, builds up an increasing charge for each serrated portion of the vertical sync pulses. Effectively, therefore, it delivers one output pulse for each complete vertical sync pulse.

summary

□ Some clamping circuits act as limiting circuits by passing only the positive or negative portions of the input signal. □ Other clamping circuits, called d-c restorers, add a d-c level to an input signal. This only changes the reference about which a signal varies; it does not alter the signal. □ If a capacitor is added to the basic diode limiting circuit, the modified circuit is a clamping circuit. □ Negative clamping results when the signal is applied to the plate or anode; positive clamping results when the signal is applied to the cathode.

□ A triode can also be used as a clamper, but can only provide positive clamping. □ In certain applications, only the positive or negative peaks are desired instead of the signal without the peaks. The circuit that passes only the peaks is called a separator or clipper circuit. □ Diodes, triodes, or transistors can also be used as separators.

□ One typical use of a separator circuit is to separate sync pulses from the composite video signal in television receivers. These sync pulses comprise the most positive portion of the video signal. □ By biasing the triode beyond cutoff (class C operation), only the sync pulses cause conduction. □ These sync pulses consist of horizontal and vertical sync pulses; a sync separator is used to separate these pulses. This circuit, unlike the standard separator circuit, which operates on amplitude variations, operates on variations in pulse repetition rate. □ A short time-constant differentiator circuit develops the horizontal sync pulses whereas a long time constant integrator circuit develops the vertical sync pulses.

review questions

1. How do standard clamping circuits and limiters differ?
2. How do standard clamping circuits and d-c restorers differ?
3. What effect does the RC time constant have on a d-c restorer?
4. Define *fluctuating dc.*
5. What type of clamper does the grid-to-cathode circuit of a triode form?
6. Why does a triode only provide positive clamping?
7. How do the outputs of a standard clamping circuit and clipper differ?
8. How do the bias voltages differ?
9. What does a sync separator consist of?
10. Why is a sync separator used instead of a clipper circuit?

AFC circuits

Automatic frequency control (AFC) circuits are used in situations where it is necessary to control accurately the frequency of an oscillator in accordance with some external signal. Basically, such a circuit does two things: (1) it *senses* the difference between the actual oscillator frequency and the frequency that is desired and produces a *control voltage* proportional to this difference, and (2) it uses the control voltage to change the oscillator back to the desired frequency.

As an example of AFC operation, consider the hypothetical case of an oscillator that is to be maintained at a frequency of 1 megacycle. When the oscillator is right on frequency, the AFC circuit delivers a control voltage of, say, 4 volts, which keeps the oscillator at 1 megacycle. Should the oscillator now drift to a frequency of 1.1 megacycle, the output of the AFC circuit rises to 4.5 volts. This increase in the control voltage brings the oscillator frequency back to 1 megacycle, and the voltage then drops to 4 volts again. The same action occurs when the oscillator frequency falls. In this case, the control voltage drops below 4 volts and increases the oscillator frequency back to 1 megacycle. This corrective action takes place continuously, so the oscillator is always kept at 1 megacycle.

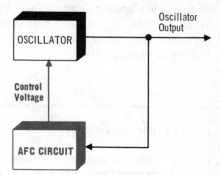

An AFC circuit senses the oscillator output frequency and generates a control voltage that brings the oscillator back to the correct frequency

In this example, an increase in oscillator frequency causes an increase in the control voltage produced by the AFC circuit, and a decrease in the oscillator frequency causes a decrease in the control voltage. In actual AFC circuits, the reverse of this can be used. The voltage can vary in the opposite direction from the change in oscillator frequency. All that is required is that the change in control voltage be *proportional* to the change in oscillator frequency, and that this change in voltage be made to bring the oscillator back to normal.

There are two types of AFC circuits: those that control the frequency of sinusoidal oscillators, and those that are used with nonsinusoidal oscillators.

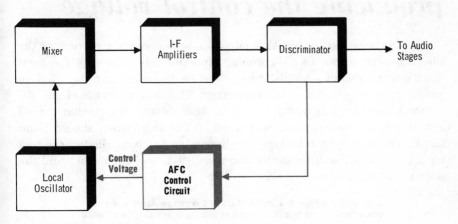

In an FM receiver, the AFC circuit controls the frequency of the local oscillator to maintain a constant receiver intermediate frequency

sinusoidal AFC circuits

Sinusoidal AFC circuits are used to control the frequency of oscillators that deliver *sine-wave outputs*. The most common use of such AFC circuits is in FM transmitters and receivers. You recall that in these equipments the intelligence carried by a signal is in the form of variations above and below some *center frequency*. It is important that this center frequency remain fixed, since if it should vary, distortion of the signal will occur.

In FM receivers, the AFC circuit controls the frequency of the local oscillator in order to maintain the correct receiver i-f frequency. The i-f should not change if the receiver is to operate properly. But if the receiver local oscillator or the transmitter oscillator tend to drift, the receiver i-f will change. The AFC circuit, though, prevents this. It does so by sensing the change in the i-f and developing a control voltage proportional to the change. It then uses the voltage to change the oscillator to the frequency that will produce the proper i-f.

Sinusoidal AFC circuits, like those used in FM receivers, take advantage of the fact that the output of a Foster-Seeley type discriminator is an audio voltage proportional to the difference between the instantaneous signal frequency and the center frequency. This means that the audio voltage is also proportional to variations in the i-f frequency, since the i-f actually consists of the center frequency and the intelligence-carrying side bands on either side of it.

producing the control voltage

All that is necessary for AFC purposes is to convert a portion of the discriminator output to a d-c voltage and use this to control the local oscillator frequency. An RC filter, like that shown, can be used to produce the required d-c control voltage. The time constant of the RC network must be *long* compared to the audio variations, so that the a-f signal will not be bypassed to ground. Remember, when the i-f is on center frequency in this type of discriminator, both diodes conduct equally, so that the drops across the resistors cancel each other and the output voltage is zero.

A d-c control voltage for operation of the AFC circuit can easily be derived from a Foster-Seeley type discriminator by filtering or averaging the a-f output

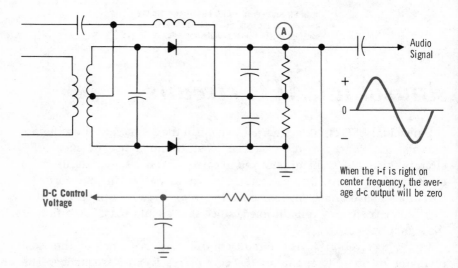

Audio Signal

When the i-f is right on center frequency, the average d-c output will be zero

D-C Control Voltage

As the i-f swings above and below the center frequency, the output swings positive and negative about zero. So, when the control voltage RC filter *averages* out the a-c swing, the control voltage will be zero when the positive and negative swings are equally around zero. This is the case when the receiver i-f is on its proper center frequency. So, when the receiver i-f is correct, the average voltage at point A is zero, and no AFC control voltage is developed. Should the i-f change, such as would occur if the local oscillator frequency drifted, an average positive or negative voltage would appear at A. The polarity of the voltage depends on whether the i-f increases or decreases, and the amplitude of the voltage is proportional to the amount of increase or decrease. The d-c control voltage will therefore be directly proportional to the change in i-f.

oscillator control
by the miller effect

Once the AFC control voltage has been developed, it must be made to control the oscillator frequency. There are various methods that can be used to accomplish this. One basic method uses the *Miller effect*. This is a characteristic of an electron tube, such that the *input capacitance* between control grid and cathode varies with changes in the voltage between them. This can be taken advantage of in AFC circuits by using a circuit arrangement like that shown.

The oscillator whose frequency is being controlled is a shunt-fed Hartley. The tube's input capacitance (C_{gk}) is effectively in parallel with part of the oscillator tank circuit. Thus, the total capacitance of the tank, and, therefore, the oscillator frequency, depend on tank capacitor C_1 and the input capacitance of the oscillator tube.

The d-c control voltage is applied to the control grid of the tube in series with its grid-leak bias resistor. As the d-c control voltage varies in amplitude with changes in the oscillator frequency, the grid-to-cathode voltage of the tube changes accordingly. This changes C_{gk} and, thus, the effective capacitance of the oscillator tank circuit; in this way, the oscillator frequency is raised or lowered to bring it back toward the right frequency.

The amount of capacitance change caused by the Miller effect is limited, so that this type of AFC only partially corrects the frequency.

The grid-to-cathode capacitance (C_{gk}) of the tube varies in accordance with the d-c control voltage as a result of the Miller effect

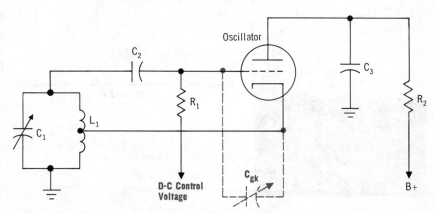

Since C_{gk} is across part of the oscillator tank circuit, as its value is changed by the d-c control voltage, it changes the resonance of the tank to bring the oscillator back on frequency

the junction diode AFC circuit

Another method, which gives a little more control over the local oscillator frequency, makes use of *junction diodes*. This method is based on the fact that when such diodes are *reverse biased,* their junction capacitance varies with the bias voltage. This is similar to the effect you learned about on the previous page.

A typical diode AFC circuit is shown. The diode, CR_1, is effectively connected across the oscillator tank circuit by means of capacitors C_1 and C_2. The oscillator is again a shunt-fed Hartley. The diode is reverse biased so that the only current that flows through it is the very small reverse current. Effectively, therefore, the diode appears as a capacitor in series with capacitors C_1 and C_2. The value of the diode's capacitance is determined by the amount of reverse bias applied to it. This is initially set for proper oscillator frequency with no d-c control voltage input. Then, when the control voltage varies, the reverse bias varies, and, therefore, so does the capacitance of CR_1. Since the series combination of C_1, C_2 and the capacitance of CR_1 is effectively in parallel with the tank-circuit capacitor, the tank capacitance and, therefore, the frequency of oscillation also vary.

The capacitance of the junction diode is varied by the d-c control voltage. This changes the tank-circuit capacitance and, therefore, the frequency of oscillation

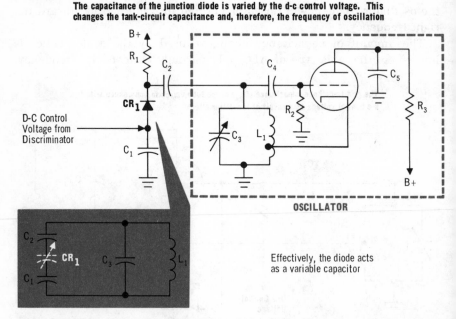

OSCILLATOR

Effectively, the diode acts as a variable capacitor

It should be noted that not all junction diodes have capacitance characteristics that are suitable for AFC use. However, certain types have been developed specifically for this purpose.

the reactance-tube AFC circuit

A method that provides more positive and complete control of the oscillator frequency makes use of a *reactance-tube* circuit. The circuit is identical to that of the reactance-tube modulator, which was described in Volume 6. Basically, the reactance tube uses the d-c control voltage to control a *reactive current* that is injected into the tank circuit of the oscillator to control its frequency.

The reactance tube changes the amplitude variations of the d-c control voltage into a varying reactance that is injected into the oscillator tank circuit

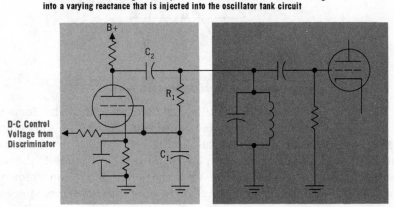

Reactance Tube   Local Oscillator

In the arrangement shown, R_1 and C_1 are in parallel with the oscillator tank circuit. R_1 is much larger than C_1, so the current through them is in phase with the tank voltage. Because of the capacitive action of C_1, however, the voltage across C_1 *lags* the current through it by 90 degrees. The phase-shifted voltage across C_1 is applied to the tube's grid and the resulting plate current also lags the current in the oscillator tank circuit by 90 degrees. A portion of this plate current is coupled into the tank circuit by capacitor C_2. Because a lagging current is an inductive current, this produces the same result as if an *inductance* were placed across the tank. The amount of this injected inductance varies in proportion to the amount of plate current provided by the reactance tube. This is determined by the d-c control voltage bias. So the total inductance of the tank and, therefore, the frequency of oscillation change in accordance with the d-c control voltage.

If the positions of R_1 and C_1 are reversed and the value of C_1 is made much larger than that of R_1, the current through C_1 and R_1 will *lead* the tank voltage. This leading phase will be dropped across R_1 and amplified by the tube to produce a plate current that leads the tank voltage. The reactance tube will inject a capacitive reactance into the oscillator tank circuit.

nonsinusoidal AFC circuits

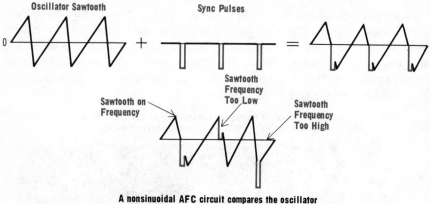

A nonsinuoidal AFC circuit compares the oscillator
frequency with externally applied sync pulses

You have seen how AFC circuits are used to control the frequency of sinusoidal oscillators. There is also a wide variety of AFC circuits that is used with nonsinusoidal oscillators, such as multivibrators and blocking oscillators. The purpose of these AFC circuits is the same as the sinusoidal kind; namely, to keep the oscillator on frequency. The way in which they work, however, is quite different from sinusoidal circuits.

The principal difference is that nonsinusoidal AFC circuits generally require synchronization, or sync, pulses for their operation. These sync pulses are supplied from some external source and occur at the repetition rate, or frequency, at which the oscillator is to be maintained. The AFC circuit compares the frequency of the oscillator with that of the sync pulses. If the two are different, it changes the oscillator frequency until it is the same as that of the sync pulses.

As an example of nonsinusoidal AFC operation, consider an oscillator that produces a sawtooth output waveform. If sharp rectangular negative sync pulses are superimposed on the sawtooth, the resulting waveform has the sync spikes riding on the negative-going portions of the sawtooth. Since these spikes are produced by the sync pulses, their positions depend on the relative phases or frequencies of the sawtooth and sync pulses. The sync pulses are fixed in frequency, so if the sawtooth frequency is lower than that of the sync pulses, the spike occurs sooner on the waveform and rides higher. If the sawtooth frequency is higher than that of the sync pulses, the spike occurs later on the waveform and rides lower. In actual AFC circuits, this varying position of the spike can be converted into a suitably varying d-c control voltage that changes the oscillator frequency until it is the same as that of the sync pulses.

the single-ended AFC circuit

One type of nonsinusoidal AFC circuit that uses the waveform comparison explained on the previous page is shown. The circuit does not compare the frequency of the sync pulses with that of the oscillator directly. Instead, the sync pulses are compared with a sawtooth wave that is derived from, and therefore has the same frequency as, the oscillator.

Without considering the sync pulses, the sawtooth wave would cause current flow into the capacitor when it is negative, and out of the capacitor when it is positive. Since the sawtooth is symmetrical about zero, the charge and discharge currents of C_3 are equal. C_3 would therefore develop zero volts. But, with the sync pulse superimposed on the sawtooth waveform, the resultant sawtooth is no longer symmetrical. Since the sync pulse is negative, the overall negative area of the waveform is greater than the positive area. Thus, there is more charge current for C_3 than discharge current, and C_3 maintains a slight negative charge.

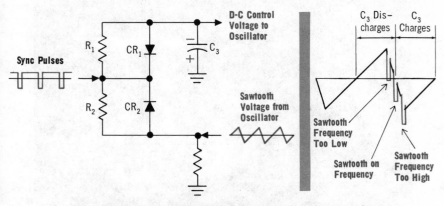

This type of AFC circuit is called single-ended because it requires sync pulses of only one polarity. The sync pulses change to the shape of the sawtooth wave to produce a negative charge on C_3. As the sawtooth shifts in frequency, the position of the sync pulse increases or decreases this d-c control voltage

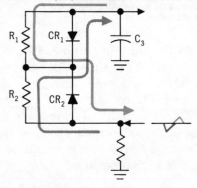

Without the sync pulses, C_3 charges and discharges equally on both halves of the sawtooth voltage. The net charge, then, would be zero volts

the single-ended
AFC circuit (cont.)

The amount of negative charge depends on the position of the negative sync pulse on the retrace of the sawtooth. If the sawtooth frequency
is too high, the sync pulse will appear later, at the lower part of the
waveform. This will make the negative part of the waveform even
greater and build more of a negative charge on C_3. If the sawtooth is
lower in frequency, the sync pulse will appear earlier, at the upper part
of the waveform. This reduces the negative part of the waveform to
cause a smaller negative charge on C_3.

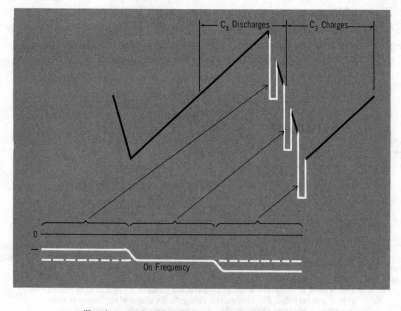

When the sync pulse rides high because the sawtooth frequency
is too low, there is less of a negative control voltage. When
the pulse rides low because of a high sawtooth frequency, there
is a greater negative control voltage

Remember that the sync is not shifting in time. It has a fixed frequency and always occurs at the same time. The sawtooth, though,
changes with the frequency of the oscillator, causing the sync pulse to
appear to ride up and down the retrace part of the waveform to vary
the d-c control voltage. The circuit is designed so that the on-frequency
control voltage occurs when the sync pulse is about in the center of
the slope. The d-c control voltage is fed to the oscillator to shift its
frequency to keep the sync pulse in that position.

the double-ended AFC circuit

Another widely used type of nonsinusoidal AFC circuit has *two* equal-amplitude but *opposite-polarity* sync pulse trains applied to it to give better control. The circuit compares the phase of these sync pulses with that of a sawtooth wave derived from the oscillator output. When the oscillator is on frequency, the phase comparison results in a zero d-c output from the circuit. If the oscillator is off frequency, the circuit delivers a positive or negative output, depending on whether the oscillator frequency is too high or too low.

Effectively, a double-ended AFC circuit operates as a *discriminator*. Each of the diodes has two voltages applied to it: the sawtooth, which is the same for both diodes, and one of the opposite-polarity sync pulses. Without the sync pulses both diodes conduct equally on the opposite polarities of the sawtooth wave. Capacitor C_3 charges and discharges equally for both polarities and thus produces a net charge of zero volts for the currents produced by the sawtooth alone. The sync pulses, though, can change this, since each pulse is fed to its own diode. When the oscillator is right on frequency, both pulses occur as the sawtooth wave is going through zero, so the pulses are equal and opposite around zero; CR_1 and CR_2 again conduct equally to keep a zero charge on C_3. But as the sawtooth wave changes in frequency, the pulses ride high or low on the waveform so that one sync pulse is greater in amplitude than the other and its respective diode will conduct more to charge C_3.

Without the sync pulses, C_3 charges and discharges equally to produce a net charge of zero volts. With the sync pulses on frequency, the net charge is still zero since the opposite polarity pulses are equally about zero. Off frequency, the pulses produce a greater positive or negative charge according to their position on the sawtooth

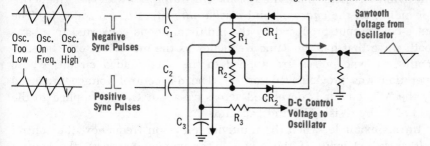

When the sawtooth wave is too low in frequency, both pulses ride high on the sawtooth and the positive pulse is greater; CR_1 conducts more and C_3 charges to a positive voltage. When the sawtooth is too high in frequency, the pulses ride low and the negative sync pulse is greater; C_3 charges to a negative voltage. The d-c control voltage charges the oscillator frequency until the positive and negative sync pulses are equal and opposite so that C_3 will produce a zero control voltage.

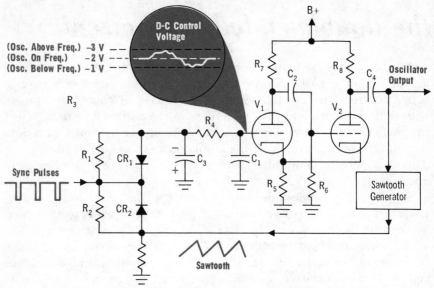

The control voltage varies the bias on stage V_1 of the cathode-coupled multivibrator to control its operating frequency

oscillator frequency control

You have seen two ways in which the d-c control voltage for non-sinusoidal AFC circuits can be developed. How this voltage controls the oscillator frequency depends on the type of oscillator used. One way that it can be done is shown.

This is a single-ended AFC circuit controlling a cathode-coupled multivibrator. The multivibrator is *free-running*, with its frequency depending on the *charging* and *discharging* times of capacitor C_2. The pulse-type output produced by the multivibrator is converted to a sawtooth wave that has the same frequency as the multivibrator. The sawtooth and sync pulses are applied to the single-ended circuit, whose operation was previously described. The d-c control voltage produced by the AFC circuit is developed across capacitor C_3 and applied to the grid of V_1 by resistor R_4 and capacitor C_1.

In this example, when the multivibrator is on frequency, the control voltage is −2 volts. If the oscillator frequency *increases*, the control voltage becomes *more negative*. This increases the bias on stage V_1, which effectively *increases* the discharge time of capacitor C_2. The result is a decrease in the multivibrator output frequency that returns it to the correct frequency. If the multivibrator drops *below* the correct frequency, the opposite action occurs. The control voltage becomes *less negative* than −2 volts and the discharge time of C_2 is *decreased*. As a result, the multivibrator frequency is raised back to normal.

oscillator
frequency control (cont.)

Another example of how the d-c control voltage can be used to control the oscillator frequency is shown here. The arrangement consists of a *double-ended* AFC circuit and a *blocking oscillator*. Again, the pulse-type output of the oscillator is converted to a sawtooth wave that has the same frequency as the oscillator. The sawtooth wave and the oppo-site-polarity sync pulses are applied to the double-ended AFC circuit, whose operation was previously discussed. The d-c control voltage produced by the circuit is coupled to the base circuit of the oscillator. When the oscillator is on frequency, the control voltage is essentially *zero* and the oscillator frequency is determined by the natural discharge time of capacitor C_4 in relation to the circuit voltages.

Should the oscillator begin to run too *fast,* the control voltage becomes *negative.* This *increases* the time required for C_4 to discharge during each oscillator cycle and results in a lowering of the oscillator frequency. If the oscillator should begin running too *slow,* the opposite action occurs. The control voltage becomes *positive, decreasing* the discharge time for capacitor C_4, and the oscillator frequency increases.

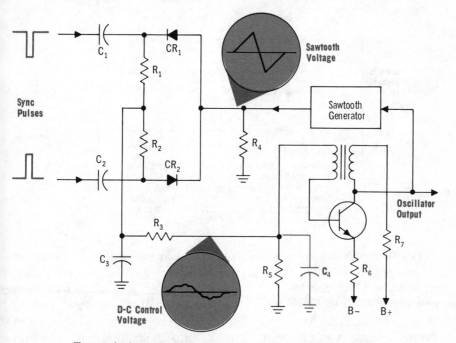

The control voltage varies the frequency of the blocking oscillator by varying the discharge time of capacitor C_4

the synchroguide circuit

Another AFC circuit that is used with a blocking oscillator is the *Synchroguide* circuit. This method of AFC uses a control tube to develop the voltage that controls the oscillator frequency.

Stage V_2 operates as a conventional ultra-audion blocking oscillator, with plate-to-grid feedback provided by the tube's interelectrode capacitances. The basic frequency of oscillation is controlled by the grid-leak blocking network consisting of capacitor C_5 and resistor R_4. The control tube, V_1, is normally kept cut off by the grid-leak action of capacitor C_1 and resistor R_1. Both the horizontal sync pulses and a feedback voltage from the oscillator output are applied to the grid of V_1.

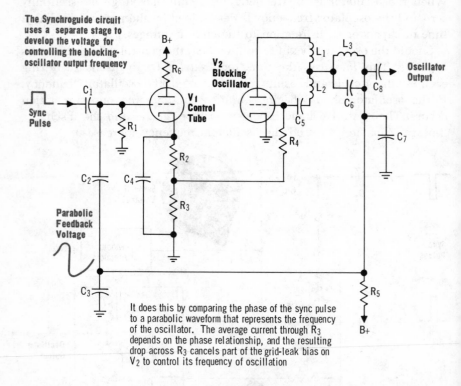

The Synchroguide circuit uses a separate stage to develop the voltage for controlling the blocking-oscillator output frequency

It does this by comparing the phase of the sync pulse to a parabolic waveform that represents the frequency of the oscillator. The average current through R_3 depends on the phase relationship, and the resulting drop across R_3 cancels part of the grid-leak bias on V_2 to control its frequency of oscillation

The feedback voltage is a parabolic-type waveform. It is produced by the action of tank circuit L_3-C_6, which generates a damped oscillation when V_2 is cut off, and R_5 and C_3, which integrate the resulting waveform to produce a parabolic shape. This parabolic feedback voltage drives V_1 close to conduction. The sync pulses, which coincide with the peaks of the parabolic waveform, then drive V_1 into conduction and into grid conduction to produce the grid-leak bias.

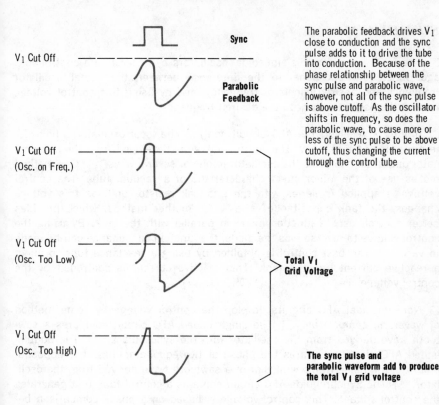

V₁ Cut Off — Sync — Parabolic Feedback

V₁ Cut Off (Osc. on Freq.)

V₁ Cut Off (Osc. Too Low) — Total V₁ Grid Voltage

V₁ Cut Off (Osc. Too High)

The parabolic feedback drives V_1 close to conduction and the sync pulse adds to it to drive the tube into conduction. Because of the phase relationship between the sync pulse and parabolic wave, however, not all of the sync pulse is above cutoff. As the oscillator shifts in frequency, so does the parabolic wave, to cause more or less of the sync pulse to be above cutoff, thus changing the current through the control tube

The sync pulse and parabolic waveform add to produce the total V_1 grid voltage

the synchroguide circuit (cont.)

The *duration* of this conduction depends on how much of the sync pulse coincides with the peaks of the feedback voltage. When the oscillator is on frequency, the tube conducts for approximately half the width of the sync pulse. The other half of the sync pulse is below cutoff. Should the oscillator frequency drift, either more or less of each sync pulse causes V_1 to conduct. In this way, the average voltage across resistor R_3 caused by current through V_1 varies in accordance with the phase difference between the feedback voltage and the sync pulses.

This voltage across R_3 controls the overall bias on the oscillator, and, therefore, also controls its frequency. When more average current flows through R_3, the resulting additional positive voltage drop cancels some of the negative grid-leak bias across it. This decreases the oscillator bias, therefore increasing the oscillator frequency. The opposite action occurs when V_1 conducts less and therefore develops a smaller average voltage across R_3. Essentially, changes in the oscillator frequency cause corresponding changes in the voltage across R_3, which in turn vary the oscillator bias to bring the oscillator back to the correct frequency.

summary

☐ The AFC circuit controls sinusoidal oscillators by generating a control voltage, which is proportional to the difference between the actual oscillator frequency and desired oscillator frequency, and by using this control voltage to shift the oscillator back to the desired frequency.

☐ In an FM receiver, the AFC circuit controls the local oscillator, which determines the i-f frequency. The control voltage is developed from the discriminator output and controls the oscillator in one of several ways. ☐ One method makes use of the Miller effect characteristic of a vacuum tube. The control voltage is applied in series with the grid-leak resistor and, as this voltage changes, the tank capacitance varies. ☐ Another method, which provides better control, uses a junction diode in parallel with the tank. By using the control voltage to reverse bias the diode, the junction capacitance can be made to vary. ☐ The best control is obtained by using a reactance tube to inject a reactive current into the tank. This reactive current is controlled by the control voltage.

☐ Nonsinusoidal AFC circuits develop the control voltage by some method of waveform comparison. ☐ The single-ended AFC circuit compares a sawtooth wave derived from the oscillator with the sync pulses. ☐ The double-ended AFC circuit compares the phase of two equal-amplitude but opposite-polarity sync pulse trains with that of a sawtooth wave derived from the oscillator. ☐ The Synchroguide AFC circuit contains a control tube that generates the control voltage. This control voltage is based on a phase comparison between sync pulses and a parabolic waveform that represents the oscillator frequency.

review questions

1. What important relationship exists between the control voltage and oscillator frequency?
2. Why is the discriminator output used to develop the control voltage?
3. What is the *Miller effect*?
4. How is the Miller effect used to control oscillator frequency?
5. How do junction diodes control oscillator frequency?
6. How do reactance tubes control oscillator frequency?
7. What is the main difference between sinusoidal and non-sinusoidal oscillators?
8. What is *waveform comparison*?
9. What determines how a control voltage is used?
10. Compare single-ended, double-ended, and Synchroguide AFC circuits.

counter circuits

Many pieces of electronic equipment require a circuit whose output depends on the *frequency* of the input. Usually, the input is a train of pulses. The output can be either a *d-c voltage* proportional to the pulse repetition rate of the input pulses, or a *series of pulses* whose own pulse repetition rate is proportional to that of the input.

One such type of counter circuit uses two diodes connected as shown. The values of R_1 and C_1 are chosen for a short time constant. For each input pulse, CR_1 conducts until C_1 charges, which occurs very rapidly. This produces a narrow voltage spike across R_1. During the negative swing of each input pulse, C_1 discharges rapidly through diode CR_2, since it is now forward biased while CR_1 is reverse biased. As this sequence occurs with each input pulse, positive voltage spikes are developed across R_1 at the same frequency as the input pulse repetition rate.

Resistor R_2 and capacitor C_2 form an integrating network to convert the spikes across R_1 into a d-c voltage. The amplitude of this voltage is proportional to the input pulse repetition rate. A voltmeter connected across the output of the circuit would indicate a small voltage for low input pulse repetition rates, and a relatively large voltage for high repetition rates.

One type of counter circuit produces a d-c voltage that is proportional to the pulse repetition rate of the input pulse train

HIGH REPETITION RATE   LOW REPETITION RATE

the step-by-step counter

The d-c output voltage of the counter described on the previous page can be made to increase in a *step-by-step* sequence by using a charging capacitor at the output of diode CR_1. Now, each time an input pulse causes CR_1 to conduct, capacitor C_2 charges while the pulse is present. However, since the pulse is narrow, C_2 only charges slightly during the pulse time. But, there is no discharge path for C_2, so it *maintains* its charge in between pulses. Each additional input pulse causes C_2 to charge up a little more.

It should be noted that the *additional* voltage developed across C_2 is progressively smaller for each succeeding input pulse because the charge on C_2 is in opposition to the input pulses. As a result, a point will eventually be reached where the voltage on C_2 is approximately equal to the amplitude of the input pulses, so the input pulses will produce no additional voltage across C_2. This point limits the number of pulses that the circuit can effectively count.

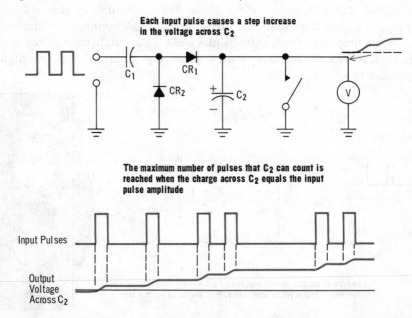

Each input pulse causes a step increase in the voltage across C_2

The maximum number of pulses that C_2 can count is reached when the charge across C_2 equals the input pulse amplitude

Input Pulses

Output Voltage Across C_2

The voltage across C_2 and, therefore, the number of pulses counted by the circuit, can be indicated on a voltmeter connected across the output of the circuit. A switch in parallel with C_2 can be used to discharge the capacitor and enable the circuit to begin counting from zero again. When the switch is open, the circuit is able to count. Closing the switch discharges C_2, thus destroying any count held by the circuit. The switch must then be opened again before another count can begin.

the frequency-divider counter

When millions of pulses have to be counted, the counter circuits described thus far are limited because the output capacitors will charge up for only a relatively few pulses. But, if a pulse train is first divided down to fewer pulses, these circuits can be used. The pulse train can be divided down by a frequency divider counter. The pulse rate can be divided down by, say, 3, or 5, or 100, or 1000, or more. For example, a counter can be used as a "by-3" divider if it delivers *one output* pulse for every *three input* pulses. Similarly, a "by-100" divider would deliver one output pulse for every 100 input pulses. Of course, when the divided-down pulses are counted, the reading must be multiplied by the proper factor to determine the original frequency.

One simple type of frequency-divider counter consists of a series gas tube and resistor that are connected across the output of the step-by-step counter previously described. The gas tube is triggered into conduction by the voltage across capacitor C_2. However, a certain number of input pulses are required before the voltage on C_2 reaches the triggering level. In the circuit shown, C_2 has sufficient voltage to trigger the gas tube after *three* input pulses are received. When the tube conducts, C_2 discharges through resistor R_1 and the tube. The discharge current produces a voltage pulse across R_1 that serves as the output. After C_2 discharges, the gas tube cuts off and remains cut off until three more input pulses again charge C_2 to the triggering level. Thus, the circuit delivers one output pulse for every three input pulses.

"BY-3" COUNTER

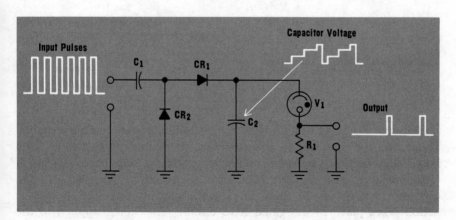

Three input pulses cause C_2 to charge to the voltage level that will ignite V_1. When V_1 conducts, it provides a discharge path for C_2. The discharge current then produces an output pulse across R_1. Thus, three input pulses cause one output pulse

gating circuits

The term *gating circuits* covers a wide variety of circuits used in many different applications. The basic thing all of these circuits have in common is that they have *two* or more separate inputs, all of which must be present for the circuit to deliver an output. If any input is present *alone,* the circuit is inoperative.

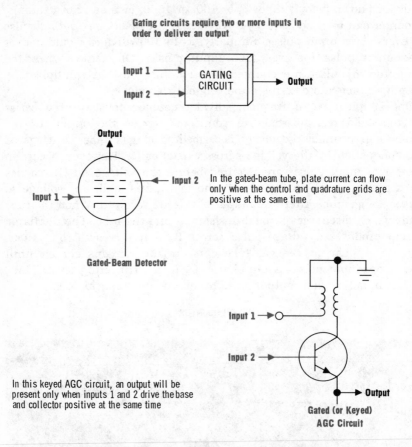

Gating circuits require two or more inputs in order to deliver an output

Input 1 → GATING CIRCUIT → Output
Input 2 →

Output

Input 2 →
Input 1 →

In the gated-beam tube, plate current can flow only when the control and quadrature grids are positive at the same time

Gated-Beam Detector

Input 1 →o
Input 2 →

In this keyed AGC circuit, an output will be present only when inputs 1 and 2 drive the base and collector positive at the same time

→ Output

Gated (or Keyed) AGC Circuit

You are already familiar with two commonly used gating circuits. These are the *gated-beam detector* and the *gated AGC* circuit. You recall that in the gated-beam detector, gating action occurs between the quadrature grid and the input grid. Plate current can flow in the tube only when both of these grids are sufficiently positive. A similar action takes place in the gated AGC circuit. The signal applied to the base can only produce an output signal during the time that a second input provides collector voltage. Thus, in both cases, an output is produced only when the two inputs are present.

the coincidence gate

In both the gated-beam detector and gated AGC circuits, one of the inputs is essentially an *intelligence-carrying* signal, while the second input serves a *timing function*. Thus, the timing input functions like a gate. When it is present, the gate is *open*, and the intelligence-carrying signal can pass through to the output. But without the timing input, the gate is *closed* and the intelligence-carrying signal cannot reach the output.

There is another type of gating circuit whose purpose is to detect the *simultaneous occurrence* of two signals and produce an output to indicate when such coincidence occurs. Such a circuit is called a *coincidence gate*. There are many circuits that can be used as coincidence gates. One type for detecting the coincidence of two *positive-going* pulses is shown in A.

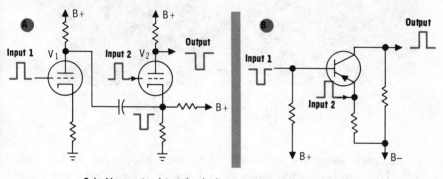

Coincidence gates detect the simultaneous occurrence of two inputs

Stage V_2 is biased well beyond cutoff by the divider network in the cathode. When positive pulse input 1 is applied to its grid, the negative-going pulse from the plate of V_1 brings V_2 *close* to the conduction point. However, it still does not conduct because the negative pulse is not quite large enough to overcome the fixed cathode bias on V_2. If a positive pulse is applied to the grid of V_2 at the same time the negative pulse is on the cathode, V_2 does conduct. Thus, a negative-going pulse is delivered by V_2 only when positive-going input pulses 1 and 2 are present *simultaneously*.

B shows a similar type of coincidence detector, except that it detects the simultaneous occurrence of a positive and a negative pulse. Reverse-bias voltage polarities are applied to both the base and emitter. The polarity of the input pulses overcomes both bias voltages to forward bias the stage, so both inputs are necessary to bias the stage into conduction. Only when they are both present does the stage conduct and deliver a positive-going output pulse.

computer AND gates

Only when both inputs are at +10 volts will the
output be +10 volts

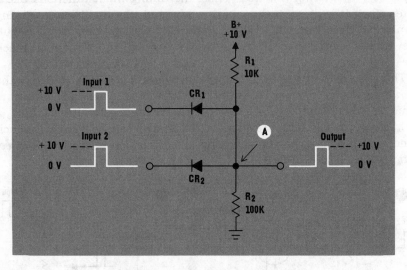

If either input is zero, its diode will conduct and
clamp the zero volts to the output

Coincidence gates are the heart of modern high-speed digital computers. Thousands of such gates are used in a typical large computer. In digital terminology these gates are referred to as *AND gates,* since they perform what is known as the logical AND function.

Most computer AND gates employ semiconductor diodes. The exact circuit arrangement depends on whether coincidence of positive- or negative-going signals is to be detected. The circuit shown is for *positive-*going signals. When either of the input signals is at the zero volt level, the corresponding diode *conducts* because it is forward biased. Since the diodes have a very low forward resistance compared to R_1, the zero volts appears at point A as the gate output, and R_1 drops the entire B+ voltage (+10 volts). When *both* inputs are at +10 volts, the two diodes are no longer forward biased. As a result, both diodes are *cut off.* The current flowing from ground through R_1 and R_2 now produces about +10 volts at point A because R_2 is so much greater than R_1. So the output of the gate is +10 volts. The same circuit can be used to detect the coincidence of three or more input signals merely by adding additional diodes.

When similar-type gate circuits are suitably modified, they can be used for negative-going input signals.

OR gates

Another type of circuit that is widely used in digital computers is the OR *circuit,* or OR gate, as it is frequently called. Unlike the AND gate, the OR gate produces an output when *either one* or *both* of the input signals are present. This is why it is called an OR circuit: either one *or* the other *or* both of the inputs will produce an output. The only time there is no output is when *neither* one of the inputs is present.

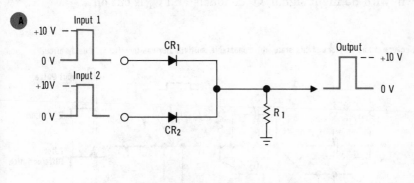

An OR circuit delivers an output when either or
both of its inputs are present

In the OR circuit shown in A, one input is applied to the anode of CR_1 and the other to the anode of CR_2. Both diodes have their cathodes returned to ground through resistor R_1. When *neither one* of the positive input pulses is present, *no current* flows in either diode, and the circuit delivers no output or zero volts. But if either one of the input pulses is present, it will *forward bias* its corresponding diode. The resulting current flow then produces a voltage drop across R_1. This voltage serves as the output of the OR circuit.

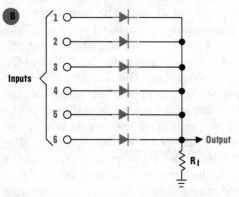

OR circuits can contain many inputs. The diodes
serve to isolate one input circuit from the others

time delay circuits

Many types of electronic equipment perform a sequence of operations. Consequently, it is often necessary to delay either the passage of a signal from one circuit to another or the initiation of some operation. Circuits that provide such delays are called *time delay circuits*. One circuit that you have already studied (Vol. 6) that can be used to provide a time delay is the *monostable multivibrator*. In the circuit shown, with no input signal, Q_2 conducts and Q_1 is cut off.

Because it has only one stable state, the monostable multivibrator can function as a delay circuit

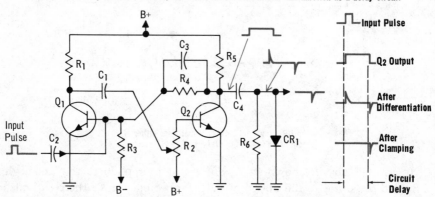

When it is triggered by an input pulse, the circuit produces one square wave. The leading edge of the square wave starts at the same time as the input pulse, but the trailing edge gives the delay. When the square wave is differentiated, the negative spike is delayed in time

When a positive input pulse is applied to the base of Q_1, it overcomes the reverse bias and drives Q_1 into conduction. This reduces the forward bias on the base of Q_2, eventually cutting Q_2 off. The new condition, with Q_1 conducting and Q_2 cut off, remains for a short time until the circuit goes back to its stable state, with Q_2 conducting and Q_1 cut off, and remains that way until another positive input pulse is applied to Q_1.

Capacitor C_4 and resistor R_6 differentiate the rectangular wave and produce sharp pulses at the leading and trailing edges of the square wave. The positive pulse at the leading edge is clamped to the ground by diode CR_1. As a result, the output of the circuit is a single sharp pulse that corresponds to the trailing edge of the Q_2 output. The time interval between the application of the input pulse to Q_1 and the delivery of the sharp output pulse is the time delay of the circuit. Since the RC time constant of C_1-R_2 determines the delay, R_2 can be adjusted to control the delay achieved.

delay lines

As you will learn later, when a signal is applied to an electrical transmission line, a delay in transmission time is produced by the inductance and capacitance that exist along the length of the line. Discrete *inductors* and *capacitors* can be connected to produce the same type of delay. A network of this type is called an *artificial delay line*.

One type of artificial delay line consists of inductors and capacitors connected as shown. When an input signal is applied, capacitor C_1 begins to charge through inductor L_1. Since the inductance of L_1 opposes the buildup of current, a certain amount of time is required for C_1 to charge. As C_1 becomes charged, C_2 begins to charge to the C_1 voltage through inductor L_2. Again, a definite time is required for C_2 to become charged because of the opposition of L_2. This same sequence occurs for each section of the line, with each capacitor taking a definite amount of time to charge. The total delay time before the signal reaches the output is therefore the *sum* of the LC charging times of each of the LC sections.

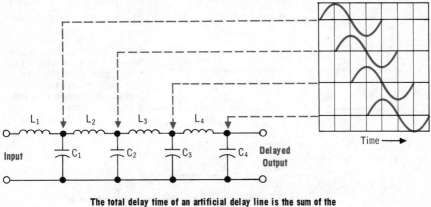

The total delay time of an artificial delay line is the sum of the delays of the individual sections. The charge of each capacitor is delayed by its associated inductor. The time delay of each LC section is $t = \sqrt{LC}$.

The delay produced by *each* LC section can be calculated from the equation $t = \sqrt{LC}$, where t is the delay time in seconds, and L and C are the values of the inductance and capacitance. Thus, if an LC section consisted of a 0.1-mh inductor and a 0.01-μf capacitor, its delay would be:

$$t = \sqrt{0.1 \times 10^{-3} \times 0.01 \times 10^{-6}} = \sqrt{1 \times 10^{-12}}$$
$$t = 1 \ \mu\text{sec}$$

Four of these sections would then provide a delay of 4 μsec.

the phantastron

In radar equipment, a frequently-used pulse-delay circuit is the *phantastron*. Like the monostable multivibrator delay circuit previously described, the phantastron has *two* operating states: one stable and the other unstable. The circuit is normally in its stable state, but when an input pulse is received, it switches to its unstable state. It remains in this state for a definite time and then automatically switches back to its stable state.

The usable delay is the rectangular pulse it delivers while it is in its unstable state. This rectangular pulse must be differentiated and clipped, as in the monostable delay circuit, to produce the required delayed pulse output. An important characteristic of the phantastron is that the delay it provides can be varied by changing the *plate voltage*. In other delay circuits, a part, such as a capacitor or resistor, must be varied to change the delay.

One type of phantastron circuit uses a pentagrid tube. Grid 1 controls the cathode emission, while grid 3 determines how much current passes through to the plate. Grids 2 and 4 are internally connected and function as the screen grid. The output of the circuit is taken from the cathode.

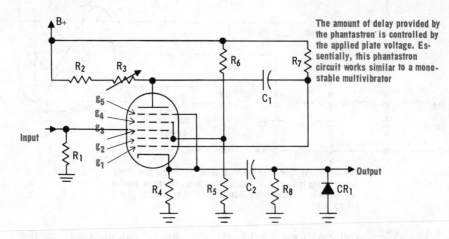

The amount of delay provided by the phantastron is controlled by the applied plate voltage. Essentially, this phantastron circuit works similar to a monostable multivibrator

With no input signal, there is a positive bias on grid 1 because it is connected through R_7 to B+. Thus, a very heavy cathode current flows. The resulting high voltage drop across cathode resistor R_4 provides a negative bias between grid 3 and the cathode that is sufficient to prevent any current from passing through grid 3 to the plate. Therefore, only grid 2, the screen grid, receives current. Essentially, plate current is cut off, but the cathode is still delivering a high current to the screen grid.

the phantastron (cont.)

When a positive pulse is applied to grid 3, the plate current cutoff bias is overcome and current flows to the plate. This causes a sharp drop in plate voltage, since plate load resistors R_2 and R_3 are very large in value. As a result, the plate voltage drops sharply; this is coupled as a negative-going pulse to grid 1 by capacitor C_1, causing a considerable decrease in cathode emission. The overall current through the tube drops considerably, but the plate voltage is still low because of the high values of R_2 and R_3. With less current through R_4, the bias on grid 3 is reduced, so plate current continues to flow even after the input pulse is gone.

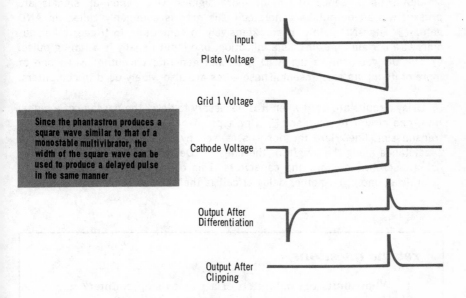

Since the phantastron produces a square wave similar to that of a monostable multivibrator, the width of the square wave can be used to produce a delayed pulse in the same manner

As long as the plate voltage is low, C_1 continues to discharge to keep the tube in this state. When C_1 finishes discharging, grid 1 again becomes positive, causing a high cathode current and bias that again cuts off grid 3. The plate current stops flowing, and the resulting rise in plate voltage is coupled by capacitor C_1 as a positive pulse to grid 1 to bring the stage quickly back to its stable state. It will stay this way until another input pulse is received. The negative-going cathode voltage that was produced during the unstable state is differentiated, and the leading spike is clamped. The trailing spike is the delayed pulse. R_3 can be adjusted to control the drop in plate voltage, and, thus, the discharge action of C_3, to determine the time delay.

summary

☐ Counters provide output pulses or voltages that are proportional to the input pulse repetition rate. ☐ The step-by-step counter provides a voltage output that increases in steps as each additional pulse is applied to the input. When the output voltage equals the peak amplitude of the input pulses, no further counting takes place. ☐ The frequency divider counter generates one output pulse whenever a certain number of input pulses have been received. One simple type of frequency divider counter consists of a gas tube connected to the output of a step-by-step counter.

☐ The gating circuit receives two or more inputs and will deliver an output only when the proper conditions are met. These conditions are usually established by the polarities of the inputs. ☐ The coincident gate senses the simultaneous presence of two or more signals. Only when all signals are present will an output be generated. This gate is commonly called an AND gate. ☐ The AND gate is used extensively in computers to trigger other circuits at a certain time. In this application, one input usually is a timing pulse. ☐ The OR gate, unlike the AND gate, will generate an output when one or more of its inputs are present. These gates are also widely used in computers.

☐ Delay circuits are used when it is necessary to delay the passage of a signal from one circuit to another. ☐ One type of delay circuit is a delay line or transmission line. Here the delay is caused by the inherent inductance and capacitance along the length of the line. ☐ Delay lines can be simulated by using discrete inductors and capacitors. This configuration is called an artificial delay line. ☐ Another delay circuit is the phantastron.

review questions

1. What limits the operation of a step-by-step counter?
2. How does a frequency divider counter operate?
3. Is the operation of the frequency divider counter limited as was the step-by-step counter? Explain.
4. Two switches connected in series between a power source and a load represent an AND function. Why?
5. What determines the circuit arrangement of an AND gate?
6. How did the OR gate get its name?
7. What is the main difference between the AND and OR gate?
8. How does an actual delay line differ from an artificial delay line?
9. What determines the total delay in an artificial delay line?
10. How can the phantastron delay be varied?

r-f signal transmission and antennas

You have now learned about many of the electronic circuits used to generate, amplify, shape, and otherwise process electrical signals. You also learned in Volume 2 how these circuits can be connected to produce many different types of electronic equipment. Much of this equipment, you recall, is used for *transmitting* and *receiving* electrical signals over long distances by means of *radio waves*. Common examples of this equipment include radio, television, and radar transmitters and receivers.

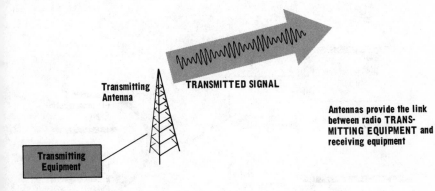

Transmitting Antenna

TRANSMITTED SIGNAL

Transmitting Equipment

Antennas provide the link between radio TRANS-MITTING EQUIPMENT and receiving equipment

The transmitting equipment generates the signal, amplifies it to a high power level, and then applies it to an antenna that *radiates* it into space. At the receiving end, an antenna *intercepts* a portion of the radiated signal and applies it to the receiver, which amplifies it to a usable level and then recovers the intelligence carried by the signal. You have already seen how the various transmitters and receivers operate. Now you will learn how *antennas* make the transmission and reception of radio waves possible.

TRANSMITTED SIGNAL

Receiving Antenna

Antennas provide the link between radio transmitting equipment and RECEIVING EQUIPMENT

Receiving Equipment

antenna reciprocity

Basically, an antenna is a length of conductor that acts as a *conversion* device. It converts an electrical signal into *electromagnetic* energy, as well as electromagnetic energy into an electrical signal. The *first* type of conversion takes place when an antenna is used for *transmitting* purposes. The transmitter output is applied to the antenna terminals and causes current to flow in the antenna. The antenna then converts the current flow into an electromagnetic signal that is radiated into space.

For most purposes, an antenna is equally good as a transmitter and receiver of electromagnetic energy

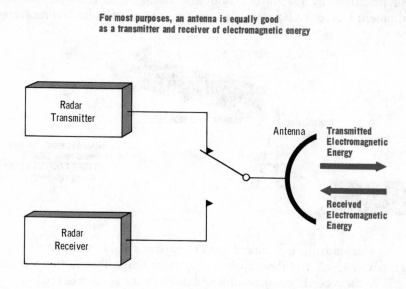

Radar equipment requires only a single antenna, which is alternately used for transmitting and receiving

The *second* type of conversion occurs when an antenna is used for *receiving*. An electromagnetic signal, when passing an antenna, induces a current in it. The current is then applied as a signal input to the receiver.

For many purposes, any antenna performs *both* types of conversion equally well. Therefore, the same antenna can often be used either for transmitting or receiving. This is known as *antenna reciprocity*. Because of antenna reciprocity, a *single* antenna can be used in applications that do not require simultaneous transmitting and receiving. The most common example of this is in radar equipment, where the antenna is alternately connected to the output of the transmitter and to the input of the receiver.

antenna current

When the output of a transmitter is applied to an antenna, current flows back and forth along the length of the antenna. However, since an antenna does not form a closed circuit, the current causes an *uneven distribution* of electrons. This is shown for a simple antenna fed at the center by the transmitter.

At a given instant, the left-hand terminal of the transmitter is negative and the right-hand terminal is positive. Thus, electrons in the antenna are repelled by the negative terminal and attracted by the positive one. This causes current to flow as shown. But since the antenna ends are *open,* the result is an increasing negative charge toward the left end of the antenna and an increasing positive charge toward the right end. At the ends of the antenna the *charge* is *maximum* and the *current* is *zero.* At the center, the *charge* is *zero* and the *current* is *maximum.*

Since the transmitter output varies *sinusoidally,* so does the polarity of its output terminals. Therefore, both the current and the charge buildup along the antenna also vary sinusoidally.

The conditions described here are ideal. They exist when the length of the antenna is equal to one-half of the wavelength of the transmitter output frequency. As you will see later, this relationship between the antenna length and the signal frequency is important if the antenna operation is to be efficient.

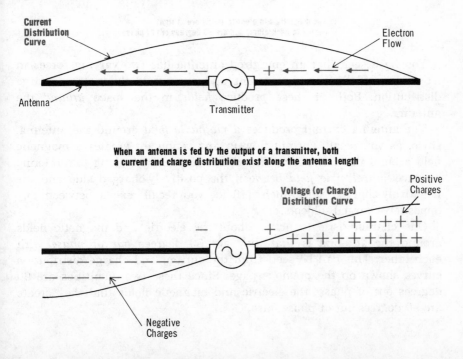

When an antenna is fed by the output of a transmitter, both a current and charge distribution exist along the antenna length

fields around an antenna

**Both a magnetic and an electric field
exist around an energized antenna**

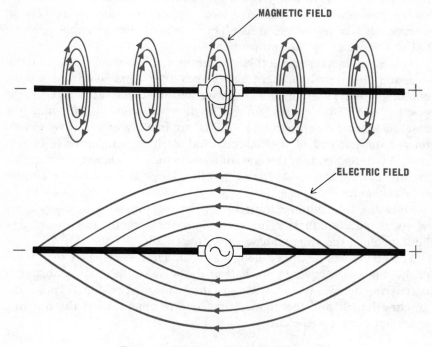

The magnetic and electric fields are at right
angles to each other, and are 90 degrees out of phase

You have seen that an energized antenna has two varying forces in it: a sinusoidally varying current and a sinusoidally varying charge distribution. Both of these produce *fields* in the space *around* the antenna.

The antenna *current* produces a *magnetic field* around the antenna, since, as you recall, current flow in any conductor creates a magnetic field around the conductor. The *charge distribution* along the antenna produces an *electric field* between the positively-charged side and the negatively-charged side. Such a field, you recall, exists between any oppositely-charged objects.

One characteristic to notice about the electric and magnetic fields around the antenna is that they are 90 degrees *out of phase* with each other. This can be seen from the current and charge distribution curves shown on the previous page. Since these two quantities are 90 degrees out of phase, the electric and magnetic fields that they create are 90 degrees out of phase, also.

the radiated field

The two fields that exist around an antenna do *not* make up the electromagnetic radiation that is emitted by the antenna and picked up by distant receivers. These fields do, however, *produce* the field that is actually radiated.

The exact way in which they do this is not completely understood, even today. However, one way of explaining it is shown. In A, the electric field around the antenna is at its *maximum* value. An instant later, in B, the field is *collapsing* back into the antenna. If the frequency of the signal applied to the antenna is low, the entire electric field will collapse back into the antenna. However, if the frequency is high, the outer parts of the field cannot move in very fast. Thus, when the charge distribution, or voltage, across the antenna is almost zero, there will still be a relatively large electric field around the antenna.

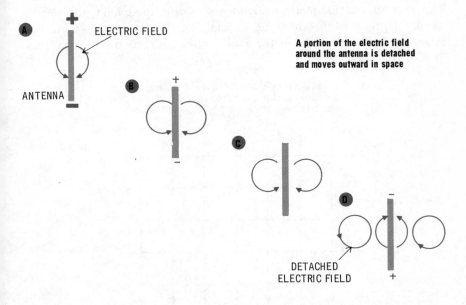

ELECTRIC FIELD

A portion of the electric field around the antenna is detached and moves outward in space

ANTENNA

DETACHED
ELECTRIC FIELD

In C, an exact *zero voltage* condition exists along the antenna. The electric field has not completely collapsed, and the portion that remains is left with no voltage to support it. This portion is then *repelled* from the antenna by the next electric field when it develops (D). The same action occurs repeatedly, so a series of detached electric fields constantly move outward from the antenna.

Magnetic lines of force are detached from the magnetic field around the antenna in the same way. They, too, then constantly move outward from the antenna.

the electromagnetic field

Thus far you have seen that detached electric and magnetic fields move outward from an energized antenna. These fields, however, are then modified according to two basic laws of electromagnetic radiation. These laws are:

1. *A moving electric field creates a magnetic field.*
2. *A moving magnetic field creates an electric field.*

These created fields are *in phase* with and have a direction *perpendicular* to the fields that cause them. So we now have *two* electromagnetic fields moving outward from the antenna, with the magnetic and electric components of each perpendicular to one another.

Although it is beyond the scope of this book, it can be shown that the two electromagnetic fields *add* together vectorially in space to produce a *single*, sinusoidally-varying electromagnetic field. This field is then the total *radio wave* that propagates outward from the antenna. The electric and magnetic components of this total field are perpendicular both to each other and to the direction of propagation. This is shown in the illustration for a field whose direction of propagation is *into* the page.

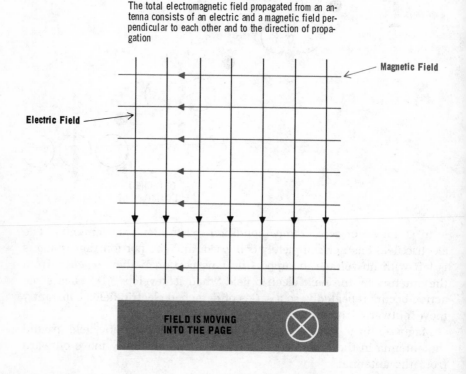

The total electromagnetic field propagated from an antenna consists of an electric and a magnetic field perpendicular to each other and to the direction of propagation

Magnetic Field

Electric Field

FIELD IS MOVING
INTO THE PAGE

wavelength

The radio waves propagated outward from an antenna travel at approximately the speed of light, which is 186,000 miles per second, or 300 million meters per second. All radio waves travel at this speed, regardless of their frequency.

An important characteristic of a radio wave is its *wavelength,* which, you recall, is the *distance* traveled by the wave in the time required for one cycle. To find the wavelength, you divide the speed of the wave by its frequency. As an equation, this is:

$$\lambda = \frac{300{,}000{,}000 \text{ meters/second}}{\text{f cycles/second}}$$

where λ is the wavelength in meters, and f is the frequency of the wave in cycles per second.

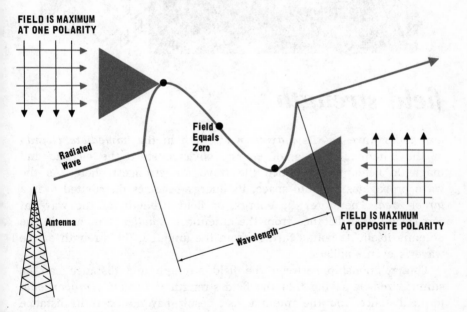

The distance traveled by a radio wave during the time required for it to go through one full cycle is the WAVELENGTH

FIELD IS MAXIMUM AT ONE POLARITY

Radiated Wave

Field Equals Zero

Antenna

FIELD IS MAXIMUM AT OPPOSITE POLARITY

Wavelength

If the wavelength of a wave is known, the frequency can be found by using the above equation in a different form:

$$\text{f} = \frac{300{,}000{,}000 \text{ meters/second}}{\lambda \text{ meters}}$$

where again f is in cycles per second, and λ is in meters.

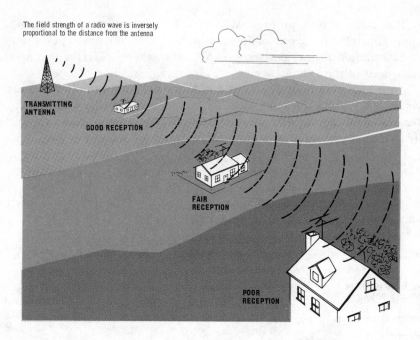

field strength

A radio wave has its *maximum* strength in the *immediate vicinity* of the antenna. This is, of course, obvious, since the electric and magnetic fields that produce the wave are strongest there. As the wave propagates out into space, its energy becomes distributed over a *larger area*. Therefore, the energy, or field strength, of the wave at some point at a distance from the antenna is *smaller* than it is at the antenna itself. At points farther from the antenna, the strength of the wave is even smaller.

This relationship between the field strength and distance can be summarized by saying that the field strength is *inversely proportional* to the distance from the antenna. As a result, beyond a certain distance the strength of a radio wave is too weak to be picked up and processed by receiving equipment.

As you will see later, there are certain conditions under which a radio wave having a usable field strength can still be received at locations that are normally too far from the antenna to receive usable signals.

directivity

Radiation emitted by a point would extend outward equally in all directions. However, an antenna is not a point. Consequently, its radiation is affected by its *shape* and is *not* uniform in all directions. In some directions the radiation is weak, or even zero. Thus, every antenna has a characteristic *radiation pattern*. Graphs, called *polar diagrams*, are commonly used to give a pictorial representation of these radiation patterns.

A polar diagram shows how the relative field strength of an antenna varies with both *distance* and *direction* from the antenna. Two typical polar diagrams are shown. Both represent the areas around a vertical antenna as seen from above.

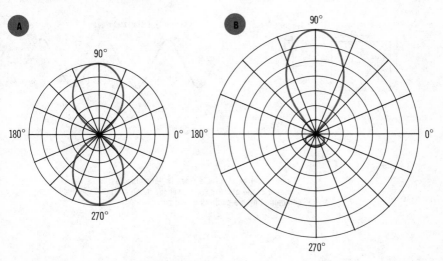

Polar diagrams are useful for graphically illustrating the directional characteristics of an antenna's radiation pattern

The antenna represented by A radiates strongly in the direction of 90 and 270 degrees. Away from these two directions the radiation falls off, until there is practically no radiation at all between approximately 160 to 200 and 20 to 340 degrees. The antenna represented by B has practically no radiation between about 160 to 20 degrees. It is therefore said to be more directional, or have better *directivity*, than the antenna of A.

Antennas are frequently selected for certain applications on the basis of their directivity. This is because some applications require good directivity, while others require a broad radiation pattern.

polarization

Another important characteristic of a radio wave emitted by an antenna is its *polarization*. This is defined as the direction of the *electric-field component* of the wave with respect to ground. If, as the wave travels through space, its electric field is vertical with respect to ground, the wave is *vertically polarized*. If the electric field is horizontal with respect to ground, it is *horizontally polarized*. With a simple antenna the *position* of the antenna determines the polarization of the wave. Vertically-positioned antennas produce vertically-polarized waves and horizontally-positioned antennas produce horizontally-polarized waves.

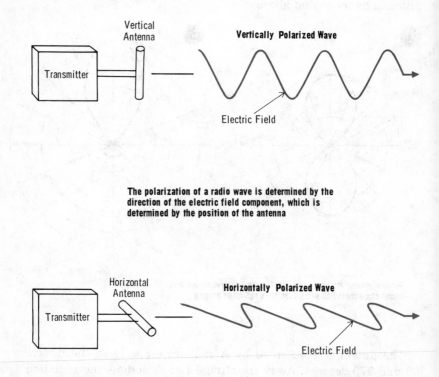

The polarization of a radio wave is determined by the direction of the electric field component, which is determined by the position of the antenna

The type of polarization used in any particular system depends upon many interrelated factors. These include the signal frequencies involved, the type of transmitting antenna and its height above ground, and the height of the receiving antenna above ground. At all but high frequencies, for best reception the orientation of the receiving antennas with respect to ground should be the same as the polarization of the received wave. In other words, if the transmitting antenna is vertical, the receiving antenna should also be vertical.

summary

☐ The antenna is the link between transmitting and receiving equipment. ☐ Transmitting antennas convert electrical signals into electromagnetic energy and radiate this energy into space. The energy is intercepted by a receiving antenna and converted back into electrical signals. ☐ In certain applications, the same antenna can be used for both transmitting and receiving. This is known as antenna reciprocity.

☐ The output of a transmitter sets up a sinusoidally varying charge on the antenna. ☐ The antenna current produces a magnetic field while the charge produces an electric field. These fields are 90 degrees out of phase with each other. ☐ Although both fields are radiated into space, they do not make up the electromagnetic wave that is intercepted by the receiving antenna. Instead, these two fields create two electromagnetic fields that add vectorially to produce the desired field. ☐ Wavelength relates the frequency of the radio wave to the distance traveled by the wave in a certain time interval. This quantity is especially important in antenna design because the length of the antenna is related to the signal frequency.

☐ The field strength of a radio wave is maximum in the immediate vicinity of the antenna and decreases as the distance from the antenna increases. ☐ Beyond certain distances, the field strength is so weak that it cannot be processed by the receiving equipment. ☐ The radiation pattern or polar diagram of an antenna shows how the field strength varies with distance and direction from the antenna. ☐ Polarization defines the orientation of the electric-field component of the wave with respect to ground. ☐ Antennas can be either horizontally polarized or vertically polarized. ☐ The transmitting and receiving antennas should both be polarized in the same direction.

review questions

1. What is an *antenna*?
2. Radar sets use one antenna to transmit and receive. Why?
3. How is current and charge distributed along an antenna?
4. What are the two basic laws of electromagnetic radiation?
5. How are these laws applied to the generation of an electromagnetic wave?
6. Calculate the wavelength of a 10-megacycle signal.
7. Why is the field strength inversely proportional to distance from the antenna?
8. What affects the radiation pattern of an antenna?
9. How is the polarization of a simple antenna determined?
10. What other factors affect polarization?

transmission paths

When a radio wave leaves an antenna, it travels outward into space. As the wave moves outward, various portions of it follow different paths and are affected by the things that lie in these paths.

One part of the wave travels along the surface of the earth, and is therefore called the *ground wave*. The remainder of the wave moves upward and outward from the antenna and makes up what is called the *sky wave*. As you shall see, each of these portions of the total wave are responsible for two distinctly different types of signal transmission. Under certain conditions, the ground wave provides the best transmission, and under other conditions the sky wave is best.

An important thing to understand is that the ground and sky waves are actually part of the *same* total wave emitted by the antenna. It is only for convenience that they are considered to be separate waves.

When a radio wave leaves an antenna, it consists of a ground wave portion and a sky wave portion

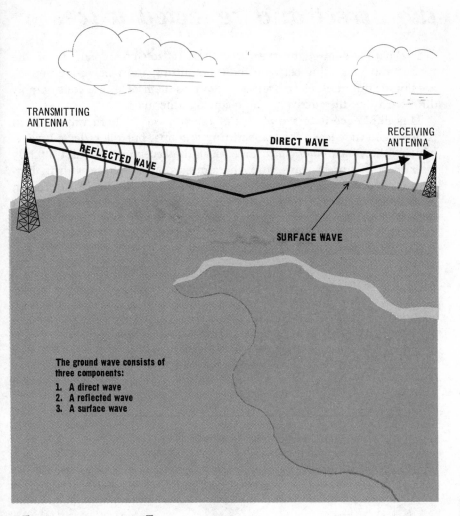

TRANSMITTING
ANTENNA

DIRECT WAVE

RECEIVING
ANTENNA

REFLECTED WAVE

SURFACE WAVE

The ground wave consists of
three components:
1. A direct wave
2. A reflected wave
3. A surface wave

the ground wave

The ground wave moves outward from the antenna both directly along the earth's surface and in the space immediately above it. Usually the wave is considered to consist of three components. One of these travels directly through space from the transmitting antenna to the receiving antenna. It is called the *direct wave*. The second component also travels in space between the transmitting and receiving antennas, but does not follow a direct path. Instead, it is reflected from the earth back up to the receiving antenna. Hence, it is called the *reflected wave*. The third component is called the *surface wave*, since it travels in contact with the earth.

the direct and reflected waves

The paths followed by the direct and reflected components of the ground wave traveling between the transmitting and receiving antennas are not too different. Nevertheless, the waves themselves are considerably different when they arrive at the receiving antenna.

This difference is in the *phases* of the two waves. Both waves are in phase when they leave the transmitting antenna, but the reflected wave, which follows a *longer path,* arrives at the receiving antenna slightly *later* than the direct wave, and, therefore, is out of phase with it. Furthermore, when reflected by the earth, the reflected wave is shifted in phase *180 degrees* in much the same way that a mirror reverses a reflected image. If it were not for the difference in the lengths of the paths that they follow, the two waves would arrive at the receiving antenna 180 degrees out of phase, and would *cancel* each other. Because of this difference in path length, however, the two waves arrive somewhat less than 180 degrees out of phase and only *partial* cancellation occurs.

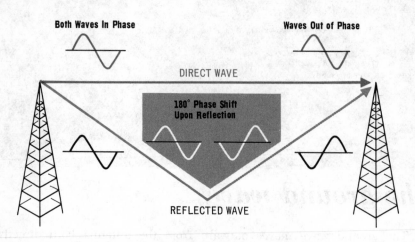

The 180° phase shift produced by reflection and the difference in path length cause the direct and reflected waves to arrive at the receiving antenna out of phase

When both the transmitting and receiving antennas are relatively close to the ground, the path lengths followed by the direct and reflected waves are not too different, and for practical purposes can be considered as equal. Under these conditions the direct and reflected waves effectively cancel each other, and only the surface wave is responsible for reception.

the surface wave

As pointed out previously, the surface wave passes along the ground as it travels to the receiving antenna. Since the earth's surface is effectively a conductor, the moving wave induces a voltage in the earth, and this voltage produces eddy currents. The energy that establishes these currents is *absorbed* from the surface wave, thereby weakening the wave as it travels outward from the antenna.

The amount of this weakening, or *attenuation,* of the wave depends on the *type of terrain* over which the wave passes. Water causes the least attenuation, while jungle, mountainous, or densely-populated terrain causes the most. This means that the surface wave has a relatively long transmission range over water, but only a short range over terrain covered with obstructions.

The *frequency* of a surface wave also greatly affects the degree to which it is attenuated by the earth. As frequency is increased, attenuation increases rapidly. Therefore, surface-wave communication is limited to relatively *low frequencies.* The effect of frequency on attenuation is shown in the graph.

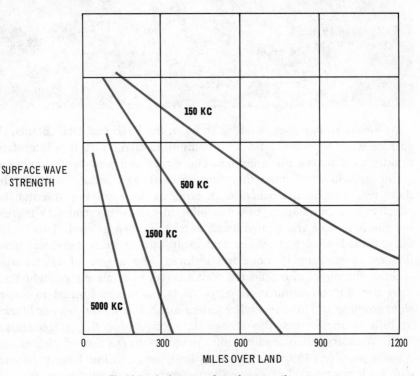

The higher the frequency of a surface wave, the
more it is attenuated by the earth's surface

communications
with the ground wave

The effectiveness of the ground wave in providing radio communication varies, depending on the *frequency* and *power* involved. At relatively *low* frequencies, such as those used in commercial AM broadcasting, the *surface-wave* component is strong. However, since it is steadily attenuated as it moves outward from the antenna, a considerable amount of power must be transmitted for long-range communication.

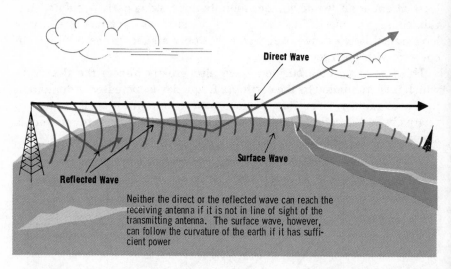

Direct Wave

Surface Wave

Reflected Wave

Neither the direct or the reflected wave can reach the receiving antenna if it is not in line of sight of the transmitting antenna. The surface wave, however, can follow the curvature of the earth if it has sufficient power

At *higher frequencies,* such as those in the VHF and UHF bands, the surface wave becomes useless for communication, since it is attenuated rapidly as it leaves the antenna. The *direct* and *reflected* components of the ground wave must therefore be used. You recall, however, that these two components cancel each other at the receiving antenna. For effective communication, this cancellation can be overcome by increasing the *height* of the transmitting antenna above ground. This causes the reflected wave to travel considerably farther than the direct wave, thereby attenuating it more and reducing the degree of cancellation.

Since the direct and reflected waves travel in relatively straight lines, their use for communication purposes is essentially limited to *line-of-sight* conditions. If the receiving antenna is below the horizon or blocked by hills or mountains, this line-of-sight communication is ineffective.

In summary, then, radio communication by means of the ground wave is possible (1) over a relatively long range, at low frequencies and with high power, and (2) over short distances, at high frequencies and with low power.

the sky wave

You have now seen how the ground wave behaves and how it can provide various types of communication. But, in addition to the ground wave, a portion of the energy radiated by an antenna moves upward and outward away from the antenna. This is called the *sky wave*, which, as you will learn, behaves very differently from the ground wave. Because of its behavior, the sky wave is responsible for practically all of the long-range radio communication in the world today. It is no exaggeration to say that were it not for the characteristics of the sky wave, long-range radio communication as we know it would be impossible.

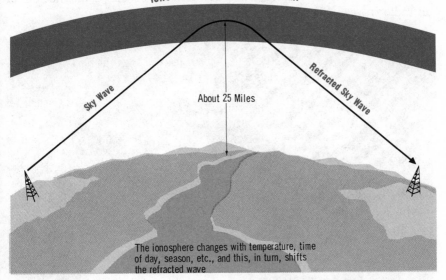

The sky wave is refracted back to the earth by the ionosphere, and, as a result, is capable of providing very-long-distance communication

IONOSPHERE (Layers of Ionized Air)

Sky Wave

Refracted Sky Wave

About 25 Miles

The ionosphere changes with temperature, time of day, season, etc., and this, in turn, shifts the refracted wave

The sky wave can transmit signals over long distances because it is *refracted,* or bent, back toward the earth by the *ionosphere.* The ionosphere is a group of layers of ionized air that starts about 25 miles up. Their electrical charge repels the radio waves to refract them. A receiving antenna located in the vicinity of the returning sky wave can thus receive strong signals even though it is hundreds of miles from the transmitting antenna. Since the ionosphere is ionized air, such factors as temperature, time of day, and season change its ionization properties.

the ionosphere

The *ionosphere* is a region of the earth's atmosphere that extends from about 25 to 350 miles above the earth. It is called the ionosphere because it contains a much greater number of negative and positive *ions* than do the other regions of the atmosphere. Ions, you recall, are formed when one or more electrons are stripped from a neutral atom or added to a neutral atom. In the ionosphere, the former occurs as a result of bombardment by ultraviolet and other radiation from the sun. At altitudes above about 350 miles, the air is too thin to permit large-scale ion formation. At altitudes below about 25 miles, not enough radiation penetrates to cause much ionization.

The *degree* of ionization that exists in the ionosphere depends on the intensity of the radiation from the sun. Consequently, the density varies both with the *time* of day and the *height* above the earth. As a result of the density variation with height, the ionosphere can be considered to be made up of different *layers*, each with a different average ion density. As you will see, each of these layers has a distinct effect on radio waves.

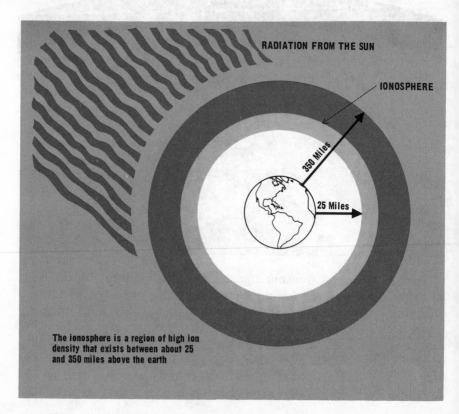

RADIATION FROM THE SUN

IONOSPHERE

350 Miles

25 Miles

The ionosphere is a region of high ion density that exists between about 25 and 350 miles above the earth

ionospheric layers

There is no sharp dividing line between the layers of the ionosphere. Each one tends to merge gradually into the next. However, for purposes of discussion, distinctly separate layers are assumed.

The *lowest* layer of the ionosphere occurs at an altitude between about 25 and 50 miles. This layer is called the *D layer*. The D layer is present only during the *day*, and even then its ionization is low. Directly above the D layer is the *E layer*, which extends from an altitude of about 50 miles to an altitude of about 90 miles. Density in the E layer is greatest at about 70 miles. The E layer is strongest during the day, although it is present, but much weaker, at night. Maximum density of the E layer occurs at about 12:00 noon.

The last layer of the ionosphere is the *F layer*, which extends from a height of 90 miles to the upper limit of the ionosphere of 350 miles. At night there is only one F layer, but during the day it often separates into two parts, designated F_1 and F_2. The F_2 layer, which is the uppermost, has the highest ion density of any of the ionospheric layers. The F_1 and F_2 layers recombine back into the F layer shortly after sunset.

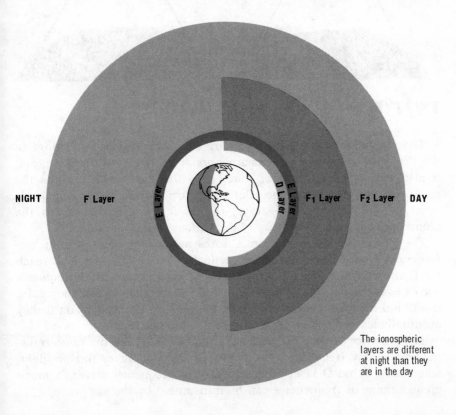

NIGHT   F Layer   E Layer   D Layer   E Layer   F₁ Layer   F₂ Layer   DAY

The ionospheric layers are different at night than they are in the day

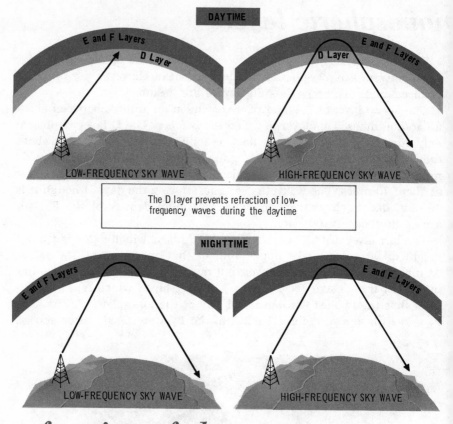

DAYTIME

LOW-FREQUENCY SKY WAVE   HIGH-FREQUENCY SKY WAVE

The D layer prevents refraction of low-frequency waves during the daytime

NIGHTTIME

LOW-FREQUENCY SKY WAVE   HIGH-FREQUENCY SKY WAVE

refraction of sky waves

The properties of the ionosphere are such that it does two things to the sky wave. It *absorbs* various amounts of energy from the wave, and it also acts as a radio mirror that *bends* the wave back towards the earth. The ability of the ionosphere to return a wave to earth depends upon the *frequency* of the wave, the *angle* at which it strikes the ionosphere, and the *ion density* of the various layers.

The D layer of the ionosphere absorbs most of the energy from *low-frequency waves*. Consequently, practically none of these waves reach the E and F layers, which are responsible for refraction. *High-frequency waves* pass through the D layer with little absorption. When they enter the E and F layers, they are bent by the ionized atmosphere until they eventually leave the ionosphere and return towards earth.

The presence of the D layer during the daytime prevents radio transmission at low frequencies by means of the sky wave. But at night, when there is no D layer to absorb the low-frequency waves, a much greater range of frequencies can be transmitted by the sky wave.

critical frequency

Although all radio waves are refracted by the atmosphere, the *degree* of refraction depends on the *frequency* of the wave. Waves that are strongly refracted are quickly bent back towards the earth. But waves that are only slightly refracted pass through the ionosphere and do not return to earth.

The amount of refraction that takes place is *inversely proportional* to the frequency of the wave. Thus, *low-frequency* waves undergo *strong* refraction, while the refraction of very *high-frequency* waves is only *slight*. This does not mean that low-frequency waves are always bent back towards earth. In the daytime, the D layer absorbs most of these waves, so that they cannot reach the E and F layers to be refracted.

Radio waves above a certain frequency pass through the ionosphere and do not return to earth. Waves in the VHF band are of this type

IONOSPHERE

IONOSPHERE

Frequency Low Enough To Be Refracted Back To Earth

Frequency Too High To Be Refracted Back To Earth

If the frequency of a wave transmitted directly upward was steadily increased, a point would be reached where the wave would pass right through the atmosphere. The frequency at which this occurs is called the *critical frequency*. All waves with frequencies higher than this will not be returned to earth. The critical frequency is not always the same. It depends on the degree of ionization of the ionosphere, which in turn depends on the time of day and the season of the year. The critical frequency is highest at noon and during midsummer.

critical angle

You saw that the frequency of a wave affects the amount of refraction it undergoes in the ionosphere and, therefore, whether or not it is returned to earth. The *angle* at which the wave enters the ionosphere has a similar effect. A wave of a given frequency will be bent back to earth if it enters the ionosphere at one angle, but will pass through the ionosphere if it enters at a different angle. The *larger* the angle, the more chance there is that the wave will *not* return to earth.

The four waves shown are of the same frequency. Wave A strikes the ionosphere at practically a 90-degree angle and is not refracted sufficiently to return to earth. Waves B and C enter the ionosphere at smaller angles, and both are returned to earth.

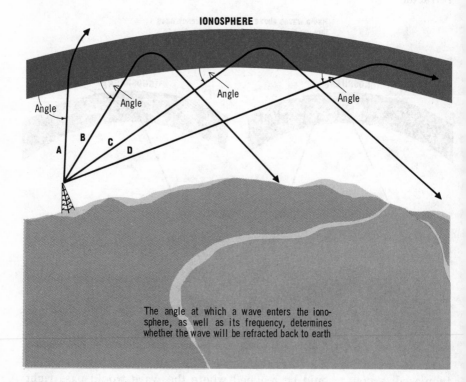

The angle at which a wave enters the iono- sphere, as well as its frequency, determines whether the wave will be refracted back to earth

The smaller the angle, the longer the path length that the wave follows in the ionosphere and the greater the distance from the antenna that it returns to earth. If the angle is too small, however, the wave will effectively *remain* in the ionosphere and not return to earth (wave D); or it could travel through the ionosphere a great distance and come out on the other side of the world.

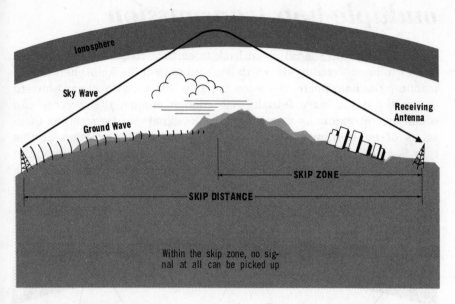

Within the skip zone, no signal at all can be picked up

skip distance and skip zone

When a radio wave is refracted by the ionosphere, it can return to earth many hundreds of miles from the transmitting antenna. The exact distance depends on many things, including the frequency of the wave, the angle at which it enters the ionosphere, and the time of day. At the point where the wave returns to earth a very strong signal can be picked up by a receiving antenna. Since the path of the wave is up to the ionosphere and back down, the strength of the received signal is not affected by things such as mountains or tall structures that lie between the transmitting and receiving antennas.

Although a refracted wave is strong at the point where it returns to earth, it is essentially *zero* between that point and the transmitting antenna. This means that a receiving antenna at the returning point will receive a strong signal, while other receiving antennas much closer to the transmitter will receive no reflected signal at all.

The distance from the transmitting antenna to the spot where the reflected wave returns to earth is frequently called the *skip distance*. At all distances less than this around the antenna, reception of a signal is only possible with the *ground wave* emitted by the transmitting antenna. However, the ground wave is completely attenuated before it covers the skip distance. Consequently, there is a zone between the point where the ground wave is attenuated and the point where the sky wave returns to earth in which *no signal* at all is received. This zone is commonly referred to as the *skip zone*.

multiple-hop transmission

When a sky wave is refracted back to earth it frequently has enough energy to be *reflected* by the earth back up toward the ionosphere. Upon reaching the ionosphere, the wave is again refracted downward toward the earth. If the wave initially has enough energy, this process can occur *several times*. As a result, a usable signal can be received thousands of miles from the transmitting antenna. Transmission of this type is called *multiple-hop transmission*. The effects of frequency and transmission angle on multiple-hop transmission are the same as those previously described for single-hop transmission.

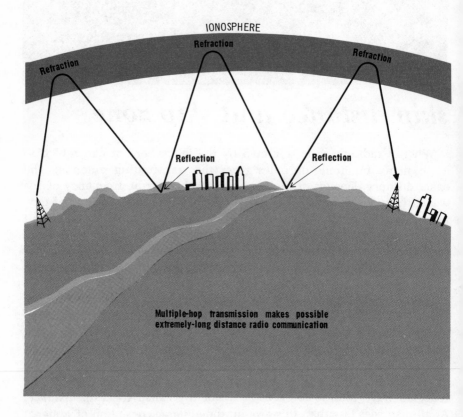

Multiple-hop transmission makes possible extremely-long distance radio communication

Although multiple-hop transmission can cover extremely long distances, a considerable amount of the wave's energy is *lost* in the repeated refractions and reflections. Consequently, if two identical signals cover the same distance, one in a single hop and the other in multiple hops, the single-hop wave will be considerably stronger when it reaches the receiving antenna.

fading

As you have seen, a transmitter radio wave can travel to a receiving antenna over a variety of paths. When the same wave reaches a receiving antenna after following *two* paths, the received signal strength may be drastically affected. This is because of the *relative phases* of the two received waves. If the two are in phase, they add; if they are out of phase, they subtract.

When both of the waves are constant, the resultant received signal is also constant. But if one or both of them vary, which frequently occurs because of rapid ionization changes in the ionosphere, the waves arrive sometimes *in phase* and sometimes *out of phase*. As a result, the received signal strength fluctuates widely. This condition is known as *fading*.

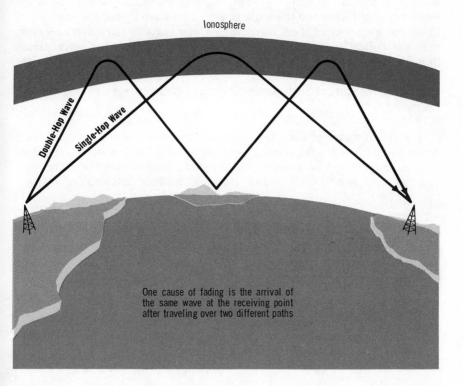

One cause of fading is the arrival of the same wave at the receiving point after traveling over two different paths

Fading can occur as a result of a single-hop and a multiple-hop wave both arriving at the same point. It can also be caused by interference between the ground and sky waves at the receiving point. Another type of especially severe fading can be caused by only a single sky wave. This occurs at points located near the outer edge of the skip zone when the sky wave alternately strikes and skips over the area.

summary

☐ Radio waves that leave an antenna travel in one of two paths. One part of the wave, called the ground wave, travels along the surface of the earth. The other part, called the sky wave, travels upward and outward from the antenna. ☐ The ground wave consists of a direct wave, a reflected wave, and a surface wave. ☐ The direct and reflected waves both travel in essentially the same path and are effective for line-of-sight communications at high frequencies. ☐ The surface wave travels along the surface of the earth and is effective for low-frequency, high-power communications. ☐ The second portion of the transmitted radio wave, the sky wave, is responsible for practically all long-range radio communications. This wave travels upward and outward from the antenna toward the ionosphere.

☐ The ionosphere consists of several layers of ionized air that refract the wave back toward the earth. ☐ The angle of refraction depends upon the frequency of the wave and the angle at which the wave strikes the ionosphere. ☐ As the frequency of the wave increases, the angle of refraction decreases until the critical frequency is reached. At this frequency, the wave passes through the ionosphere. ☐ Increasing the angle at which the wave strikes the ionosphere has the same effect on the angle of refraction as increasing the frequency. The critical angle is the angle at which the wave passes through the ionosphere.

☐ The skip distance or skip zone is the distance between the point the wave leaves the earth and is refracted back to earth. ☐ When the wave is refracted back to earth, it can be reflected, by the earth, back toward the ionosphere. This can occur several times and is called multiple-hop transmission.

review questions

1. How do the paths of the direct and reflected waves differ?
2. Why does the antenna height affect the range of direct and reflected waves?
3. Under what conditions are ground waves effective?
4. What is the *ionosphere*?
5. How does the ionosphere affect the range of a sky wave?
6. How do frequency and signal angle affect angle of refraction?
7. What occurs when a wave is transmitted at the critical frequency or critical angle?
8. How does the wave frequency affect the skip distance?
9. What causes multiple-hop transmission?
10. What are some conditions that affect fading?

antenna length

When an antenna is energized by r-f energy from a transmitter, current and voltage variations occur along the length of the antenna. The current and voltage then produce the electromagnetic field that is radiated by the antenna. Since the strength of the radiated field depends on the amplitude of the antenna voltage and current, a large amount of r-f energy must be supplied by the transmitter. However, for the r-f energy from the transmitter to produce a large voltage and current in the antenna, a certain relationship must exist between the frequency (or wavelength) of the energy and the length of the antenna.

Basically, this relationship requires that the frequency of the applied energy be such that the antenna appears to the transmitter as a *resonant circuit*. For this to occur, the antenna length must be some multiple of the wavelength of the applied r-f energy. Most commonly, this multiple is one-half—in other words, an antenna whose length is equal to one-half the wavelength of the applied r-f energy. Such an antenna is called a *half-wave antenna*.

The reason for this relationship between antenna length and the wavelength of the applied energy will become obvious when you study r-f transmission lines.

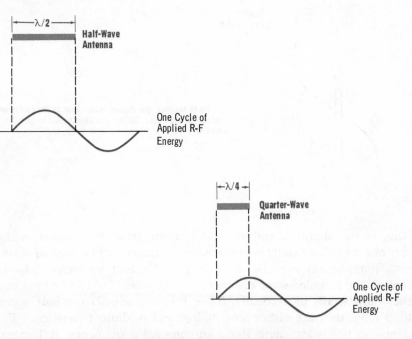

For best operation, the length of an antenna must be some
multiple of the wavelength of the applied r-f energy

the hertz antenna

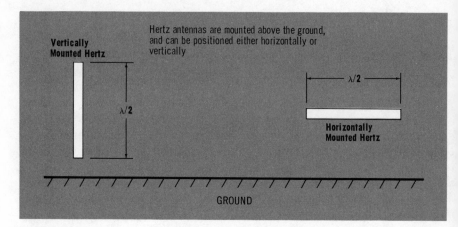

Hertz antennas are mounted above the ground, and can be positioned either horizontally or vertically

Vertically Mounted Hertz

λ/2

λ/2

Horizontally Mounted Hertz

GROUND

There is almost a limitless variety of antennas in use today. These range in complexity from a simple, single conductor to elaborate arrays containing many elements. For any particular application, the type of antenna used depends on the requirements of the system. These include frequency, directivity, polarization, and range.

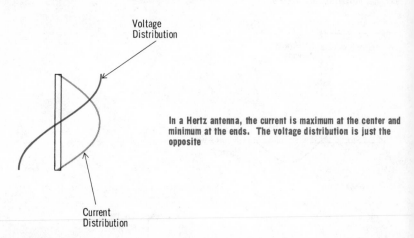

Voltage Distribution

In a Hertz antenna, the current is maximum at the center and minimum at the ends. The voltage distribution is just the opposite

Current Distribution

One of the simplest, and yet widely used, types of antenna is the *Hertz* antenna. Essentially, a Hertz is any antenna that is *one-half wavelength* long, or any even or odd multiple of a half wavelength. Hertz antennas are installed some distance *above ground,* and can be mounted either horizontally or vertically. Since they are usually one-half wavelength long, they are rather long at low and medium frequencies. For example, a half wavelength Hertz antenna for a frequency of 1 megacycle would be over 300 yards long.

the marconi antenna

A Hertz antenna for low and medium frequencies is very long. Such a long length is highly undesirable, and often completely unfeasible, when the antenna is to be used with *portable* transmitting equipment. This length disadvantage can be overcome somewhat by using a *Marconi* antenna.

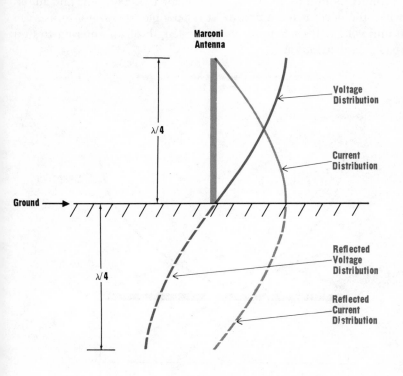

Physically, a Marconi Antenna is a quarter wavelength long, but it operates as a half-wave antenna

Essentially, a Marconi antenna operates as a half-wave antenna, but *physically* it is only a *quarter wavelength* long. This is possible because a Marconi is operated in conjunction with *ground*. One end is fed near ground. Thus, the ground provides a *reflection* of the current and voltage distribution set up in the antenna. The result is that a wave is emitted from the antenna/ground combination that is the same as the wave emitted by a Hertz antenna operated at the same frequency. Electrically, therefore, a Marconi is the same as a Hertz. Physically, however, it is only half as long.

antenna impedance

For maximum transfer of *power* from a transmitter to an antenna, the output impedance of the transmitter must be *matched* to the impedance of the antenna. Therefore, the impedance of the particular antenna that is used must be known. However, the impedance of an antenna *varies* along the antenna's length. As in any electrical circuit, this impedance is minimum when the current is maximum, and maximum when the current is minimum. It is possible, therefore, to use the current and voltage distributions along the length of an antenna to find the impedance distribution.

The impedance of a half-wave Hertz is minimum at the center and maximum at the ends

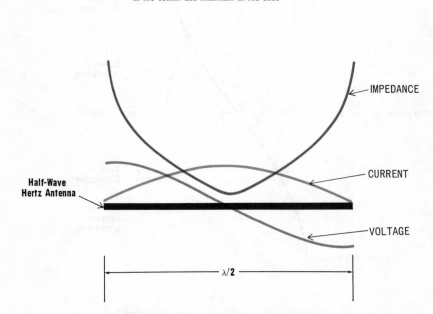

For a half-wave Hertz antenna, the impedance distribution is as shown. You can see that the *minimum* impedance exists at the *center,* where the current is maximum. If this antenna were connected to a transmitter having a low output impedance, the antenna would have to be driven at the center for maximum transfer of power. If a high output-impedance transmitter were used, the antenna would have to be driven at one of the *ends,* where the impedance is *maximum.* The actual impedance at the center of a half-wave Hertz is approximately 73 ohms. The impedance at the ends is about 2400 ohms.

In a Marconi antenna, the low-impedance point is at the grounded end, and the highest impedance occurs at the other end.

antenna electrical length

It has been assumed that the *physical* length of an antenna is the same as its *electrical* length. In other words, a half-wave antenna for a 10-meter wave is 5 meters long. Actually, this is correct only for an antenna that is *perfectly isolated* in space, an ideal condition never realized in practice. Nearby objects, such as the insulators used for support, introduce capacitance on the antenna, and, as a result, the antenna's dielectric constant is greater than 1. This causes the velocity of wave travel along the antenna to be less than the wave velocity in free space, and, in effect, makes the antenna *too long*. To compensate for this, the physical length of an antenna must be made about 5 percent *less* than the corresponding wavelength in free space.

For a half-wave antenna, the proper physical length for any given frequency can be found from the equation L = 468/f, where L is the antenna length in feet, and f is the frequency in megacycles. Consider a half-wave antenna for a frequency of 1 megacycle. The wavelength of a 1 megacycle wave in meters is: 300/f (mc) = 300/1 = 300, so the wavelength in feet is 3.26 × 300, or 978. The electrical length of the half-wave antenna is therefore:

$$1\lambda = 978 \text{ feet} \qquad \lambda/2 = 489 \text{ feet}$$

The physical length of the antenna is: 468/f (mc) = 468/1 = 468 feet. So the physical length is 21 feet less than the electrical length.

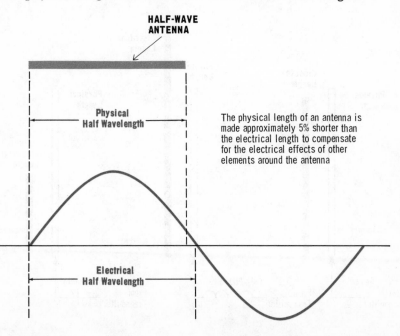

HALF-WAVE ANTENNA

Physical Half Wavelength

Electrical Half Wavelength

The physical length of an antenna is made approximately 5% shorter than the electrical length to compensate for the electrical effects of other elements around the antenna

antenna tuning

Very often an antenna does not have the correct length for the frequency at which it is to operate. This can occur when available space limits the size of the antenna, or when the antenna must operate over a range of different frequencies. Since physically changing the antenna's length is normally either difficult or impossible, some other means must be used to adjust the electrical length for efficient operation.

This can be done at the transmitter by *electrically* lengthening or shortening the antenna. Such a process is called *antenna tuning,* and is accomplished by adding either *inductance* or *capacitance* to the antenna at the point where it is fed by the transmitter. When inductance is added, the antenna is resonant at a lower frequency, which means that electrically it has a longer wavelength. Similarly, added capacitance causes the antenna to be resonant at a higher frequency, which means that electrically it has a shorter wavelength.

In summary, then, added *inductance* has the property of *lengthening* the antenna, while added *capacitance* has the property of *shortening* it. Thus, by adding the proper amount of either inductance or capacitance, the length of an antenna can be continuously varied over a certain range.

Adding inductance to an antenna effectively increases
its length, and adding capacitance decreases its length

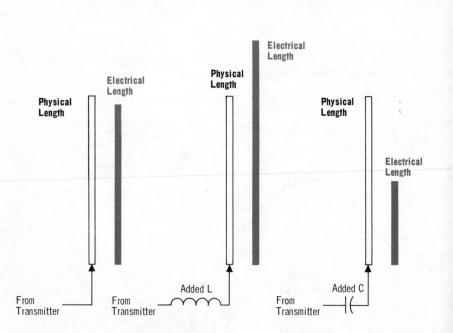

summary

□ The physical length of the antenna affects the strength of the electro-magnetic field. □ To maximize the electromagnetic field, the antenna must appear as a resonant circuit to the transmitter. This is accomplished by de-signing an antenna whose physical length equals some multiple of the wave-length of the r-f energy. Usually, this multiple is one-half, and the resultant antenna is called a half-wave antenna. □ A Hertz antenna is the simplest and most widely used antenna. Any antenna that is one-half wavelength long or any even or odd multiple of a half wavelength is called a Hertz antenna. □ The Hertz antenna can be mounted, either vertically or horizontally, above the ground.

□ The Marconi antenna operates as a half-wave antenna but is physically only one-quarter wavelength long. One end of this antenna is grounded and the ground provides a reflection of the voltage and current distribution. □ For maximum power transfer between the transmitter and antenna, the impedance of the antenna must match the output impedance of the transmitter. □ In the Hertz antenna, the impedance is minimum at the center and maximum at the ends. □ In the Marconi antenna, the impedance is minimum at the grounded end and maximum at the other end.

□ In actual practice, the physical and electrical lengths of an antenna differ. Usually the physical length is made five percent less than the electrical length to compensate for this. □ Antenna tuning provides a method of electrically lengthening or shortening the antenna by adding capacitance or inductance at the point where the antenna is fed.

review questions

1. How does the signal frequency affect antenna length?
2. What should the length of a half-wave antenna be to trans-mit a 30-megacycle signal under ideal conditions?
3. How are Hertz antennas polarized?
4. What is the disadvantage of the Hertz antenna?
5. Why is the Marconi antenna only half as long as the Hertz antenna for a given frequency?
6. How can impedance distribution be found?
7. Compare the impedance distribution in the Hertz and Mar-coni antennas.
8. Why do the physical and electrical lengths of an antenna differ?
9. What should the actual physical length of a half-wave an-tenna be to transmit a 30-megacycle signal?
10. How does the addition of capacitance or inductance affect the electrical length of an antenna?

antenna arrays

The antennas you have learned about so far have been very simple, consisting merely of a single conductor driven by the output of a transmitter. These antennas provide satisfactory operation for applications where directivity is *not* an important consideration, such as in much of commercial broadcasting. However, when it is necessary to produce a concentration of radio waves in a *specific direction*, more complex antennas must be used. These highly *directional antennas* are especially important for VHF and UHF communication, where the transmitted energy is concentrated in the direct-wave component of the ground wave.

Directional antennas usually consist of a number of separate elements that function together to provide the required directivity. These multi-element arrangements are called *antenna arrays*, and have characteristics that are determined by the number and types of elements they use. Three commonly-used elements for antenna arrays are *dipoles*, *reflectors*, and *directors*. A dipole is essentially a single-conductor antenna fed at the center and usually operated half-wave. Reflectors and directors are directive elements that alter the normal radiation pattern of a dipole.

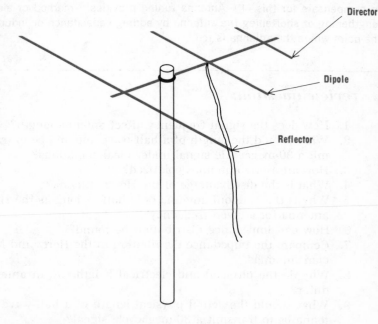

An antenna array has a highly directive radiation
pattern. Generally, the more elements in an
array, the more directive is its pattern

reflectors

When a half-wave dipole antenna is energized, its radiation pattern has the shape of a donut that surrounds the antenna. If a conductor is placed close to the dipole, a *current* will be induced in it by the electromagnetic radiation from the dipole. This current will then cause the conductor to act as an antenna, and it will emit its own radiation. Two radiation fields will thus exist in the area around the dipole and conductor, and they will interact to produce a *single* resultant field. The exact manner in which the two fields interact depends on the relative *lengths* of the dipole and conductor as well as on the *distance* between them.

Although it is beyond the scope of this book, it can be shown that if the two elements are separated by about 15 percent of the wavelength, and the conductor is slightly longer than the dipole, the two fields will combine to produce the radiation pattern shown. You can see that practically all of the radiation is on the side of the dipole *away* from the conductor. The conductor thus acts like a reflector, since it directs most of the radiation to the other side of the dipole. Because of this, the conductor is called a *reflector*.

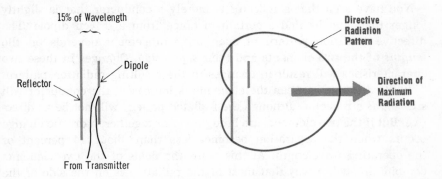

A reflector acts like a reflecting mirror for waves
traveling in its direction from the driven dipole

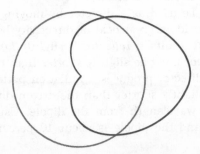

This shows how the reflector changes
the pattern of the antenna

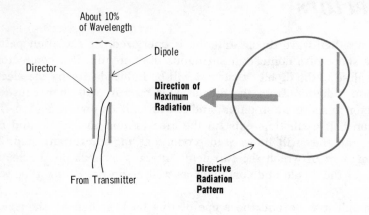

A director is shorter than the driven dipole.
It produces a directive radiation pattern
opposite to that produced by a reflector

directors

You have seen that a reflector is merely a conductor that is slightly longer than and located a certain distance from a driven dipole. The directive radiation pattern of such an arrangement depends on the *lengths* of the two elements and their *separation*. Changes in these two characteristics will result in changes in the resulting radiation pattern.

If the distance between the elements is increased, the conductor will still act as a reflector, although the radiated pattern will not be as directive. But if the two elements are brought closer together, a drastic change occurs when the separation becomes less than about 14 percent of the operating wavelength. At this point the fields of the two elements combine in such a way that most of the radiation is on the side of the reflector *away* from the dipole. The pattern is thus just the *opposite* of what it is when the elements are 15 percent of a wavelength apart. A conductor used in this way is called a *director*.

Although a reflector could be used as a director by moving it closer to the dipole, it would not provide a great deal of directivity because of its length. For best directional results, a *reflector* is slightly *longer* than the driven dipole. But a *director* must be slightly *shorter* than the dipole to give best results. Thus, a director produces a radiation pattern opposite to that of a reflector, is slightly shorter than the driven dipole, and is less than 14 percent of a wavelength from the dipole. Usually, the distance between a director and the dipole is about 10 percent of the wavelength.

parasitic arrays

In a reflector-dipole or director-dipole combination, such as you have just seen, only the dipole receives electrical energy from the transmitter. The reflector or director receives its energy from the dipole radiation. Consequently, reflectors and directors are called *parasitic elements,* and antenna systems that use them are called *parasitic arrays.*

Because of the opposite directivity they provide, a reflector and a director can be used together to provide a very directive radiation pattern. When used this way they are placed on *opposite sides* of the driven dipole, and their directive characteristics combine to produce a very narrow beam of radiation in the direction of the director. A parasitic array of this type having a dipole, one reflector, and one director is called a *three-element array.*

For even greater directivity, additional parasitic elements are frequently added to an array. Such multielement arrays usually have one reflector and two or more directors. In effect, each director acts as the driven element for the succeeding director.

Parasitic arrays are frequently referred to as *yagi* antennas. Thus, a three-element yagi is a three-element parasitic array.

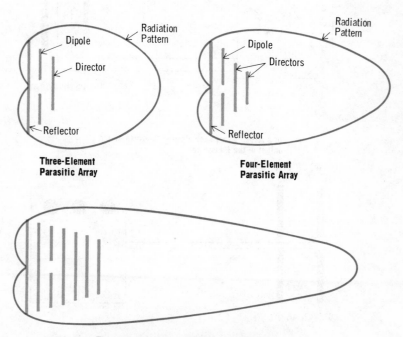

A parasitic array is also called a yagi antenna

Three-Element Parasitic Array

Four-Element Parasitic Array

The more reflectors and directors that are used, the longer and narrower becomes the radiation pattern

driven arrays

In a parasitic array, each of the parasitic elements causes some power loss from the system. Consequently, such antennas are generally best suited for applications where only a *moderate* amount of power is to be transmitted. For high-power applications, directional patterns can be produced with little power loss by antenna systems called *driven arrays*.

Basically, driven arrays consist of two or more elements, usually half-wave dipoles, with *each* element being driven by the output of the transmitter. As with parasitic arrays, the radiation pattern of a driven array depends on the interaction of the fields produced by the individual elements. This means, therefore, that the resultant pattern is affected by the *number* of elements, their *physical placement* with respect to each other, and the *spacing* between them. In addition, though, since each element is driven, the resultant pattern also depends on the *phase relationship* of the energy supplied to each.

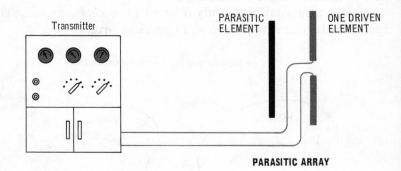

PARASITIC ARRAY

In a driven array, each element is driven by the output of the transmitter

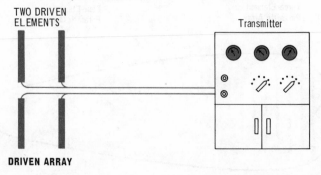

DRIVEN ARRAY

types of driven arrays

Although driven arrays can take many forms, they can be divided into three basic types. These are called *broadside, end-fire,* and *collinear* arrays. A simple broadside array consists of two half-wave elements placed one-half wave apart and parallel to each other. The two elements are excited *in phase,* and produce a radiation pattern like that shown in A. You can see that most of the radiation occurs in the *two directions* broadside to the array, as seen looking down on the elements.

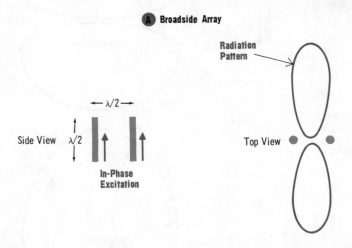

In a simple end-fire array, two half-wave ($\lambda/2$) elements are placed parallel to each other and a certain fraction of a wavelength apart, such as one-half ($\lambda/2$) or one-quarter ($\lambda/4$) wave. The two elements are then driven out of phase by the same fraction of a wavelength. The radiation pattern is directional in the *plane* of the array, as shown in B. If the elements are one-half wave apart and are driven one-half cycle, or 180 degrees, out of phase, the radiation occurs in *two directions* outward from the array. And if the elements are one-quarter wave apart and excited one-quarter cycle out of phase, the pattern is in *one direction,* similar to the pattern from a parasitic array.

In a simple collinear array, two half-wave elements are placed end-to-end and excited in phase. The radiation pattern of such an array extends 360 degrees around the antenna, but it is very directive in the *plane* of the array. This means that if a collinear array is mounted vertically, little of the radiation is directed upward toward the sky or downward toward the ground.

Each of the driven arrays described has consisted of only two elements. In actual driven arrays, though, many more than two elements are often used to provide greater directivity.

types of driven arrays (cont.)

B End-Fire Array

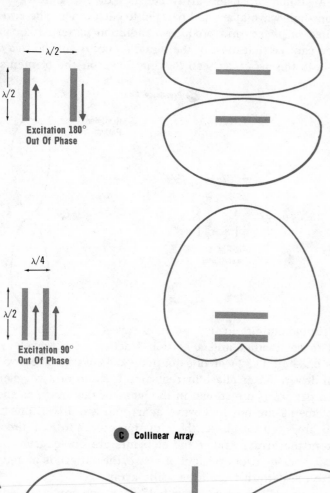

$\lambda/2$

$\lambda/2$

Excitation 180°
Out Of Phase

$\lambda/4$

$\lambda/2$

Excitation 90°
Out Of Phase

C Collinear Array

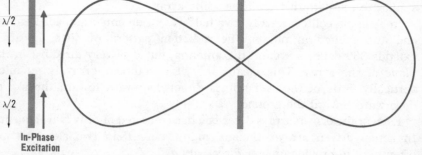

$\lambda/2$

$\lambda/2$

In-Phase
Excitation

loop and folded antennas

For maximum power to be delivered to an antenna, the impedance of the antenna at the point where it is driven must be the same as the output impedance either of the transmitter or the transmission line that connects the antenna to the transmitter. Very often these impedances are quite different, and some sort of *impedance-matching* device must be used for efficient operation. This is particularly a problem at high frequencies and in multielement arrays, where the antenna impedance is very low. To overcome this problem the *folded dipole* was developed.

Essentially, a folded dipole is *two* half-wave conductors connected at the ends, with one of them fed at the center. Actually, a folded dipole is often made by folding a full wavelength conductor to form the two half-wave elements. When energy is applied to the driven element of a folded dipole, the field produced by the driven element induces a current in the second element. This induced current is essentially the same as that in the driven element. It can be shown mathematically that this *doubling* of the current has the effect of increasing the input impedance of the antenna by a factor of *four*. In other words, the impedance increases according to the *square* of the number of elements. If three elements are used in a folded dipole, the impedance is nine times the impedance of a simple dipole.

Except for the increased impedance, a folded dipole functions electrically the same as a single dipole.

If a folded dipole is opened up to form a circle, it is called a *loop antenna*. This arrangement gives the antenna increased directivity along the plane of the loop.

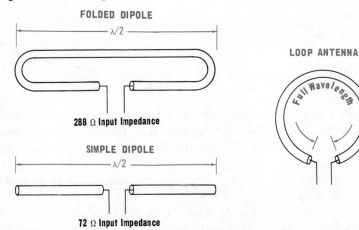

FOLDED DIPOLE

λ/2

288 Ω Input Impedance

LOOP ANTENNA

Full Wavelength

SIMPLE DIPOLE

λ/2

72 Ω Input Impedance

Both the folded dipole and the loop antenna are
variations of the basic dipole

reflector antennas

You saw how a simple reflector element can provide directivity for a driven dipole. However, a far greater degree of directivity can be obtained by using more elaborate reflector arrangements. Various such arrangements are possible, depending on the required directivity and the frequency involved.

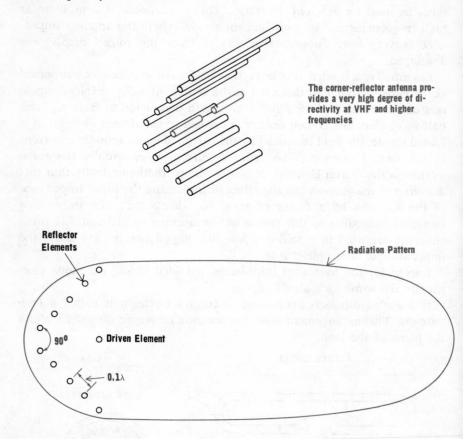

The corner-reflector antenna provides a very high degree of directivity at VHF and higher frequencies

Reflector Elements

Radiation Pattern

90°   Driven Element

0.1λ

One such type of antenna is called a *corner reflector,* since it contains two rows of parasitic reflecting elements that form a 90-degree angle. The driven dipole is located along the line that bisects the 90-degree angle, about one-half wavelength from the point where the two rows of reflectors converge. The reflector elements are spaced about 10 percent of a wavelength apart.

The corner reflector is highly directive in the forward direction. The radiation emitted towards the back and sides is actually about 1000 times less than that in the forward direction.

parabolic reflectors

Another highly-directive type of antenna for VHF and UHF frequencies uses a reflecting surface curved in the shape of a *parabola*. Because of the characteristics of this parabolic reflecting surface, radiation is emitted from this antenna in a very narrow beam.

The driven element in a parabolic reflecting antenna is placed at what is called the *focal point* of the reflector. This is the point to which all incoming horizontal radiation would be reflected by the parabolic reflector, and, in fact, this characteristic is used when such an antenna is used for receiving purposes.

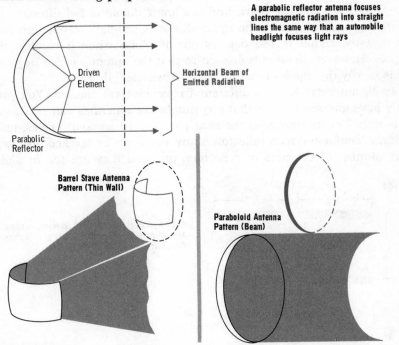

A parabolic reflector antenna focuses electromagnetic radiation into straight lines the same way that an automobile headlight focuses light rays

Driven Element

Horizontal Beam of Emitted Radiation

Parabolic Reflector

Barrel Stave Antenna Pattern (Thin Wall)

Paraboloid Antenna Pattern (Beam)

The characteristic that makes the reflector useful for transmitting purposes is shown. When radiation from the driven element is reflected by the reflector, it travels outward in straight horizontal lines. A few of the possible paths for the reflected radiation are shown. The *total length* of every path, from the driven element to the reflector to line A, is the *same;* all of the radiation emitted by the driven element and then reflected arrives at line A at the same time and in phase. The antenna therefore radiates a narrow circular beam outward. This is true of only a full parabola reflector. If part of the reflector is removed from the top and bottom of the full parabola, a barrel-stave parabolic reflector is produced, which is highly directive in only one plane.

stacked antennas

Besides using directors and reflectors, antennas can be made more effective, directive, and sensitive by stacking two or more antennas. If the antennas are fed so that the signal phases on each antenna in the stack are such that the antennas work together, the directivity and sensitivity of each antenna will add. A simple method of stacking antennas is shown.

These antennas are called lazy "H" arrays because they look like an H lying on its side. Each antenna section is a full-wave dipole and both are fed so that their currents are in phase. In A, the dipoles are a half wavelength apart, and the lower dipole is fed directly. The *matching stub* of line to the upper dipole is one-half wavelength long, so that the signal is 180 degrees out of phase when it reaches that dipole. However, the line is crossed so that the antenna is fed in phase. This is why the dipoles must be one-half wavelength apart.

In B, antennas for two different frequencies are stacked. You probably have guessed by now that any number of antennas can be stacked this way. This is shown on the next page for 16 stacked dipoles, using a large, common-screen reflector. Many yagis can be stacked also, with any number of directors or reflectors, provided they are *fed in phase*.

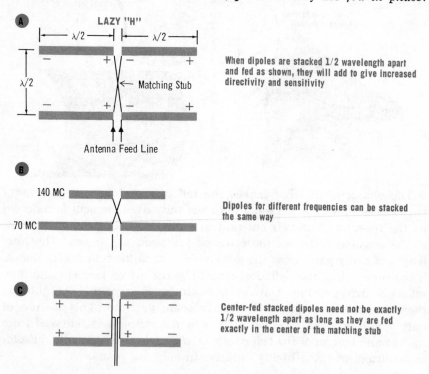

A LAZY "H"

|◄— λ/2 —►| |◄— λ/2 —►|

λ/2

← Matching Stub

Antenna Feed Line

When dipoles are stacked 1/2 wavelength apart and fed as shown, they will add to give increased directivity and sensitivity

B

140 MC

70 MC

Dipoles for different frequencies can be stacked the same way

C

Center-fed stacked dipoles need not be exactly 1/2 wavelength apart as long as they are fed exactly in the center of the matching stub

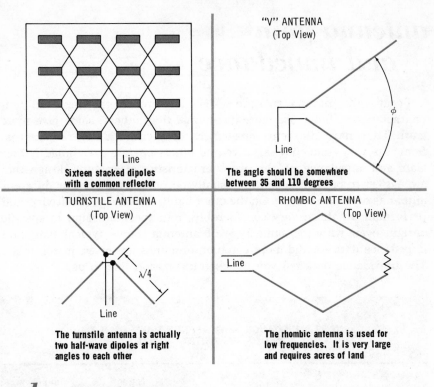

Sixteen stacked dipoles
with a common reflector

"V" ANTENNA
(Top View)

The angle should be somewhere
between 35 and 110 degrees

TURNSTILE ANTENNA
(Top View)

The turnstile antenna is actually
two half-wave dipoles at right
angles to each other

RHOMBIC ANTENNA
(Top View)

The rhombic antenna is used for
low frequencies. It is very large
and requires acres of land

other antennas

By now, you can see that antennas come in many sizes and shapes. The dipoles are the most common, but other more elaborate types are also frequently used. One such type is the V antenna, which is comprised of two end-fed antenna lines at an angle somewhere between 35 and 110 degrees. The patterns of each leg of the "V" add together to give better directivity according to the angle used. The antenna is simple, has high gain, and can work over bands that are harmonically related.

The *turnstile* antenna, which is commonly used with television transmitters is actually two half-wave dipoles at right angles to each other. Since each dipole radiates in two directions, the turnstile antenna gives good coverage in a 360-degree circle.

The *rhombic* antenna is used at low r-f frequencies and is usually large and complicated to design. It takes up acres of land. The *conical* antenna, which is not shown, uses a cone-shaped array that is essentially many "V" antennas positioned around a common apex. It can also be a continuous metal cone that is solid or screened. It has good directional characteristics and is a broadband antenna. A simple version of the conical antenna only uses two "V" sections projecting forward from a common apex.

antenna gain and impedance

Because the antenna types are designed differently, they have different characteristics. Some are more directional than others; some give more gain. They have different impedances or produce different patterns. Some are very frequency selective and others operate over broad bands. Gain and impedance are the two characteristics of antenna design that are easiest to predict since they usually do not vary much for different antennas of the same type. On the other hand, directivity, sensitivity, and performance pattern vary considerably from specific design to specific design, even with the same type of antenna. Some typical gain and impedance data for the more common antennas are given in the table. The impedance data tell you which transmission line to use.

INPUT IMPEDANCE AND APPROXIMATE GAIN OF VARIOUS PARASITIC ARRAYS

Type of Antenna	Input Impedance (ohms)	Gain Over Dipole (db)
Dipole	72	0
Folded Dipole	300	0
Dipole and Reflector	60	3 to 4
Folded Dipole and Reflector	250	3 to 4
Dipole, Reflector, and Director	20 to 30	4 to 6
Folded Dipole, Reflector, and Director	80 to 120	4 to 6
Stacked Dipoles	35 to 40	3 to 4
Stacked Folded Dipoles	150	3 to 4
Stacked Dipoles and Reflectors	25 to 30	6 to 7
Stacked Folded Dipoles and Reflectors	100 to 120	6 to 7
Dipole Turnstile	35 to 40	−1.5
Folded Dipole Turnstile	150	−1.5

summary

☐ Antenna arrays consist of separate elements that provide the required directivity. The dipole, reflector, and director are the most commonly used elements. ☐ The dipole is essentially a single-conductor antenna, fed at the center, and usually operated half wave. ☐ The reflector and director are both conductors placed a certain distance from the dipole. This distance determines whether the element acts as a reflector or director.

☐ The basic dipole with a reflector or director is called a parasitic array because only the dipole is driven by the transmitter. ☐ A driven array is a multielement array in which all elements are driven by the transmitter. The broadside, end-fire, and collinear arrays are types of driven arrays. ☐ Driven arrays differ in their physical makeup and, as a result, their radiation patterns differ. ☐ The folded dipole is actually a full-wave dipole that is folded back to half-wave length.

☐ Many different elements can be combined to provide a highly directive antenna. Some of these are reflector antennas, parabolic antennas, and stacked antennas. ☐ Reflector antennas, such as the corner reflector, use several parasitic reflectors to provide high directivity. ☐ The parabolic antenna uses a parabolic reflecting surface to provide a very narrow beam. ☐ The stacked antenna uses two or more antennas, one above the other. ☐ By controlling the signal phases applied to each antenna, the overall array can be made highly directive and selective. ☐ Although all antennas perform the same basic function, individual requirements dictate the exact type of antenna to be used.

review questions

1. What determines the characteristics of an antenna array?
2. How do the reflector and director affect the dipole radiation pattern?
3. What is a *parasitic element*? A *parasitic array*?
4. What factors affect the pattern of a driven array?
5. Describe the physical makeup of the broadside, end-fire, and collinear driven arrays.
6. What is a *loop antenna*?
7. Why is a corner reflector highly directive?
8. How do the radiation patterns of a parabolic and barrel-stave antenna differ?
9. What affects the directivity and sensitivity of stacked antennas?
10. Why is it important to know the antenna impedance?

receiving antennas

You have now seen the various types of antennas that are used to transmit radio waves. To pick up the radio waves so that the intelligence they carry can be recovered, *receiving antennas* are used. When a transmitted wave passes a receiving antenna it induces a current in it as a result of *electromagnetic induction*. This current varies according to the amplitude and frequency of the wave, and thus carries the same signal intelligence as the wave. The current then serves as the input to the receiving equipment.

Any type of antenna can be used for receiving purposes

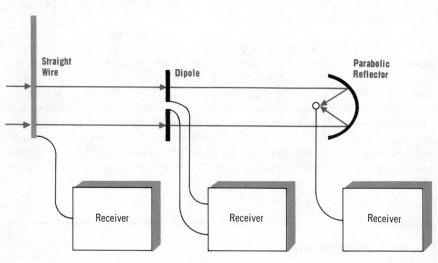

Simple straight wires are suitable for many applications, while complex types, such as parabolic reflectors, are required for others

It was pointed out previously that because of the principle of *antenna reciprocity* an antenna is equally efficient for transmitting or receiving. Therefore, the transmitting antennas you have learned about can also be used for receiving. In actual practice, however, the requirements for receiving antennas are often much less severe than those for transmitting antennas, so relatively simple types can be used. These include straight pieces of wire, coils of wire, and basic dipoles. Of course, using the more sophisticated parasitic and stacked arrays will allow the antenna to be more directive and sensitive to weak signals.

r-f transmission lines

Very often, practical considerations require that an antenna be located some distance from its associated transmitter or receiver. Some means must, therefore, be used to *transfer* the electrical energy between the equipment and antenna. This is done by conductors called *r-f transmission lines*. Basically, an r-f transmission line merely serves to electrically connect an antenna and transmitter, or receiver. However, it must do so as efficiently as possible. In other words, with a minimum loss of power. This creates special problems because of the frequencies involved.

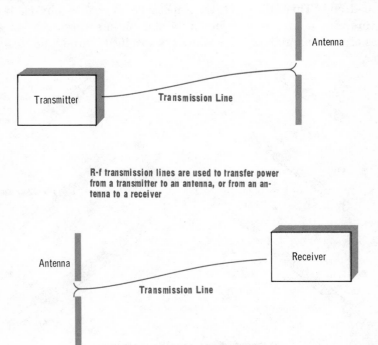

R-f transmission lines are used to transfer power from a transmitter to an antenna, or from an antenna to a receiver

At r-f frequencies, the effects of the capacitance and inductance of any conductor become significant. This is especially true of transmission lines that are relatively long. As the r-f energy applied at the input propagates down such a line, it is *retarded* by the capacitance and inductance, which is effectively *distributed* all along the length of the line. Because of this, the input energy, or voltage, can go through a complete cycle before the voltage at the start of the cycle reaches the load at the other end of the line. As you will see, this creates special problems and considerations in the use of these lines as efficient conductors.

characteristic impedance

Every transmission line has resistance. It also has inductance and capacitance distributed along its length. These three quantities combine to give the line a value of impedance. You would expect that the impedance value of any particular line would depend on the type of line and its length, and, strictly speaking, this is so. However, a transmission line also has a property called *characteristic impedance*, designated Z_0, which is independent of its length.

Essentially, the characteristic impedance of a particular type of line is the impedance it would have if it were *infinite* in *length* and *open* at the load end. This is, of course, impossible to realize physically and measure. But it can be determined by suitable measurements on short pieces of the line, and its value is always specified by the manufacturer.

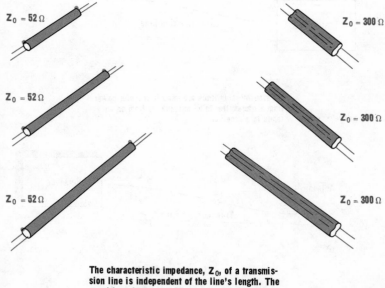

The characteristic impedance, Z_0, of a transmission line is independent of the line's length. The usual impedances are 52, 72, 150, and 300 ohms

The characteristic impedance of a transmission line is important for impedance matching. If the impedance of the load connected to the line is different from the characteristic impedance, some of the energy applied to the line will be *reflected* from the load back to the source. This represents a loss of power. But if the load impedance is the same as the line's characteristic impedance, all of the energy applied to the line will be absorbed by the load. The common impedances of transmission lines are 52, 72, 150, and 300 ohms.

standing waves

It was pointed out on the previous page that if the load impedance is different from the characteristic impedance of a transmission line, part of the energy will be reflected from the load back down the line toward the source. When this happens, there are *two waves* moving along the line in opposite directions: the *applied wave* going from source to load, and the *reflected wave* going from load to source. At any point on the line the two waves add vectorially to produce a resultant wave, which is *stationary* on the line. In other words, when the two oppositely-traveling waves combine, they cause the various points along the line to have *constant* values of voltage and current.

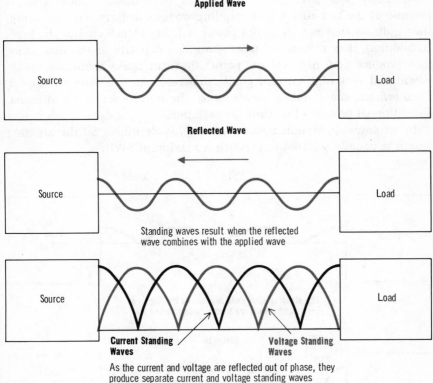

Applied Wave

Source   Load

Reflected Wave

Source   Load

Standing waves result when the reflected
wave combines with the applied wave

Source   Load

**Current Standing
Waves**   **Voltage Standing
Waves**

As the current and voltage are reflected out of phase, they
produce separate current and voltage standing waves

The resultant stationary wave actually represents a series of amplitude alternations, called *standing waves*. There are standing waves of current and standing waves of voltage. The two types are separated in phase, since the current and voltage waves are reflected out of phase from the load.

standing-wave ratio

To express the standing-wave conditions existing on a transmission line, a quantity called the *standing-wave ratio* (SWR) is used. This is the ratio of the maximum effective value of the standing waves to their minimum effective value. The SWR is also equal to the ratio of the characteristic impedance of the line to the impedance of the load, or vice versa. For example, if the line has a characteristic impedance of 300 ohms and the load impedance is 50 ohms, the SWR is 300/50, or 6. You can see, therefore, that the *higher* the SWR, the *greater* is the *mismatch* between the line and the load. An SWR of 1 indicates that there are no standing waves on the line, and all the power is absorbed by the load.

Generally, *low* SWR's are wanted on transmission lines. This is because of the bad effects that standing waves can have. For one thing, they indicate that not all of the power is being transferred to the load. In addition, they reduce the power-handling capacity of the line, since they produce very high voltage points that can cause insulation break-down, and very high current points that result in excessive I^2R losses. Furthermore, the standing waves cause the line to act as an antenna, so additional power is lost through radiation.

In an *antenna,* standing waves are *highly desirable.* So the antenna length is usually selected to produce a maximum SWR.

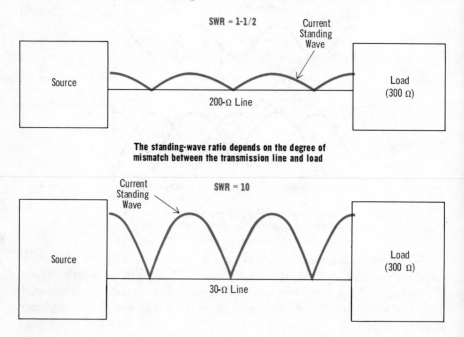

The standing-wave ratio depends on the degree of mismatch between the transmission line and load

terminations

You have seen that the presence or absence of standing waves depends on the impedance match between the transmission line and the load. When the load impedance equals the Z_0 of the line, no standing waves are produced. However, for this to be true, the load reactance must be *resistive*. If it is capacitive or inductive, even though it equals Z_0, standing waves will be produced. This is why an antenna should have a length that makes it resonant at the operating frequency. If it is resonant, its impedance is resistive, and it will absorb all of the energy from the transmission line.

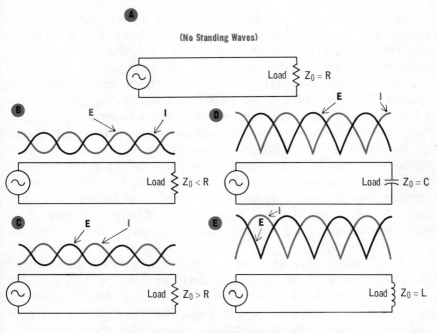

Only when the load resistance is resistive and
equal to Z_0 will no standing waves be produced

When the load impedance is resistive, but not equal to the Z_0 of the line, standing waves are produced, although they are relatively small (low SWR). As shown in B and C, the relative phases of the current and voltage standing waves depend on whether the resistive load impedance is larger or smaller than Z_0.

When the load impedance equals Z_0, but is *inductive* or *capacitive*, fairly large standing waves are produced (large SWR). The relative phases of the voltage and current standing waves depend on whether the load impedance is inductive or capacitive. This is shown in D and E.

The use of a particular type of transmission line depends on the
frequency, power, type of installation involved, and cost

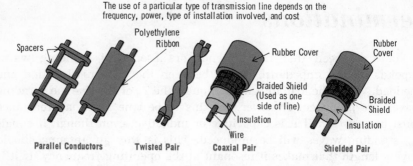

Parallel Conductors   Twisted Pair   Coaxial Pair   Shielded Pair

types of transmission line

Various types of r-f transmission line are widely used. Each has advantages as well as disadvantages, and the choice of a specific type usually depends on the requirements of the particular application.

One of the most common types of transmission line consists of *two parallel conductors* maintained a fixed distance apart by insulating spacers. This type of line is relatively cheap and efficient, but as it has a fairly high radiation loss it cannot be used near metal objects. Also, the distance between the two wires is not fixed where there is no spacer, so impedance tends to change at those points. In another version of this type of line, the two conductors are embedded in a thin ribbon of polyethylene to keep their distance fixed all along the line. This is the familiar *twin lead* used for television receiver installations. The characteristic impedance of twin lead is determined by the diameter of the wires and their spacing. The two most common values available are 75 and 300 ohms.

Another simple type of transmission line is called a *twisted pair*, since it consists of two insulated conductors twisted together. The twisting holds the lines together at a relatively fixed distance apart and at the same time balances them against the effects of nearby magnetic and electric fields since the alternating wires in the twist pattern tend to cancel any induced pickup. Characteristic impedances of twisted pairs are between 70 and 100 ohms.

Another type of line is called a *shielded pair*. It consists of two parallel conductors separated from each other and surrounded by solid insulation. The conductors are electrically shielded by a copper braid wrapped around the dielectric. The principal advantage of the shielded pair is that both conductors are perfectly balanced to ground by means of the braid, and are shielded from stray signals.

A coaxial transmission line is similar to the shielded pair, except it only has one wire. The shielding braid is used as the other wire and is usually grounded. Coaxial lines are covered next.

coaxial line

Coaxial lines, or coaxial cables as they are called, are the most widely used type of r-f transmission line. They consist of a hollow, tubular outer conductor, and a second conductor held in place exactly at the center of the outer conductor by insulating spacers. In some types, a solid, continuous, insulating material is used in place of the spacers between the inner and outer conductors.

The principal advantage of the coaxial line is its ability to eliminate radiation losses. No radiation, either magnetic or electrostatic, extends outside of the outer conductor. Thus, the coaxial line is a perfectly shielded line. Coaxial lines have the disadvantages of being relatively costly and difficult to install.

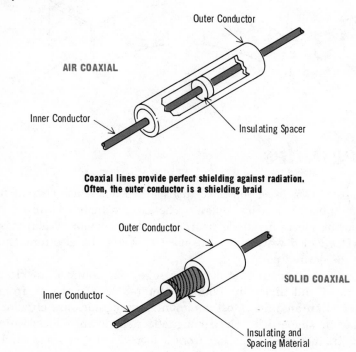

Coaxial lines provide perfect shielding against radiation. Often, the outer conductor is a shielding braid

The characteristic impedance of a coaxial line depends on the inner diameters of the conductors. It can be calculated from the equation:

$$Z_0 = 138 \log_{10} \frac{D}{d}$$

where D is the inner diameter of the outer conductor and d is the diameter of the inner conductor. Often, the outer conductor is a shielding braid that shields the inner wire from stray pickup.

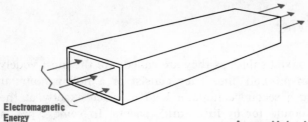

A waveguide is a hollow device used for transferring high-frequency electromagnetic energy

Electromagnetic Energy

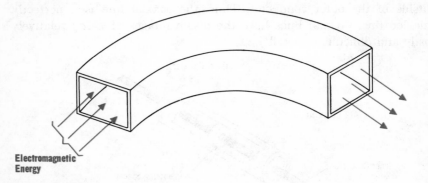

Electromagnetic Energy

waveguides

The transmission lines you have just learned about use current flow in wires to transfer electrical energy. The same transfer, however, can be made using electromagnetic fields instead of current. When this is done, devices called waveguides are used to direct the electromagnetic field over the desired path.

Essentially, a waveguide is a hollow tube that confines an electromagnetic field and makes it follow a required path, such as from a transmitter to an antenna. Most commonly, waveguides are circular or rectangular in shape. The electromagnetic field is introduced into a waveguide by means of radiation from a loop of wire or some kind of probe. The field passes through the waveguide and emerges at the other end.

Waveguides are not too practical to use at frequencies lower than about 3000 megacycles. This is because their cross-sectional dimensions must be about one-half of the wavelength of the energy involved or else the wave will not be propagated through the waveguide. So, at low frequencies, a waveguide would have to be prohibitively large. At the frequencies at which they are practical, waveguides have lower total losses than do other types of r-f transmission lines.

summary

☐ Receiving antennas pick up the transmitted radio waves so that the intelligence can be recovered. ☐ Although all transmitting antennas can be used as receiving antennas, the requirements of a receiving antenna are much less severe. ☐ Transmission lines are used to transfer electrical energy between the antenna and the equipment with a minimum loss of power. ☐ All transmission lines have a characteristic impedance that depends on their resistance and distributed capacitance and inductance. ☐ If the characteristic impedance of the transmission line is different than the load resistance, part of the energy is reflected back to the source. This reflected wave plus the original wave add vectorially to produce standing waves.

☐ The standing-wave ratio (SWR) expresses the effect of standing waves. Low SWR's are desirable in the transmission line, but high SWR's are desirable at the antenna. ☐ Standing waves are also produced if the load impedance is inductive or capacitive, even though the load impedance matches the transmission line impedance. ☐ If only a resistive mismatch occurs, the standing waves are relatively small. However, even a small reactive mismatch will produce fairly large standing waves.

☐ Various types of transmission lines are in common use. These include the twin lead, twisted pair, and shielded pair, all of which have two separate insulated leads. ☐ Another transmission line is the coaxial line, which consists of a hollow tubular outer conductor and a second conductor held exactly in the center of the outer conductor. ☐ Still another type is the waveguide, which is a hollow tube. In this type of transmission line, an electromagnetic field instead of current is used to transfer energy.

review questions

1. How are radio waves picked up by a receiving antenna?
2. Which characteristics of a transmission line retard the flow of r-f energy?
3. What is *characteristic impedance*?
4. How are standing waves produced?
5. What does a high SWR indicate in terms of impedance match?
6. How does the antenna length affect the SWR?
7. How do resistive and reactive mismatches affect the SWR?
8. Describe the physical construction of the twin-lead, twisted-pair, and shielded-pair transmission lines.
9. What are the advantages and disadvantages of coaxial lines?
10. What factor limits the use of waveguides? Why?

designing a hertz antenna

You have seen that a basic Hertz antenna is nothing more than a straight piece of conductor whose electrical length is one-half the wavelength of the energizing frequency, and whose physical length is approximately five percent shorter than the electrical length. The design of such an antenna is therefore a relatively simple matter. The basic equation for wavelength, you recall, is:

$$\text{Wavelength } (\lambda) = \frac{300,000,000}{\text{frequency}}$$

where the wavelength is in meters and the frequency is in cps. Since one meter equals 3.28 feet, this equation can be changed to a form that will give the wavelength in feet. This form is:

$$\text{Wavelength (feet)} = \frac{984,000,000}{\text{frequency (cps)}}$$

So, if a Hertz antenna is to operate at a frequency of 3 megacycles, its electrical length is found by first calculating the wavelength of a 3-megacycle wave:

$$\text{Wavelength} = \frac{984,000,000}{3,000,000} = 328 \text{ feet}$$

The electrical length of the antenna is one-half of this, or 164 feet. The physical length is five percent shorter than this, or:

$$0.05 \times 164 \text{ feet} = 8.2 \text{ feet}$$
$$164 - 8.2 = 155.8 \text{ feet}$$

You can see from this example that Hertz antennas are very long at low frequencies. As a result, they are generally used only for frequencies higher than a few megacycles.

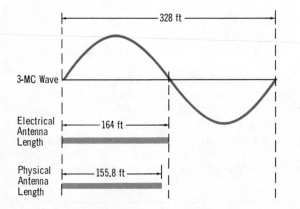

A 3-mc Hertz antenna has a physical length of 155.8 feet. It is slightly less (5%) than one-half wavelength long

designing a marconi antenna

The Marconi antenna operates as a half-wave antenna. Actually, however, it is only one-quarter wavelength long, since the ground image supplies another quarter wavelength. The first step in designing a Marconi is to calculate the wavelength of the operating frequency.

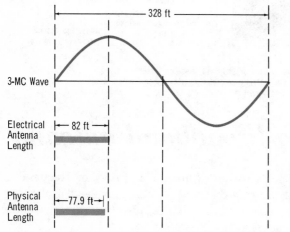

A 3-mc Marconi antenna has a physical length of 77.9 feet. It is slightly less (5%) than one-quarter wavelength long

As an example, consider a Marconi that is to operate at 3 megacycles. The wavelength at this frequency is:

$$\text{Wavelength} = \frac{984,000,000}{3,000,000} = 328 \text{ feet}$$

The electrical length of the Marconi is one-quarter of this, or 328 feet/4 = 82 feet. The physical length, which is five percent less, is therefore:

$$0.05 \times 82 = 4.1 \text{ feet}$$
$$82 - 4.1 = 77.9 \text{ feet}$$

As another example, consider a Marconi for 500 kilocycles. The wavelength is: 984,000,000/500,000, or 1968 feet. One-quarter wavelength, therefore, is 1968 feet/4, or 492 feet. Its physical length is five percent less, or: 0.05 × 492 = 24.6 feet. So, the length of the antenna is: 492 − 24.6 = 467.4 feet.

It was previously shown that the physical length of a 3-megacycle Hertz antenna is 155.8 feet. A Marconi for the identical frequency is, therefore, only half as long. You can see then that when an installation imposes limitations on the physical length of an antenna, the Marconi has a decided advantage over the Hertz. This is especially true at the lower frequencies, where Hertz antennas would often be prohibitively long.

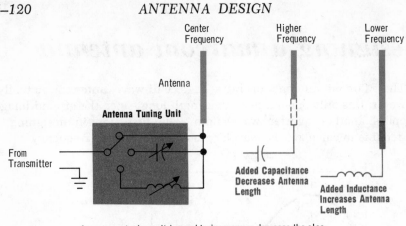

An antenna tuning unit is used to increase or decrease the electrical length of an antenna so that it is resonant at the operating frequency. In this way, the antenna can be used over a broad band of frequencies

designing a broadband antenna

Frequently, an antenna is used to transmit a variety of frequencies. It is usually impractical to use a different antenna for every frequency, so a *single* antenna must be designed that is adequate over the entire range of frequencies to be used.

One way to do this is to use an antenna that is designed for the *center* frequency of the band of frequencies. Such an antenna would be most efficient at the center, and less efficient at the higher and lower frequencies. But an *antenna tuning unit* would then be used to lengthen or shorten the antenna electrically in accordance with the exact operating frequency. For example, if a half-wave antenna was to operate from 50 to 100 megacycles, its physical length would be designed for 75 megacycles. The wavelength at this frequency is: 984,000,000/ 75,000,000 = 13.12 feet. One-half wave is, therefore, 13.12 feet/2, or 6.56 feet. The antenna is made five percent shorter than this, or: 0.05 × 6.56 = 0.328 feet. So, the antenna would be 6.56 − 0.328 = 6.23 feet long.

An antenna tuning unit is connected between the transmitter and the 6.23-foot antenna. When the operating frequency is *less* than 75 megacycles, the antenna is *too short*. The tuning unit is adjusted so that it adds *inductance* in series with the antenna to increase its electrical length to the correct electrical length for the operating frequency. When the operating frequency is *higher* than 75 megacycles, the antenna is *too long*. Now the tuning unit is adjusted so that it adds capacitance in series with the antenna to shorten its electrical length. In spite of its fixed length, therefore, the antenna is always made electrically resonant at the operating frequency.

designing parasitic arrays

The design of a parasitic array is more complicated than the design of either a Hertz or Marconi antenna. Not only must the length of the driven dipole be calculated, but the lengths of the reflectors and directors and the distance from the dipole must also be determined. As an example, consider a parasitic array having one reflector and one director that is to operate at 100 megacycles. The wavelength at this frequency is: 984,000,000/100,000,000, or 9.84 feet. One-half wavelength is, therefore, 9.84 feet/2, or 4.92 feet. The physical length of the driven dipole is five percent less than this: 0.05 × 4.92 = 0.246 feet. So the antenna is 4.92 − 0.246 = 4.67 feet long.

The reflector is made slightly longer than the driven dipole, and the director is made slightly shorter. Exactly how much longer and shorter these two elements are depends on how sharp a frequency characteristic is desired from the antenna. The closer the lengths of the two elements are to the length of the dipole, the narrower is the band of frequencies that the antenna will transmit and receive effectively.

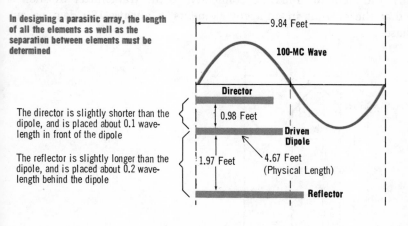

In designing a parasitic array, the length of all the elements as well as the separation between elements must be determined

The director is slightly shorter than the dipole, and is placed about 0.1 wavelength in front of the dipole

The reflector is slightly longer than the dipole, and is placed about 0.2 wavelength behind the dipole

The last thing to be determined is the distance between the dipole and the parasitic elements. The reflector can be placed about 0.2 wavelength in back of the dipole, and the director about 0.1 wavelength in front of it. Thus, the distance between the dipole and the reflector is: 0.2 × 9.84 feet = 1.97 feet. And the distance between the dipole and director is: 0.1 × 9.84 feet = 0.98 feet.

Any additional directors that are used are made progressively shorter; additional reflectors are made progressively longer. An additional director is placed 0.1 wavelength before the following *director,* and the additional reflector is placed 0.2 wavelength behind the preceding *reflector.*

designing driven arrays

The design of driven arrays is quite complex, since it involves not only the lengths of the elements and the separation between them, but the relative phase of the excitation applied to the various elements as well. As an example of such a design, consider a simple six-element end-fire array to be used at 80 megacycles. All elements are one-half wave long and are separated from each other by a half wave. The first step, therefore, is to find the wavelength involved. This is found by:

$$\text{Wavelength} = \frac{984,000,000}{80,000,000} = 12.3 \text{ feet}$$

So, one-half wavelength is 12.3 feet/2, or 6.15 feet. This is the separation between elements. The physical length of the elements is five percent shorter than this.

$$0.05 \times 6.15 = 0.308 \text{ feet}$$
$$6.15 - 0.308 = 5.84 \text{ feet}$$

Finally, the elements must be connected to the transmitter in such a way that the current in adjacent elements is always 180 degrees out of phase.

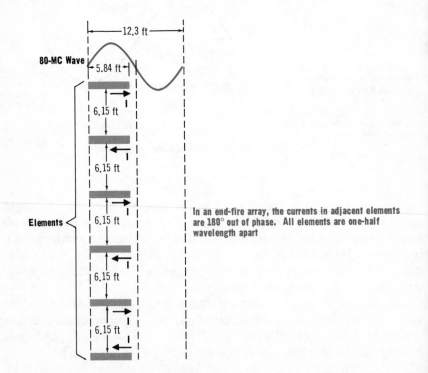

In an end-fire array, the currents in adjacent elements are 180° out of phase. All elements are one-half wavelength apart

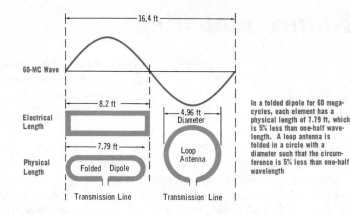

In a folded dipole for 60 megacycles, each element has a physical length of 7.79 ft, which is 5% less than one-half wavelength. A loop antenna is folded in a circle with a diameter such that the circumference is 5% less than one-half wavelength

designing
loop and folded antennas

The folded dipole antenna is frequently used because its impedance is four times that of a conventional dipole. If a conventional dipole is fed by a 300-ohm transmission line, which is commonly used, an impedance-matching device is required to match the 72-ohm antenna impedance to the 300-ohm line. But a folded dipole, although it functions as a half-wave antenna, has an impedance of 288 ohms, and can be fed from a 300-ohm line directly.

Each element in a folded dipole is one-half wavelength long. This wavelength is calculated the same way as it is done for a conventional dipole. For example, for a folded dipole for 60-megacycles use, the wavelength is: 984,000,000/60,000,000, or 16.4 feet. The electrical length of *each* element in the folded dipole is one-half this length, or 8.2 feet. The physical length of the elements is made five percent smaller than the electrical length: 0.05 × 8.2 = 0.41 feet; 8.2 − 0.41 = 7.79 feet.

Since a folded dipole can be made by taking a conductor one full wavelength long and bending it to form two dipoles, the length can also be calculated on the basis of a full wavelength. For example, to find the length of conductor needed to make a folded dipole for 40 megacycles, you first find the corresponding wavelength: 984,000,000/ 40,000,000, or 24.6 feet. The physical length of the required conductor is five percent less than this, or: 0.05 × 24.6 = 1.23 feet; 24.6 − 1.23 = 23.4 feet. A conductor this length, then, could be bent to form a folded dipole for 40 megacycles. This method can also be used to find the length of conductor required to form a loop antenna that operates as a dipole. The only difference is that, for a loop antenna, the length of the conductor is folded into a circular shape.

impedance matching

Since the signal picked up by the antenna is usually *very small* to begin with, it is important that the signal be transferred from the antenna to the receiver with as little loss as possible. For this to be realized, the *impedances* of the antenna, transmission line, and receiver input must be *matched* as closely as possible.

There are many ways to provide the required impedance match, with the best method in a particular case depending on such factors as the frequencies involved, the amount of mismatch present, and the signal strength. One method is to insert an *impedance-matching transformer* between the transmission line and the receiver input. The transformer primary is in the transmission line circuit and the secondary forms part of the receiver input circuit.

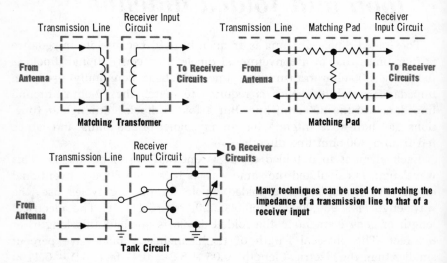

Many techniques can be used for matching the impedance of a transmission line to that of a receiver input

Another method of obtaining the required impedance match is to use a *matching pad* between the transmission line and the receiver input. Such a pad is nothing more than a network of resistors whose values are chosen to provide the necessary impedance characteristics.

Still another method of impedance matching can be used when the receiver input is in the form of a *tank circuit*. The input from the transmission line can be applied to the tank through any one of a number of taps on the tank coil. Because of their different positions with respect to the tank, each tap presents a different impedance to the transmission line. The tap that has an impedance closest to that of the transmission line is selected. The total impedance of the tank is unaffected by which tap is selected on the coil. This total impedance is matched to that of the following receiver circuit.

typical radiation and reception patterns

These polar diagrams show the relative directivity of some basic antenna constructions for both vertically and horizontally polarized antennas. In the first two diagrams, only the major lobe patterns are shown. There are usually many minor lobes, as illustrated in the third diagram. Also, the distance between the antenna and ground greatly affects the major and minor lobe pattern distribution.

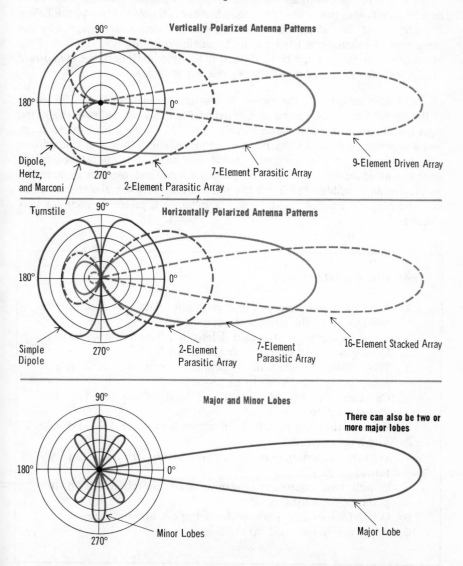

summary

☐ In any transmitting system, proper design of the antenna is important to achieve the desired directivity, sensitivity, and gain. ☐ One of the main design criteria is the physical length. ☐ The length of both the Hertz and Marconi antennas can be found once the wavelength of the frequency is known. ☐ In a broadband antenna, where many frequencies are to be transmitted, the length is usually designed around the center frequency. Antenna tuning units can then be used to lengthen or shorten the antenna electrically.

☐ The design of a parasitic array is more complicated because, in addition to the length of the driven element, the lengths of the parasitic elements must be calculated. Also the distance between the parasitic elements and the driven elements must be calculated. ☐ Design of the driven array requires the same type of calculations used for the parasitic array with one addition: Each of the driven elements must be connected to the transmitter so that the current in adjacent elements is always 180 degrees out of phase.

☐ The folded dipole, like the dipole, is one-half wavelength long. The length of the overall conductor can be calculated on the basis of one wavelength and then the length is folded to form two dipoles. ☐ The length of the loop antenna is also calculated on the basis of one wavelength, but it is shaped into a circle. ☐ Because the received signal is very small, it is important that the impedance between the antenna, transmission line, and receiver be matched as closely as possible. ☐ Often the impedances between the transmission line and receiver are matched by using transformers, matching pads, or tank circuits.

review questions

1. How do the lengths of the parasitic elements compare to the length of the driven element?
2. What determines the actual length of parasitic elements?
3. How would you design a driven array?
4. Why must the current in adjacent elements of a driven array be 180 degrees out of phase?
5. Compare the impedance of a folded dipole to that of a standard dipole.
6. What is the only physical difference between a folded dipole and loop antenna?
7. Why is impedance matching important in receiving systems?
8. Which two components are usually matched by an impedance-matching device?
9. What factors affect methods of impedance matching?
10. What are *major* and *minor* lobes?

cumulative index

cumulative index